CALCULUS

with analytic geometry

CALCULUS

■ ■ ■——SECOND EDITION
with supplementary exercises

with analytic geometry

Richard E. Johnson

Fred L. Kiokemeister

ALLYN and BACON, Inc.   Boston, 1960

First printing . . . . January, 1960
Second printing . . . . June, 1960
Third printing . . . . . . November, 1960

Library of Congress Catalog Card Number: 59-10051

Preface

THIS SECOND EDITION differs from the first in that some of the chapters have been improved and modified in the light of experience, a new chapter on three-dimensional vector analysis has been added, and supplementary exercises have been included.

Chapter 6 as now presented stresses graphical methods for determining extrema of a function. Rolle's theorem and the mean value theorem are introduced here (rather than in Chapter 14 as in the first edition). This is followed up by a section on intermediate value theorems in Chapter 8, on the definite integral. An intuitive discussion of the derivative of exponential functions is now included in Chapter 10. The section on two-dimensional vector algebra in Chapter 15 has been rewritten from an algebraic standpoint. This leads naturally to the three-dimensional vector analysis of Chapter 18. A recent elementary proof of the fundamental theorem of algebra has been added to Chapter 19, on partial differentiation.

The appendix has been enlarged to include a list of formulas from trigonometry and tables of exponential, logarithmic, and trigonometric functions. Additional exercises for each of the chapters are included in the set of supplementary exercises.

It is our conviction that college students, particularly in the first two years, not only are able to understand and appreciate rigorous mathematical theory but also are more interested in courses containing both rigorous proofs and applications of the theorems. This conviction led us to write a book containing a theoretical basis of the calculus together with applications of the methods and results. An early start in theoretical mathematics has an added advantage in that it allows a wide selection of meaningful courses in the last two years of college for those students continuing in mathematics. Equally important, students taking only two years of mathematics will get an insight into the methods as well as the applications of the calculus.

Although this is primarily a calculus book, enough analytic geometry has been included to make it self-contained in that respect. For students who have had analytic geometry, Chapter 2 on the line and the part of Chapter 7 on conic sections may be omitted without affecting the continuity of the book. The book has been designed to be used by students having good training in algebra, plane geometry, and trigonometry.

Every effort has been made to give an intuitive discussion of each new concept prior to its rigorous development. The more difficult theoretical parts have been put in separate sections, and may be omitted at the discretion of the instructor. Following the theory, the natural geometrical and physical applications have been presented.

Some of the other unusual features of the book follow:

In Chapter 4, limits of the linear, quadratic, reciprocal, and square-root functions are discussed before the statement of the limit theorems. Then the limit theorems are shown to follow from these special limits and a general composite limit theorem.

A particularly complete treatment of extrema of a function is given in Chapter 6. A novel feature of this chapter is the emphasis on graphical means of determining extrema.

The completeness property of the real number system is stated in terms of least upper bounds and greatest lower bounds in Chapter 8, and then is used in the definition of lower and upper integrals of a continuous function. The equality of the lower and upper integrals is proved on the assumption that a function continuous in a closed interval has a simply stated uniform continuity property in that interval. This proof may be replaced by a geometrical argument if the instructor feels that it is too complicated for his class. A similar treatment of the double integral is to be found in Chapter 20.

Sequences are introduced in Chapter 9 for the specific purpose of showing that the integral equals the limit of a sequence of Riemann sums. The sigma and delta notations are used for the first time in this chapter.

A full account of the differential calculus of the elementary transcendental functions is given in Chapter 10. Special sections on inverse functions, exponential laws of growth and decay, and the definition of partial derivatives are also included.

The formal integration of Chapters 11 and 12 contains a section on separable differential equations. Featured in the latter chapter is a general substitution formula that validates trigonometric and related substitutions for evaluating integrals.

A transition from the elementary topics of differentiation and integration to some of the deeper properties of functions occurs in Chapter 14. Here the boundedness properties of a continuous function are proved, and the mean value theorem is brought into play in the discussion of indeterminate forms, improper integrals, and the finite Taylor's theory.

Vectors are introduced in Chapter 15 and studied further in Chapter 18, where three-dimensional vector analysis is applied to geometric and physical problems. Solid analytic geometry is studied first in Chapter 17 without vectors, and then again in Chapter 18 with the aid of vectors.

A thorough treatment of elementary convergence theory of infinite series is given in Chapter 16. Least upper bounds are again used in defining the radius of convergence of a power series. Proofs are given that a power series may be differentiated and integrated termwise within its interval of convergence.

Chapters 19 and 20 are given over to a brief introduction to the calculus of functions of several variables.

The final chapter on differential equations features a complete discussion of second-order linear differential equations with constant coefficients.

We have attempted to make the chapters as independent of each other as possible so that the book might be used for a second calculus course following a variety of different first courses. Essentially all of the material in this book has been tested in the classroom by the authors and their colleagues and has been improved as a result of this experience. The publishers have also had many critical readings of the book by other teachers. To these and the many other people who have helped so greatly in the formation of this book we express our deep appreciation.

R.E.J.

F.L.K.

Contents

ix

may be combined into one as follows:

$$ab = 0 \quad \text{if and only if} \quad a = 0 \text{ or } b = 0.$$

2. Inequalities

An important property of the system of real numbers is that the set (or collection) of nonzero numbers can be separated into two parts, one part made up of the positive numbers and the other part the negative numbers. Thus each real number is either a positive number, zero, or a negative number.

Two nonzero numbers a and b either *agree in sign* (that is, both are positive or both are negative) or *differ in sign* (that is, one is positive and one is negative). If a and b agree in sign, ab and a/b are positive numbers, whereas if a and b differ in sign, ab and a/b are negative numbers. The nonzero numbers a and $1/a$ always agree in sign; a and $-a$ always differ in sign. The sum of two positive numbers is positive, of two negative numbers is negative.

If $a \neq b$, one of the numbers a and b is greater than the other. We write

$$a > b$$

if a is greater than b, and

$$a < b$$

if a is less than b (which is to say that b is greater than a). The symbols $<$ and $>$ may be defined as follows:

1.1 Definition. If a and b are real numbers, then

  (i) $a > b$ if $a - b$ is a positive number.
  (ii) $a < b$ if $a - b$ is a negative number.

An expression of the form

$$a > b \quad \text{or} \quad a < b$$

is called an *inequality*. For example,

$$9 > 5 \quad \text{and} \quad \frac{13}{2} < 7,$$

since $9 - 5 = 4$, a positive number and $\frac{13}{2} - 7 = -\frac{1}{2}$, a negative number. Clearly

$$a > b \quad \text{and} \quad b < a$$

have the same meaning.

If a is a positive number, $a - 0$ is positive and $a > 0$ according to the definition above. Conversely, if $a > 0$, then $a = a - 0$ is a positive number. Therefore,

the number a is positive if and only if $a > 0$,

and, similarly,

the number a is negative if and only if $a < 0$.

The following laws of inequalities will be useful in the sequel.

1.2 If $a > b$ and $b > c$, then $a > c$.

1.3 If $a > b$, then $a + c > b + c$ for every number c.

1.4 If $a > b$ and c is positive, then $ac > bc$.

1.5 If $a > b$ and c is negative, then $ac < bc$.

Particular note is to be made of the distinction between 1.4 and 1.5. Thus multiplication by a positive number maintains the direction of the inequality, whereas multiplication by a negative number reverses the direction of the inequality.

These laws may be proved by using the properties of positive and negative numbers and Definition 1.1. We illustrate this fact by proving one of the laws.

Proof of 1.4: Since $a > b$, both $a - b$ and c are positive numbers. Hence $(a - b)c$, which is equal to $ac - bc$, is a positive number, and $ac > bc$ according to 1.1.

The laws 1.2–1.5 remain valid if the direction of each inequality is reversed. We restate these laws after this reversal:

1.2′ If $a < b$ and $b < c$, then $a < c$.

1.3′ If $a < b$, then $a + c < b + c$ for every number c.

1.4′ If $a < b$ and c is positive, then $ac < bc$.

1.5 If $a < b$ and c is negative, then $ac > bc$.

We may write

$$a < x < b \quad \text{or} \quad b > x > a$$

if $a < x$ and $x < b$. In this case, x is a number between a and b. In a continued inequality such as this, the inequality signs will always have the same direction. Thus, we shall never write

$$a < x > b \quad \text{or} \quad a > x < b.$$

Other useful symbols are $\geq$ and $\leq$ which are defined in an obvious way:

$$a \geq b \quad \text{if either} \quad a > b \quad \text{or} \quad a = b,$$

and similarly for $a \leq b$. A continued inequality such as

$$a \leq x < b$$

indicates that either x is between a and b or $x = a$.

Example 1. Solve the inequality $7x - 5 > 3x + 4$.

Solution: If x is a number such that

$$7x - 5 > 3x + 4,$$

then $\qquad\qquad 7x - 5 + 5 > 3x + 4 + 5$ $\qquad\qquad$ (by 1.3).

and $\qquad\qquad\qquad 7x > 3x + 9.$

Adding $-3x$ to each side of this inequality, we have

$$4x > 9 \qquad\qquad\qquad \text{(by 1.3)}.$$

We may multiply each side of this inequality by $\frac{1}{4}$, a positive number, to get

$$x > \frac{9}{4} \qquad\qquad\qquad \text{(by 1.4)}.$$

Each of the steps we have carried out is reversible. That is, we may begin with the inequality

$$x > \frac{9}{4},$$

multiply each side by 4, add $3x$ to each side of the resulting inequality, and then add -5 to each side to obtain the given inequality

$$7x - 5 > 3x + 4.$$

Consequently,

$$7x - 5 > 3x + 4 \quad \textit{if and only if} \quad x > \frac{9}{4}.$$

The set of all numbers x greater than $\frac{9}{4}$ is the *solution* of the given inequality in that a number x satisfies the given inequality if and only if $x > \frac{9}{4}$.

Example 2. Solve the inequality $-3 < 1 - 2x < 4$.

Solution: If we add -1 to each member of the inequality, we get

$$-4 < -2x < 3.$$

We may multiply each member of this new inequality by $-\frac{1}{2}$, a negative number, to obtain (by 1.5′)

$$2 > x > -\frac{3}{2},$$

or, what is the same thing,

$$-\frac{3}{2} < x < 2.$$

Therefore the solution of the given inequality consists of the set of all numbers x between $-\frac{3}{2}$ and 2.

Example 3. Show that

$$(x + 2)(x + 1) > 0 \quad \text{and} \quad \frac{x + 2}{x + 1} > 0$$

for every number $x < -2$.

Solution: We only need show that $x + 2$ and $x + 1$ agree in sign. Since $x < -2$,

$$x + 2 < -2 + 2 \quad \text{and} \quad x + 1 < -2 + 1 \qquad \text{(by 1.3′)}.$$

Hence

$$x + 2 < 0 \quad \text{and} \quad x + 1 < -1.$$

Since $-1 < 0$, both $x + 2$ and $x + 1$ are negative, and therefore

$$(x + 2)(x + 1) > 0 \quad \text{and} \quad \frac{x + 2}{x + 1} > 0.$$

If $a \geq 0$, then it is false that $a < 0$. That is to say, if $a \geq 0$ then a is *nonnegative*. The nonnegative numbers consist of the positive numbers and the number 0. If a is a nonzero number, then $a^2 > 0$ since the two factors in the product $a \cdot a = a^2$ agree in sign. Also, $0^2 = 0$, and we may make the following statement.

1.6 The square of every real number a is nonnegative, i.e.,

$$a^2 \geq 0.$$

The number $\sqrt{a}$ is real if and only if $a \geq 0$. If $a < 0$, $\sqrt{a}$ is an imaginary number. We recall that, by definition, $\sqrt{a}$ is the *nonnegative number* b such that $b^2 = a$.

Example 4. For what numbers x is $\sqrt{1 - 2x}$ a real number?

Solution: The number $\sqrt{1 - 2x}$ is real if and only if $1 - 2x \geq 0$, or, if and only if

$$x \leq \frac{1}{2}.$$

Between any two unequal rational numbers a and b is always another rational number. It may be verified, for example, that the *arithmetic average*, $(a + b)/2$, of a and b is between a and b.

An important property of the real number system is that between any two unequal real numbers is at least one rational number. This property allows us to approximate each real number by a rational number. For example, if a is a real number then there is some rational number b such that

$$a < b < a + .01.$$

The rational number b so chosen approximates the real number a to within .01 of a unit.

■ ■ ■ EXERCISES

In each of Exercises 1–10, solve the given inequality.

1. $3x + 1 < x + 5$.

2. $1 - 2x < 5x - 2$.

3. $3 - 2x > 0$.

4. $\dfrac{3x}{4} - \dfrac{1}{2} < 0$.

5. $\dfrac{3x - 5}{2} \leq 0$.

6. $.01x - 2.32 \geq 0$.

7. $-.1 < x - 5 < .1$.

8. $-.01 < x + 3 < .01$.

9. $-.03 \leq \dfrac{2x + 3}{5} \leq .03$.

10. $-.001 \leq \dfrac{5 - 2x}{4} \leq .001$.

In each of Exercises 11–14, determine the numbers x for which the given square root is a real number.

11. $\sqrt{2x-8}$.
12. $\sqrt{3+4x}$.
13. $\sqrt{b^2-4ax}$.
14. $\sqrt{16-7x}$.

In each of Exercises 15–20, find all numbers x satisfying the given conditions.

15. $x+1>0$ and $x-3<0$.　**16.** $x-1<0$ and $x+2>0$.

17. $\dfrac{1}{x+3}<0$.　**18.** $\dfrac{1}{2x-5}>0$.

19. $3x-2\geq 0$ and $5x-1\leq 0$.　**20.** $2x+1>0$ and $x-1>0$.

21. Prove 1.2, 1.3, and 1.5 of the text.

22. If $a<b$ and $c\leq d$, prove that $a+c<b+d$.

23. If $a\neq b$, prove that $(a+b)/2$ is between a and b.

24. If $a>0$ and $b>0$, and if $a\neq b$, prove that $\sqrt{ab}$ (called the *geometric average* of a and b) is between a and b.

25. If $a\geq 0$ and $b\geq 0$, prove that $a^2=b^2$ if and only if $a=b$.

26. If $a>b>0$, prove that $a^2>b^2$.

3. Absolute values

Each real number a is either a negative number or a nonnegative number, and if a is negative, then $-a$ is a positive number. In other words, corresponding to each real number a is a nonnegative number which is either a itself or $-a$. This nonnegative number is called the *absolute value* or *numerical value* of a and is designated by the symbol $|a|$. The precise definition of the absolute value of a is as follows.

1.7 Definition. Let a be a real number. If $a\geq 0$, then $|a|=a$, and if $a<0$, then $|a|=-a$.

For example,

$$|2|=2,\quad \left|\frac{1}{3}\right|=\frac{1}{3},\quad |\pi|=\pi,\quad |0|=0,$$

since 2, $\frac{1}{3}$, π, and 0 are nonnegative numbers. On the other hand

$$|-2|=-(-2)=2,\quad |-\pi|=-(-\pi)=\pi,$$

since -2 and $-\pi$ are negative. Since $\sqrt{2}-1$ and $\pi-3$ are nonnegative, we have that

$$|\sqrt{2}-1|=\sqrt{2}-1,\quad |\pi-3|=\pi-3,$$

but

$$|\sqrt{3}-3|=-(\sqrt{3}-3)=3-\sqrt{3},$$

and

$$\left|\pi-\frac{29}{7}\right|=-\left(\pi-\frac{29}{7}\right)=\frac{29}{7}-\pi,$$

since $\sqrt{3}-3$ and $\pi-\frac{29}{7}$ are negative numbers.

If $a\geq 0$, then $a=|a|$, whereas if $a<0$, $a<0<|a|$. Thus $a\leq |a|$ for every number a. Similarly, if $a\geq 0$, then $-|a|\leq 0\leq a$; and if $a<0$,

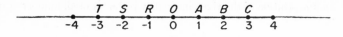

Figure 1.1

Let O and A be any two distinct points on a line L. We assign to O the number 0 and to A the number 1. We shall call O the *origin*, A the *unit point*, and OA the *unit segment* of L. With the point B on the opposite side of A from O and such that segment OA is congruent to segment AB (written $OA = AB$) we assign the number 2. With the point R on the opposite side of O from A and such that $OA = OR$ we assign the number -1. Continuing in this fashion, we may assign all the integers to equi-spaced points on the line L as indicated in Figure 1.1.

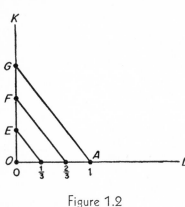

Figure 1.2

On each of the congruent segments OA, AB, BC, OR, RS, ST, and so on, n equispaced points may be selected for any positive integer n. Having done so, to the mth point on the unit segment OA (counting from O to A) we assign the rational number m/n; to the mth point on AB we assign the rational number $1 + m/n$; and so on. To points on the opposite side of the origin from A we assign the negative rational numbers. In this way, all the rational numbers can be assigned to points of the line L. These points are called the *rational points* on L.

The usual method of dividing a segment into n congruent parts is indicated in Figure 1.2 for $n = 3$. The points E, F, and G are chosen on line K (any line on O other than L) so that $OE = EF = FG$. Then lines are constructed on E and F parallel to line GA. These parallel lines divide segment OA into three congruent parts.

There are many points on line L that are not rational points. To each of the nonrational points on L may be assigned an irrational number. Considerations of rational approximations of the irrational number p and the positions of the corresponding rational points on L allow us to select that point P to which the number p may be assigned.

The number p assigned to the point P on L is called the *coordinate* of P. The notation $P(p)$ will be used to signify that P is the point that has coordinate p. We assume henceforth that each point on L has a co-ordinate and that each real number is the coordinate of a point on L. A given assignment of coordinates is called a *coordinate system*, and the line L together with a coordinate system is called a *coordinate line*.

1.15 Definition. If $P(p)$ and $Q(q)$ are points on a coordinate line, the *length* of the segment PQ is designated by $|PQ|$ and is defined to be

$$|PQ| = |q - p|.$$

The number $|PQ|$ is also called the *distance* between P and Q.

The length of a segment of a line obviously depends on the coordinate system. For example, a segment of length 24 units on a line marked off in inches has length 2 units if the line is marked off in feet. Since $|p - q| = |q - p|$, it follows that

$$|PQ| = |QP|;$$

that is, that the length of a segment PQ does not depend on the relative positions of P and Q. We note that the distance between the origin $O(0)$ and the point $P(p)$ is just $|p|$.

A coordinate system on a line L sets up a correspondence between real numbers and points in such a way that with each real number p is associated a unique point $P(p)$, and with each point P is associated a unique real number p, the coordinate of P. This correspondence is such that if L is thought of as a horizontal line,

$a < b$ if and only if $A(a)$ is to the left of $B(b)$,

and if A, B, C, and D are four points on L,

$AB = CD$ if and only if $|AB| = |CD|$.

It is possible to define a directed distance on a coordinate line as follows:

1.16 Definition. The *directed distance* from the point $P(p)$ to the point $Q(q)$ on a coordinate line is designated by $\overline{PQ}$ and is defined to be

$$\overline{PQ} = q - p.$$

Since $\overline{PQ} = q - p$ and $\overline{QP} = p - q$, it is evident that

$$\overline{PQ} = -\overline{QP}.$$

Also, we have that

$$|\overline{PQ}| = |PQ|.$$

On a horizontal coordinate line, if point $Q(q)$ is to the right of point $P(p)$, it follows that $q > p$ and hence that $\overline{PQ} = q - p > 0$. On the other hand, if $Q(q)$ is to the left of $P(p)$, then $q < p$ and $\overline{PQ} = q - p < 0$. Thus directed distance indicates clearly the relative positions of the points $P(p)$ and $Q(q)$. In particular, the directed distance from the origin to the point $P(p)$ is just p, the coordinate of P.

Example 1. Given the points $O(0)$, $A(-11/4)$, $B(1)$, $C(3)$, and $D(7/2)$, (Figure 1.3), find $\overline{AC}$, $\overline{BA}$, $\overline{AB}$, $\overline{DB}$, $\overline{OA}$, $|CD|$, $|OC|$, and $|BA|$.

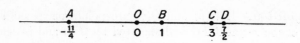

Figure 1.3

Solution:

$$\overline{AC} = 3 - (-11/4) = 23/4, \quad \overline{BA} = -11/4 - 1 = -15/4,$$
$$\overline{AB} = 1 - (-11/4) = 15/4, \quad \overline{DB} = 1 - 7/2 = -5/2,$$
$$\overline{OA} = -11/4 - 0 = -11/4, \quad |CD| = |7/2 - 3| = 1/2,$$
$$|OC| = |3 - 0| = 3, \quad |BA| = |-11/4 - 1| = 15/4.$$

Example 2. Give a geometric interpretation of the solution of the inequality $x - 1 < 2x + 1$.

Solution: The inequality has the solution

$$x > -2.$$

Hence x satisfies the given inequality if and only if the point $X(x)$ is to the right of $A(-2)$ as in Figure 1.4. The solution therefore consists of the set of all co-ordinates of points (excluding A) on the half-line with the end point A and to the right of A.

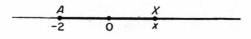

Figure 1.4

1.17 Theorem. If $P(p)$ and $Q(q)$ are points on a coordinate line, then

$$\frac{p + q}{2}$$

is the coordinate of the mid-point of the segment PQ.

Proof: If $M(m)$ is the mid-point of PQ, then

$$\overline{PM} = \overline{MQ}.$$

Hence

$$m - p = q - m,$$
$$2m = p + q,$$
$$m = \frac{(p + q)}{2}.$$

According to 1.17, the coordinate of the mid-point of a segment is the arithmetic average of the coordinates of the end points.

Example 3. Find the midpoint of the segment AD of Figure 1.3.

Solution: If $M(m)$ is the mid-point of AD, then

$$m = \frac{-\frac{11}{4} + \frac{7}{2}}{2} = \frac{3}{8}.$$

Hence $M(\frac{3}{8})$ is the mid-point of AD.

5. Intervals

If $A(a)$ and $B(b)$ are two points on a coordinate line with $a < b$, the point $X(x)$ is on the segment AB if and only if $a \leq x \leq b$. If X is between A and B (so that X is neither A nor B), then $a < x < b$.

1.18 Definition. The *open interval* determined by the numbers a and b, where $a < b$, is the set of all real numbers x such that $a < x < b$. The *closed interval* determined by a and b is the set of all x such that $a \leq x \leq b$. If just one of a or b is excluded from this closed interval, the resulting set of numbers is called a *half-open interval*.

The open interval determined by a and b will be designated by

$$(a,b),$$

whereas the closed interval will be designated by

$$[a,b].$$

The two half-open intervals are designated by

$$[a,b) \quad \text{and} \quad (a,b].$$

Thus

x is in the interval (a,b) if and only if $a < x < b$;
x is in the interval $[a,b]$ if and only if $a \leq x \leq b$;
x is in the interval $[a,b)$ if and only if $a \leq x < b$;
x is in the interval $(a,b]$ if and only if $a < x \leq b$.

Each interval clearly determines a segment of a coordinate line. For example, the interval $[a,b]$ determines the segment AB, where $A(a)$ and $B(b)$, in the sense that a point $C(c)$ is on AB if and only if the number c is in the interval $[a,b]$.

The symbol ∞, called *infinity*, is useful in many situations where large numbers are involved. However, in using this symbol, we must realize that it is not a number in the ordinary sense of the word. For example, we cannot add 3 to ∞ or divide 1 by ∞.

We shall use the notation

$$(a,\infty)$$

to designate the set of all numbers greater than a, and the notation

$$(-\infty,a)$$

to designate the set of all numbers less than a. Also, $[a,\infty)$ will designate the set of all numbers $x \geq a$, and similarly for $(-\infty,a]$. Continuing, one could use the notation $(-\infty,\infty)$ for the set of all real numbers.

Example 1. Give the interval solution of the inequality

$$|x - 2| < 1.$$

Solution: By 1.9, $|x - 2| < 1$ if and only if

$$-1 < x - 2 < 1,$$

or $$1 < x < 3.$$

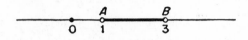

Figure 1.5

Thus the solution of the given inequality is the open interval (1,3) in the sense that the number x satisfies the given inequality if and only if x is in the interval (1,3). Geometrically the solution is represented by the open segment AB (excluding A and B, as is indicated by the hollow dots at A and B in Figure 1.5).

Example 2. Give the interval solution of the inequality

$$3x - 1 < 5x + 2.$$

Solution: The solution is obtained as follows:

$$3x - 1 < 5x + 2,$$
$$-2x < 3,$$
$$x > -\frac{3}{2}.$$

Thus the solution consists of the infinite interval $(-\frac{3}{2}, \infty)$.

Example 3. For the inequality

$$|5x + 10| < .01,$$

(a) find its interval solution.
(b) express the solution as an interval of the form $(a - c, a + c)$ having midpoint a.
(c) find a condition on $|x + 2|$ that implies the original inequality.

Solution: The solution is found as in Example 1:

$$|5x + 10| < .01,$$
$$-.01 < 5x + 10 < .01,$$
$$-.002 < x + 2 < .002,$$
$$-2.002 < x < -1.998.$$

Clearly the answer to (a) is the open interval $(-2.002, -1.998)$. The midpoint of this interval is -2. Thus the answer to (b) is $(-2 - .002, -2 + .002)$. Since x satisfies the given inequality if and only if $-.002 < x + 2 < .002$, the answer to (c) is $|x + 2| < .002$.

■ ■ ■ EXERCISES

In each of the following, give the interval solution of the inequality. Also sketch the corresponding segment of a coordinate line.

1. $-3 < x + 3 < 2.$

2. $1 < 2x - 1 < 3.$

3. $|x - 5| \leq 1.$

4. $|x + 2| \leq .1.$

5. $2 \leq 3 - 4x < 3.$

6. $5 < 5x + 1 \leq 7.$

7. $|2x + 3| < .01.$

8. $|3 - x| < .02.$

9. $-1 < 4 + 2x \leq 0.$

10. $-5 < 1 - 3x \leq 4.$

11. $|x - .01| \leq .001.$

12. $|.1x + 3| < .12.$

13. $-9 \leq 3x - 6 < 0.$

14. $x^2 < 4.$

15. $\dfrac{1}{x} > 10.$

16. $\dfrac{2}{x - 1} > -1.$

17. Show that if $|x| > b$ where $b > 0$, then x lies outside the interval $[-b,b]$.

18. Give a geometric solution of the inequality $|x - 1| > 5.$

19. Let ϵ (epsilon) be a positive number. Find the interval solution of the inequality

$$|5x + 10| < \epsilon.$$

Find a condition on $|x + 2|$ that implies the given inequality.

20. Let a and b be any numbers and m and ϵ be positive numbers. Find the interval solution of the inequality

$$|(mx + b) - (ma + b)| < \epsilon.$$

Find a condition on $|x - a|$ that implies the given inequality.

21. Note that

$$|\sqrt{x} - 2| = \frac{|x - 4|}{\sqrt{x} + 2} \leq \frac{|x - 4|}{2},$$

and therefore that $|\sqrt{x} - 2| < .01$ if $|x - 4| < .02$. Hence the interval $(3.98, 4.02)$ is a solution (although not the largest interval solution) of the inequality $|\sqrt{x} - 2| < .01$. In a similar way, find an interval solution of the inequality $(a > 0, \epsilon > 0)$

$$|\sqrt{x} - \sqrt{a}| < \epsilon.$$

22. Note that if $x > \frac{3}{2}$, then

$$\left|\frac{1}{x} - \frac{1}{3}\right| = \frac{|x - 3|}{3x} \leq \frac{2}{9}|x - 3|.$$

Hence $|1/x - 1/3| < .01$ if $|x - 3| < .045$, and $(3 - .045, 3 + .045)$ is an interval solution (although not the largest one) of the inequality $|1/x - 1/3| < .01$. In a similar way, find an interval solution of the inequality $(a > 0, \epsilon > 0)$

$$\left|\frac{1}{x} - \frac{1}{a}\right| < \epsilon.$$

intersection of L and the line L' through P which is perpendicualr to L (Figure 2.1). If P lies on L, P is its own projection on L.

For a point P in the plane, let $A(a)$ and $B(b)$ be the projections of P on the x-axis and y-axis, respectively (Figure 2.2). Then the numbers a and b are called the *coordinates* of P and we write $P(a,b)$ to indicate that P has x-coordinate (or *abscissa*) a and y-coordinate (or *ordinate*) b.

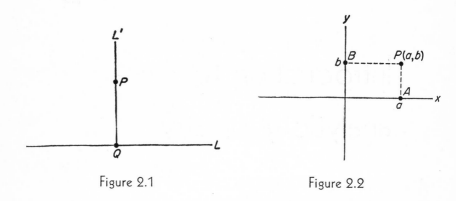

Figure 2.1   Figure 2.2

In this way there is associated with each point P on the plane a pair (a,b) of numbers. Conversely, with each pair (a,b) of numbers there is associated the point $P(a,b)$ of intersection of the line perpendicular to the x-axis at the point $A(a)$ and the line perpendicular to the y-axis at the point $B(b)$ (as in Figure 2.2). This association of pairs of numbers with points is called a *rectangular coordinate system* in the plane, and a plane together with a coordinate system is called a *coordinate plane*. Some examples of points with their coordinates are given in Figure 2.3.

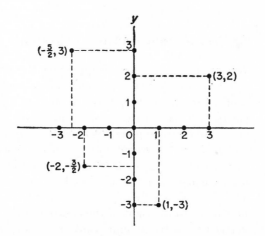

Figure 2.3

The coordinate axes divide the plane into four parts, or *quadrants*, numbered as in Figure 2.4. Each point in the plane is either on a coordinate axis or in one of the four quadrants. The point $P(a,b)$ is in the first quadrant if and only if $a > 0$ and $b > 0$. Similar statements may be made for the points in the other quadrants.

Since the pair of coordinates completely specifies the point, it is customary when convenient to designate the point $P(a,b)$ by the number pair (a,b) without the letter P. We recall that (a,b) is also used to designate an open interval. No confusion should result from this, since the context will always clearly indicate which use of the notation (a,b) is meant.

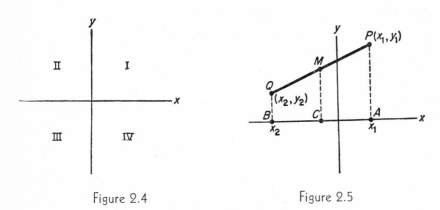

Figure 2.4   Figure 2.5

The point $A(a)$ on the x-axis will have the origin as its projection on the y-axis and hence will be the point $(a,0)$ on the plane. Similarly, the point $B(b)$ on the y-axis will be the point $(0,b)$ on the plane. The point of intersection of the two axes is called the *origin* of the coordinate system, and has coordinates $(0,0)$. The projections of the point (a,b) on the x- and y-axes will be the points $(a,0)$ and $0,b)$, respectively.

2.1 Theorem. If $P(x_1,y_1)$ and $Q(x_2,y_2)$ are two points on a coordinate plane, then

$$M\left(\frac{x_1 + x_2}{2}, \frac{y_1 + y_2}{2}\right)$$

is the mid-point of the line segment PQ.

Proof: The projections on the x-axis of P and Q are the points $A(x_1,0)$ and $B(x_2,0)$, respectively (Figure 2.5). The projection C of M on the x-axis is the mid-point of the segment AB according to a result of Euclidean geometry. Thus, by 1.17, C has coordinates

$$\left(\frac{x_1 + x_2}{2}, 0\right).$$

Hence, by definition, $(x_1 + x_2)/2$ is the abscissa of M. A similar argument relative to the y-axis shows that M has ordinate $(y_1 + y_2)/2$.

of the given equation for which $x < -1$ or $y < 0$. A selection of points on the graph is given by the following table of values:

x	-1	0	1	2	3	4	5	6	7	8
y	0	1	$\sqrt{2}$	$\sqrt{3}$	2	$\sqrt{5}$	$\sqrt{6}$	$\sqrt{7}$	$2\sqrt{2}$	3

Using these points, the graph is sketched in Figure 2.8.

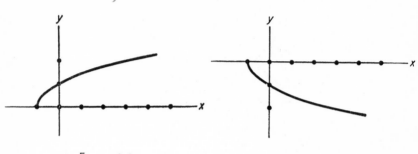

Figure 2.8   Figure 2.9

Example 2.   Sketch the graph of the equation

$$y = -\sqrt{x + 1}.$$

Solution: It is clear that for every point (a,b) on the graph of $y = \sqrt{x + 1}$, the point $(a,-b)$ is on the graph of $y = -\sqrt{x + 1}$. For example,

$$(-1,0), \quad (0,-1), \quad (2,-\sqrt{3}), \quad (3,-2), \quad (8,-3)$$

are on the graph of $y = -\sqrt{x + 1}$. The graph is sketched in Figure 2.9.

Example 3.   Sketch the graph of the equation

$$y^2 = x + 1.$$

Solution: If $y^2 = x + 1$, then either

$$y = \sqrt{x + 1} \quad \text{or} \quad y = -\sqrt{x + 1}.$$

Thus a point is on the graph of $y^2 = x + 1$ if and only if it is on the graph of $y = \sqrt{x + 1}$ or on the graph of $y = -\sqrt{x + 1}$. Hence the graph of $y^2 = x + 1$ is the composite of the two previous graphs, and is sketched in Figure 2.10.

This graph is a parabola, and we may say that $y^2 = x + 1$ is an equation of the parabola. Furthermore, $y = \sqrt{x + 1}$ is an equation of the upper half of the parabola and $y = -\sqrt{x + 1}$ is an equation of the lower half.

Example 4.   Sketch the graph of the equation

$$y = |x|.$$

Solution: Since $|x| = x$ if $x \geq 0$, the graphs of $y = |x|$ and $y = x$ coincide if $x \geq 0$. Thus this part of the graph is a straight line bisecting the first quadrant. On the other hand, $|x| = -x$ if $x \leq 0$; and therefore the graphs of

$$y = |x| \quad \text{and} \quad y = -x$$

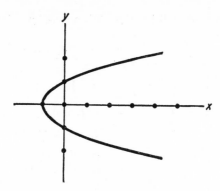

Figure 2.10

coincide if $x \leq 0$.   This part of the graph is a straight line bisecting the second quadrant.   Hence the total graph of $y = |x|$ consists of two half-lines emanating from the origin as in Figure 2.11.

With proper labeling of axes, the graph of the equation

$$v^2 = u + 1$$

will be the same as the graph of $y^2 = x + 1$, namely, the parabolic curve of Figure 2.10.   Also, the equation

$$s = |t|$$

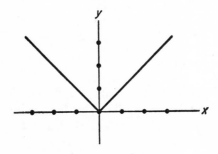

Figure 2.11

has the same graph as $y = |x|$ if t- and s-axes are used in place of x- and y-axes.

Example 5.   Find an equation for the line on the point $A(-1,2)$ parallel to the x-axis; parallel to the y-axis.

Solution: Let L be the line on A parallel to the x-axis.   Then a point $P(x,y)$ lies on L if and only if its projection on the y-axis is the point $(0,2)$; i.e., if and only if $y = 2$.   Thus

$$y = 2$$

is an equation of L.

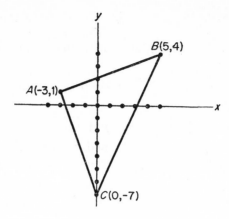

Figure 2.14

Solution: We have by the distance formula that

$$|AB| = \sqrt{(5 - (-3))^2 + (4 - 1)^2}$$
$$= \sqrt{73},$$
$$|AC| = \sqrt{(0 - (-3))^2 + (-7 - 1)^2}$$
$$= \sqrt{73},$$
$$|BC| = \sqrt{(0 - 5)^2 + (-7 - 4)^2}$$
$$= \sqrt{146}.$$

Since $|AB|^2 + |AC|^2 = 73 + 73 = 146 = |BC|^2,$

the triangle has a right angle at vertex A. It happens that this triangle also is isosceles, since $|AB| = |AC|$.

The area of the right triangle ABC is given by

$$\frac{1}{2}|AB| \cdot |AC| = \frac{1}{2}\sqrt{73} \cdot \sqrt{73} = \frac{73}{2}.$$

4. Circles

A circle may be defined as a curve in a plane all of whose points are equidistant from a fixed point. The distance formula of the previous section can be used to give the following analytic description of a circle.

2.4 Theorem. The circle with center $C(h,k)$ and radius r has equation

$$(x - h)^2 + (y - k)^2 = r^2.$$

Proof: The point $P(x,y)$ is on the given circle if and only if

$$|PC| = r,$$

that is, if and only if

$$\sqrt{(x - h)^2 + (y - k)^2} = r,$$

or $$(x - h)^2 + (y - k)^2 = r^2.$$

This equation, satisfied by the coordinates of those and only those points on the given circle, is therefore an equation of the circle.

In the light of the definition of the graph of an equation (2.2), we have also proved that the *graph of the equation*

$$(x - h)^2 + (y - k)^2 = r^2$$

is the circle with center $C(h,k)$ and radius r.

As a particular case,

$$x^2 + y^2 = r^2$$

is an equation of a circle of radius r and with center at the origin.

Example 1. Find an equation of the circle with center $C(4,-3)$ and radius 6.

Solution: In this example,

$$h = 4, \quad k = -3, \quad r = 6.$$

By 2.4, $$(x - 4)^2 + [y - (-3)]^2 = 6^2,$$

or $$(x - 4)^2 + (y + 3)^2 = 36$$

is an equation of the circle. After noting that $(x - 4)^2 = x^2 - 8x + 16$ and $(y + 3)^2 = y^2 + 6y + 9$, we may also write the following equation of the circle:

$$x^2 + y^2 - 8x + 6y - 11 = 0.$$

The circle is drawn in Figure 2.15.

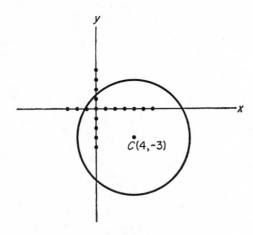

Figure 2.15

Example 2. Show that the graph of the equation

$$x^2 + y^2 + 4x - 2y - 1 = 0$$

is a circle, and find its center and radius.

Solution: The given equation is equivalent to the equation

$$x^2 + y^2 + 4x - 2y = 1.$$

Adding the numbers 4 and 1 to each side of this equation to complete squares, we have

$$x^2 + 4x + 4 + y^2 - 2y + 1 = 1 + 4 + 1,$$

or
$$(x + 2)^2 + (y - 1)^2 = (\sqrt{6})^2.$$

We recognize this to be the equation of a circle with center $C(-2,1)$ and radius $r = \sqrt{6}$ (Figure 2.16).

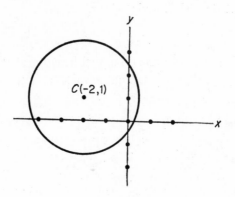

Figure 2.16

A set of points defined geometrically is sometimes called a *locus*. Thus a circle is a locus of points all at a given distance from a fixed center. The locus of points equidistant from the points $A(-1,0)$ and $B(1,0)$ is the perpendicular bisector of the line segment AB, i.e., the y-axis.

Example 3. Find an equation of the locus of all points $P(x,y)$ in a coordinate plane such that the distance between P and $A(5,1)$ is three times the distance between P and $B(-3,1)$.

Solution: Let $P(x,y)$ be a point on the locus (Figure 2.17). It is given that

$$|PA| = 3|PB|,$$

and therefore, using the distance formula,

$$\sqrt{(x - 5)^2 + (y - 1)^2} = 3\sqrt{(x + 3)^2 + (y - 1)^2}.$$

Since $P(x,y)$ is on the locus if and only if the coordinates of P satisfy the above equation, this is an equation of the locus.

If we observe that the quantities under the radical signs in the above equation are nonnegative for every choice of x and y, then it is clear x and y satisfy the above equation if and only if they satisfy the equation

$$(x - 5)^2 + (y - 1)^2 = 9[(x + 3)^2 + (y - 1)^2].$$

This also must be an equation of the locus. In turn, this latter equation can

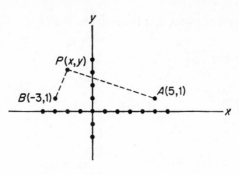

Figure 2.17

be changed into an equivalent form

$$8x^2 + 8y^2 + 64x - 16y + 64 = 0,$$

or $$x^2 + y^2 + 8x - 2y + 8 = 0.$$

Upon completing squares, we get

$$(x + 4)^2 + (y - 1)^2 = 9.$$

From this final form of the equation, we deduce that the given locus is a circle with center $C(-4,1)$ and radius $r = 3$.

■ ■ ■ EXERCISES

In each of Exercises 1–6, show that ABC is a right triangle. Use the fact that the center of the circle circumscribed about ABC is the mid-point of the hypotenuse to find the equation of each circumscribed circle. Sketch.

1. $A(1,0)$, $B(5,3)$, $C(4,-4)$.
2. $A(1,0)$, $B(4,2)$, $C(-3,6)$.
3. $A(4,4)$, $B(1,5)$, $C(-2,-4)$.
4. $A(3,-2)$, $B(4,3)$, $C(-6,5)$.
5. $A(0,1)$, $B(2,3)$, $C(0,5)$.
6. $A(1,-2)$, $B(0,0)$, $C(-2,-1)$.

In each of Exercises 7–12, find an equation of the circle. Sketch.

7. Center $(-1,-3)$, radius $r = 3$.
8. Center $(3,0)$, radius $r = 5$.
9. Center $(2,4)$, passing through the origin.
10. Center $(0,0)$, passing through the point $(3,7)$.
11. Radius $r = 4$, tangent to both coordinate axes, lying in the second quadrant.
12. Radius $r = 1$, tangent to both coordinate axes, lying in the fourth quadrant.

In each of Exercises 13–20, find the center and radius of the circle with given equation. Sketch.

13. $x^2 + y^2 - 16 = 0.$

14. $x^2 + y^2 - 2x - 4y + 1 = 0.$

15. $x^2 + y^2 + 6x - 10y + 25 = 0.$

16. $4x^2 + 4y^2 + 16x + 15 = 0.$

17. $2x^2 + 2y^2 + 4y + 1 = 0.$

18. $x^2 + y^2 + 6x + 8y = 0.$

19. $9x^2 + 9y^2 - 6x + 12y + 4 = 0.$

20. $4x^2 + 4y^2 + 4x - 12y + 7 = 0.$

21. Find an equation of the locus of all points $P(x,y)$ in a coordinate plane twice as far from the point $A(1,0)$ as from the point $B(-2,0)$.

22. Find an equation of the locus of all points $P(x,y)$ in a coordinate plane equidistant from the points $A(2,1)$ and $B(4,-1)$.

23. Show that the point $P(x,y)$ is equidistant from the point $(0,4)$ and the x-axis if and only if $x^2 - 8y + 16 = 0.$

24. Find the center and radius of the circle with equation

$$x^2 + y^2 + ax + by + c = 0.$$

Under what conditions on a, b, and c will the equation have no graph? Is the graph ever just a point?

5. Slope of a line

It is convenient to think of an angle between two lines in a plane as being formed by rotating one of the lines, about the fixed vertex of the angle, until it coincides with the other line. The angle has positive measure if the rotation is counterclockwise and negative measure otherwise.

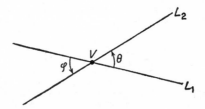

Figure 2.18

Given two lines L_1 and L_2 intersecting at V, the *angle from L_1 to L_2* is defined to be the angle of least positive measure formed by rotating L_1 about V to L_2. The congruent angles θ and ϕ of Figure 2.18 are the angles from L_1 to L_2. It is clear that the angle from L_1 to L_2 has measure between

0° and 180° (or, between 0 and π radians). We shall follow the conventional practice of considering parallel lines as intersecting in an angle of measure 0°.

Useful concepts in the determination of an equation of a straight line in a coordinate plane are inclination and slope as defined below.

2.5 Definition. The *inclination* of a line is the angle α from the x-axis to the line. The *slope m* of the line is given by

$$m = \tan \alpha.$$

The inclination α of a line L satisfies the inequality

$$0° \le \alpha < 180°,$$

with $\alpha = 0°$ if and only if L is parallel to the x-axis. A line parallel to the y-axis has an inclination of 90°.

For each number r there exists a unique angle α, $0° \le \alpha < 180°$, such that $\tan \alpha = r$. Thus the slope of a line can be any real number. *The slope of a line parallel to the x-axis is zero.* Since tan 90° does not exist, *a line parallel to the y-axis does not have slope.* Conversely, a line that does not have slope is parallel to the y-axis.

Since $\tan \alpha > 0$ if $0° < \alpha < 90°$, the lines that are rising (as we move from left to right along the line) have positive slope; and since $\tan \alpha < 0$ if $90° < \alpha < 180°$, the lines that are falling have negative slope.

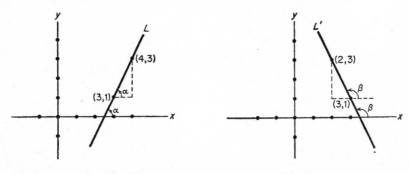

Figure 2.19   Figure 2.20

Example 1. Construct the line on the point (3,1) that has slope 2; that has slope -2.

Solution: Start from the point (3,1) and construct a right triangle with altitude twice its base as in Figure 2.19. Then draw the line L on the vertices (3,1) and (4,3) of this triangle. The inclination α of L is an angle of the right triangle, and we see that $\tan \alpha = 2$. The line L of slope 2 is rising.

In order to construct a line of slope -2, start from the point (3,1) and construct a right triangle with altitude twice its base as in Figure 2.20. Then draw the line L' on the vertices (3,1) and (2,3) of this right triangle. The inclination β is the supplement of the angle α of the right triangle, and therefore

$$\tan \beta = -\tan \alpha = -2.$$

The line L' of slope -2 is falling.

Given two distinct points on a line not parallel to the y-axis the slope of the line may be found by the following theorem.

2.6 Theorem. The slope m of the line L on the points $P(x_1,y_1)$ and $Q(x_2,y_2)$ is given by

$$m = \frac{y_2 - y_1}{x_2 - x_1}, \qquad x_2 \neq x_1.$$

Proof: Let us assume that $y_1 < y_2$, so that Q is above P. Construct a line x' through P and parallel to the x-axis (Figure 2.21). Then the

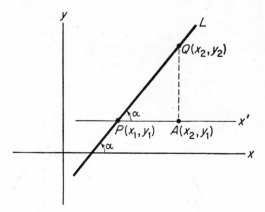

Figure 2.21

inclination α of L is the same relative to both the x-axis and the x'-axis. By definition (notation of Figure 2.21),

$$\tan \alpha = \frac{\overline{AQ}}{\overline{PA}};$$

and since $\overline{AQ} = y_2 - y_1$ and $\overline{PA} = x_2 - x_1$,

$$m = \tan \alpha = \frac{y_2 - y_1}{x_2 - x_1}.$$

If $y_2 < y_1$, we construct the line x' through Q and obtain by the same reasoning as above that

$$m = \frac{y_1 - y_2}{x_1 - x_2}.$$

Since

$$\frac{y_2 - y_1}{x_2 - x_1} = \frac{y_1 - y_2}{x_1 - x_2},$$

this agrees with the previous result.

If $y_1 = y_2$, the line L is parallel to the x-axis and $m = 0$.　Since

$$\frac{y_2 - y_1}{x_2 - x_1} = 0$$

in this case, the formula again gives the correct result.

Example 2.　Find the slope m of the line on the points $(3,4)$ and $(5,-1)$.

Solution: We identify one of these points, say $(3,4)$, with $P(x_1,y_1)$ and the other, $(5,-1)$, with $Q(x_2,y_2)$ in 2.3.　Hence

$$m = \frac{-1 - 4}{5 - 3} = -\frac{5}{2}.$$

If we let P be $(5,-1)$ and Q be $(3,4)$, we again obtain

$$m = \frac{4 - (-1)}{3 - 5} = -\frac{5}{2}.$$

6. Parallel and perpendicular lines

If the lines L_1 and L_2 are parallel, then their inclinations and slopes are equal.　Conversely, if the slopes of lines L_1 and L_2 are equal, then so are their inclinations, and lines L_1 and L_2 are parallel.　We state these observations in the following compact form.

2.7 Theorem.　The lines L_1 and L_2 with slopes m_1 and m_2, respectively, are parallel if and only if $m_1 = m_2$.

A test for the perpendicularity of two lines is given by the next theorem.

2.8 Theorem.　The lines L_1 and L_2 with slopes m_1 and m_2, respectively, are perpendicular if and only if

$$m_1 = -\frac{1}{m_2}.$$

Proof: If α_1 and α_2 are the inclinations of L_1 and L_2, we assume the notation is so chosen that $\alpha_2 > \alpha_1$ (Figure 2.22).

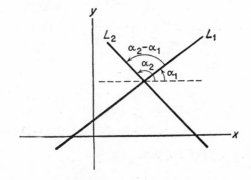

Figure 2.22

If L_1 and L_2 are perpendicular, then $\alpha_2 - \alpha_1 = 90°$, and since $\cos 90° = 0$

$$\cos (\alpha_2 - \alpha_1) = \cos \alpha_2 \cos \alpha_1 + \sin \alpha_2 \sin \alpha_1 = 0.$$

Therefore

$$\frac{\sin \alpha_1}{\cos \alpha_1} = -\frac{\cos \alpha_2}{\sin \alpha_2}, \quad \tan \alpha_1 = -\frac{1}{\tan \alpha_2}, \quad m_1 = -\frac{1}{m_2}.$$

Conversely, if $m_1 = -1/m_2$, a reversal of the argument of the previous paragraph proves that $\cos (\alpha_2 - \alpha_1) = 0$ and hence that $\alpha_2 - \alpha_1 = 90°$. Thus L_1 and L_2 are perpendicular.

According to this theorem, two lines (neither of which is parallel to an axis) are perpendicular if and only if their slopes are *negative reciprocals* of each other.

Example 1. Show that the triangle with vertices $A(-1,-1)$, $B(-9,6)$, and $C(-2,14)$ is a right triangle.

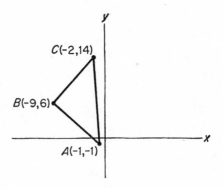

Figure 2.23

Solution: The slopes of the sides of triangle ABC (Figure 2.23) are as follows:

$$\text{slope of } AB = \frac{6 - (-1)}{-9 - (-1)} = -\frac{7}{8},$$

$$\text{slope of } AC = \frac{14 - (-1)}{-2 - (-1)} = -15,$$

$$\text{slope of } BC = \frac{14 - 6}{-2 - (-9)} = \frac{8}{7}.$$

Since $-\frac{7}{8}$ and $\frac{8}{7}$ are negative reciprocals, sides AB and BC are perpendicular. Hence ABC is a right triangle with right angle at B.

Example 2. Show that the points $A(-1,4)$, $B(0,2)$, $C(2,-2)$ are collinear.

Solution: If m_1 is the slope of AB, then

$$m_1 = \frac{4 - 2}{-1 - 0} = -2.$$

If m_2 is the slope of BC, then

$$m_2 = \frac{2 - (-2)}{0 - 2} = -2,$$

and $m_1 = m_2$. The lines AB and BC have the point B in common, and since there is one and only one line L on B with given slope, it follows that A, B, C lie on L.

Example 3. Determine y so that the point $P(1,y)$ lies on the perpendicular bisector of the line segment whose endpoints are $A(-1,2)$ and $B(-3,0)$.

Solution: The mid-point of the line segment AB is the point $M(-2,1)$. The slope of AB is $m = 1$. Hence the point $P(1,y)$ will lie on the perpendicular bisector of AB if and only if the slope of PM is $-1/m = -1$, i.e., if and only if

$$\frac{y - 1}{1 - (-2)} = -1,$$

or
$$y = -2.$$

∎ ∎ ∎ EXERCISES

1. Show that $(0,3)$, $(-2,12)$, $(-4,11)$, and $(2,4)$ are vertices of a rectangle.
2. Determine x so that the line on the points $A(2,-3)$ and $P(x,3)$ has slope 2.

In each of Exercises 3–6, show by means of slopes that the three points are collinear.

3. $(1,-1)$, $(-2,5)$, $(3,-5)$.   4. $(2,0)$, $(4,1)$, $(-6,-4)$.
5. $(-1,1)$, $(2,3)$, $(-4,-1)$.   6. $(-6,3)$, $(4,-1)$, $(3,-\frac{3}{5})$.
7. Show that the point $P(6,3)$ is on the perpendicular bisector of the line segment with end points $A(3,2)$ and $B(7,6)$.
8. Determine y so that the point $P(1,y)$ lies on the perpendicular bisector of the segment AB in Exercise 7.
9. Show that if $x \neq 2$, the line on the points $A(2,-1)$ and $P(x,3-2x)$ has slope -2.
10. Given the line L on the point $A(-1,-1)$ with slope 2, show that for every number x the point $P(x,2x+1)$ lies on L. (Consider the two cases $x = -1$ and $x \neq -1$.)
11. Given the line L on the point $A(3,1)$ with slope $-\frac{1}{2}$, show that for every number x the point $P(x,-\frac{1}{2}x+\frac{5}{2})$ lies on L.
12. Determine y so that the line L on the points $A(1,-1)$ and $P(x,y)$ will have slope 3 where $x \neq 1$.
13. Show that $y = 3x - 4$ is an equation of the line L in Exercise 12.
14. Find an equation of the line on the points $A(1,2)$ and $B(-5,3)$.
15. Given points $A(-1,-1)$, $B(-9,6)$, and $C(-2,14)$, so that the triangle ABC has a right angle at B (see Example 1 above in the text), find coordinates of the point D such that $ABCD$ is a rectangle.

7. *Equations of lines*

The line on the point (a,b) and parallel to the y-axis has equation

$$x = a,$$

since a point $P(x,y)$ is on this line if and only if $x = a$ (Figure 2.24). Similarly, the line on the point (a,b) and parallel to the x-axis has equation

$$y = b,$$

since a point is on this line if and only if it has coordinates of the form (x,b) (Figure 2.24).

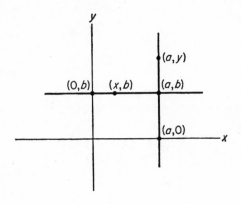

Figure 2.24

An equation of a line not parallel to a coordinate axis may be obtained in the following way. Let L be a line with given slope m that passes through a given point $Q(x_1,y_1)$ as in Figure 2.25. Then a point $P(x,y)$, different from Q, is on L if and only if the line on P and Q has slope m, that is, if and only if the coordinates of P satisfy the equation

$$m = \frac{y - y_1}{x - x_1}, \qquad x \neq x_1.$$

When this equation is written in the form

2.9 $$y - y_1 = m(x - x_1),$$

it is called the *point-slope form* of the equation of the line passing through the point (x_1,y_1) and with slope m. Note that the coordinates of $Q(x_1,y_1)$ as well as those of the points $P(x,y)$ on L different from Q satisfy 2.9, since trivially

$$y_1 - y_1 = m(x_1 - x_1).$$

Example 1. Find an equation of the line on the points $(-1,4)$ and $(5,6)$ (Figure 2.26).

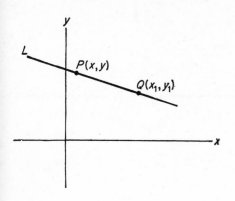

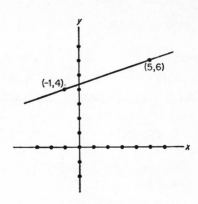

Figure 2.25   Figure 2.26

Solution: The slope of the line is given by

$$m = \frac{6-4}{5+1} = \frac{1}{3}.$$

Taking $(-1,4)$ as the given point (x_1, y_1) and $m = \frac{1}{3}$, we have by 2.9 that an equation of the line is

$$y - 4 = \frac{1}{3}(x + 1).$$

This may be simplified to the form

(1) $x - 3y + 13 = 0.$

Had we chosen $(5,6)$ for the point (x_1, y_1) in 2.9, we would have obtained

$$y - 6 = \frac{1}{3}(x - 5)$$

as an equation of the line. However, it may be verified that this reduces to the previous equation (1).

Example 2. Find an equation of the line on the point $(3,-2)$ and perpendicular to the line of the previous example (Figure 2.27).

Solution: Since the slope of the line of Example 1 is $\frac{1}{3}$, the slope of the line in question is the negative reciprocal of $\frac{1}{3}$, that is, -3. Hence its equation is

$$y + 2 = -3(x - 3),$$

or $3x + y - 7 = 0.$

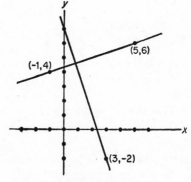

Figure 2.27

If a line L crosses the x-axis at the point $(a,0)$, then the number a is called the *x-intercept* of L. Similarly, if L crosses the y-axis at $(0,b)$, the number b is called the *y-intercept* of L.

An equation of the line having slope m and passing through the point

$(0,b)$ is, by 2.9,
$$y - b = m(x - 0),$$
or

2.10 $y = mx + b.$

This is called the *slope-intercept form* of the equation of L, since it involves only the slope m and the y-intercept b of L.

For example,
$$y = -3x + 7$$
is an equation of the line with slope -3 and y-intercept **7**. This is the line of Figure 2.27.

An equation of the form

2.11 $Ax + By + C = 0,$

where A, B, and C are given numbers with not both A and B equal to zero, is called an *equation of the first degree* in x and y. It is clear from our previous results that every straight line has an equation of the first degree. We shall now show that, conversely, the graph of every first-degree equation is a straight line.

If $B = 0$, then $A \neq 0$ and 2.11 has the form
$$Ax + C = 0,$$
or, equivalently,
$$x = -\frac{C}{A},$$
which is an equation of a straight line parallel to the y-axis. Multiplication of both sides of an equation by a nonzero number or transposition of terms in an equation does not change the graph of the equation. Hence, if $B = 0$, the graph of 2.11 is a straight line parallel to the y-axis.

If $B \neq 0$, Equation 2.11 may be put in the form
$$y = -\frac{A}{B}x - \frac{C}{B},$$
which is the slope-intercept form of an equation of a line with slope $-A/B$ and y-intercept $-C/B$. Hence, if $B \neq 0$, the graph of 2.11 is a straight line.

This proves what we started out to show, namely, that the graph of every equation of the first degree in x and y is a straight line. Since the graph of every first-degree equation is a straight line, such an equation is frequently called a linear equation.

An easy way to graph a linear equation is to put the equation in the slope-intercept form, as illustrated in the following example.

Example 3. Sketch the graph of the linear equation
$$3x + 4y - 6 = 0.$$

Solution: The given equation may be solved for y as follows:

$$4y = -3x + 6,$$

$$y = -\frac{3}{4}x + \frac{3}{2}.$$

We recognize this equation to be the equation of the line with slope $-\frac{3}{4}$ and y-intercept $\frac{3}{2}$. Its graph is sketched in Figure 2.28. The x-intercept of the

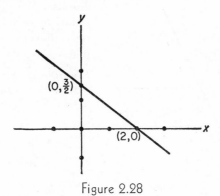

Figure 2.28

line is 2, as may be seen by letting $y = 0$ in the equation and solving the resulting equation for x.

Two nonparallel lines have a point of intersection. This point can be found by solving simultaneously the equations of the lines, since a point lies on two graphs if and only if its coordinates satisfy the equations of both graphs.

Example 4. Find the point of intersection of the lines with equations

$$6x - 3y - 10 = 0 \quad \text{and} \quad 2x + 6y - 1 = 0.$$

Solution: The coordinates of the point of intersection of these two lines must satisfy both equations; that is, they must be the simultaneous solution of these equations. The given equations have slope-intercept form

$$y = 2x - \frac{10}{3} \quad \text{and} \quad y = -\frac{1}{3}x + \frac{1}{6}.$$

Their simultaneous solution may be found by eliminating y as follows:

$$2x - \frac{10}{3} = -\frac{1}{3}x + \frac{1}{6},$$

$$12x - 20 = -2x + 1,$$

$$14x = 21,$$

$$x = \frac{3}{2}.$$

Then
$$y = 2 \cdot \frac{3}{2} - \frac{10}{3} = -\frac{1}{3},$$

so that $(\frac{3}{2}, -\frac{1}{3})$ is the required point of intersection (see Figure 2.29).

The points of intersection of any two graphs can be found similarly by solving simultaneously the equations of the graphs. We illustrate this procedure by finding the points of intersection of a circle and a straight line.

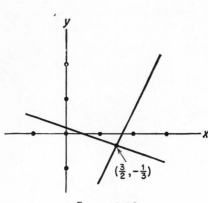

Figure 2.29

Example 5. Find the points of intersection of the circle with equation

$$x^2 - 8x + y^2 + 11 = 0$$

and the line with equation

$$x + y - 5 = 0.$$

Solution: The slope-intercept form of the equation of the line is

$$y = -x + 5.$$

Substituting this value of y in the equation of the circle, we obtain

$$x^2 - 8x + (-x + 5)^2 + 11 = 0,$$

which reduces to

$$x^2 - 9x + 18 = 0.$$

This quadratic equation may be factored to yield

$$(x - 3)(x - 6) = 0.$$

Thus $x = 3$ and $x = 6$ are the abscissas of the points of intersection of the line

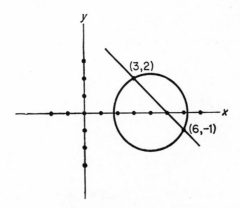

Figure 2.30

and the circle. The ordinate of each point may be found by substituting each x value in the second of the given equations and solving for y. Thus, if $x = 3$, $y = -3 + 5 = 2$; if $x = 6$, $y = -6 + 5 = -1$. The points of intersection are $(3,2)$ and $(6,-1)$, as sketched in Figure 2.30.

■ ■ ■ EXERCISES

In each of Exercises 1–12, find an equation of the line satisfying the given conditions.

1. On $(5,1)$ and $(-1,-1)$.

2. On $(3,3)$ and $(7,6)$.

3. With slope 3 and y-intercept -3.

4. With slope $-\frac{1}{2}$ and passing through the point $(-3,-5)$.

5. With slope 4 and passing through the point $(1,6)$.

6. With x-intercept 3 and y-intercept 2.

7. With x-intercept $-\frac{1}{3}$ and slope 6.

8. On $(-1,2)$ and $(-1,-3)$.

9. On $(-4,1)$ and $(3,1)$.

10. With x-intercept a and y-intercept b.

11. With x-intercept a and slope m.

12. With inclination $135°$ and y-intercept -2.

In each of Exercises 13–20, find the slope and intercepts, and sketch the line with given equations.

13. $2x - y + 3 = 0$.

14. $3x - 2y + 2 = 0$.

15. $x + 2y + 6 = 0$.

16. $5x + y - 2 = 0$.

17. $3x + 5 = 0$.

18. $4y - 1 = 0$.

19. $5x + y + 15 = 0$.

20. $2x + 4y - 1 = 0$.

In each of Exercises 21–26, find the equations of the lines on the given point that are, respectively, parallel and perpendicular to the given line. Sketch.

21. $(3,3)$, $2x + y - 1 = 0$.

22. $(-1,4)$, $3x - y + 5 = 0$.

23. $(2,-1)$, $3x - 2y - 8 = 0$.

24. $(5,1)$, $2x - 4y - 5 = 0$.

25. $(0,0)$, $4x + 7y - 1 = 0$.

26. $(-1,-1)$, $3x + 7 = 0$.

In each of Exercises 27–30, find the point of intersection of the lines with given equations.

27. $3x - y + 4 = 0$
$x - 2y + 18 = 0$.

28. $2x + y - 3 = 0$
$x - 3y - 12 = 0$.

29. $3x + 2y - 7 = 0$
$2x + 3y + 2 = 0$.

30. $5x + y - 2 = 0$
$3x - 2y + 7 = 0$.

In each of Exercises 31–34, find the points of intersection of the line and circle with given equations.

31. $4x - 3y - 10 = 0$
$x^2 + y^2 - 2x + 4y - 20 = 0$.

32. $x - y + 1 = 0$
$x^2 + y^2 + 6x - 10y + 9 = 0$.

33. $3x - 4y + 10 = 0$ **34.** $x - y - 5 = 0$
      $x^2 + y^2 - 10x = 0.$ $x^2 + y^2 - 4y - 1 = 0.$

35. Show that $Ax + By = Ax_1 + By_1$ is an equation of the line on the point (x_1, y_1) and parallel to the line $Ax + By + C = 0$.

36. Show that $Bx - Ay = Bx_1 - Ay_1$ is an equation of the line on the point (x_1, y_1) and perpendicular to the line $Ax + By + C = 0$.

In Exercises 37–39, sketch the graph of the equation.

37. $y = |x - 2|$.   (Consider $x \geq 2$ and $x \leq 2$.)

38. $|x| + |y| = 1$.   **39.** $|x + y| = 1$.

8. Analytic methods in geometry

The methods of analytic geometry may be used to solve problems of Euclidean geometry. This is done by considering the geometric configuration under study to be on a coordinate plane. Lines, circles, and other curves of the configuration may be thought of as graphs of certain equations. Properties of the geometric configuration then can be derived from algebraic considerations of the corresponding equations.

We illustrate such analytic methods in geometry in the following examples. In each example, the coordinate system is chosen as advantageously as possible to simplify the algebraic calculations.

Example 1. Prove that the mid-points of the sides of a quadrilateral are the vertices of a parallelogram.

Solution: Let us choose the coordinate axes so that the vertices A and B of the quadrilateral $ABCD$ are on the x-axis as in Figure 2.31. Let E, F, G, and H be the mid-points of sides AB, BC, CD, and DA, respectively. We shall prove that opposite sides of the quadrilateral $EFGH$ are parallel. The slope of EF

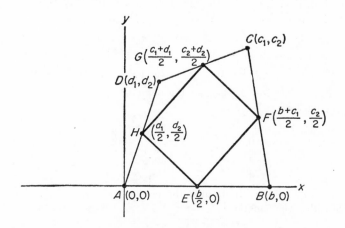

Figure 2.31

is given by

$$\frac{c_2/2}{[(b + c_1)/2] - b/2} = \frac{c_2}{(b + c_1) - b} = \frac{c_2}{c_1},$$

that of GH by

$$\frac{[(c_2 + d_2)/2] - d_2/2}{[(c_1 + d_1)/2] - d_1/2} = \frac{c_2}{c_1}.$$

Thus sides EF and GH are parallel. The proof that FG and EH are parallel is similar, and so is omitted.

Example 2. A *parabola* may be defined as the locus of all points equidistant from a fixed point (called the *focus*) and a fixed line (called the *directrix*). Find an equation of the parabola with focus $(0,1)$ and directrix $y = -1$ in a coordinate plane.

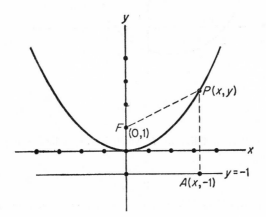

Figure 2.32

Solution: The point $P(x,y)$ in the plane will be on the given parabola if and only if (Figure 2.32)

$$|PF| = |PA|.$$

Thus

$$\sqrt{x^2 + (y - 1)^2} = |y + 1|$$

is an equation of the parabola. Any point $P(x,y)$ satisfying this equation also satisfies the equation

$$x^2 + (y - 1)^2 = (y + 1)^2,$$

and conversely. Hence

$$x^2 + y^2 - 2y + 1 = y^2 + 2y + 1,$$

or

$$x^2 = 4y$$

also is an equation of the given parabola.

Example 3. Find an equation of the tangent line to the circle with equation

$$x^2 + y^2 + 2x - 4y - 5 = 0$$

at the point $P(2,1)$.

$$3$$

Functions

■ ■ ■ ■ ■ A GENERAL THEORY of the calculus is not possible without the use of functions. Indeed, it is significant that the word "function," with its strict mathematical meaning, was introduced by Leibnitz, one of the discoverers of the calculus. Therefore, before getting into the calculus proper, it is fitting that we first discuss functions.

1. Definitions

The word *function*, as used in mathematics, is a purely technical word that will be defined in this section. In defining a function, we shall use the word *correspondence*. Although this latter word will not be defined, its meaning will be made clear by some examples.

As a first example, there is a correspondence between the collection of cards in the index file of a library and the collection of books in the library. Thus, to each card of the index file there corresponds a book, namely, the book described on the card.

Associated with each person in this country is a surname. Thus there is a correspondence set up between the collection of all people in this country and the collection of all surnames. Corresponding to each house in a city is an address. And so on, with examples of correspondences existing all about us.

We are primarily interested in the calculus with cor-

respondences between sets of real numbers.   Certain types of such correspondences will be called functions.   Before being more precise about
functions, let us give some examples.

The formula
$$S = 6x^2$$

gives the area S of the surface of a cube in terms of the length x of an edge.
According to this formula, to each positive number x there corresponds
another positive number S.   For example, if $x = 1$ in., then $S = 6$ in.²;
if $x = 3$ in., then $S = 54$ in.².   Such a correspondence which associates
with each positive number x a positive number S is an example of a
function.

The linear equation
$$y = 3x - 2$$

defines a correspondence: to each real number x there corresponds the real
number y given by this equation.   For example, if $x = 0$, then $y = -2$;
if $x = 2$, then $y = 4$; if $x = -\frac{5}{2}$, then $y = -\frac{19}{2}$.   This correspondence
which associates with each real number x a real number y is a second
example of a function.

The equation
$$s = 16t^2$$

gives the distance s, in feet, that an object falls in t seconds from rest if
the only force acting on the object is that of gravity.   This equation
defines a function; the function that associates with each nonnegative
number t the nonnegative number s.   For example, if $t = 0$, $s = 0$; if
$t = 1$, $s = 16$; if $t = \sqrt{2}$, $s = 32$; if $t = 5$, $s = 400$.   That is to say, the
object falls 16 feet in 1 second, 400 feet in 5 seconds, and so on.

To each real number x there corresponds the nonnegative number $|x|$.
The correspondence that associates with each number its absolute value
also is an example of a function.   It is the function defined by the equation

$$y = |x|.$$

3.1 Definition.   A *function* is a correspondence that associates with
each number x of some given set of numbers one and only one number y.

The set of numbers x over which the function is defined is called the
domain of definition, or just *domain*, of the function.   On the other hand,
the set of all numbers y corresponding to some x in the domain of the function is called the *range* of the function.

We do not allow a function to be defined by an equation such as

$$y = \pm\sqrt{x},$$

since to each positive number x there correspond *two* numbers y.   Of
course, we can break the equation down into two equations

$$y = \sqrt{x}, \qquad y = -\sqrt{x},$$

and then each of these equations defines a function.

Corresponding to each positive number r is a number V, the volume of a sphere of radius r. This correspondence defines a function, regardless of whether or not we can express V in terms of r by an actual formula. A function need not be defined by an equation, as we shall show by example below.

Just as we use the letters x, y, a, b, and so on to designate numbers, so shall we use letters to designate functions. The letters f, g, F, and G are commonly used for this purpose. If f is a given function, then*

$$f(x),$$

read "f of x," will designate the number associated with x by the function f. Thus, if f is a function, then f is a correspondence that associates with each number x in its domain one and only one number $f(x)$ in its range. We give now some examples of functions and of the use of the functional notation.

Example 1. Let f be the function defined by the equation

$$f(x) = x^3 - 1.$$

The domain of f is the set of all real numbers. The function f associates with each real number x the real number $x^3 - 1$. For example,

$$f(0) = 0^3 - 1 = -1; \quad f(1) = 1^3 - 1 = 0; \quad f(3) = 3^3 - 1 = 26;$$

$$f(-4) = (-4)^3 - 1 = -65; \quad f(\sqrt[3]{2}) = (\sqrt[3]{2})^3 - 1 = 1.$$

Example 2. Let G be the function defined by the equation

$$G(u) = \sqrt{u - 3}.$$

Since $\sqrt{u - 3}$ is a real number if and only if $u \geq 3$, the domain of G is the set of all numbers $u \geq 3$. The function G associates with each real number u of its domain the real number $\sqrt{u - 3}$. For example, G associates with 4 the number $\sqrt{4 - 3} = 1$; with 8 the number $\sqrt{8 - 3} = \sqrt{5}$; with $\frac{13}{4}$ the number $\sqrt{\frac{13}{4} - 3} = \frac{1}{2}$. In other words

$$G(4) = 1, \quad G(8) = \sqrt{5}, \quad G\left(\frac{13}{4}\right) = \frac{1}{2}.$$

While the letter u was used in the above definition of G, we could just as well have defined G by the equation

$$G(x) = \sqrt{x - 3},$$

or by the equation

$$G(z) = \sqrt{z - 3}.$$

A function need not be defined by an equation such as in the two examples above. Other ways of defining functions are given below.

---

* This functional notation is due to the Swiss mathematician Leonard Euler (1707–1783), probably the most prolific mathematician of all time. The form of many of our present-day textbooks is due to Euler.

Example 3. The following table is taken from a railroad timetable. It gives the time taken by a train to travel certain distances. As such, it defines a function T, where $T(d)$ is the number of minutes taken by the train in traveling d miles from Chicago. Thus, from the table,

$$T(0) = 0, \quad T(92.9) = 162, \quad T(141.4) = 208, \quad T(164.3) = 233,$$

and so on. The domain of T is made up of 7 numbers (the first column of the table).

d	City	Time	$T(d)$
0.0 miles	Chicago	4:00 P.M.	0 min
92.9	Niles	6:42	162
141.4	Kalamazoo	7:28	208
164.3	Battle Creek	7:53	233
209.4	Jackson	8:39	279
247.6	Ann Arbor	9:18	318
283.5	Detroit	10:00	360

Example 4. It costs 4 cents per ounce or fraction thereof to send a parcel by first-class mail. Any parcel of weight not exceeding 20 lb may be sent by first-class mail. If we let

$$F(w)$$

be the cost in cents of sending a parcel of weight w ounces, then

$$F(w) = 4 \text{ if } 0 < w \le 1,$$
$$F(w) = 8 \text{ if } 1 < w \le 2,$$
$$- - - - - - - - - - - - -$$
$$- - - - - - - - - - - - -$$
$$F(w) = 4n \text{ if } n - 1 < w \le n,$$
$$- - - - - - - - - - - - -$$

This defines a function F with the set of all positive numbers not exceeding 320 (ounces) as its domain.

Example 5. If $f(x) = \dfrac{2x}{x-3}$, $x \ne 3$, find $f(2), f(a), f(a+h)$, and $\dfrac{f(a+h) - f(a)}{h}$, $h \ne 0$.

Solution: If $f(x) = \dfrac{2x}{x-3}$, then

$$f(2) = \frac{2 \cdot 2}{2 - 3} = -4.$$

$$f(a) = \frac{2a}{a-3}, \quad a \ne 3; \quad f(a+h) = \frac{2(a+h)}{a+h-3}.$$

$$\frac{f(a+h) - f(a)}{h} = \frac{[2(a+h)/(a+h-3)] - [2a/(a-3)]}{h}$$

$$= \frac{(2a + 2h)(a-3) - 2a(a+h-3)}{h(a+h-3)(a-3)}$$

$$= \frac{-6h}{h(a+h-3)(a-3)}$$

$$= \frac{-6}{(a+h-3)(a-3)}, \quad h \ne 0.$$

■ ■ ■ EXERCISES

If $f(x) = x^2 - 3x + 1$, find:

1. $f(0); f(1); f(-1); f(3); f(-\sqrt{3}); f(h)$.

2. $f(1 + h); f(-2 + h); f(x + h)$.

3. $\dfrac{f(1 + h) - f(1)}{h}, h \neq 0; \dfrac{f(x + h) - f(x)}{h}, h \neq 0$.

4. $\dfrac{f(x) - f(3)}{x - 3}, x \neq 3; \dfrac{f(x) - f(a)}{x - a}, x \neq a$.

If $g(x) = \dfrac{x - 1}{x + 1}, x \neq -1$, find:

5. $g(0); g(1); g(-3); g(a^2); g(z)$.

6. $g(1 + h); g(-2 + h); g(x + h)$.

7. $\dfrac{g(1 + h) - g(1)}{h}, h \neq 0; \dfrac{g(x + h) - g(x)}{h}, h \neq 0$.

8. $\dfrac{g(4) - g(2)}{2}; \dfrac{g(x) - g(2)}{x - 2}, x \neq 2$.

If $f(x) = 2x^2 - 5x$, find an equation of the line through the following two points:

9. $(0, f(0))$ and $(1, f(1))$.

10. $(2, f(2))$ and $(\tfrac{5}{2}, f(\tfrac{5}{2}))$.

11. $(3, f(3))$ and $(3 + h, f(3 + h)), h \neq 0$.

12. $(a, f(a))$ and $(b, f(b)), a \neq b$.

13. $(2, f(2))$ and $(2 + h, f(2 + h)), h \neq 0$.

14. $(a, f(a))$ and $(a + h, f(a + h)), h \neq 0$.

15. If $f(x) = x^2 - 3x + 1$, for what numbers x is $f(x) = f(2x)$? Is $f(x) = f(ax)$? Is $2f(x) = f(2x)$?

16. If $F(x) = \sqrt{x}, x > 0$, show that

$$\frac{F(x + h) - F(x)}{h} = \frac{1}{\sqrt{x + h} + \sqrt{x}}, \qquad h \neq 0.$$

Write an equation which defines each of the functions in Exercises 17–20.

17. The function f such that $f(r)$ is the area of a circle of radius r.

18. The function F such that $F(r)$ is the surface area of a sphere of radius r.

19. The function G such that $G(A)$ is the surface area of a sphere with great circles of area A.

20. The function g such that $g(h)$ is the volume of a cone having a vertex angle of 90° and height h.

2. Types of functions

If the range of a function f consists of just one number, say c, then f is called a *constant function*, or simply a *constant*. Thus $f(x) = c$ for every number x, and f associates with all numbers x the same number c.

If $a_0, a_1, \cdots, a_n$ are given numbers and n is a given nonnegative integer, then an expression of the form

$$a_0 x^n + a_1 x^{n-1} + \cdots + a_{n-1} x + a_n$$

is called a polynomial. For example

$$8x^3 - x^2 + 2x - 5, \quad x^5 + 1, \quad 3x^2 - x + 1, \quad -5x + 2$$

are polynomials.

A *polynomial function* is any function f defined by an equation of the form

$$f(x) = a_0 x^n + a_1 x^{n-1} + \cdots + a_{n-1} x + a_n,$$

with n a nonnegative integer. The domain of any polynomial function may be taken to be the set of all real numbers.

Special polynomial functions are the *linear function* f defined by

$$f(x) = a_0 x + a_1,$$

the *quadratic function* f defined by

$$f(x) = a_0 x^2 + a_1 x + a_2, \quad a_0 \neq 0,$$

and the *cubic function* f defined by

$$f(x) = a_0 x^3 + a_1 x^2 + a_2 x + a_3, \quad a_0 \neq 0.$$

A *rational function* is a function defined by a quotient of two polynomials. For example,

$$f(x) = \frac{x^2 - 3x + 1}{x + 2}$$

defines a rational function f having as its domain the set of all numbers $x \neq -2$.

A function defined in terms of polynomials and roots of polynomials is called an *algebraic function*. For example,

$$f(x) = \frac{x - 1}{x\sqrt{x^2 + 1}}$$

defines an algebraic function f. Its domain is the set of all nonzero real numbers.

Examples of nonalgebraic functions are the six trigonometric functions sine, cosine, tangent, cotangent, secant, and cosecant, the logarithmic function f defined by

$$f(x) = \log_a x,$$

and the exponential function g defined by

$$g(x) = a^x.$$

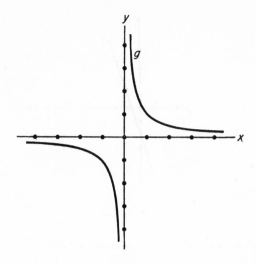

Figure 3.4

Thus, for positive values of x, the smaller is x the larger is $1/x$; and the larger is x the smaller is $1/x$. Similar statements can be made for negative values of x.

From these remarks, we conclude that the graph of g fits in the first and third quadrants as sketched in Figure 3.4. The graph approaches the x-axis for large values of $|x|$; and it approaches the y-axis for small values of $|x|$.

Example 5. Determine the graph of the postage function (Example 4 of Section 1).

Solution: For this function F,

$$F(x) = 4n \quad \text{if} \quad n - 1 < x \leq n,$$

with n a positive integer. The graph of F is the graph of the equation

$$y = 4n \quad \text{if} \quad n - 1 < x \leq n.$$

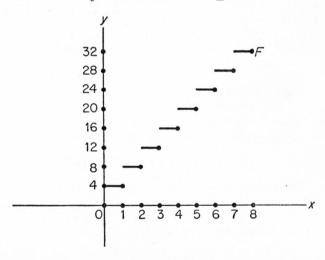

Figure 3.5

Thus the graph is made up of "steps,"

$$y = 4 \quad \text{if} \quad 0 < x \le 1,$$
$$y = 8 \quad \text{if} \quad 1 < x \le 2,$$
$$y = 12 \quad \text{if} \quad 2 < x \le 3,$$

and so on. It is sketched in Figure 3.5.

■ ▣ ■ EXERCISES

Sketch the graph of the function defined as follows:

1. $f(x) = 2x - 1.$ 2. $g(x) = 1 - 3x.$

3. $G(x) = 3 - 5x.$ 4. $F(x) = (2 + x)/3.$

5. $F(x) = x^2/2.$ 6. $G(x) = 2/x^2, x \ne 0.$

7. $g(t) = |t + 1|.$ 8. $f(s) = |2 - s|.$

9. $f(r) = 2/r, r \ne 0.$ 10. $g(t) = t/2.$

11. $f(x) = \sqrt{1 - x}, x \le 1.$ 12. $G(x) = -\sqrt{1 - x}, x \le 1.$

13. $f(x) = -1$ if $x < 0; f(x) = 1$ if $x \ge 0.$

14. $g(x) = x$ if $x > 1; g(x) = -x$ if $x < -1.$

15. $G(x) = x^2$ if $x \ge 0; G(x) = -x^2$ if $x < 0.$

16. $F(x) = \sqrt{4 - x^2}$ if $x \ge 0; F(x) = -\sqrt{4 - x^2}$ if $x < 0.$

17. $F(x) = n$ if $n \le x < n + 1,$ n an integer.

18. $F(x) = -n$ if $n \le x < n + 1,$ n an integer.

4. Combinations of functions

Just as we can combine numbers with the operations of addition, subtraction, multiplication, and division, so can we combine functions with
these operations.

The function F is called the *sum* of the functions f and g if

$$F(x) = f(x) + g(x)$$

for every number x in the domain of both f and g. If

$$F(x) = f(x) - g(x),$$

F is called the *difference* of f by g. Similarly, G is called the *product* of f
and g if

$$G(x) = f(x) \cdot g(x)$$

for every number x in the domain of both f and g; and G is called the
quotient of f by g if

$$G(x) = \frac{f(x)}{g(x)}.$$

Clearly we must exclude from the domain of the quotient function G all
numbers x for which $g(x) = 0.$

If, for example,

$$F(x) = 3x^2 + 5,$$

then F is the sum of the functions f and g defined by

$$f(x) = 3x^2, \qquad g(x) = 5.$$

If $\qquad\qquad G(x) = (x^2 + 1)(3x - 4),$

then G is the product of the functions f and g defined by

$$f(x) = x^2 + 1, \qquad g(x) = 3x - 4.$$

If $\qquad\qquad F(x) = \dfrac{\sqrt{x + 3}}{x^2},$

then F is the quotient of f by g where

$$f(x) = \sqrt{x + 3}, \qquad g(x) = x^2.$$

The domain of F is the set of all numbers $x \geq -3$, $x \neq 0$.
It is customary to write

$$f^2(x) = f(x) \cdot f(x)$$

for the product of the function f with itself. Similarly

$$f^3(x) = f(x) \cdot f(x) \cdot f(x).$$

The meaning of $f^n(x)$ is clear for an integer n, $n \geq 2$.

Another important combination of the functions f and g is the *composite function F* of f by g defined by

$$F(x) = f(g(x)).$$

The domain of F is the set of all numbers x such that $g(x)$ is in the domain of f.

For example, the function F defined by

$$F(x) = \sqrt{x^2 + 1}$$

is a composite of the square-root function and a polynomial function. Thus, if

$$f(x) = \sqrt{x} \quad \text{and} \quad g(x) = x^2 + 1,$$

$$F(x) = f(g(x)) = \sqrt{g(x)} = \sqrt{x^2 + 1}.$$

The domain of g is the set of all real numbers, whereas the domain of f is the set of all nonnegative numbers. Since $g(x) > 0$ for every number x, the range of g lies in the domain of f for every number x and hence the domain of F is the set of all real numbers.

■ ■ ■ EXERCISES

1. If $f(x) = x^2 - 1$ and $g(x) = 3x + 1$, define:
   (a) The sum of f and g.   (b) The difference of f by g.

(c) The product of f and g.

(d) The quotient of f by g.

(e) The composite of f by g.

(f) The composite of g by f.

2. Do the same as in Example 1 for

$$f(x) = \sqrt{x - 1}, \quad x \geq 1, \quad g(x) = x^2 + 1.$$

3. Do the same as in Example 1 for

$$f(x) = \frac{1}{x + 1}, \quad x \neq -1, \quad g(x) = \frac{x}{x - 1}, \quad x \neq 1.$$

4. Do the same as in Example 1 for

$$f(x) = \frac{1}{x^2}, \quad g(x) = \sqrt{x}, \quad x \geq 0.$$

5. If $f(x) = x^2$, find a function g such that $f(g(x)) = x$. Is $g(f(x)) = x$ also?

6. If $f(x) = \sqrt[3]{x}$, find a function g such that $f(g(x)) = x$. Is $g(f(x)) = x$ also?

7. If $f(x) = |x|$, find $f(f(x))$.

8. If $f(x) = ax^2 + bx + c$, and $f(x + h) = f(x) + f(h)$ for all real numbers x and h, what can be said about the numbers a, b, and c?

5. *Increasing and decreasing functions*

The function f defined by

$$f(x) = x^2$$

is increasing in the interval $[1,3]$ in the sense that $f(x)$ steadily grows larger as x ranges from 1 to 3.   Similarly, f is decreasing in the interval $[-4,0]$ in the sense that $f(x)$ steadily grows smaller as x ranges from -4 to 0. Actually, f is decreasing in the infinite interval $(-\infty,0]$ and increasing in the infinite interval $[0,\infty)$ according to the following definition.

3.3 Definition.   A function f defined in an interval is

(1) *increasing* in that interval if $f(x_1) < f(x_2)$ whenever $x_1 < x_2$, x_1 and x_2 any numbers in the interval.

(2) *decreasing* in that interval if $f(x_1) > f(x_2)$ whenever $x_1 < x_2$, x_1 and x_2 any numbers in the interval.

Geometrically, if we imagine a point moving along the graph of f from left to right (i.e., in the direction of increasing x numbers), then the point is rising where f is increasing and falling where f is decreasing.

If the function f is increasing in a closed interval $[a,b]$, then $f(a)$ is the minimum value and $f(b)$ is the maximum value of f in this interval.   More generally, the maximum and minimum values of a function in an interval are defined as follows.

3.4 Definition.   If for the numbers u and v contained in an interval,

$$f(u) \leq f(x) \leq f(v)$$

for every number x in the interval, then $f(u)$ is the *minimum value* and $f(v)$ the *maximum value* of the function f in the interval.

A function might have an *absolute minimum* value $f(u)$ in the sense that $f(u) \leq f(x)$ for every number x in the domain of f; and similarly, it might have an *absolute maximum* value.

For example, if

$$f(x) = x^2,$$

then $f(0) = 0$ is an absolute minimum value of the function f.

Example 1. If

$$g(x) = 4 - x^2,$$

find where the function g is increasing and where it is decreasing.

Solution: In the first place, we see that $g(0) = 4$ is an absolute maximum value of g. If $x_1 < x_2 < 0$, then $x_1^2 > x_2^2$ and $4 - x_1^2 < 4 - x_2^2$. Thus $g(x_1) < g(x_2)$ and we conclude that g is increasing in the interval $(-\infty,0]$. If $0 < x_1 < x_2$, then $x_1^2 < x_2^2$ and $4 - x_1^2 > 4 - x_2^2$. Thus $g(x_1) > g(x_2)$ and g is decreasing in the interval $[0,\infty)$.

Example 2. If

$$f(x) = (x + 2)^4,$$

find where the function f is increasing and where it is decreasing.

Solution: The minimum value of f occurs when $x = -2$, in which case $f(-2) = 0$. If $x_1 < x_2 < -2$, then $x_1 + 2 < x_2 + 2 < 0$ and $|x_1 + 2| > |x_2 + 2|$. Hence $(x_1 + 2)^4 > (x_2 + 2)^4$ and $f(x_1) > f(x_2)$. Thus f is decreasing in the interval $(-\infty,-2]$. It may be shown in a similar way that f is increasing in the interval $[-2,\infty)$.

Example 3. If

$$g(x) = 4 - x^2,$$

find the maximum and minimum values of g in the interval $[-1,3]$.

Solution: According to Example 1, g is increasing in the interval $[-1,0]$ and decreasing in the interval $[0,3]$. Therefore $g(-1) = 3$ is the minimum value and $g(0) = 4$ is the maximum value of g in $[-1,0]$; and $g(0)$ is the maximum value and $g(3) = -5$ is the minimum value of g in $[0,3]$. Hence $g(0) = 4$ and $g(3) = -5$ are the respective maximum and minimum values of g in the whole interval $[-1,3]$.

■ ■ ■ EXERCISES

Find where each of the following functions is increasing and where it is decreasing. Also find the maximum and minimum values of the function in the given interval. Sketch the graph of each function.

1. $f(x) = -2x + 1$; $[-2,1]$.   **2.** $g(x) = x^2 + 3$; $[2,5]$.

3. $F(x) = x^2 + 2x + 2$; $[-4,4]$.   **4.** $g(x) = \dfrac{4}{1 + x^2}$; $[-2,2]$.

5. $G(x) = \dfrac{1}{x}$; $[-7,-1]$.   **6.** $F(x) = \sqrt{1 + x}$; $[-1,\infty)$.

7. $f(x) = \dfrac{1}{\sqrt{x^2 + 1}}; \; (-\infty, \sqrt{3}]$.   8. $G(x) = |x|; \; [-3,3]$.

9. $g(x) = x^3; \; [0,20]$.   10. $F(x) = 1 - x^3; \; [-3,5]$.

11. Let the function f be defined and be nonnegative (i.e., $f(x) \geq 0$) in some interval, and let $f(u)$ be the minimum and $f(v)$ be the maximum values of f in this interval. Prove that $[f(u)]^2$ and $[f(v)]^2$ are the minimum and maximum values respectively of the function f^2 in this interval. If $F(x) = \sqrt{f(x)}$, find the minimum and maximum values of F in the same interval.

12. Let the functions f and g be defined and increasing in an interval. Prove that the sum of f and g also is increasing in this interval. Show by the example $f(x) = x + 1$, $g(x) = x - 1$ that the product of two increasing functions need not be increasing. Prove that if the functions f and g are both positive in the given interval, then their product is increasing in the interval. What can be said if both functions are negative in the given interval?

13. Let the function g be defined and increasing in the interval $[a,b]$, and let the function f be defined and increasing in the interval $[g(a),g(b)]$. Prove that the composite of f by g is increasing in $[a,b]$.

4

Limits
and derivatives

■ ■ ■ ■ ■ IN THIS CHAPTER we lay a foundation for the calculus.
This foundation will consist of definitions and basic theorems. The new concepts of limit, continuity, and derivative play a fundamental role throughout the calculus.

The introduction of limits allows one to proceed from
elementary mathematics consisting mainly of algebra and
geometry to higher mathematics consisting of the calculus
and all its ramifications. Early in our mathematical
training we were faced with problems whose solutions involved the use of limits, although we were probably
unaware of it at the time. To select just one example,
the area of a circle of radius r is πr^2 according to a formula
of geometry, where π is a number approximately equal to
3.1416. How is such a formula derived? The usual way
is to inscribe regular polygons in the circle, find the areas
of these polygons, and then determine the "limiting value"
of these areas as the numbers of sides of the polygons
increase without bound. Thus even such a seemingly
simple formula as that for the area of a circle depends on
the concept of limit for its derivation.

60

1. *Introduction to limits*

We shall put off the formal definition of limit to the next section.   Let us first discuss informally the meaning of this concept.

If x is a number close to 2, then the number $3x + 5$ is close to 11.   An inspection of the accompanying table of values bears out this contention. While $3x + 5$ equals 11 when x equals 2, this is

x	1.8	1.9	1.95	1.999	2.0001	2.1	2.2
$3x + 5$	10.4	10.7	10.85	10.997	11.0003	11.3	11.6

not of primary concern to us at the moment.   Since $3x + 5$ is close to 11 provided that x is close to (but unequal to) 2, we shall say that the limit of $3x + 5$ as x approaches 2 is 11, and we shall write symbolically

$$\lim_{x \to 2} (3x + 5) = 11.$$

Similarly,

$$\lim_{x \to -1} \frac{2x}{x + 2} = -2,$$

since $2x/(x + 2)$ is close to -2 provided that x is close to -1.

Consider now the more complicated problem of evaluating

$$\lim_{x \to 0} \left(\frac{1}{2}\right)^{1/x^2}.$$

We cannot predict the answer, as we could in the previous examples, by giving x the value 0, since $(\frac{1}{2})^{1/0}$ is meaningless.   However, an inspection of the accompanying table leads us to believe that

x	± 1	$\pm \frac{1}{2}$	$\pm \frac{1}{3}$	$\pm \frac{1}{4}$	$\pm 1/n$
$(\frac{1}{2})^{1/x^2}$	$\frac{1}{2}$	$\frac{1}{16}$	$\frac{1}{512}$	$1/2^{16}$	$1/2^{n^2}$

$(\frac{1}{2})^{1/x^2}$ is close to 0 provided that x is close to 0, that is to say,

$$\lim_{x \to 0} \left(\frac{1}{2}\right)^{1/x^2} = 0.$$

These examples are but instances of the limit of a function f.   We shall say that the limit of f as x approaches a equals b, written symbolically as

$$\lim_{x \to a} f(x) = b,$$

if the *number* $f(x)$ is close to b provided that x is close to (but unequal to) a.

Let us look at some more examples of limits.

Example 1.   Find $\displaystyle\lim_{y \to 3} \frac{1/y - \frac{1}{3}}{y - 3}.$

Solution: If we define the function g by

$$g(y) = \frac{1/y - \frac{1}{3}}{y - 3}, \quad y \neq 3,$$

then we are asked to find

$$\underset{y \to 3}{\text{limit}}\, g(y).$$

It is clear that the answer is not to be found by letting $y = 3$ in $g(y)$, since $g(3)$ is undefined.   However, if $y \neq 3$,

$$g(y) = \frac{1/y - \frac{1}{3}}{y - 3} = \frac{(3 - y)/3y}{y - 3} = -\frac{y - 3}{3y(y - 3)} = -\frac{1}{3y},$$

since the *nonzero* factor $y - 3$ can be canceled out of the numerator and denominator.   Evidently $-1/3y$ is close to $-\frac{1}{9}$ if y is close to 3, and therefore the number $g(y)$ is close to $-\frac{1}{9}$ if y is close (but unequal) to 3.   Hence

$$\underset{y \to 3}{\text{limit}}\, \frac{1/y - \frac{1}{3}}{y - 3} = -\frac{1}{9}.$$

Example 2.   Find $\underset{x \to 1}{\text{limit}}\, \dfrac{\sqrt{x} - 1}{x - 1}.$

Solution: If the function f is defined by

$$f(x) = \frac{\sqrt{x} - 1}{x - 1}, \quad x \geq 0, \quad x \neq 1,$$

then we are asked to find

$$\underset{x \to 1}{\text{limit}}\, f(x).$$

As in the previous example, we cannot guess the answer by letting $x = 1$, since $f(1)$ is undefined.   However, since $x \geq 0$,

$$x - 1 = (\sqrt{x} - 1)(\sqrt{x} + 1),$$

and therefore

$$f(x) = \frac{\sqrt{x} - 1}{x - 1} = \frac{1}{\sqrt{x} + 1}, \quad x \neq 1.$$

Now it is clear that $f(x)$ is close to $\frac{1}{2}$ if x is close (but unequal) to 1.   Hence

$$\underset{x \to 1}{\text{limit}}\, \frac{\sqrt{x} - 1}{x - 1} = \frac{1}{2}.$$

Example 3.   Find $\underset{h \to 0}{\text{limit}}\, \dfrac{(2 + h)^2 - 4}{h}.$

Solution: If the function G is defined by

$$G(h) = \frac{(2 + h)^2 - 4}{h}, \quad h \neq 0,$$

then we wish to find

$$\underset{h \to 0}{\text{limit}}\, G(h).$$

Again, we cannot find this limit by letting $h = 0$, since $G(0)$ is undefined.   So we proceed as before by simplifying $G(h)$:

$$G(h) = \frac{(4 + 4h + h^2) - 4}{h} = \frac{4h + h^2}{h} = 4 + h$$

since $h \neq 0$. Then it is clear that $G(h)$ is close to 4 if h is close (but unequal) to 0, that is,

$$\lim_{h \to 0} \frac{(2 + h)^2 - 4}{h} = 4.$$

The next example illustrates the use of limits in a geometrical problem.

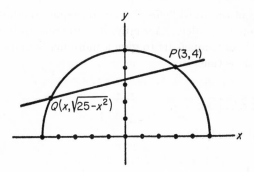

Figure 4.1

Example 4. Let $P(3,4)$ and $Q(x,\sqrt{25 - x^2})$ be two distinct points on the semi-circle (Figure 4.1) with equation

$$y = \sqrt{25 - x^2},$$

and let $M(x)$ designate the slope of the secant line through P and Q. Find

$$\lim_{x \to 3} M(x).$$

Solution: We cannot let $x = 3$ in $M(x)$, since the points P and Q coincide if $x = 3$ and the secant line is not well defined.   Clearly

$$M(x) = \frac{\sqrt{25 - x^2} - 4}{x - 3}, \quad x \neq 3.$$

We may rationalize the numerator of $M(x)$ as follows:

$$M(x) = \frac{(\sqrt{25 - x^2} - 4)(\sqrt{25 - x^2} + 4)}{(x - 3)(\sqrt{25 - x^2} + 4)}$$

$$= \frac{(25 - x^2) - 16}{(x - 3)(\sqrt{25 - x^2} + 4)} = \frac{9 - x^2}{(x - 3)(\sqrt{25 - x^2} + 4)}$$

$$= -\frac{x + 3}{\sqrt{25 - x^2} + 4}, \quad x \neq 3.$$

If x is close to 3, $\sqrt{25 - x^2}$ is close to 4 and $M(x)$ is close to $-\frac{6}{8}$, that is,

$$\lim_{x \to 3} M(x) = -\frac{3}{4}.$$

The slope of the radius OP is $\frac{4}{3}$, and therefore the slope of the tangent line to the circle at P is $-\frac{3}{4}$, which is the same as the limit of $M(x)$ as x approaches 3.

for every x (other than a) that is within δ of a, i.e., for which

$$0 < |x - a| < \delta.$$

The number δ depends on ϵ. In general, the smaller the value of ϵ, the smaller the corresponding value of δ. However, and this fact is very important, once we have chosen a δ corresponding to some given ϵ, *any positive $\delta' < \delta$ may be used in place of δ to yield the desired conclusion.* Thus, if it is true that

$$|f(x) - b| < \epsilon \text{ for every } x \text{ satisfying } 0 < |x - a| < \delta,$$

then certainly for any positive $\delta' < \delta$, it is true that

$$|f(x) - b| < \epsilon \text{ for every } x \text{ satisfying } 0 < |x - a| < \delta',$$

since every x satisfying $0 < |x - a| < \delta'$ also satisfies $0 < |x - a| < \delta$.
Let us return to the first example of Section 1 and *prove* that

$$\lim_{x \to 2} (3x + 5) = 11.$$

If, for example, we select $\epsilon = .3$, then we wish to find a positive number δ such that

$$|(3x + 5) - 11| < .3 \text{ for every } x \text{ satisfying } 0 < |x - 2| < \delta.$$

The inequality $|(3x + 5) - 11| < .3$ holds provided that

$$|3x - 6| < .3,$$

and in turn this inequality holds provided that

$$|x - 2| < .1.$$

Thus

$$|(3x + 5) - 11| < .3 \text{ for every } x \text{ satisfying } |x - 2| < .1,$$

and δ may be chosen equal to .1 or any positive number less than .1.
More generally, for every $\epsilon > 0$,

$$|(3x + 5) - 11| < \epsilon \text{ provided that } |x - 2| < \frac{\epsilon}{3},$$

and therefore for every $\epsilon > 0$ there exists $\delta = \epsilon/3$ such that

$$|(3x + 5) - 11| < \epsilon \text{ for every } x \text{ satisfying } 0 < |x - 2| < \delta.$$

This *proves* that

$$\lim_{x \to 2} (3x + 5) = 11.$$

In other examples, it might be much more difficult to select a δ corresponding to each ϵ. Before giving some more complicated examples, let us prove the following generalization of the preceding example.

4.2 $$\lim_{x \to a} (mx + b) = ma + b.$$

Let us first assume that $m \neq 0$. Then for every $\epsilon > 0$,

$$|(mx + b) - (ma + b)| < \epsilon$$

provided that
$$|m(x - a)| < \epsilon,$$
and this inequality holds provided that

$$|x - a| < \frac{\epsilon}{|m|}.$$

Thus, for $\delta = \epsilon/|m|$,

$|(mx + b) - (ma + b)| < \epsilon$ for every x satisfying $0 < |x - a| < \delta$,

and 4.2 is proved. Note that in the example above $|m| = 3$.

If $m = 0$, $(mx + b) - (ma + b) = 0$ for every x, and therefore $|(mx + b) - (ma + b)| < \epsilon$ for every x satisfying $|x - a| < \delta$, where δ is *any* positive number. This proves 4.2 in case $m = 0$.

As special cases of 4.2, we have

4.3 $$\lim_{x \to a} b = b,$$

4.4 $$\lim_{x \to a} x = a.$$

Formula 4.3 is obtained from 4.2 by letting $m = 0$, whereas 4.4 is obtained by letting $m = 1$ and $b = 0$.

As the first general limit theorem, let us prove that if the limit of $f(x)$ as x approaches a exists, then

4.5 $$\lim_{x \to a} k \cdot f(x) = k \lim_{x \to a} f(x)$$

for every number k.

In order to prove 4.5, let

$$\lim_{x \to a} f(x) = b.$$

Then we wish to prove that

$$\lim_{x \to a} k \cdot f(x) = kb,$$

that is, that for every number $\epsilon > 0$ there exists a number $\delta > 0$ such that

$$|kf(x) - kb| < \epsilon$$

provided that

$$0 < |x - a| < \delta.$$

Now 4.5 is obvious if $k = 0$, so let us assume that $k \neq 0$. Then $|kf(x) - kb| < \epsilon$ if and only if

$$|f(x) - b| < \epsilon',$$

where $\epsilon' = \epsilon/|k|$. Since $\lim_{x \to a} f(x) = b$, we know that for the number $\epsilon' > 0$ there exists a number $\delta > 0$ such that

$$|f(x) - b| < \epsilon'$$

provided that

$$0 < |x - a| < \delta.$$

5. If $f(x) = 5x^2 - 3x + 1$, show that

$$\lim_{x \to 1} f(x) = f(1).$$

6. If $g(x) = 2x^2 - 5x + 3$, show that

$$\lim_{x \to 3} g(x) = g(3).$$

7. Prove that $\lim_{x \to a} |x - a| = 0$ and that $\lim_{x \to a} k|x - a| = 0$.

8. Prove that $\lim_{x \to a} (x - a)^3 = 0$. (*Hint:* cf. proof of 4.6.)

Then prove that $\lim_{x \to a} x^3 = a^3$. (*Hint:* cf. proof of 4.7.)

9. Prove that if

$$\lim_{x \to a} f(x) = b \quad \text{and} \quad \lim_{x \to a} f(x) = c,$$

then $b = c$.

10. Prove that if

$$\lim_{x \to a} f(x) = b \quad \text{and} \quad \lim_{x \to a} g(x) = c,$$

then

$$\lim_{x \to a} [f(x) - g(x)] = b - c.$$

Find each of the following limits, using the limit theorems 4.2–4.8:

11. $\lim_{x \to 2} \dfrac{x^2 - 4}{x - 2}$.

12. $\lim_{h \to 0} \dfrac{(1 + h)^2 - 1}{h}$.

13. $\lim_{x \to 1} \dfrac{x^3 - 1}{x - 1}$.

14. $\lim_{h \to 0} \dfrac{(3 + h)^3 - 27}{h}$.

15. $\lim_{h \to 0} \dfrac{(1 + h)^3 - h - 1}{h}$.

16. $\lim_{x \to -2} \dfrac{x^3 - 3x + 2}{x + 2}$.

3. Two special limits

If we recall that $|c| < d$ if and only if $-d < c < d$ (1.9), then it is clear that the definition of limit has the following alternate form.

4.9 The limit of the function f as x approaches a equals b,

$$\lim_{x \to a} f(x) = b,$$

if for every number $\epsilon > 0$ there exists a number $\delta > 0$ such that

$$-\epsilon < f(x) - b < \epsilon$$

for every x satisfying

$$-\delta < x - a < \delta, \quad x \neq a.$$

We shall use this form of the definition of limit to establish the following limit.

4.10

$$\lim_{x \to a} \frac{1}{x} = \frac{1}{a}, \quad a \neq 0.$$

Proof: We shall assume throughout that $a > 0$. The proof for $a < 0$ is similar, and so is omitted.

We wish to prove that for every number $\epsilon > 0$, there exists a number $\delta > 0$ such that

(1) $\quad -\epsilon < \dfrac{1}{x} - \dfrac{1}{a} < \epsilon$ provided that $-\delta < x - a < \delta, \quad x \neq a$.

If we can prove that for every ϵ between 0 and $1/a$,

(2) $$0 < \epsilon < \frac{1}{a},$$

there exists a number $\delta > 0$ such that (1) holds, then the proof will be complete. We need not worry about any $\epsilon \geq 1/a$, since for these *large* values of ϵ, (1) holds for *any* δ associated with some ϵ satisfying (2).

So let us assume that we have chosen some number ϵ satisfying (2), or, equivalently,

$$1 - \epsilon a > 0.$$

Then the number x satisfies the inequality

(3) $$-\epsilon < \frac{1}{x} - \frac{1}{a} < \epsilon$$

provided that it satisfies

$$\frac{1}{a} - \epsilon < \frac{1}{x} < \frac{1}{a} + \epsilon,$$

or $$\frac{1 - \epsilon a}{a} < \frac{1}{x} < \frac{1 + \epsilon a}{a}.$$

And x satisfies this latter inequality provided that it satisfies

$$\frac{a}{1 - \epsilon a} > x > \frac{a}{1 + \epsilon a},$$

or $$\frac{a}{1 + \epsilon a} - a < x - a < \frac{a}{1 - \epsilon a} - a.$$

This latter inequality may be put in the form

(4) $$-\frac{\epsilon a^2}{1 + \epsilon a} < x - a < \frac{\epsilon a^2}{1 - \epsilon a}.$$

Now if we choose

$$\delta = \frac{\epsilon a^2}{1 + \epsilon a},$$

which is the *smaller* of the two numbers $\epsilon a^2/(1 + \epsilon a)$ and $\epsilon a^2/(1 - \epsilon a)$, then for every x satisfying

$$-\delta < x - a < \delta,$$

necessarily x satisfies (4) and (3). Thus (1) has been proved, and 4.10 holds.

The second special limit theorem we wish to establish is as follows:

4.11 $\text{limit}_{x \to a} \sqrt{x} = \sqrt{a}, \quad a \geq 0.$

Proof: Let us assume that $a > 0$, leaving the case $a = 0$ for the reader to prove.

We wish to prove that for every number $\epsilon > 0$, there exists a number $\delta > 0$ such that

(1) $-\epsilon < \sqrt{x} - \sqrt{a} < \epsilon$ provided that $-\delta < x - a < \delta, \quad x \neq a.$

As discussed in the proof by 4.10, no loss of generality results if we assume ϵ restricted as follows:

(2) $0 < \epsilon < \sqrt{a}.$

If ϵ is chosen so as to satisfy (2), then

(3) $-\epsilon < \sqrt{x} - \sqrt{a} < \epsilon$

provided that

$$\sqrt{a} - \epsilon < \sqrt{x} < \sqrt{a} + \epsilon.$$

Since each member of this inequality is a positive number, we may square each member to obtain the equivalent inequality

$$(\sqrt{a} - \epsilon)^2 < x < (\sqrt{a} + \epsilon)^2.$$

Hence x satisfies (3) if and only if it satisfies

$$(\sqrt{a} - \epsilon)^2 - a < x - a < (\sqrt{a} + \epsilon)^2 - a,$$

or

(4) $-[a - (\sqrt{a} - \epsilon)^2] < x - a < (\sqrt{a} + \epsilon)^2 - a.$

If we choose δ to be the *smaller* of the two positive numbers

$$a - (\sqrt{a} - \epsilon)^2, \qquad (\sqrt{a} + \epsilon)^2 - a,$$

then every x satisfying

$$-\delta < x - a < \delta$$

also satisfies (4), and finally, (3). Thus (1) is satisfied for this choice of δ, and 4.11 has been proved.

By almost the same argument used in proving 4.11, we may prove the following limit theorem.

4.12 $\text{limit}_{x \to a} \sqrt[n]{x} = \sqrt[n]{a}, \quad a \geq 0, \quad n$ a positive integer.

Example. Find $\text{limit}_{x \to 4} (x^2 + 5\sqrt{x}).$

Solution: By the sum formula (4.8),

$$\text{limit}_{x \to 4} (x^2 + 5\sqrt{x}) = \text{limit}_{x \to 4} x^2 + \text{limit}_{x \to 4} 5\sqrt{x}.$$

Hence

$$\underset{x\to 4}{\text{limit}}\,(x^2 + 5\sqrt{x}) = \underset{x\to 4}{\text{limit}}\,x^2 + 5\underset{x\to 4}{\text{limit}}\,\sqrt{x} \qquad \text{(by 4.5)}$$

$$= 16 + 5\sqrt{4} \qquad \text{(by 4.7, 4.11)}$$

$$= 26.$$

■ ■ ■ EXERCISES

Find each of the following limits by use of limit theorems 4.2–4.8, 4.10–4.12.

1. $\underset{x\to 9}{\text{limit}}\,(x^2 - 3x + 4\sqrt{x}).$

2. $\underset{x\to 8}{\text{limit}}\,(3x + 4\sqrt[3]{x}).$

3. $\underset{x\to -2}{\text{limit}}\,\dfrac{x^3 - 3x + 1}{x}$

4. $\underset{y\to 2}{\text{limit}}\,\dfrac{5y\sqrt{y} - 2}{y}.$

5. $\underset{z\to 4}{\text{limit}}\,\dfrac{z - 4}{\sqrt{z} - 2}.$

6. $\underset{h\to 1}{\text{limit}}\,\dfrac{h\sqrt[3]{h} + 3}{h}.$

7. Prove that $\underset{x\to 0}{\text{limit}}\,\sqrt{x} = 0.$ (*Hint:* If $x \ge 0$, $\sqrt{x} < \epsilon$ if and only if $x < \epsilon^2$.)

8. Prove 4.12 for $a > 0$. (*Hint:* Let $0 < \epsilon < \sqrt[n]{a}$, and follow the proof of 4.11.)

9. Prove 4.12 for $a = 0$.

10. Prove that $\underset{x\to a}{\text{limit}}\,\dfrac{1}{x} = \dfrac{1}{a}$ if $a < 0$. (*Hint:* Let $0 < \epsilon < -1/a$, so that $1 + \epsilon a > 0$, and proceed as in the proof of 4.10.)

11. (a) Prove that $\underset{x\to a}{\text{limit}}\,f(x) = b$ if and only if $\underset{x\to a}{\text{limit}}\,|f(x) - b| = 0$. (*Hint:* Note that $\||f(x) - b| - 0| = |f(x) - b|$.)

(b) Prove that if for some open interval containing a, $0 \le F(x) \le G(x)$, and if $\underset{x\to a}{\text{limit}}\,G(x) = 0$, then $\underset{x\to a}{\text{limit}}\,F(x) = 0$. (*Hint:* Note that $|G(x) - 0| = G(x)$ and $|F(x) - 0| = F(x)$.)

(c) Use (a) and (b) together with Exercise 7 of the previous section to prove that $\underset{x\to a}{\text{limit}}\,\dfrac{1}{x} = \dfrac{1}{a}$, $a > 0$. (*Hint:* Note that $0 \le \left|\dfrac{1}{x} - \dfrac{1}{a}\right| = \left|\dfrac{x - a}{xa}\right| < \dfrac{2}{a^2}\,|x - a|$ provided that $\dfrac{a}{2} < x$.)

4. Graphical interpretation of limit

If $\underset{x\to a}{\text{limit}}\,f(x) = b$, the question naturally arises as to the nature of the graph of the function f near $x = a$. Whether or not $f(a)$ exists is of no immediate concern in the discussion of this limit.

By definition (4.9), the above limit exists if for every number $\epsilon > 0$, there exists a number $\delta > 0$ such that

(1) $$b - \epsilon < f(x) < b + \epsilon$$

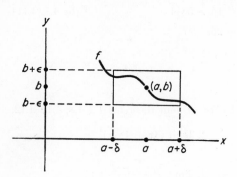

for every x satisfying

$$(2)\ a - \delta < x < a + \delta,\ x \neq a.$$

In terms of the graph of f, (1) states that the point $(x, f(x))$ of the graph lies between the two lines $y = b - \epsilon$ and $y = b + \epsilon$ provided that, (2), x lies in the open interval $(a - \delta, a + \delta)$, $x \neq a$. This is to say that as long as x is in the interval $(a - \delta, a + \delta)$, $x \neq a$, the graph of f lies within the rectangle bounded by the lines

Figure 4.2

$$y = b - \epsilon,\quad y = b + \epsilon,\quad x = a - \delta,\quad x = a + \delta,$$

and whose center is the point (a, b) (Figure 4.2). Since $x \neq a$, nothing is said about the point (a, b) being on or not on the graph of f. The number ϵ can be chosen as small as we wish, so that the rectangle can be made to have as small an altitude (2ϵ) as we wish. Thus it is clear that the graph of f must "approach" the point (a, b) as x "approaches" a.

If, now, $b > 0$ we may choose ϵ such that $0 < \epsilon < b$ (as is illustrated in Figure 4.2). (We might choose $\epsilon = b/2$.) Then $b - \epsilon > 0$, and the line $y = b - \epsilon$ lies above the x-axis. If x is in the interval $(a - \delta, a + \delta)$, the graph of f must lie above the x-axis, or in other words, $f(x) > 0$. We state this result as follows.

4.13 If $\lim\limits_{x \to a} f(x) = b$ and if $b > 0$, then there is an interval $(a - \delta, a + \delta)$ such that $f(x) > 0$ if x is in the interval $(a - \delta, a + \delta)$, $x \neq a$.

An obvious analogue of this theorem can be stated for the case where $b < 0$. Clearly no conclusion can be drawn when $b = 0$.

5. Continuity

The most natural value for $\lim\limits_{x \to a} f(x)$ to be is $f(a)$, provided, of course, that $f(a)$ exists. This situation arises often enough to be given a special name, as indicated in the following definition.

4.14 Definition. The function f is *continuous* at the number a in the domain of f if

$$\lim\limits_{x \to a} f(x) = f(a).$$

This definition really makes three statements.   Thus f is continuous at a if $f(a)$ exists, limit $f(x)$ exists, and
$$\text{limit}_{x \to a} f(x) = f(a).$$

Going back to the definition of limit, f is continuous at a if for every $\epsilon > 0$ there exists some $\delta > 0$ such that
$$f(a) - \epsilon < f(x) < f(a) + \epsilon \text{ for every } x \text{ satisfying } a - \delta < x < a + \delta.$$
Note that we no longer need insist that $x \neq a$, since trivially
$$f(a) - \epsilon < f(a) < f(a) + \epsilon.$$

If the function f is continuous at a, then there are points on the graph of f arbitrarily close to the point $(a, f(a))$ (which is also on the graph of f). To be more precise, for every $\epsilon > 0$ there exists some $\delta < 0$ such that $f(x)$ is in the interval $(f(a) - \epsilon, \ f(a) + \epsilon)$ for every x in $(a - \delta, a + \delta)$. In terms of the graph (Figure 4.3), this means that the graph of f between $x = a - \delta$ and $x = a + \delta$ is completely contained in the rectangle $ABCD$. Thus, for every choice of the lines
$$y = f(a) - \epsilon \quad \text{and} \quad y = f(a) + \epsilon,$$
there exist lines
$$x = a - \delta \quad \text{and} \quad x = a + \delta$$
such that the graph of f between $x = a - \delta$ and $x = a + \delta$ is completely contained in the rectangle determined by these four lines.

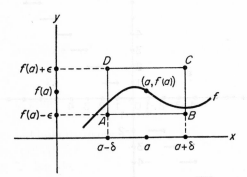

Figure 4.3

The function f might be continuous at every number in a given interval, in which case we shall say that f is *continuous in the interval*.

For example, the function f defined by
$$f(x) = x^2$$
is continuous at every number a, since
$$\text{limit}_{x \to a} f(x) = a^2 = f(a).$$

5. $\displaystyle\lim_{y\to5}\frac{\dfrac{y+1}{y-1}-\dfrac{3}{2}}{y-5}$.

6. $\displaystyle\lim_{x\to4}\frac{\dfrac{1}{\sqrt{x}}-\dfrac{1}{2}}{x-4}$.

7. $\displaystyle\lim_{x\to a}\frac{\dfrac{1}{x^3}-\dfrac{1}{a^3}}{x-a}$.

8. $\displaystyle\lim_{x\to a}\frac{\dfrac{1}{x^2+1}-\dfrac{1}{a^2+1}}{x-a}$.

9. $\displaystyle\lim_{x\to a^3}\frac{\sqrt[3]{x}-a}{x-a^3}$.

10. $\displaystyle\lim_{y\to b^2}\frac{\dfrac{y}{b^2}-\dfrac{b^4}{y^2}}{y-b^2}$.

11. If the functions f and g are continuous at a and if $g(a)\neq0$, then prove that the functions F and G also are continuous at a, where

$$F(x) = f(x)g(x), \qquad G(x) = f(x)/g(x).$$

12. If the function g is continuous at a and the function f is continuous at $g(a)$, show that the composite of f by g is continuous at a.

13. Prove that if the function f is continuous at c and $f(x) < W$ for every x in the domain of f, and if

$$g(x) = \frac{1}{W-f(x)},$$

then g is continuous at c.

14. Prove that $\displaystyle\lim_{x\to0}\frac{1}{x}$ does not exist. $\left(\text{Assume that there is a number } b \text{ such}\right.$

that $\displaystyle\lim_{x\to0}\frac{1}{x} = b$. Consider that $\displaystyle\lim_{x\to0}\frac{x}{x} = \lim_{x\to0}x\frac{1}{x}.\Big)$

7. The derivative of a function

The first important use we shall make of the limit concept is to define the derivative of a function. Much of the calculus is concerned with properties and applications of the derivative.

4.24 Definition. The *derivative* of the function f at the number x is

$$\lim_{h\to0}\frac{f(x+h)-f(x)}{h},$$

if this limit exists. If this limit does not exist, f does not have a derivative at x.

The notation $f'(x)$, read "f prime of x," is commonly used to designate the number which is the derivative of f at x. Thus

$$f'(x) = \lim_{h\to0}\frac{f(x+h)-f(x)}{h}.$$

The function f' so defined is called the *derivative* of f. The domain of f'

is the set of all numbers x for which

$$\lim_{h \to 0} \frac{f(x + h) - f(x)}{h}$$

exists.

A *differentiable* function is a function that has a derivative. Thus the function f is differentiable at a if $f'(a)$ exists.

If the function g is continuous at a, then the value of the limit $g(x)$ is just $\lim_{x \to a} g(a)$. The limit that defines the derivative is not so easily evaluated: one cannot give h the value 0 in the equation

$$g(h) = \frac{f(x + h) - f(x)}{h}$$

to compute $\lim_{h \to 0} g(h)$, since this substitution yields

$$\frac{f(x) - f(x)}{0} = \frac{0}{0},$$

a meaningless expression.

Some examples of the method of computing a derivative are given now.

Example 1. If $f(x) = x^2$, find $f'(x)$.

Solution: By definition,

$$f'(x) = \lim_{h \to 0} \frac{f(x + h) - f(x)}{h}.$$

Thus

$$f'(x) = \lim_{h \to 0} \frac{(x + h)^2 - x^2}{h}$$

$$= \lim_{h \to 0} \frac{2xh + h^2}{h} = \lim_{h \to 0} (2x + h) = 2x.$$

Since this limit exists for every x, the domain of f' is the set of all real numbers.

Example 2. If $g(x) = 1/x$, $x \neq 0$, find $g'(3)$.

Solution: The steps in finding $g'(3)$ are as follows:

$$g'(3) = \lim_{h \to 0} \frac{1/(3 + h) - \frac{1}{3}}{h} = \lim_{h \to 0} \frac{-h}{3h(3 + h)}$$

$$= \lim_{h \to 0} \frac{-1}{3(3 + h)} = -\frac{1}{9}.$$

Example 3. If $F(z) = \sqrt{z}$, find $F'(z)$.

Solution: The domain of F is the set of all nonnegative numbers. By definition,

$$F'(z) = \lim_{h \to 0} \frac{\sqrt{z + h} - \sqrt{z}}{h}$$

if the limit exists. Since

$$\frac{\sqrt{z + h} - \sqrt{z}}{h} = \frac{(\sqrt{z + h} - \sqrt{z})(\sqrt{z + h} + \sqrt{z})}{h(\sqrt{z + h} + \sqrt{z})}$$

$$= \frac{(z + h) - z}{h(\sqrt{z + h} + \sqrt{z})} = \frac{1}{\sqrt{z + h} + \sqrt{z}}$$

if $h \neq 0$,

$$F'(z) = \lim_{h \to 0} \frac{1}{\sqrt{z + h} + \sqrt{z}} = \frac{1}{2\sqrt{z}}$$

provided that $z \neq 0$. Thus the domain of F' is the set of all positive numbers, and it differs from the domain of F in that 0 is excluded.

By definition, the derivative of the function f at the number x is

(1) $$f'(x) = \lim_{h \to 0} \frac{f(x + h) - f(x)}{h}.$$

Similarly, the derivative of f at the number a is

(2) $$f'(a) = \lim_{h \to 0} \frac{f(a + h) - f(a)}{h}.$$

The difference between (1) and (2) is just notational. We have merely replaced x by a in (1) to obtain (2).

If we define the function F by the equation

$$F(x) = \frac{f(x) - f(a)}{x - a},$$

then by 4.23

$$\lim_{x \to a} F(x) = \lim_{h \to 0} F(a + h)$$

provided either of these limits exists. Thus

$$\lim_{x \to a} \frac{f(x) - f(a)}{x - a} = \lim_{h \to 0} \frac{f(a + h) - f(a)}{h},$$

and we conclude that an alternate way of defining the derivative of a function is as follows:

4.25 $$f'(a) = \lim_{x \to a} \frac{f(x) - f(a)}{x - a}.$$

■ ■ ■ EXERCISES

1. If $f(x) = x^2 + 3x - 1$, use 4.24 to find:
(a) $f'(2)$.   (b) $f'(-1)$.   (c) $f'(a)$.   (d) $f'(x)$.

2. If the function f is defined as follows, use 4.24 to find $f'(x)$:
(a) $f(x) = kx$.   (b) $f(x) = kx^2$.   (c) $f(x) = kx^3$.

3. If $g(x) = 1/(x + 1)$, $x \neq -1$, use 4.25 to find:
(a) $g'(0)$.   (b) $g'(1)$.   (c) $g'(a)$, $a \neq -1$.

4. Let $f(x) = \sqrt{x}$, $x > 0$. Use 4.25 to find:
(a) $f'(1)$.   (b) $f'(4)$.   (c) $f'(3)$.   (d) $f'(a)$, $a > 0$.

5. If $F(x) = x^2 + 2$, find $F'(x)$. Then use the function F' to find:
(a) $F'(-3)$.   (b) $F'(-2)$.   (c) $F'(0)$.   (d) $F'(1)$.

6. If $G(x) = x - 3/x$, $x \neq 0$, find $G'(x)$. Then use the function G' to find:
(a) $G'(-3)$.   (b) $G'(-1)$.   (c) $G'(2)$.   (d) $G'(5)$.

Find the derivative of each function defined as follows:

7. $f(x) = 3x^2 - 2x$.   **8.** $g(y) = y - y^2$.

9. $F(z) = z/(2 - z)$, $z \neq 2$.   **10.** $G(x) = (3x + 1)/x$, $x \neq 0$.

11. $S(t) = 16t^2$, $t \geq 0$.   **12.** $F(u) = 1/\sqrt{u}$, $u > 0$.

13. $f(x) = \sqrt{x^2 + 1}$.   **14.** $F(t) = 4/t^2$, $t \neq 0$.

15. $g(x) = x\sqrt{x}$, $x \geq 0$.   **16.** $g(x) = \sqrt[3]{x}$.

17. Let f be a function and a be a number such that $f'(a)$ exists. If the function F is defined by the equation

$$F(x) = \frac{f(x) - f(a)}{x - a}, \quad x \neq a, \quad F(a) = f'(a),$$

show that F is continuous at a.

8. Tangent lines

One of the many applications of the derivative is to the problem of finding the tangent line to the graph of a function at some point on the graph.

It is possible to define the tangent line to a circle at a point P on the circle either as the line perpendicular to the radius at P or as the line intersecting the circle in only one point P. Neither one of these definitions of a tangent line will carry over to a general curve. In Figure 4.6, for

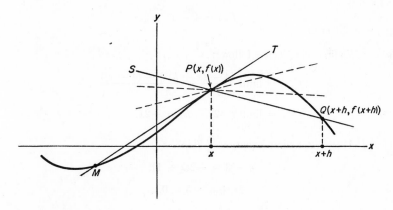

Figure 4.6

example, the tangent line T at P intersects the curve in another point M.

The tangent line T at P to a curve such as in Figure 4.6 should be the line on P that is nearest to the curve in the neighborhood of P. We interpret this to mean that each secant line S on P and some other point Q of the curve should be close to T when Q is close to P. The limiting position of the secant line S as Q approaches P should be the tangent line T.

These rather vague statements as to the nature of the tangent line to the graph of f at the point $P(x,f(x))$ can be made precise by use of slopes. If $Q(x + h, f(x + h))$ is another point on the graph of f (Figure 4.6), then the slope $m(h)$ of the secant line S on P and Q is given by

$$m(h) = \frac{f(x + h) - f(x)}{h}.$$

Since we are thinking of x as a fixed number, the slope of S just depends on h for its value. The slope of the tangent line at P then is defined to be

$$\lim_{h \to 0} m(h) = \lim_{h \to 0} \frac{f(x + h) - f(x)}{h},$$

if this limit exists. Since this limit is exactly the derivative of f at x, we are led to defining the tangent line as follows.

4.26 Definition. The tangent line to the graph of f at the point $P(x,f(x))$ is the line on P with slope $f'(x)$.

The slope of the tangent line T to the graph of f at the point $(a,f(a))$ evidently is $f'(a)$. Thus the equation of T is

4.27 $$y - f(a) = f'(a)(x - a).$$

This is based on the assumption, of course, that $f'(a)$ exists.

Example 1. Find an equation of the tangent line T to the graph of the function f defined by

$$f(x) = 4 - x^2$$

at the point $(1,3)$.

Solution: We first find $f'(x)$ as follows:

$$f'(x) = \lim_{h \to 0} \frac{[4 - (x + h)^2] - (4 - x^2)}{h}$$

$$= \lim_{h \to 0} (-2x - h) = -2x.$$

Thus $f'(1) = -2$, and an equation of T is

$$y - 3 = -2(x - 1),$$

or $$2x + y - 5 = 0.$$

The curve is sketched in Figure 4.7.

Example 2. Find an equation of the tangent line T to the graph of

$$g(x) = \frac{1}{x}, \quad x \neq 0,$$

at the point $(3, \frac{1}{3})$.

Solution: An equation of T is

$$y - \frac{1}{3} = g'(3)(x - 3).$$

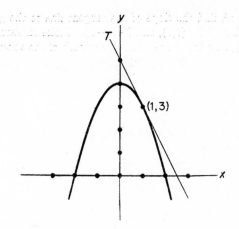

Figure 4.7

By Example 2 of the previous section, $g'(3) = -\frac{1}{9}$. Thus an equation of T is

$$y - \frac{1}{3} = -\frac{1}{9}(x-3),$$

or $x + 9y - 6 = 0.$

Example 3. Find an equation of the tangent line T to the graph of

$$F(x) = \sqrt{1+x}, \quad x \geq -1,$$

at the point $(0,1)$.

Solution: The slope m of T is given by

$$m = \lim_{h\to 0} \frac{F(h) - F(0)}{h} = \lim_{h\to 0} \frac{\sqrt{1+h} - 1}{h}.$$

However, if $h \neq 0$, then

$$\frac{\sqrt{1+h} - 1}{h} = \frac{(1+h) - 1}{h(\sqrt{1+h} + 1)} = \frac{1}{\sqrt{1+h} + 1},$$

and $m = \lim\limits_{h\to 0} \dfrac{1}{\sqrt{1+h} + 1} = \dfrac{1}{2}.$

Hence the equation of T is given by

$$y - 1 = \frac{1}{2}(x - 0),$$

or $x - 2y + 2 = 0.$

■ ■ ■ EXERCISES

1. If $g(x) = x^2$, find the slope of the tangent line to the graph of g at each of the points

$$(-2,g(-2)), \quad (-1,g(-1)), \quad (0,g(0)), \quad (1,g(1)), \quad (2,g(2)).$$

Sketch the graph of g and the tangent lines at each of the above points.

2. If $f(x) = x^3$, find the slope of the tangent line to the graph of f at each of the points $(0,0)$, $(1,1)$, and $(-1,-1)$. Make an accurate sketch of the graph of f, showing the tangent line at each of the above points.

In each of the following exercises, find an equation of the tangent line to the graph of the given function at the given point.

3. $f(x) = 3x^2 + 1$; $(-1, f(-1))$.

4. $g(x) = 1/x^2$, $x \neq 0$; $(2, g(2))$.

5. $F(x) = 1/(x - 1)$, $x \neq 1$; $(2, F(2))$.

6. $G(x) = 10/(x^2 + 1)$; $(3, G(3))$.

7. $g(x) = 2\sqrt{x}$, $x \geq 0$; $(1, g(1))$.

8. $F(x) = 1/\sqrt{x}$, $x > 0$; $(2, F(2))$.

9. $G(x) = 1 - x^3$; $(-1, G(-1))$.

10. $f(x) = x^4$; $(1, f(1))$.

11. $f(x) = x^2 - x^4$; $(\sqrt{2}, f(\sqrt{2}))$.

12. If $f(x) = kx^2$, show that the tangent line to the graph of f at the point $(c, f(c))$ is parallel to the secant line on the points $(a, f(a))$ and $(b, f(b))$ if and only if $c = (a + b)/2$.

13. Find the area of the triangle formed by the coordinate axes and the tangent line to the graph of $f(x) = x^2 - 9$ at the point $(2, -5)$.

9. Continuity of a differentiable function

The condition on a function of possessing a derivative is stronger than that of being continuous, as we shall now prove.

4.28 Theorem. If the function f is differentiable at a, then f is continuous at a.

Proof: By assumption and by 4.25, a is in the domain of f and

$$\lim_{x \to a} \frac{f(x) - f(a)}{x - a} = f'(a).$$

It is possible to write $f(x) - f(a)$ as a product in the following way,

$$f(x) - f(a) = \frac{f(x) - f(a)}{x - a} \cdot (x - a), \quad x \neq a.$$

Hence, by the product limit theorem,

$$\lim_{x \to a} [f(x) - f(a)] = \lim_{x \to a} \frac{f(x) - f(a)}{x - a} \cdot \lim_{x \to a} (x - a)$$

$$= f'(a) \cdot 0$$

$$= 0.$$

Thus
$$\lim_{x \to a} f(x) = f(a)$$

and the theorem is proved.

The converse of this theorem is not true. That is, there are functions continuous but not differentiable at some number. The example below illustrates this fact.

Example. If f is the absolute-value function,

$$f(x) = |x|,$$

show that f is continuous but not differentiable at the number 0.

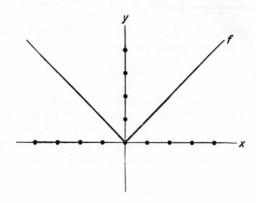

Figure 4.8

Solution: The graph of f, consisting of two half-lines meeting at the origin, is sketched in Figure 4.8. By definition,

$$f(x) = x \quad \text{if} \quad x \geq 0; \qquad f(x) = -x \quad \text{if} \quad x \leq 0.$$

We shall show that f is continuous at every number a. By 1.14,

$$|x| = \sqrt{x^2}.$$

Hence

$$\text{limit}_{x \to a} |x| = \text{limit}_{x \to a} \sqrt{x^2} = \sqrt{\text{limit}_{x \to a} x^2} = \sqrt{a^2} = |a|,$$

and f is continuous at a.

In order to prove that f is not differentiable at 0, we must show that

$$\text{limit}_{h \to 0} \frac{f(0 + h) - f(0)}{h} = \text{limit}_{h \to 0} \frac{|h|}{h}$$

does not exist. Assume, on the contrary, that

$$\text{limit}_{h \to 0} \frac{|h|}{h} = b.$$

Then for every $\epsilon > 0$ there must exist some $\delta > 0$ such that

$$b - \epsilon < \frac{|h|}{h} < b + \epsilon \text{ for every } h \text{ satisfying } -\delta < h < \delta, h \neq 0.$$

In particular, if we let $\epsilon = 1$, there must exist some $\delta > 0$ such that

$$b - 1 < \frac{|h|}{h} < b + 1 \text{ for every } h \text{ satisfying } -\delta < h < \delta, h \neq 0.$$

Thus the inequality

(1) $$b - 1 < \frac{|h|}{h} < b + 1$$

must be satisfied for both positive and negative values of h. However,

(2)   if $h > 0$, $\dfrac{|h|}{h} = 1$ and $1 < b + 1$ according to (1);

(3)   if $h < 0$, $\dfrac{|h|}{h} = -1$ and $b - 1 < -1$ according to (1).

From (2) we conclude that $b > 0$, whereas $b < 0$ according to (3). Since no such number b exists, our assumption that

$$\lim_{h \to 0} \frac{|h|}{h}$$

exists must be false. Thus f is not differentiable at 0.

It is geometrically evident that the graph of f (Figure 4.8) has no tangent line at 0. The secant lines on 0 and a point Q to the right of the origin all have slope 1, whereas those on 0 and a point Q to the left of the origin all have slope -1. Clearly these slopes are not approaching some fixed number as Q approaches 0.

■ ■ ■ EXERCISES

1. Let g be a function such that:
   (i) $\lim\limits_{x \to a} g(x) = 0$,
   (ii) $g(x) \neq 0$ for every $x \neq a$ in some open interval containing a.

   Prove the following theorems:

   (a) If $\lim\limits_{x \to a} \dfrac{f(x)}{g(x)}$ exists, then $\lim\limits_{x \to a} f(x) = 0$.

   (*Hint:* Note that $f(x) = \dfrac{f(x)}{g(x)} \cdot g(x)$, $x \neq a$.)

   (b) $\lim\limits_{x \to a} \dfrac{1}{g(x)}$ does not exist.

2. Show that if $F(x) = \sqrt[3]{x}$, then F is continuous at 0 and $F'(0)$ does not exist.

3. Define the function f by
   $$f(x) = x^2/2 \text{ if } x \geq 0; \qquad f(x) = -x^2/2 \text{ if } x < 0.$$
   Sketch the graph of f and prove that $f'(x) = |x|$ for all x.

4. If $g(x) = |x|$, prove that $g'(x) = |x|/x$ for all $x \neq 0$.

5. Let the function f be defined and increasing in the interval $[a,b]$ and let c be a number in (a,b). Prove that if $f'(c)$ exists, then $f'(c)$ is not negative, i.e., $f'(c) \geq 0$. Using $f(x) = x^3$ and the interval $[-1,1]$, show that both $f'(x) = 0$ and $f'(x) > 0$ are possible values for the derivative of an increasing function.

Differentiation of algebraic functions

5

■ ■ ■ ■ ■   WE RECALL FROM the previous chapter that the derivative f' of a function f is defined by

5.1 $$f'(x) = \lim_{h \to 0} \frac{f(x + h) - f(x)}{h}.$$

The domain of the function f' is the set of all numbers x in the domain of f for which the limit above exists.

The process of finding the derivative of a function is called *differentiation*. This chapter is devoted to the development of various differentiation formulas that will allow us to find the derivative of every algebraic function.

There are many symbols for the derivative of a function f. We shall use the symbols

$$f'(x) \quad \text{and} \quad D_x f(x)$$

interchangeably to designate the derivative of f at x. If the notation

$$y = f(x)$$

is used, then the derivative of f at x may also be designated by any one of the following symbols:

$$y', \quad D_x y, \quad \frac{dy}{dx}, \quad \frac{d}{dx} f(x).$$

constant times the derivative of the function.   The proof of 5.7 is given below.

$$D_x[k \cdot f(x)] = \lim_{h \to 0} \frac{[k \cdot f(x + h)] - [k \cdot f(x)]}{h}$$

$$= k \lim_{h \to 0} \frac{f(x + h) - f(x)}{h} = k \, D_x f(x).$$

The two formulas above along with the formulas of the previous section will allow us to differentiate any polynomial function, as is illustrated in the following examples.

Example 1.   Differentiate f if

$$f(x) = 4x^2 - 8x + 3.$$

Solution: This is done as follows.

$$
\begin{aligned}
D_x f(x) &= D_x(4x^2) - D_x(8x) + D_x 3 & \text{(by 5.6),}\\
&= 4D_x x^2 - 8D_x x + D_x 3 & \text{(by 5.7),}\\
&= 4(2x) - 8(1) + 0 & \text{(by 5.5, 5.3, 5.2),}\\
&= 8x - 8.
\end{aligned}
$$

Example 2.   Find $D_x(6x^5 - x^4 + \sqrt{3}x^3 + x - 7)$.

Solution: We have

$$D_x(6x^5 - x^4 + \sqrt{3}x^3 + x - 7) = 6D_x x^5 - D_x x^4 + \sqrt{3}D_x x^3 + D_x x - D_x 7,$$

$$= 30x^4 - 4x^3 + 3\sqrt{3}x^2 + 1.$$

■ ■ ■ EXERCISES

Show that:

1. If $f(x) = x^{10}/10 - x^5$, then $f'(x) = x^9 - 5x^4$.
2. If $g(x) = 5x^3 - 3x^2 + 1$, then $g'(x) = 15x^2 - 6x$.
3. If $F(x) = x^7 - 7x^6 - 3x + 4$, then $D_x F(x) = 7x^6 - 42x^5 - 3$.
4. $D_x(mx + b) = m$.
5. Prove that if $D_x f(x)$ exists and $k \neq 0$, then

$$D_x \frac{f(x)}{k} = \frac{D_x f(x)}{k},$$

and find:

(a) $D_x \dfrac{3x^2 + 2x - 5}{4}$.   (b) $D_x \dfrac{x^3 - 6x + 3}{3}$.

6. If $g(x) = \dfrac{2x^3 - 3x^2 + 12x}{6}$, find:

(a) $g'(x)$.   (b) $g'(2)$.   (c) $g'(a)$.   (d) $g'(b^2 + 1)$.   (e) $g'(1 - x)$.

Differentiate each of the following:

7. $f(x) = x^3 - 2x^2 + 5x + 7$.   8. $g(x) = 5x^4 - x^3 + 7x^2 - 3$.

9. $F(t) = \frac{1}{5}t^5 - \frac{1}{3}t^3$.

10. $G(y) = 3y^7 - 7y^3 + 21y.$

11. $G(x) = \dfrac{k}{n+1}\, x^{n+1}$, n a positive integer.

12. $H(z) = \sqrt{5}(z^2 - z)$.

13. $N(u) = \dfrac{u^2 + 1}{\pi + 1}$.

14. $S(t) = 16t^2 - 50t + 100$.

In each of the following, find $\dfrac{dy}{dx}$:

15. $y = 5x^2 - 2x + 1$.

16. $y = ax^3 + bx^2 + cx + d$.

17. $y = (x^2 + 1)^2$.

18. $y = (3x + 1)^3$.

19. $y = \dfrac{5x^3 - 8x^2}{6}$.

20. $y = (x + 2)^4$.

21. If $f(x) = x^3 - 3x$, find equations of the tangent lines to the graph of f at the points $(-1,f(-1))$, $(0,f(0))$, and $(1,f(1))$. Then sketch the graph of f, showing the tangent lines found above.

22. If $g(x) = -(x^2 + 4x + 2)$, find equations of the tangent lines to the graph of f at the points $(-3,g(-3))$, $(-2,g(-2))$, and $(-1,g(-1))$. Then sketch the graph of f, showing the tangent lines found above.

23. Use the definition of the derivative to prove that if $f'(x)$ exists and $f(x) \neq 0$, then

$$D_x \frac{1}{f(x)} = -\frac{D_x f(x)}{f^2(x)}.$$

Find:

(a) $D_x \dfrac{1}{x^2 + 1}$.

(b) $\dfrac{d}{dx} \dfrac{5}{x + 2}$.

(c) $\dfrac{d}{dx} \dfrac{3}{x^3 + 1}$.

24. Prove the power formula (5.5) using the alternate definition of the derivative (4.25).

3. The product and quotient formulas

The derivative of the product of two functions is not the product of the derivatives of the two functions as one might suspect in view of the sum formula (5.6). The correct formula is derived below.

Let f and g be functions, each of which has a derivative at x. Then

$$D_x[f(x)g(x)] = \lim_{h \to 0} \frac{[f(x + h)g(x + h)] - [f(x)g(x)]}{h},$$

if, indeed, the derivative exists. It is not evident how to evaluate the above limit. We would like to separate the functions f and g, as in the proof of the sum formula, if possible. The following device of adding and subtracting a term allows us to make such a separation.

$$\frac{f(x+h)g(x+h) - f(x)g(x)}{h}$$

$$= \frac{f(x+h)g(x+h) - f(x+h)g(x) + f(x+h)g(x) - f(x)g(x)}{h},$$

$$= \frac{f(x+h)[g(x+h) - g(x)] + g(x)[f(x+h) - f(x)]}{h},$$

$$= f(x+h)\frac{g(x+h) - g(x)}{h} + g(x)\frac{f(x+h) - f(x)}{h}.$$

Hence, using the limit theorems,

$$D_x[f(x)g(x)]$$

$$= \lim_{h\to 0} f(x+h) \lim_{h\to 0} \frac{g(x+h) - g(x)}{h} + g(x) \lim_{h\to 0} \frac{f(x+h) - f(x)}{h},$$

$$= f(x) D_x g(x) + g(x) D_x f(x).$$

Since f has a derivative at x, f is continuous at x and

$$\lim_{h\to 0} f(x+h) = f(x).$$

We have proved the following product formula.

5.8 $D_x[f(x)g(x)] = f(x) D_x g(x) + g(x) D_x f(x).$

In words, the *derivative of the product of two functions is the first function times the derivative of the second one plus the second function times the derivative of the first one.*

Example.   Find $D_x(x^3 - 3x^2 + 1)(x^5 + 4x^2 + 2x - 5)$.

Solution: By 5.8 we have

$$D_x(x^3 - 3x^2 + 1)(x^5 + 4x^2 + 2x - 5)$$

$$= (x^3 - 3x^2 + 1) D_x(x^5 + 4x^2 + 2x - 5) +$$
$$(x^5 + 4x^2 + 2x - 5) D_x(x^3 - 3x^2 + 1)$$

$$= (x^3 - 3x^2 + 1)(5x^4 + 8x + 2) + (x^5 + 4x^2 + 2x - 5)(3x^2 - 6x).$$

The formula for the derivative of a quotient of two functions is derived in a similar way, as we now will show.

$$D_x\left[\frac{f(x)}{g(x)}\right] = \lim_{h\to 0} \frac{\frac{f(x+h)}{g(x+h)} - \frac{f(x)}{g(x)}}{h} = \lim_{h\to 0} \frac{f(x+h)g(x) - f(x)g(x+h)}{hg(x)g(x+h)},$$

$$= \lim_{h\to 0} \frac{f(x)g(x) - f(x)g(x+h) - f(x)g(x) + f(x+h)g(x)}{hg(x)g(x+h)},$$

$$= \lim_{h\to 0} \frac{g(x)\left[\frac{f(x+h) - f(x)}{h}\right] - f(x)\left[\frac{g(x+h) - g(x)}{h}\right]}{g(x)g(x+h)},$$

$$= \frac{g(x) D_x f(x) - f(x) D_x g(x)}{g^2(x)}.$$

This proves the quotient formula:

5.9 $$D_x\left[\frac{f(x)}{g(x)}\right] = \frac{g(x)\,D_xf(x) - f(x)\,D_xg(x)}{g^2(x)}.$$

In words, the *derivative of the quotient of two functions is the denominator times the derivative of the numerator minus the numerator times the derivative of the denominator all divided by the square of the denominator.*

Example. Find $D_x\left[\dfrac{x^2-4}{x^3+2x-5}\right]$.

Solution: We first use 5.9, and then proceed as indicated below.

$$D_x\left[\frac{x^2-4}{x^3+2x-5}\right] = \frac{(x^3+2x-5)\,D_x(x^2-4) - (x^2-4)\,D_x(x^3+2x-5)}{(x^3+2x-5)^2},$$

$$= \frac{(x^3+2x-5)(2x) - (x^2-4)(3x^2+2)}{(x^3+2x-5)^2},$$

$$= \frac{-x^4+14x^2-10x+8}{(x^3+2x-5)^2}.$$

If n is a positive integer, then by 5.9 and the power formula,

$$D_x\left[\frac{1}{x^n}\right] = \frac{x^n\,D_x1 - 1\,D_xx^n}{(x^n)^2} = \frac{-nx^{n-1}}{x^{2n}} = \frac{-n}{x^{n+1}}.$$

Writing this result in terms of negative exponents, we have

$$D_xx^{-n} = -nx^{-n-1}.$$

In other words, if r is a negative integer,

$$D_xx^r = rx^{r-1},$$

which is just the same as the power formula. We conclude that

5.10 $$D_xx^r = rx^{r-1} \quad \text{for every integer } r.$$

For example,

$$D_xx^{-2} = -2x^{-3}, \quad D_xx^{-12} = -12x^{-13}, \quad D_xx^0 = 0x^{-1} = 0.$$

■ ■ ■ EXERCISES

Differentiate:

1. $f(x) = (2x+1)(1-2x+4x^2)$. **2.** $F(x) = (x^2+3x-1)(x^2-3x-1)$.

3. $g(y) = (\pi y^2 + \sqrt{2})(y^3\sqrt{5}-1)$. **4.** $G(t) = (3t^2+1)^2$.

5. $f(z) = z^3(3z^2-7z+5)$. **6.** $g(x) = (x^3+1)(x^4-x+5)$.

Find:

7. $D_x\left[\dfrac{x-1}{x+1}\right]$, $x \neq -1$. **8.** $D_x\left[\dfrac{x^2-a^2}{x^2+a^2}\right]$.

9. $D_x\left[\dfrac{x^2-2x+2}{x-1}\right]$, $x \neq 1$. **10.** $D_x\left[\dfrac{x-1}{x^2-2x+2}\right]$.

11. $D_y \left[\dfrac{y^3 - a^3}{y^3 + a^3} \right]$, $y \neq -a$.   **12.** $D_z \left[\dfrac{z^4 - 16}{z^4 + 16} \right]$.

Find $f'(x)$ if $x \neq 0$ and:

13. $f(x) = x^3 + \dfrac{1}{x^3}$.   **14.** $f(x) = \dfrac{x^3 - 3x^2 - 6x + 1}{x^2}$.

15. $f(x) = \left(1 + \dfrac{2}{x} \right) \left(2 + \dfrac{1}{x} \right)$.   **16.** $f(x) = \dfrac{1 + \dfrac{2}{x}}{2 + \dfrac{1}{x}}$, $x \neq -\dfrac{1}{2}$.

17. $f(x) = \left(x + \dfrac{1}{x} \right)^2$.   **18.** $f(x) = \left(x^2 - \dfrac{1}{x^2} \right)^2$.

19. Construct a proof of 5.8 by using the device of adding and subtracting the term $f(x)g(x + h)$.

20. Construct a proof of 5.9 by using the device of adding and subtracting the term $f(x + h)g(x + h)$.

21. Let $u = F(x)$, $v = G(x)$, and $w = H(x)$. Prove that if the functions F, G, and H are differentiable at x, then (using 5.8)

$$D_x uvw = uv\, D_x w + uw\, D_x v + vw\, D_x u.$$

What would the generalization of this be to a product of n functions?

22. Using the previous exercise, find:
(a) $D_x[(2x + 1)(3x - 1)(x - 2)]$.
(b) $D_x[(3x - 2)^2(2x + 3)]$.

23. Using 5.8, find $D_x f^2(x)$; $D_x f^3(x)$. What do you think $D_x f^n(x)$ is, where n is any positive integer?

24. Using 5.9, find $D_x[f(x)]^{-1}$. Then use 5.8 to find $D_x f^{-2}(x)$; $D_x f^{-3}(x)$. What do you think $D_x f^{-n}(x)$ is, where n is any positive integer?

4. The chain rule

If f and g are functions, then the composite of f by g was defined previously. For example, if

$$f(x) = x^{20}, g(x) = x^2 + 1,$$

then the composite of f by g is given by

$$f(g(x)) = (x^2 + 1)^{20}.$$

We shall show in this section that if the function g has a derivative at x and the function f has a derivative at $g(x)$, then the composite of f by g has a derivative at x given by the so-called *chain rule:*

5.11 $D_x f(g(x)) = f'(g(x))g'(x)$.

For example, if $f(x) = x^{20}$ and $g(x) = x^2 + 1$, then

$$f'(x) = 20x^{19}, \quad f'(g(x)) = 20(x^2 + 1)^{19}, \quad g'(x) = 2x,$$

and

$$D_x(x^2 + 1)^{20} = 20(x^2 + 1)^{19} \cdot 2x = 40x(x^2 + 1)^{19}.$$

Before proving the chain rule, we establish the following simple but useful lemma.

5.12 Lemma. If $f'(b)$ exists and if the function G is defined by

$$G(z) = \frac{f(z) - f(b)}{z - b}, \quad \text{if } z \neq b, \quad G(b) = f'(b),$$

then: (i) G is continuous at the number b,
and   (ii) $f(z) - f(b) = G(z)(z - b)$ for every number z in the domain of f.

Proof: By the alternate definition of the derivative (4.25),

$$f'(b) = \lim_{z \to b} \frac{f(z) - f(b)}{z - b} = \lim_{z \to b} G(z).$$

Since $G(b) = f'(b)$ by definition and $\lim\limits_{z \to b} G(z) = f'(b)$, evidently G is continuous at b and (*i*) is proved.

Clearly

$$G(z)(z - b) = f(z) - f(b), \quad z \neq b,$$

from the definition of G. Even if $z = b$, however,

$$G(z)(z - b) = f(z) - f(b)$$

since each side of the equation is zero. This proves (ii).

Let us use this lemma now to prove the chain rule. For convenience, let F be the composite of f by g, so that

$$F(x) = f(g(x)).$$

By definition (4.25),

$$F'(a) = \lim_{x \to a} \frac{f(g(x)) - f(g(a))}{x - a},$$

if this limit exists. Let the function G be defined precisely as in the lemma above, with

$$b = g(a).$$

Then, by 5.12 (ii),

$$f(z) - f(g(x)) = G(z)[z - g(a)],$$

and for every x in the domain of g such that $g(x)$ is in the domain of f,

$$f(g(x)) - f(g(a)) = G(g(x))[g(x) - g(a)].$$

Hence, by 5.12 (i),

$$F'(a) = \lim_{x \to a} G(g(x)) \frac{g(x) - g(a)}{x - a}$$

and $\qquad\qquad F'(a) = f'(g(a))g'(a)$

provided that g has a derivative at a and f has a derivative at $g(a)$. This is the chain rule 5.11 with a in place of x.

The principal use of the chain rule at the present is to aid in the differ-

it for the special cube root function. The proof in the general case runs parallel to the case $n = 3$, as the reader may easily verify.

By definition,

$$D_x x^{1/3} = \lim_{h \to 0} \frac{(x + h)^{1/3} - x^{1/3}}{h}.$$

If we use identity 5.4 with $n = 3$, $u = (x + h)^{1/3}$, and $v = x^{1/3}$, we obtain

$$h = (x + h)^{3/3} - x^{3/3} = [(x + h)^{1/3} - x^{1/3}][(x + h)^{2/3} + (x + h)^{1/3}x^{1/3} + x^{2/3}]$$

Hence
$$\frac{(x + h)^{1/3} - x^{1/3}}{h} = \frac{1}{(x + h)^{2/3} + (x + h)^{1/3}x^{1/3} + x^{2/3}},$$

and
$$D_x x^{1/3} = \lim_{h \to 0} \frac{1}{(x + h)^{2/3} + (x + h)^{1/3}x^{1/3} + x^{2/3}}$$

$$= \frac{1}{x^{2/3} + x^{1/3}x^{1/3} + x^{2/3}},$$

$$= \frac{1}{3x^{2/3}} = \frac{1}{3} x^{-2/3} = \frac{1}{3} x^{1/3-1}.$$

This clearly yields 5.14 if $n = 3$.

Finally, let us prove that the following general power formula holds:

5.15 $D_x x^r = rx^{r-1}$, r a rational number.

If $x \neq 0$ and $r = m/n$, m and n integers with $n > 0$, then

$$D_x x^{m/n} = D_x (x^{1/n})^m$$

$$= m(x^{1/n})^{m-1} D_x x^{1/n} \qquad \text{(by 5.13)}$$

$$= mx^{(m-1)/n} \cdot \frac{1}{n} x^{1/n-1} \qquad \text{(by 5.14)}$$

$$= \frac{m}{n} x^{m/n-1}.$$

Thus $D_x x^r = rx^{r-1}$, and 5.15 is proved.

The power function f defined by

$$f(x) = x^r$$

has a derivative at 0 for certain powers r. Since $f(0)$ is undefined if $r \leq 0$, $f'(0)$ does not exist in this case. If $r > 0$, then

$$f'(0) = \lim_{x \to 0} \frac{x^r - 0^r}{x - 0} = \lim_{x \to 0} x^{r-1}.$$

If $r \geq 1$, this latter limit exists and equals 0, whereas, if $r < 1$, this limit does not exist, as will be shown in Chapter 7. Thus, 5.15 also holds if $x = 0$ and $r \geq 1$.

Another proof of this power formula, showing that it is actually valid for any real number power r, is given in Chapter 10.

From 5.15 and the chain rule, we obtain the following general form of **5.13**:

5.16 $\qquad D_x g^r(x) = rg^{r-1}(x) D_x g(x)$, $\quad r$ a rational number.

Example 1. Find $D_x[x\sqrt{x^2 + 4}]$.

Solution: We first use the product formula and then continue as indicated below.

$$D_x[x(x^2 + 4)^{1/2}] = (x^2 + 4)^{1/2} D_x x + x D_x (x^2 + 4)^{1/2}$$

$$= (x^2 + 4)^{1/2} + x \cdot \frac{1}{2} (x^2 + 4)^{-1/2} D_x(x^2 + 4)$$

$$= (x^2 + 4)^{1/2} + \frac{x}{2} (x^2 + 4)^{-1/2}(2x)$$

$$= \sqrt{x^2 + 4} + \frac{x^2}{\sqrt{x^2 + 4}}$$

$$= \frac{2x^2 + 4}{\sqrt{x^2 + 4}}.$$

Example 2. Find $\quad D_x \left[\dfrac{x^2}{\sqrt[3]{3x + 1}} \right]$.

Solution: We proceed as follows:

$$D_x \left[\frac{x^2}{\sqrt[3]{3x + 1}} \right] = \frac{2x\sqrt[3]{3x + 1} - x^2 D_x(3x + 1)^{1/3}}{(\sqrt[3]{3x + 1})^2}$$

$$= \frac{2x\sqrt[3]{3x + 1} - x^2 \cdot \frac{1}{3} (3x + 1)^{-2/3} D_x(3x + 1)}{(3x + 1)^{2/3}}$$

$$= \frac{2x(3x + 1) - x^2}{(3x + 1)^{4/3}} = \frac{5x^2 + 2x}{\sqrt[3]{(3x + 1)^4}}.$$

■ ■ ■ EXERCISES

Differentiate:

1. $f(x) = x\sqrt{1 - x^2}$.

2. $g(y) = (1 - 2y)\sqrt{y^2 + 2y + 3}$.

3. $h(z) = \sqrt{\dfrac{1 - z}{1 + z}}$.

4. $F(t) = (2t + t^2)^{3/2}$.

5. $S(t) = \sqrt[3]{3t + 1}$.

6. $h(x) = \dfrac{\sqrt{x^2 - 4}}{x}$.

7. $g(x) = \dfrac{\sqrt{x^2 + 4}}{x}$.

8. $f(x) = \sqrt{x + \dfrac{1}{x}}$.

9. $F(y) = \left(y - \dfrac{1}{y} \right)^{3/2}$.

10. $G(z) = \sqrt{2z} + \sqrt{\dfrac{z}{2}}$.

Find $\dfrac{dy}{dx}$:

11. $y = 3x^2 - x + 5 - x^{-1/2}$.

12. $y = \sqrt{3 + 2x^2}$.

13. $y = \sqrt{5x} - \sqrt{\dfrac{5}{x}}$.

14. $y = \dfrac{1}{\sqrt{x^2 + 1}}$.

15. $y = x^3\sqrt[3]{x + 1}$.

16. $y = \sqrt{1 + \sqrt{x}}$.

17. $y = \dfrac{\sqrt{3x + 1} - 1}{5}$.

18. $y = \dfrac{\sqrt{x} - 1}{\sqrt{x} + 1}$.

19. $y = \dfrac{x}{\sqrt{2x + 1}}$.

20. $y = \sqrt[5]{x^5 + 1}$.

21. Derive Formula 5.14 for n any positive integer.

22. Find the equation of the tangent line to the graph of the equation $y = \sqrt[3]{x}$ at the point (8,2). Sketch the graph and the tangent line.

Given that $D_x \sin x = \cos x$, find:

23. $D_x\sqrt{\sin x}$.

24. $D_z\sqrt{1 - \sin^2 z}$.

25. $D_y\sqrt{3 - 2 \sin y}$.

26. $D_x\sqrt{\sin 5x}$.

27. $D_t \dfrac{\sin t}{\sqrt{1 - \sin t}}$.

28. $D_y\sqrt[3]{y - 5 \sin y}$.

29. $D_x \dfrac{5}{\sqrt{3 - \sin^2 3x}}$.

30. $D_t\sqrt{4 + 3 \sin 2\pi t}$.

6. Implicit differentiation

Most of the functions we have differentiated up to this point have been *explicitly* defined by an algebraic equation. If, for example,

$$f(x) = x^3 + 1,$$

then the function f is explicitly defined by an algebraic equation.

Not all functions are defined in such an explicit way. An equation in x and y such as

$$x^3 - x = y^3 - y^2 + 24,$$

for example, is not easily solved for y in terms of x. However, there might exist a function f such that

$$y = f(x)$$

satisfies the given equation; that is, such that

$$x^3 - x = f^3(x) - f^2(x) + 24$$

holds for every value of x in the domain of f. Such a function as f is said to be defined *implicitly* by the given equation. The properties of f are implied by the equation which it satisfies.

The derivative of a function defined implicitly by an equation in x and y can often be found without solving the equation for y. The process of finding the derivative of a function defined implicitly by an equation is called *implicit differentiation*.   We illustrate this process by the following examples.

Example 1.   On the assumption that there is a differentiable function f defined implicitly by the equation

$$x^3 - x = y^3 - y^2 + 24,$$

find the derivative of f.

Solution: By assumption,

$$x^3 - x = f^3(x) - f^2(x) + 24$$

holds for every x in the domain of f.   Now each side of this equation defines a function: thus the left side defines the function F, where

$$F(x) = x^3 - x,$$

and the right side defines the function G, where

$$G(x) = f^3(x) - f^2(x) + 24.$$

Since $F(x) = G(x)$ for every x in the domain of f,

$$D_x F(x) = D_x G(x)$$

for every x at which f has a derivative.   However,

$$D_x F(x) = 3x^2 - 1 \quad \text{and} \quad D_x G(x) = 3f^2(x)\, D_x f(x) - 2f(x)\, D_x f(x),$$

so that

$$3x^2 - 1 = [3f^2(x) - 2f(x)]\, D_x f(x).$$

This equation may be solved for $D_x f(x)$, yielding the desired derivative

$$D_x f(x) = \frac{3x^2 - 1}{3f^2(x) - 2f(x)}.$$

Example 2.   Two differentiable functions are defined by the equation

$$x^2 + y^2 = 16$$

of a circle, namely, those defined by the equations

$$y = \sqrt{16 - x^2} \quad \text{and} \quad y = -\sqrt{16 - x^2}.$$

Find the derivative of each of these two functions.

Solution: The implicit differentiation of the given equation may be carried out as follows (thinking of y as $f(x)$, where f is either one of the functions defined by the equation).

$$D_x(x^2 + y^2) = D_x 16,$$

$$2x + 2y\, D_x y = 0,$$

$$D_x y = -\frac{x}{y}.$$

Thus

$$D_x \sqrt{16 - x^2} = -\frac{x}{\sqrt{16 - x^2}} \quad \text{and} \quad D_x(-\sqrt{16 - x^2}) = \frac{x}{\sqrt{16 - x^2}}.$$

The example above illustrates the fact that implicit differentiation gives the derivative of every differentiable function defined by the given equation.

Example 3. Find the derivative of every differentiable function defined implicitly
by the equation

$$x^3 + x^2 y^2 = x + 2y - 1.$$

Solution: For simplicity, we will not actually replace y by $f(x)$ as we did in
Example 1. However, the following calculations are based on the assumption
that $y = f(x)$, where f is a differentiable function defined implicitly by the given
equation.

$$D_x(x^3 + x^2 y^2) = D_x(x + 2y - 1),$$

$$3x^2 + D_x(x^2 y^2) = 1 + 2 D_x y - 0,$$

$$3x^2 + (x^2 \cdot 2y\, D_x y + y^2 \cdot 2x) = 1 + 2 D_x y,$$

$$3x^2 + 2x^2 y\, D_x y + 2xy^2 = 1 + 2 D_x y,$$

$$(2x^2 y - 2)\, D_x y = 1 - 3x^2 - 2xy^2,$$

$$D_x y = \frac{1 - 3x^2 - 2xy^2}{2x^2 y - 2}.$$

■ ■ ■ EXERCISES

1. (a) Find two differentiable functions $y = y(x)$ defined by the equation
      $y^2 = 4x$.
   (b) Graph the equation $y^2 = 4x$ and indicate on your graph the graphs
      of the two functions in part (a).
   (c) Find $y'(x)$ for each of the two functions of part (a).
   (d) Find dy/dx by implicit differentiation of the equation $y^2 = 4x$, and
      verify that this result agrees with your results in part (c).
   (e) Find the slopes of the tangent lines to the graph of $y^2 = 4x$ at the
      following points: $(1,2)$; $(1,-2)$; $(4,4)$; $(4,-4)$.

2. (a) Find two differentiable functions $y = y(x)$ defined by the equation
      $x^2 + 4y^2 = 4$.
   (b) Graph the equation $x^2 + 4y^2 = 4$, and indicate on your graph the
      graphs of the two functions in part (a).
   (c) Find $y'(x)$ for each of the two functions of part (a).
   (d) Find dy/dx by implicit differentiation of the equation $x^2 + 4y^2 = 4$,
      and verify that this result agrees with your results in part (c).
   (e) Find the slopes of the tangent lines to the graph of $x^2 + 4y^2 = 4$ at
      the points where $x = \pm 1$.

Assuming that $y = f(x)$ and that $f'(x)$ exists, find dy/dx in each of the following:

3. $y^2 = 2x$.   4. $xy = 1$.

5. $x^2 - y^2 = 1$.   6. $9x^2 + 16y^2 = 144$.

7. $x^2 + y^2 = 25$.   8. $y^2 + 2x = y$.

9. $xy + x^2 = 5$.   10. $3x^2 + xy^2 - y^3 = 0$.

11. $x + \sqrt{xy} = 2y$.   12. $\dfrac{x}{y} - 2y = x$.

13. $\sqrt[3]{xy} + x = \sqrt[3]{y^2}.$

14. $\dfrac{x - y}{x + y} = x.$

15. $x^2 y^2 = 4.$

16. $y + \sqrt{xy} = x^2.$

17. $\dfrac{y^2}{x + y} = 1 - x^2.$

18. $x\sqrt{1 + 2y} + y = x^2.$

19. Prove Formula 5.15 as follows. If we let $f(x) = x^{m/n}$, m and n integers with $n > 0$, and if we assume that the function f has a derivative, then it may be found by implicit differentiation of the equation $f^n(x) = x^m$.

20. Prove Formula 5.16 by the method suggested in the preceding exercise.

7. Higher derivatives

If f' is the derivative of the function f, then f' is called the *first derivative* of f. The derivative of f' is designated by f'' and is called the *second derivative* of f. Similarly, the derivative f''' of f'' is called the *third derivative* of f, and so on. In terms of the other notations for the derivative the higher derivatives of f at x are designated as follows:

$f(x)$	$f'(x)$	$f''(x)$	$f'''(x)$	$\cdots$	$f^{[n]}(x)$
$f(x)$	$D_x f(x)$	$D_x^2 f(x)$	$D_x^3 f(x)$	$\cdots$	$D_x^n f(x)$
y	$\dfrac{dy}{dx}$	$\dfrac{d^2 y}{dx^2}$	$\dfrac{d^3 y}{dx^3}$	$\cdots$	$\dfrac{d^n y}{dx^n}$

We use $f^{[n]}(x)$ to designate the nth derivative of f at x, so as to distinguish it from the nth power $f^n(x) = [f(x)]^n$ of $f(x)$.

Example. Find the first four derivatives of f if

$$f(x) = x\sqrt{x} - 3x^2 + 5x - 4.$$

Solution: We have

$$f(x) = x^{3/2} - 3x^2 + 5x - 4,$$

$$f'(x) = \frac{3}{2} x^{1/2} - 6x + 5,$$

$$f''(x) = \frac{3}{4} x^{-1/2} - 6,$$

$$f'''(x) = -\frac{3}{8} x^{-3/2},$$

$$f^{[4]}(x) = \frac{9}{16} x^{-5/2}.$$

■ ■ ■ EXERCISES

Find the first and second derivatives of the following:

1. $f(x) = x^3 - 3x^2 - 3x + 7.$

2. $S(t) = 16t^2 - 50t + 48.$

3. $F(y) = y^5 - 3y^3 + 7y - 4.$

4. $G(x) = x^4 - 7x^2 + x - 5.$

5. $g(t) = t^2\sqrt{t} - 3t + 5.$

6. $f(z) = \sqrt[3]{z^5} - \sqrt[3]{z} + 6.$

7. $f(x) = \sqrt{x} - \dfrac{1}{\sqrt{x}}.$

8. $g(x) = \sqrt{x^2 + 1}.$

9. $F(x) = \dfrac{1}{\sqrt{3 - 2x^2}}.$

10. $f(y) = \dfrac{1 - \sqrt{y}}{1 + \sqrt{y}}.$

Find $\dfrac{dy}{dx}, \dfrac{d^2y}{dx^2},$ and $\dfrac{d^3y}{dx^3}$ of the following:

11. $y = x^3 - 4x^2 + 3x - 7.$

12. $y = 5x^4 - x^2 + \sqrt{2}.$

13. $y = \sqrt{3 + x}.$

14. $y = \sqrt{2x - 1}.$

15. $y = x^{7/2} - 3x^{5/2} + 4x^{1/2}.$

16. $y = \dfrac{x}{x + 1}.$

17. $y = \sqrt[3]{4x + 1}.$

18. $y = \dfrac{x - 1}{x + 1}.$

19. $y = \dfrac{1}{\sqrt{3x + 1}}.$

20. $y = x\sqrt{x + 1}.$

6

Applications of
the derivative

■ ■ ■ ■ ■ WE HAVE ALREADY discussed one application of the derivative, namely, to the problem of finding tangent lines to the graph of a function. This application will be discussed in more detail in the present chapter.

One of the most useful and interesting applications of the derivative is to aid in the determination of the maximum and minimum values of a function. Many so-called practical problems seeking the "best" way to do something can be formulated as problems to find maximum or minimum values of a function. Much of this chapter is devoted to the study of maxima and minima.

A derivative may be thought of as the instantaneous rate of change of a function. When thought of in this way, many physical applications of the derivative present themselves. The most obvious application of the derivative of this type is that of finding the velocity and acceleration of a moving object. This is discussed toward the end of the present chapter.

109

1. Tangent and normal lines

If $f'(a)$ exists, then the *tangent line* T to the graph of the function f at the point $P(a,f(a))$ is that line through P with slope $f'(a)$. An equation of T is therefore

$$y - f(a) = f'(a)(x - a).$$

The differentiation formulas of the previous chapter greatly simplify the problem of finding tangent lines. (Compare with Section 8 of Chapter 4.)

The *normal line* N to the graph of f at the point $P(a,f(a))$ is defined to be that line through P which is perpendicular to the tangent line. It follows that if $f'(a) \neq 0$, the slope of N is $-1/f'(a)$. Thus an equation of N is

$$y - f(a) = -\frac{1}{f'(a)}(x - a).$$

If $f'(a) = 0$, then T is a horizontal line with equation

$$y = f(a)$$

and N is a vertical line with equation

$$x = a.$$

Example 1. If

$$f(x) = x^2 + x - 6,$$

find equations for the tangent line and the normal line to the graph of f at the point where $x = 1$.

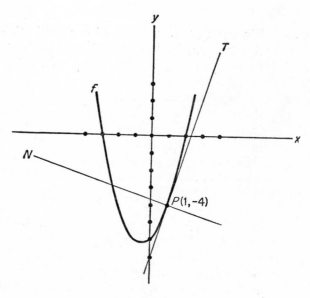

Figure 6.1

Solution: The graph of f is sketched in Figure 6.1 from the accompanying table of values. The curve is a parabola.

x	0	1	2	3	−1	−2	−3
$f(x)$	−6	−4	0	6	−6	−4	0

Since $f(1) = -4$, we are seeking the tangent line T and the normal line N to this parabola at the point $P(1,-4)$. Now

$$f'(x) = 2x + 1,$$

and $\qquad\qquad\qquad f'(1) = 3.$

Hence the slope of T is 3 and the slope of N is $-\frac{1}{3}$. Thus

$$y - (-4) = 3(x - 1),$$

or $\qquad\qquad\qquad 3x - y - 7 = 0$

is an equation of T, and

$$y - (-4) = -\tfrac{1}{3}(x - 1),$$

or $\qquad\qquad\qquad x + 3y + 11 = 0$

is an equation of N.

Example 2. Find equations of the tangent and normal lines to the graph of the equation

$$3x^2 - xy + y^2 = 3$$

at the point $(1,1)$.

Solution: We may differentiate implicitly the given equation to obtain

$$6x - y - x\,D_xy + 2y\,D_xy = 0,$$

$$(2y - x)\,D_xy = y - 6x,$$

$$D_xy = \frac{y - 6x}{2y - x}.$$

If $x = 1$ and $y = 1$,

$$D_xy = -5.$$

Thus the slope of the tangent line T at the point $(1,1)$ is -5, and an equation of T is

$$y - 1 = -5(x - 1),$$

or $\qquad\qquad\qquad 5x + y - 6 = 0.$

The slope of the normal line N at $(1,1)$ is $-1/(-5) = \frac{1}{5}$, and an equation of N is

$$y - 1 = \frac{1}{5}\,(x - 1),$$

or $\qquad\qquad\qquad x - 5y + 4 = 0.$

The graph of a function f might have a clearly defined tangent line at some point $(a, f(a))$ and yet $f'(a)$ might not exist.

As a simple example of this possibility, let the function g be defined by

$$g(x) = \sqrt{4 - x^2}.$$

The graph of g is the semicircle of radius 2 sketched in Figure 6.2; it has a tangent line at each of its points.   The tangent line T at the point (2,0)

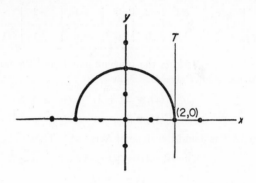

Figure 6.2

is vertical and has no slope, and therefore we can expect that $g'(2)$ does not exist.   This is indeed the case, since

$$g'(x) = -\frac{x}{\sqrt{4 - x^2}}$$

and $g'(2)$ is undefined.

We should be able to decide if the graph of a function has a vertical tangent line, as in the example above, much as we did for nonvertical tangent lines, by a consideration of secant lines.   Thus, let $P(a,f(a))$ and $Q(a + h, f(a + h))$ be distinct points on the graph of f and let L be the

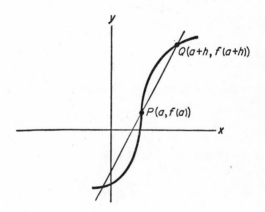

Figure 6.3

secant line on P and Q as in Figure 6.3.   If α is the inclination of L, then

$$\cot \alpha = \frac{h}{f(a + h) - f(a)},$$

and, since $\cot 90° = 0$, then L will approach a vertical position as Q approaches P if

$$\lim_{h \to 0} \cot \alpha = 0,$$

that is, if

$$\lim_{h \to 0} \frac{h}{f(a + h) - f(a)} = 0.$$

These considerations lead us to make the following definition.

6.1 Definition. If the function f is continuous at the number a and if

$$\lim_{h \to 0} \frac{h}{f(a + h) - f(a)} = 0,$$

then the tangent line to the graph of f at the point $(a,f(a))$ is the vertical line $x = a$.

Returning to the semicircle

$$g(x) = \sqrt{4 - x^2}$$

discussed above (Figure 6.2), we see that

$$\frac{h}{g(2 + h) - g(2)} = \frac{h}{\sqrt{4 - (2 + h)^2}}, \quad h < 0$$

$$= \frac{h\sqrt{-4h - h^2}}{-4h - h^2} = -\frac{\sqrt{-4h - h^2}}{4 + h}.$$

Hence

$$\lim_{h \to 0} \frac{h}{g(2 + h) - g(2)} = 0,$$

and the graph of g has a vertical tangent line at $(2,0)$ according to 6.1. Thus our definition is consistent with the geometric definition of the tangent line to a circle.

If the graph of a function f is discontinuous at some point $(a,f(a))$, then the derivative $f'(a)$ does not exist and f has no clearly defined tangent line at $(a,f(a))$. For example, the greatest integer function F (p. 76) has no tangent line at $(n,F(n))$, n an integer.

The absolute value function f defined by

$$f(x) = |x|$$

is continuous at the point $(0,0)$. However, for this graph, there is no clearly defined tangent line at the point $(0,0)$.

Example 3. Show that the graph of the function f defined by

$$f(x) = (x - 1)^{2/3} + 2$$

has a vertical tangent line at the point $(1,2)$.

Solution: Since

$$f'(x) = \frac{2}{3(x - 1)^{1/3}},$$

$f'(1)$ does not exist.   However,

$$\text{limit}_{h \to 0} \frac{h}{f(1+h) - f(1)} = \text{limit}_{h \to 0} \frac{h}{(h^{2/3} + 2) - 2}$$

$$= \text{limit}_{h \to 0} h^{1/3} = 0,$$

and the graph of f has a vertical tangent line at the point (1,2) according to Definition 6.1.   The graph of f is sketched in Figure 6.4 from the accompanying table of values.

x	0	1	2	9	-7
$f(x)$	3	2	3	6	6

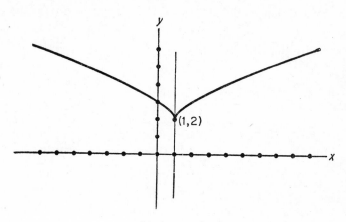

Figure 6.4

■ ■ ■ EXERCISES

Find equations for the tangent line and the normal line to each of the following graphs at the indicated point:

1. $f(x) = x^2 - 3x + 2,$ $(-2, f(-2))$.

2. $g(x) = x^2 + 4x,$ $(1, g(1))$.

3. $F(x) = x^3 - 1,$ $(-1, F(-1))$.

4. $f(x) = \sqrt{1 - 4x},$ $(-2, f(-2))$.

5. $G(x) = 1/\sqrt{3x},$ $(3, G(3))$.

6. $g(x) = \sqrt[3]{x},$ $(8, g(8))$.

7. $F(x) = (x - 1)^{2/3} + 2,$ $(9, F(9))$.

8. $f(x) = (x^2 - 4)^2,$ $(0, f(0))$.

9. $x^2 + 2y^2 = 3,$ $(1, -1)$.

10. $x^3 + x^2 y + y^3 + 8 = 0,$ $(2, -2)$.

Show that the graph of each of the following functions has a vertical tangent line at the indicated point and sketch the graph:

11. $f(x) = \sqrt{x}$,   (0,0).

12. $g(x) = \sqrt[3]{x}$,   (0,0).

13. $F(x) = 1 - (x + 1)^{1/3}$, $(-1,F(-1))$.

14. $f(x) = -x^{2/5}$,   (0,0).

15. $G(x) = (x + 3)^{2/3}$, $(-3,G(-3))$.

16. $F(x) = \sqrt{2x - 3}$, $(\frac{3}{2},F(\frac{3}{2}))$.

Two graphs are said to be *orthogonal* if their tangent lines are perpendicular at each point of intersection. Show that the graphs of each of the following pairs of equations are orthogonal:

17. $xy = 4$, $x^2 - y^2 = 15$.

18. $x^2 + y^2 - y = 0$, $x^2 + y^2 - x = 0$.

19. $x^2 + 3y^2 = 24$, $3x^2 - y^2 = 12$.

20. $y^2 = 4x + 4$, $y^2 = -6x + 9$.

21. Show that the graphs of the equations

$$y = 3x^2, \qquad y = 2x^3 + 1,$$

are tangent at the point (1,3), that is, that they have a common tangent line at this point. Sketch the graphs.

22. Show that there are exactly two tangent lines to the graph of $y = (x + 1)^3$ which pass through the origin, and find their equations.

23. Let
$$F(x) = (x - a)^{m/n}G(x) + H(x),$$

where: $0 < m < n$, G is continuous at a and $G(a) \neq 0$, $H'(a)$ exists. Prove that the graph of F has a vertical tangent at $(a,F(a))$. (This theorem covers Exercises 11 through 15; it also covers Exercise 16 if we rewrite F as $F(x) = \sqrt{2}(x - \frac{3}{2})^{1/2}$.)

24. Let $F(x) = 2x\sqrt{x + 1} + 3\sqrt[3]{x - 7}$ $(x \geq -1)$. Show that the graph of F has vertical tangents at $(-1,-6)$ and $(7,28\sqrt{2})$. (*Hint:* See Exercise 23.)

25. Let the graph of a function f have a vertical tangent at $(a,f(a))$. Prove that f is not differentiable at a. (*Hint:* Use 5.1 and Exercise 1, Section 9, Chapter 4.)

2. Increasing and decreasing functions

A function f continuous in a closed interval $[a,b]$ might have the unbroken graph given in Figure 6.5. According to definitions given in Chapter 3, this function f is increasing in the interval $[a,c]$, decreasing in the interval $[c,d]$, increasing in the interval $[d,e]$, and again decreasing in the interval $[e,b]$. In geometric language, the graph of f is rising from A to C, falling from C to D, rising again from D to E, and finally falling from E to B.

We have also defined $f(c)$ to be the maximum (or minimum) value of f in an interval containing c if $f(c) \geq f(x)$ (or $f(c) \leq f(x)$) for every number x in the interval.   Figure 6.5 indicates, for example, that $f(e)$ is the maximum value of f in each of the intervals $[d,e]$, $[d,b]$, and $[e,b]$.   Also, $f(d)$ is the minimum value of f in each of the intervals $[c,d]$, $[d,e]$, and $[c,e]$.   The maximum value of f in $[a,b]$ is apparently $f(c)$ and the minimum value $f(b)$.

In this section, we shall develop a method for determining where a function is increasing and where it is decreasing.   This method relates the increasing or decreasing of a function to the sign of the derivative. Referring to Figure 6.5, it is reasonable to expect that the function f is increasing in an interval such as $[a,c]$ where the derivative (i.e., the slope of the tangent line) is positive and is decreasing in an interval such as $[c,d]$ where the derivative is negative.   We shall presently prove that these statements hold in general.

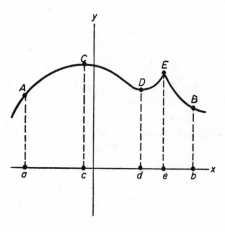

Figure 6.5

6.2 Theorem.   If the function f is continuous in the closed interval $[a,b]$, then there exist numbers u and v in $[a,b]$ such that $f(u)$ is the minimum value and $f(v)$ is the maximum value of f in $[a,b]$.

The proof of this theorem will be given in Chapter 14, after a more detailed analysis of the real number system has been carried out.

To illustrate this theorem, let

$$f(x) = 4 - x^2.$$

The function f is continuous in $(-\infty,\infty)$, and therefore, in particular, in the interval $[-2,2]$.   It is evident from the graph of f (Figure 6.6) that $f(0) = 4$ is the maximum value and $f(2) = f(-2) = 0$ is the minimum value of f in $[-2,2]$.   In the notation of 6.2, $v = 0$ and $u = 2$ or $u = -2$.

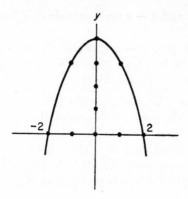

Figure 6.6

As another example, let

$$g(x) = \frac{1}{x}.$$

The function g is undefined at 0 but defined and continuous at every $x \neq 0$. Although g is continuous in the half-open interval $(0,2]$, it is clear that g does not have a maximum value in this interval. Thus, if N is any large positive number, $g(x) > N$ for any positive number $x < 1/N$.

The example above shows the necessity of having the interval $[a,b]$ in Theorem 6.2 *closed*. The function g above is continuous in the closed interval $[1,2]$, and has maximum value $g(1) = 1$ and minimum value $g(2) = \frac{1}{2}$. In the infinite interval $[1,\infty)$, g has maximum value $g(1) = 1$ but has no minimum value.

6.3 Theorem.   Let the function f be defined in some open interval containing the number c.   If $f'(c) \neq 0$, then $f(c)$ is neither the maximum nor the minimum value of f in the interval.   More specifically,

(1) if $f'(c) > 0$, then there exists an interval $(c - \delta, c + \delta)$ such that $f(x) < f(c)$ for every x in $(c - \delta, c)$; $f(x) > f(c)$ for every x in $(c, c + \delta)$.

(2) if $f'(c) < 0$, then there exists an interval $(c - \delta, c + \delta)$ such that $f(x) > f(c)$ for every x in $(c - \delta, c)$; $f(x) < f(c)$ for every x in $(c, c + \delta)$.

Proof of (1):   By assumption,

$$f'(c) = \lim_{x \to c} \frac{f(x) - f(c)}{x - c} > 0.$$

Hence, by 4.13, there exists an interval $(c - \delta, c + \delta)$ such that

$$\frac{f(x) - f(c)}{x - c} > 0, \quad x \text{ in } (c - \delta, c + \delta), \quad x \neq c.$$

Therefore, $f(x) - f(c)$ and $x - c$ must agree in sign for every x in $(c - \delta,c)$ or $(c,c + \delta)$.

If x is in $(c - \delta,c)$ then $x - c < 0$ and therefore $f(x) - f(c) < 0$, or $f(x) < f(c)$. If x is in $(c,c + \delta)$, then $x - c > 0$ and therefore $f(x) - f(c) > 0$, or $f(x) > f(c)$. This proves (1).

The proof of (2) is similar, and is omitted for that reason.

Geometrically, the theorem above states that if $f'(c) \neq 0$, then the graph of f crosses the line $y = f(c)$ at the point $(c,f(c))$. This is illustrated in Figure 6.7 for the case $f'(c) > 0$. The conclusions of the theorem are geometrically evident once we realize that the assumptions imply that the graph of f has a rising or falling tangent line at $(c,f(c))$.

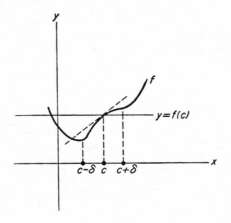

Figure 6.7

Some useful consequences of 6.3 are stated in the following theorem. The proof of this theorem is left to the reader.

6.4 Theorem. Let the function f be continuous in the closed interval $[a,b]$, and let c be a number in the open interval (a,b).

(1) If $f'(c) > 0$, then $f(c)$ is neither the minimum value of f in $[a,c]$ nor the maximum value of f in $[c,b]$.

(2) If $f'(c) < 0$, then $f(c)$ is neither the maximum value of f in $[a,c]$ nor the minimum value of f in $[c,b]$.

(3) If $f(c)$ is the maximum or minimum value of f in $[a,b]$, then either $f'(c) = 0$ or $f'(c)$ does not exist.

Example 1. The function f defined by

$$f(x) = 4 - x^2$$

is continuous in $(-\infty,\infty)$. Illustrate Theorem 6.3 for $c = -1$.

Solution: We have $f'(x) = -2x$ and $f'(-1) = 2 > 0$. It is clear from the graph of f (Figure 6.6) that $\delta = 1$ will yield the desired conclusions that

$$f(x) < f(-1) \quad \text{if} \quad x \text{ is in } (-2,-1); \quad f(x) > f(-1) \quad \text{if} \quad x \text{ is in } (-1,0).$$

Actually, any positive number $\delta \le 2$ would give the desired conclusions.

6.5 Theorem. Let the function f be continuous in the closed interval $[a,b]$.

(1) If $f'(x) > 0$ in (a,b), then f is increasing in $[a,b]$.

(2) If $f'(x) < 0$ in (a,b), then f is decreasing in $[a,b]$.

Proof of (1): To prove that f is increasing in $[a,b]$, we must show that if x_1 and x_2 are any numbers in $[a,b]$ with $x_1 < x_2$, then $f(x_1) < f(x_2)$.

With this aim in mind, let c be any number in (x_1,x_2). By assumption, $f'(c) > 0$. Since f is continuous in $[x_1,c]$, f has a minimum value $f(u)$ in this interval by 6.2. By 6.4 (1), $f(c)$ is not the minimum value of f in $[x_1,c]$, and therefore $u < c$. Actually, $u = x_1$. For if $u > x_1$, then $f'(u) > 0$ by assumption and therefore $f(u)$ could not be the minimum value of f in $[x_1,u]$, let alone in $[x_1,c]$, according to 6.4 (1). Since $f(x_1)$ is the minimum value of f in $[x_1,c]$ (and $f(c)$ is not), we have proved that

$$f(x_1) < f(c).$$

A similar argument shows that $f(x_2)$ is the maximum value of f in $[c,x_2]$, and that

$$f(c) < f(x_2).$$

Combining the two inequalities above, we have that $f(x_1) < f(x_2)$, and (1) is proved.

The proof of 6.5(2) is similar and is therefore omitted.

If $f'(x) > 0$ for every $x > a$, then f is increasing in every closed interval $[a,b]$, by the theorem above. In this case, f is increasing in the infinite interval $[a,\infty)$. If $f'(x) > 0$ for every $x < a$, then f is increasing in the infinite interval $(-\infty,a]$. Similar remarks hold for $f'(x) < 0$, in which case f is decreasing.

Example 2. If $f(x) = (x+1)^2$, determine where f is increasing and where f is decreasing.

Solution: We have $f'(x) = 2(x+1)$, and therefore

$$f'(x) < 0 \quad \text{if} \quad x < -1, \quad f'(x) > 0 \quad \text{if} \quad x > -1.$$

Hence f is decreasing (and the graph of f is falling) in the interval $(-\infty,-1]$ and f is increasing (and the graph of f is rising) in the interval $[-1,\infty)$. From this it is clear that $f(-1) = 0$ is the absolute minimum value of f, and that f has no absolute maximum value.

mum as defined in Chapter 3. For example, the function f defined by

$$f(x) = x^3 + 3x^2 - 1$$

has $f(-2) = 3$ as a relative maximum value (Figure 6.8). This is not an absolute maximum since, for example, $f(2) = 19$, a larger number than 3. This function has no absolute maximum or minimum value. The number $f(0) = -1$ is a relative minmum value of f.

We have already noted in 6.4(3) that if $a < c < b$ and $f(c)$ is the maximum or minimum value of f in $[a,b]$, then either $f'(c) = 0$ or $f'(c)$ does not exist. Therefore, the extrema of a function must occur at the critical numbers of f as defined below.

6.7 Definition. If c is a number in the domain of f such that either $f'(c) = 0$ or $f'(c)$ does not exist, then c is called a *critical number* of f.

Although it is true that the relative extrema of a function f must occur at critical numbers of f, it is not true that if c is a critical number of f then necessarily $f(c)$ is an extremum. For example, if

$$f(x) = x^3,$$

then $f'(x) = 3x^2$ and 0 is a critical number of f. Since $f'(x) > 0$ if $x \neq 0$, f is increasing in both of the intervals $(-\infty,0]$ and $[0,\infty)$ (and therefore in the interval $(-\infty,\infty)$). Thus $f(0)$ is not an extremum.

6.8 Rolle's theorem.* If f is a continuous function in the closed interval $[a,b]$ and if $f(a) = f(b)$, then f has at least one critical number in the open interval (a,b).

Proof: If $f(x) = f(a)$ for every x in $[a,b]$, then f is a constant function and $f'(x) = 0$. Hence every x in (a,b) is a critical number. If $f(x) \neq f(a)$ for some x in (a,b), then either the maximum value (if $f(x) > f(a)$) or the minimum value (if $f(x) < f(a)$) of f occurs at a number c in (a,b). The number c is a critical number of f by 6.4(3).

To illustrate Rolle's theorem, consider

$$f(x) = 4 - x^2$$

(Figure 6.6). Since $f(-2) = 0$ and $f(2) = 0$, f has a critical number between -2 and 2. We know that 0 is such a critical number.

If

$$f(x) = |x|,$$

then $f(-1) = 1$ and $f(1) = 1$. Hence f has a critical number between -1 and 1 by Rolle's theorem. Such a number is 0, since $f'(0)$ does not exist.

We return now to the main problem of this section, that of finding the extrema of a function. This problem may be solved in many cases by using Theorem 6.5 of the preceding section. Since 6.5 is useful in finding extrema of a function, it is frequently called the *first derivative test* for finding extrema.

Example 3 of the preceding section,

$$f(x) = x^3 + 3x^2 - 1,$$

---

* Michel Rolle (1652–1719) was a French mathematician principally known for his book, *Traité d'algèbre*, published in 1690.

illustrates the use of the first derivative test.   Since
$$f'(x) = 3x(x + 2),$$
$f'(x)$ exists at each number x and is zero at 0 and -2.   Thus 0 and -2 are the critical numbers of f.   Since $f'(x) > 0$ in $(-\infty, -2)$, f is increasing in $(-\infty, -2]$ by 6.5; and since $f'(x) < 0$ in $(-2,0)$, f is decreasing in $[-2,0]$ by 6.5.   Hence $f(-2) = 3$ is a (relative) maximum value of f.   Since f is decreasing in $[-2,0]$ and increasing in $[0,\infty)$, $f(0) = -1$ is a (relative) minimum value of f.

Actually, the relative extrema of a function f can be found just by comparing the values of f at the critical numbers (and, perhaps, at a few other numbers).   This will follow from the next theorem, a converse of 6.5.

6.9 Theorem.   If the function f is continuous in the interval $[a,b]$ and has no critical number in the open interval (a,b), then $f(a) \neq f(b)$.   Furthermore,

(1) if $f(a) < f(b)$, then $f'(x) > 0$ in (a,b) and f is increasing in $[a,b]$.

(2) if $f(a) > f(b)$, then $f'(x) < 0$ in (a,b) and f is decreasing in $[a,b]$.

Proof: That $f(a) \neq f(b)$ is an immediate consequence of Rolle's theorem. To prove (1), we first note that $f'(x) \neq 0$ for every x in (a,b) since f has no critical number in (a,b).   By 6.3, neither the maximum nor the minimum value of f in $[a,b]$ can occur at a number between a and b.   Therefore, since $f(a) < f(b)$ by assumption, necessarily $f(a)$ is the minimum and $f(b)$ is the maximum value of f in $[a,b]$.

If c is any number in (a,b), then $f(a)$ is the minimum value of f in $[a,c]$ since it is the minimum value of f in the larger interval $[a,b]$.   The maximum value of f in $[a,c]$ cannot occur between a and c by 6.3.   Hence $f(c)$ must be the maximum value of f in $[a,c]$.   We know that $f'(c) \neq 0$. According to 6.4(2), we cannot have $f'(c) < 0$.   Hence $f'(c) > 0$.   Thus $f'(x) > 0$ for every x in (a,b) and f is increasing in $[a,b]$ by 6.5(1).

The proof of 6.9(2), being similar, is left to the reader.

This theorem will be used to find extrema of a function f in the following way.

(1) Find the critical numbers of f.

(2) If f is continuous in $[a,b]$ and if c is the only critical number of f in (a,b), then

(a) $f(c)$ is a maximum value of f if $f(a) < f(c)$ and $f(c) > f(b)$.

(b) $f(c)$ is a minimum value of f if $f(a) > f(c)$ and $f(c) < f(b)$.

(c) $f(c)$ is not an extremum otherwise.

The following examples illustrate this graphical method.

Example 1.   Find the extrema of the function f defined by
$$f(x) = 10x^3(x - 1)^2.$$
Solution: The function f is continuous in $(-\infty,\infty)$.   We have
$$f'(x) = 30x^2(x - 1)^2 + 20x^3(x - 1)$$
$$= 10x^2(x - 1)(5x - 3),$$

so that $f'(x) = 0$ if $x = 0$, $x = 1$, or $x = \frac{3}{5}$. These are the critical numbers of f. From the accompanying table of values we conclude that $f(0)$ is not an extremum,

x	-1	0	$\frac{3}{5}$	1	2
$f(x)$	-40	0	$\frac{216}{625}$	0	80

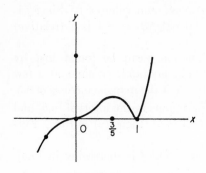

since

$$f(-1) < f(0) < f(\tfrac{3}{5});$$

that $f(\frac{3}{5})$ is a maximum value of f since

$$f(0) < f(\tfrac{3}{5}), \qquad f(\tfrac{3}{5}) > f(1);$$

that $f(1)$ is a minimum value of f since

$$f(\tfrac{3}{5}) > f(1), \qquad f(1) < f(2).$$

The graph of f is sketched in Figure 6.9.

Figure 6.9

Example 2. Find the extrema of the function g defined by

$$g(x) = x^3 + \frac{3}{x}.$$

Solution: The function g is continuous at every number $x \neq 0$. The derivative of g is given by

$$g'(x) = 3x^2 - \frac{3}{x^2}$$

$$= \frac{3(x^4 - 1)}{x^2}.$$

Clearly the only critical numbers of g are 1 and -1. ($g'(0)$ is undefined. Why isn't 0 a critical number of g?)

From the accompanying table of values, we conclude that $g(-1)$ is a maximum

x	-2	-1	$-\frac{1}{2}$	$\frac{1}{2}$	1	2
$g(x)$	$-\frac{19}{2}$	-4	$-\frac{49}{8}$	$\frac{49}{8}$	4	$\frac{19}{2}$

value of g since

$$g(-2) < g(-1), \qquad g(-1) > g(-\tfrac{1}{2}),$$

and that $g(1)$ is a minimum value of g. The graph of g is sketched in Figure 6.10.

Example 3. Find the extrema of the function F defined by

$$F(x) = x^{1/3}(x - 7)^2.$$

Solution: The function F is continuous in the interval $(-\infty, \infty)$. Its derivative is given by

$$F'(x) = \frac{1}{3} x^{-2/3}(x - 7)^2 + 2x^{1/3}(x - 7)$$

$$= \frac{1}{3} x^{-2/3}(x - 7)[(x - 7) + 6x]$$

$$= \frac{7(x - 7)(x - 1)}{3x^{2/3}}.$$

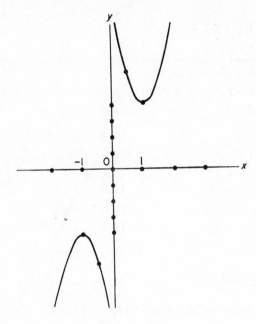

Figure 6.10

The critical numbers of F are 1 and 7, at which $F'(x) = 0$, and 0, at which the derivative is undefined. Since $F(-1) < F(0) < F(1)$, $F(0)$ is not an extremum. We see from the table that $F(1)$ is a maximum value of F and that $F(7)$ is a

x	-1	0	1	7	8
$F(x)$	-64	0	36	0	2

minimum value.   The graph of F is sketched in Figure 6.11.

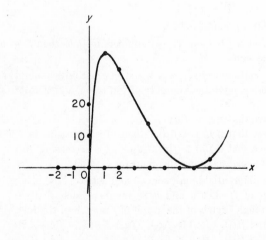

Figure 6.11

■ ■ ■ EXERCISES

Use the graphical method of this section to find the extrema of the following functions and sketch their graphs.

1. $f(x) = x^3 + 3x^2 - 9x + 1.$

2. $g(x) = x^3 + 3x^2 + 3x - 2.$

3. $h(x) = x^3 + 3x^2.$

4. $F(x) = x^2 + 2.$

5. $F(x) = \dfrac{12}{x^2 + 2}.$

6. $f(x) = (x - 2)^4.$

7. $g(x) = x^4 - 2x^2.$

8. $G(x) = 2x^3 - 3x^2.$

9. $f(x) = x^2(x - 3)^3.$

10. $g(x) = (2x^2 - 3x - 2)^2.$

11. $g(x) = x^{2/3}(x - 5).$

12. $h(x) = x^{1/3}(x - 8).$

13. $F(x) = x\sqrt[3]{3x - 4}.$

14. $f(x) = \sqrt[3]{x - 1} + \sqrt{x + 1}, x \geq -1.$

15. $f(x) = \sqrt[3]{x^3 - 9x}.$

16. $F(x) = \sqrt[3]{x^2 - 2x}.$

17. $F(x) = -x^{1/5}.$

18. $f(x) = x^2 + \dfrac{4}{x^2}.$

19. $G(x) = x^2 + \dfrac{1}{x^2}.$

20. $g(x) = \dfrac{x - 1}{x^2 + 3}.$

For each of the following polynomial functions find the extrema and sketch the graph.

21. $f(x) = x^2 - 4x + 4.$

22. $g(x) = 4 - x^2.$

23. $F(x) = 3 - 5x - x^2.$

24. $G(x) = 3x^2 - 4x + 7.$

25. $g(x) = 2x^2 + 3x - 1.$

26. $f(x) = x^3 - 6x^2 + 9x - 2.$

27. $G(x) = x^3 + x^2 + x - 4.$

28. $F(x) = x^4 - x^3.$

29. $g(x) = (x + 2)^2(x - 3)^3.$

30. $h(x) = (x + 2)^2(x - 3)^2.$

31. $f(x) = (x^2 - 4)^2.$

32. $g(x) = x^2(x^2 - 1)^2.$

33. $F(x) = 3x^5 - 25x^3 + 60x.$

34. $G(x) = x^4 - 4x.$

35. Show that for all x, $x^2 - x + 1 > 0$. (Find the minimum value of f where $f(x) = x^2 - x + 1$.)

36. Write out a proof of 6.9(2).

37. Prove that if f has no critical numbers in $[a,b]$ then $f'(a)$ and $f'(b)$ have the same sign.

38. Let f be continuous in $(-\infty,\infty)$, and let c be a critical number of f. Assume that there is no critical number of f in (c,∞), and that d is a number such that $c < d$.

(a) Prove that $f(c) \neq f(d)$.

(b) Prove that if $f(c) < f(d)$, then f is increasing in $[c,\infty)$.

(c) Prove that if $f(c) > f(d)$, then f is decreasing in $[c,\infty)$.

(d) State corresponding theorems for $(-\infty,c)$.

39. Let f be differentiable in $(-\infty,\infty)$ and let $c_1 < c_2 < c_3$ be all of the critical numbers of f. Let a and b be numbers such that $a < c_1$ and $c_3 < b$. Give a rough sketch of the graph of f in each of the following cases.

(a) $f(a) < f(c_1)$, $f(c_1) > f(c_2)$, $f(c_2) > f(c_3)$, $f(c_3) < f(b)$.

(b) $f(a) > f(c_1)$, $f(c_1) < f(c_2)$, $f(c_2) > f(c_3)$, $f(c_3) < f(b)$.

(c) $f(a) > f(c_1) > f(c_2) > f(c_3) > f(b)$.

40. If p and q are integers and $f(x) = (x - 1)^p(x + 1)^q$, $p \geq 2$, $q \geq 2$, show that f has the three critical numbers, $-1, \dfrac{q - p}{q + p}, 1$. Find the extrema of f in case:

(a) p and q are both even.
(b) p is even and q is odd.
(c) p is odd and q is even.
(d) p and q are both odd.

4. End-point extrema

A point $(c, f(c))$ is called an *end point* of the graph of the function f if there exists an interval (a,b) containing c such that every number in the interval (a,c) is in the domain of f whereas no number of the interval (c,b) is, or vice versa.

If $(c, f(c))$ is an end point of the graph of f such that $f(c)$ is the maximum or minimum value of f in some interval containing c, then $f(c)$ is called an *end-point extremum* of f. Note the difference between this definition and that of a relative extremum, in which it is assumed that some open interval containing c is contained in the domain of the function.

The graph of the function f, where

$$f(x) = \sqrt{4 - x^2},$$

is a semicircle. Clearly $f(-2) = 0$ and $f(2) = 0$ are end-point extrema of f; they are minimum values of f. Also, $f(0) = 2$ is a (relative) maximum value of f.

If $f(c)$ is an end-point extremum of f, the number c need not be a critical number of f, as the following example shows.

Example. Find the extrema of the function f defined by

$$f(x) = 3x - (x - 1)^{3/2}.$$

Solution: Since $(x - 1)^{3/2}$ is a real number only if $x \geq 1$, the domain of f is the set of all numbers $x \geq 1$. Thus $(1,3)$ is an end point of the graph of f. Since

$$f'(x) = 3 - \frac{3}{2}(x - 1)^{1/2},$$

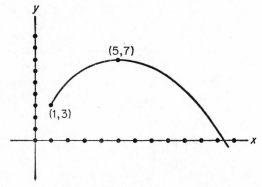

Figure 6.12

the function f' has the same domain as f.   If

$$3 - \frac{3}{2}(x-1)^{1/2} = 0,$$

then $\sqrt{x-1} = 2$, $x - 1 = 4$, and $x = 5$.   Therefore 5 is the only critical number of f.

Since f is continuous, and the point $(5,7)$ is above the point $(1,3)$, then $(1,3)$ is an end-point minimum of the graph of f.   And since the point $(10,3)$ is below the point $(5,7)$, then $(5,7)$ is a maximum point of the graph of f.   The graph is sketched in Figure 6.12 with the aid of the accompanying table of values.

x	1	2	5	10
$f(x)$	3	5	7	3

■ ■ ■ EXERCISES

Determine the extrema of the following functions graphically, and sketch their graphs.

1. $F(x) = (x+3)\sqrt{x}$.

2. $F(x) = (x-3)\sqrt{x}$.

3. $f(x) = x^2 - 2x + 1$, $0 \le x \le 3$.

4. $f(x) = x(x+5)^{3/2}$.

5. $g(x) = x^3 + 6x^2$, $-4 \le x \le 0$.

6. $F(x) = (x-1)(x+2)^2$, $-1 \le x \le 3$.

7. $f(x) = x^2(x-2)^3$, $0 \le x \le 2$.

8. $g(x) = \sqrt{9 - x^2}$.

9. $G(x) = \frac{2}{3}(x+2)^{3/2} - x$.

10. $g(x) = x^{2/3}\sqrt{9 - x^2}$.

11. $f(x) = x^{5/2} - 20x$.

12. Let p, q, n be integers and

$$f(x) = x^{p/q}(x-1)^n, \qquad 0 < p < q, \qquad n \ge 2.$$

The fraction p/q is assumed to be in lowest form.   Show that 0, $p/(p + nq)$, 1 are the critical numbers of f.   Find the extrema of f for all possible choices of p, q, and n as even or odd integers.

13. Let $g(x) = x^{3/2} + mx$ where m is a real number.   Find the extrema of g when m is positive, zero, and negative.

5. Concavity

Just as the sign of the first derivative of a function f tells us about the rising and falling of the graph of f, so does the sign of the second derivative

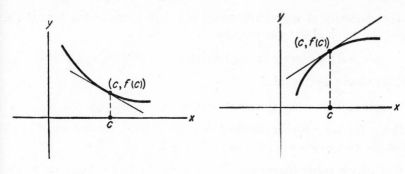

Figure 6.13   Figure 6.14

of f tell us about the concavity of the graph of f. The concavity of a graph is defined as follows.

6.10 Definition. The graph of a function f is *concave upward* at the point $(c,f(c))$ if there exists an open interval (a,b) containing c such that the graph of f between $x = a$ and $x = b$ is above the tangent line at $(c,f(c))$. Downward concavity is defined analogously.

In Figure 6.13, for example, the graph is concave upward at the point $(c,f(c))$; in Figure 6.14, the graph is concave downward at $(c,f(c))$.

If $f'(c)$ exists, then

$$y - f(c) = f'(c)(x - c)$$

is an equation of the tangent line T to the graph of f at $(c,f(c))$. Hence the *directed distance* $g(x)$ from T to the graph of f at x, measured parallel to the y-axis, is given by (Figure 6.15)

$$g(x) = f(x) - [f(c) + f'(c)(x - c)].$$

Since $g(x)$ is a directed distance, the point $(x,f(x))$ is above T if $g(x) > 0$ and below T if $g(x) < 0$. Clearly $g(c) = 0$.

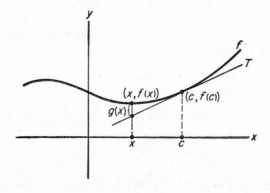

Figure 6.15

The concavity of a graph is easily stated in terms of the function g. Thus, the graph of f is concave upward at $(c, f(c))$ if

$g(x) > 0$ for every x in some interval (a,b) containing c, $x \neq c$,

and is concave downward if

$g(x) < 0$ for every x in some interval (a,b) containing c, $x \neq c$.

Before further studying the function g, we establish the important mean value theorem which will be used in the discussion to follow.

6.11 Mean value theorem. If the function f is continuous in the closed interval $[a,b]$ and if the derivative f' is defined in the open interval (a,b), then there exists a number z in (a,b) such that

$$f(b) - f(a) = (b - a)f'(z).$$

Proof: If we form the function F from f as follows,

$$F(x) = f(x)(b - a) - x[f(b) - f(a)],$$

then

$$F(a) = f(a)(b - a) - a[f(b) - f(a)] = bf(a) - af(b) = F(b).$$

The derivative of F, given by

$$F'(x) = f'(x)(b - a) - [f(b) - f(a)],$$

is defined wherever f' is defined. Thus F' is defined in the open interval (a,b).

We verify that the conditions of Rolle's theorem are satisfied by the function F: that is, F is continuous in $[a,b]$ and $F(a) = F(b)$. Hence F has a critical number z in (a,b). Since $F'(z)$ exists, necessarily $F'(z) = 0$. Therefore

$$F'(z) = f'(z)(b - a) - [f(b) - f(a)] = 0,$$

and we have proved that

$$f(b) - f(a) = (b - a)f'(z)$$

as desired.

We return now to the function g defined above and note that $g(x)$ may be written in the form

$$g(x) = [f(x) - f(c)] - (x - c)f'(c).$$

By the mean value theorem,

$$f(x) - f(c) = (x - c)f'(z)$$

for some number z between x and c. Hence

$$g(x) = (x - c)[f'(z) - f'(c)].$$

If we knew that $x - c$ and $f'(z) - f'(c)$ had the same sign for all $x \neq c$ in some open interval containing c, then we would also know that the graph of f is concave upward at $(c,f(c))$. A condition that assures us that $x - c$ and $f'(x) - f'(c)$ have the same sign, and hence that $x - c$ and $f'(z) - f'(c)$ have the same sign, in some open interval containing c is given in Theorem 6.3, namely $f''(c) > 0$.

These remarks give an outline of the proof of part of the following theorem. We leave the details to the reader.

6.12 Test for concavity. If f is a function such that its derivative f' is defined in some open interval containing the number c, then:

(1) The graph of f is concave upward at $(c,f(c))$ if $f''(c) > 0$.
(2) The graph of f is concave downward at $(c,f(c))$ if $f''(c) < 0$.

For example, the graph of the function f defined by

$$f(x) = x^2 + 2x + 1$$

is a parabola. Since $f''(x) = 2$, a positive number, this parabola is concave upward at each point on it.

6.13 Definition. The point $(c,f(c))$ is a *point of inflection* of the graph of f if there exists an interval (a,b) containing c such that the graph of f is

concave upward at each point $(x,f(x))$, x in (a,c),

and

concave downward at each point $(x,f(x))$, x in (c,b),

or vice versa.

It is clear from Theorem 6.12 (and 4.13) that if $(c,f(c))$ is a point of inflection of the graph of f and if the function f'' is continuous in some open interval containing c, then necessarily $f''(c) = 0$. The following theorem also is a consequence of 6.12.

6.14 Theorem. The point $(c,f(c))$ is a point of inflection of the graph of f if there exists an open interval (a,b) containing c such that

$$f''(x) > 0 \text{ for every } x \text{ in } (a,c),\ f''(x) < 0 \text{ for every } x \text{ in } (c,b),$$

or vice versa.

This theorem offers a criterion for the location of inflection points.

Example. If

$$f(x) = x^3 - 3x^2,$$

test the graph of f for concavity and find the points of inflection.

Solution: Evidently

$$f'(x) = 3x^2 - 6x,$$

$$f''(x) = 6(x - 1).$$

Since $f''(1) = 0$, $f''(x) > 0$ if $x > 1$, and $f''(x) < 0$ if $x < 1$, the graph is concave upward if $x > 1$ and concave downward if $x < 1$. In view of the previous theorem, $(1,-2)$ is a point of inflection of the graph. Note that the tangent line cuts the graph of f at this point. (Figure 6.16).

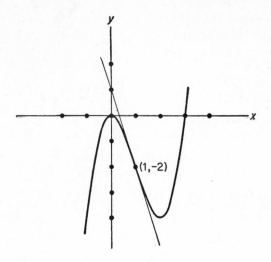

(1,−2)

Figure 6.16

6. Second derivative test for extrema

The relationship between the second derivative of a function and the concavity of the graph leads us to the following useful test for extrema.

6.15 Second derivative test for extrema.   If $f'(c) = 0$ and $f'(x)$ exists for every x in some open interval containing c, then:

(1) $f(c)$ is a maximum value of f if $f''(c) < 0$.
(2) $f(c)$ is a minimum value of f if $f''(c) > 0$.

Proof: If $f''(c) < 0$, then the graph of f is concave downward at $(c,f(c))$, that is, the graph is below the horizontal tangent line drawn at $(c,f(c))$. Hence $f(c)$ is a maximum value of f.

The proof of (2) is similar, and is omitted for this reason.

If c is a critical number of f for which either $f''(c) = 0$ or $f''(c)$ does not exist, then the second derivative test cannot be applied.

Example 1.   If
$$f(x) = x^2 - 6x + 3,$$
find the extrema of the function f.

Solution: Since
$$f'(x) = 2x - 6,$$
f has one critical number, namely, 3.   For every number x,
$$f''(x) = 2,$$
a constant, and therefore
$$f''(3) > 0.$$

Hence $f(3) = -6$ is a minimum value of f by the second derivative test.   This is the only extremum of f.

Example 2. If

$$f(x) = x^4 - 4x^3 + 10,$$

find the extrema of the function f, and also the points of inflection of its graph.

Solution: Since

$$f'(x) = 4x^3 - 12x^2 = 4x^2(x - 3),$$

the critical numbers of f are 0 and 3. The second derivative of f is given by

$$f''(x) = 12x^2 - 24x = 12x(x - 2).$$

Thus the points of inflection can occur only at $x = 0$ and $x = 2$.

Since $f''(3) > 0$, the number $f(3) = -17$ is a minimum value of f. On the other hand, $f''(0) = 0$ and the second derivative test does not apply to the critical number 0. However,

$$f''(x) > 0 \quad \text{if} \quad x < 0, \quad f''(x) < 0 \quad \text{if} \quad 0 < x < 2,$$

and therefore $(0,10)$ is an inflection point of the graph of f. Thus $f(0)$ is not an extremum of f. Also,

$$f''(x) < 0 \quad \text{if} \quad 0 < x < 2, \quad f''(x) > 0 \quad \text{if} \quad x > 2,$$

and we conclude that $(2,-6)$ is a point of inflection of the graph. The graph of f is sketched in Figure 6.17.

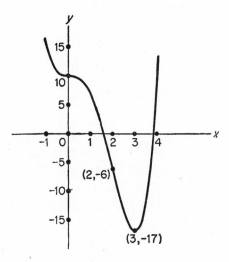

Figure 6.17

When the second derivative test fails, one can always return to the first derivative test. For some functions, it may be inconvenient to compute the second derivative, in which case the first derivative test would again be used.

■ ■ ■ EXERCISES

In the following exercises, find the extrema of each function, using the second derivative test.

1. $f(x) = 5x^2 - 2x + 1.$ **2.** $g(x) = 3 + x - x^2.$

3. $g(x) = x^3 + 3x^2 - 9x + 10.$ **4.** $F(x) = x^3 + 4x^2 - 3x - 9.$

5. $F(x) = \dfrac{x^2}{4} + \dfrac{4}{x}.$ **6.** $f(x) = x^3 + \dfrac{3}{x}.$

7. $f(x) = \dfrac{1}{\sqrt{x}} + \dfrac{\sqrt{x}}{9}.$ **8.** $g(x) = \dfrac{x^3}{x^2 + 1}.$

In the following exercises, find the extrema of each function, using the second derivative test. Also find the points of inflection, and sketch the graph.

9. $G(x) = 3 - 2x - x^2.$ **10.** $F(x) = x^2 - 4x + 5.$

11. $F(x) = x^3 - x^2 - x + 2.$ **12.** $F(x) = x^3 - 5x^2 - 8x + 20.$

13. $f(x) = 3x^4 - 4x^3 - 12x^2 + 3.$ **14.** $g(x) = x^5 - 5x + 2.$

In the following exercises, find the extrema of each function, using either the first or the second derivative test, whichever is more convenient.

15. $g(x) = x^3 - 15x.$ **16.** $F(x) = x^{7/5}.$

17. $G(x) = x^{5/3}(x - 1).$ **18.** $g(x) = \dfrac{ax}{x^2 + a^2}, a \neq 0.$

19. $F(x) = x\sqrt{x + 3}.$ **20.** $G(x) = 6\sqrt[3]{x} + x^2.$

21. $f(x) = x^{2/3}(x - 2)^2.$ **22.** $f(x) = 5x^{2/5} + 2x.$

23. $g(x) = \dfrac{x + a}{\sqrt{x^2 + 1}}, a \neq 0.$ **24.** $g(x) = \dfrac{x + 2}{x^2 + 2x + 4}.$

25. Find the points of inflection of the graph of

$$y = \frac{1}{x^2 + 3}.$$

Sketch this graph, showing the tangent lines at the points of inflection.

26. Find the points of inflection and extrema of the graph of

$$y = x^{1/3}(x - 4).$$

Sketch this graph, showing the tangent lines at the points of inflection.

27. Find the point of inflection of the graph of

$$y = x^2 - \frac{1}{6x^3}.$$

Find the equation of the tangent line to the graph at this point.

28. Let $f(x) = 2x^3 - 3(a + b)x^2 + 6abx.$ Find the extrema of f if (1) $a < b$; (2) $a = b.$

29. Determine a and b so that 1 is a critical number of the function f defined by

$$f(x) = x^3 + ax^2 + bx, \quad f(1) = -3.$$

Is $(1, -3)$ a maximum or minimum point on the graph of f?

30. Determine a and b so that 2 is a critical number of the function g defined by

$$g(x) = \frac{a}{x} + bx, \quad g(2) = 1.$$

Is $(2,1)$ a maximum or minimum point on the graph of f?

31. Prove that the graph of the equation

$$y = x^3 + ax^2 + bx + c$$

has no extremum if and only if $a^2 \leq 3b$.

32. Let k be a rational number, $k > 1$, and let the function f be defined by the equation

$$f(x) = (1 + x)^k - (1 + kx), \quad x \geq -1.$$

Show that f has an absolute minimum value 0 and that this occurs at the unique number $x = 0$. [*Hint:* Show that 0 is the only critical number of f.] This result will be used later in the following form: if k is an integer, $k > 1$, and if $x > -1$, $x \neq 0$, then $(1 + x)^k > 1 + kx$.

33. The mean value theorem is concerned with a function f continuous in an interval $[a,b]$ and differentiable in (a,b). Show that the conclusion of the mean value theorem has the following geometrical significance: Some tangent line to the graph of f between $x = a$ and $x = b$ is parallel to the secant line of the graph joining the points $(a,f(a))$ and $(b,f(b))$.

7. Applications of the theory of extrema

It is frequently possible to solve a problem which asks for the largest area, or the least volume or the lowest cost by recognizing that the solution of the problem is a maximum or minimum value of some function. We illustrate the procedure with the following examples.

Example 1. A rectangular field is to be adjacent to a river and is to have fencing on three sides, the side on the river requiring no fencing. If 100 rods of fencing is available, find the dimensions of the field with largest area.

Solution: Let the two sides of the field which are perpendicular to the river each have length x rods. Then the side parallel to the river has length $100 - 2x$ rods, since the sum of the lengths of the three sides is 100 rods (Figure 6.18). Clearly $0 < x < 50$.

The area of the field is described by the function f where

$$f(x) = x(100 - 2x) = 100x - 2x^2,$$
$$0 < x < 50.$$

The field of Figure 6.18 will have the largest possible area if $f(x)$ is the maximum value of f.

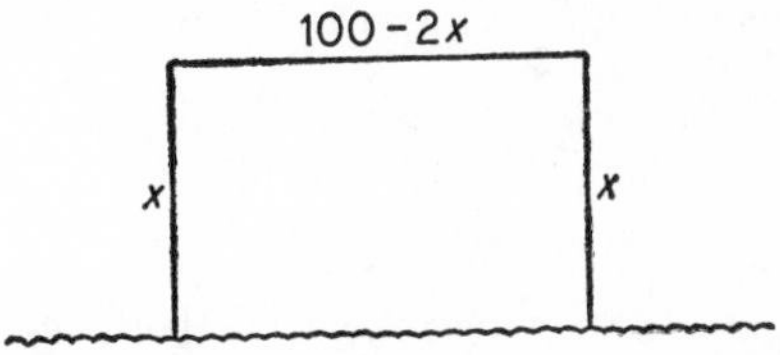

Now

$$f'(x) = 100 - 4x,$$

and $f'(x) = 0$ only if $x = 25$. Thus 25 is the critical number of f. Since

$$f''(x) = -4,$$

Figure 6.18

$f''(25) = -4$ and $f(25)$ is a maximum value of f.   The dimensions of this field of largest area are $x = 25$ rods and $100 - 2x = 50$ rods; its area is 1250 square rods.

The graph of the function f is sketched in Figure 6.19.   The ordinate $f(x)$ of each point $(x,f(x))$ on the graph is the area of the field with given width x.

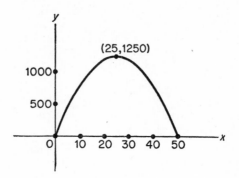

Figure 6.19

We might have started differently, letting z be the length of the side of the field parallel to the river.   Then each of the other two sides would have length $(100 - z)/2 = 50 - z/2$, and the area of the field would be given by

$$g(z) = z\left(50 - \frac{z}{2}\right) = 50z - \frac{1}{2}z^2.$$

Since

$$g'(z) = 50 - z,$$

we would discover that $g(50)$ is a maximum value of g, and since

$$g(50) = 1250,$$

the same field would be determined.   Thus there are at least two functions which give us a solution of the problem.

In some problems, it may be that one function is easier to recognize or easier to handle than another.   However, in the example above, the choice would not be important.

Example 2.   Show that a tin can of specified volume K will be made of the least amount of metal if its height equals the diameter of the base.

Solution: We are assuming, of course, that the tin can is in the form of a right circular cylinder and has both top and bottom.   The least amount of metal will be used when the surface area of the cylinder is a minimum.   Let r be the radius of the base and h be the height of the cylinder (Figure 6.20).   Then the area of the base is πr^2 as is the area of the top.   The lateral area is $2\pi rh$, the product of the circumference and the height of the cylinder.   Thus the total area A is given by

$$A = 2\pi rh + 2\pi r^2.$$

The volume of the cylinder has been specified as a (positive) number K, and hence

$$K = \pi r^2 h.$$

We can solve this equation for h,

$$h = \frac{K}{\pi r^2},$$

and then express A in terms of r (by replacing h by $K/\pi r^2$) as follows:

$$A = \frac{2K}{r} + 2\pi r^2.$$

We can now say that the area of the cylinder is described by the function f, where

$$f(r) = \frac{2K}{r} + 2\pi r^2, \quad r > 0.$$

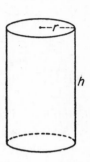

Figure 6.20

We seek a minimum value of the function f. Since

$$f'(r) = -\frac{2K}{r^2} + 4\pi r$$

for every positive number r, the critical numbers of f are the positive solutions of the equation

$$-\frac{2K}{r^2} + 4\pi r = 0,$$

or

$$\frac{2}{r^2}[-K + 2\pi r^3] = 0.$$

Thus the only critical number of f is

$$r = \sqrt[3]{\frac{K}{2\pi}}.$$

Since

$$f''(r) = \frac{4K}{r^3} + 4\pi,$$

$f''(r) > 0$ for every positive number r. Hence

$$f\left(\sqrt[3]{\frac{K}{2\pi}}\right)$$

is a minimum value of f.

We have shown above that $h = K/\pi r^2$, and therefore

$$\frac{h}{r} = \frac{K}{\pi r^3}.$$

At $r = \sqrt[3]{K}/2\pi$,

$$\frac{h}{r} = \frac{K}{\pi \dfrac{K}{2\pi}} = 2,$$

and

$$h = 2r.$$

This proves that the height and diameter of the tin can of least area are equal.

We might have solved the equation $K = \pi r^2 h$ for r, getting

$$r = \sqrt{\frac{K}{\pi h}},$$

and then used the function g given by

$$g(h) = 2\sqrt{K \pi h} + \frac{2K}{h}$$

to describe the area of the cylinder. However, the function f is somewhat easier to handle than g.

Example 3. Find a triangle of maximum area inscribed in a circle of radius r.

Solution: If triangle ABC is inscribed in a circle and if $AC \neq BC$, then there exists a triangle $AC'B$ inscribed in the circle with $AC' = BC'$ and with greater area than the given triangle, as can be seen from Figure 6.21. Thus it is clear geometrically that a triangle of maximum area inscribed in a circle is equilateral.

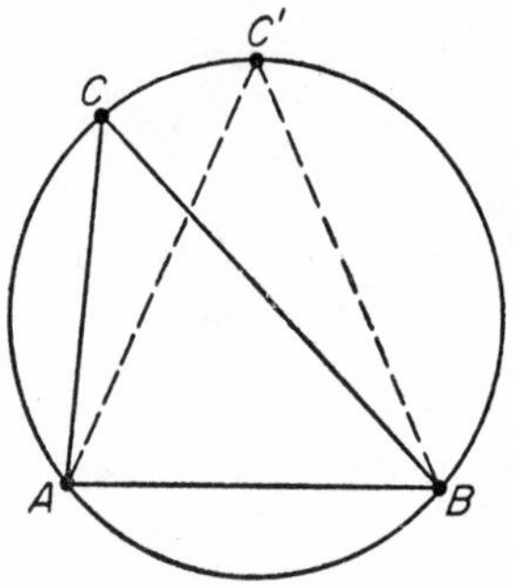

We see from the previous example that not all problems in maxima and minima require the calculus for their solution. As another example, it is obvious that if

$$f(x) = \frac{1}{1 + x^2},$$

then $f(0) = 1$ is the only maximum value of f.

Example 4. Find the point of the graph of the equation

$$y = x^2$$

that is nearest the point $A(3,0)$.

Figure 6.21

Solution: For every real number x, the point $P(x, x^2)$ is on the graph of the given equation (Figure 6.22), and

$$|PA|^2 = (x - 3)^2 + (x^2)^2$$
$$= x^4 + x^2 - 6x + 9.$$

If we let

$$g(x) = \sqrt{x^4 + x^2 - 6x + 9},$$

then $g(x)$ is just the distance between P and A, and we wish to find a minimum value of g. Now

$$g'(x) = \frac{1}{2}(4x^3 + 2x - 6)(x^4 + x^2 - 6x + 9)^{-1/2},$$

and $g'(x) = 0$ only if

$$4x^3 + 2x - 6 = 0.$$

It is clear by inspection that $x = 1$ is a solution of this equation. By dividing

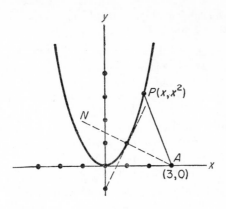

Figure 6.22

the polynomial $4x^3 + 2x - 6$ by $x - 1$, we see that

$$4x^3 + 2x - 6 = (x - 1)(4x^2 + 4x + 6),$$

and, since the equation

$$4x^2 + 4x + 6 = 0$$

has no real solution, that 1 is the only critical number of g.

Clearly $g'(0) < 0$ and $g'(2) > 0$, and $g(1) = \sqrt{5}$ is a minimum value of g. The point on the graph nearest A is $(1,1)$.

Since $D_x x^2 = 2x$, the slope of the tangent line T to the graph of $y = x^2$ at the point $P(1,1)$ is 2. The slope of the line AP is $-\frac{1}{2}$, and therefore A lies on the normal line N of the graph at $P(1,1)$ (Figure 6.22).

Example 5. An apple orchard now has 30 trees per acre, and the average yield is 400 apples per tree. For each additional tree planted per acre, the average yield per tree is reduced by approximately 10 apples. How many trees per acre will give the largest crop of apples?

Solution: If x is the number of new trees planted per acre, then there are $30 + x$ trees per acre having an average yield of $400 - 10x$ apples per tree. Hence the total yield y of apples per acre is given by

$$y = (30 + x)(400 - 10x)$$

$$= 12{,}000 + 100x - 10x^2.$$

Since
$$\frac{dy}{dx} = 100 - 20x,$$

$dy/dx = 0$ if $x = 5$. Hence an addition of 5 trees per acre will give the largest crop; then there will be 35 trees per acre, each yielding an average of 350 apples.

■ ■ ■ EXERCISES

1. A man has 600 yards of fencing which he is going to use to enclose a rectangular field and then subdivide the field into two plots with a fence

parallel to a side.   Of all the possible fields that can be so fenced, what are the dimensions of the one of maximum area?

2. Generalize Exercise 1 by dividing the field into n garden plots.

3. An open box is to be made by cutting out squares from the corners of a rectangular piece of cardboard and then turning up the sides.   If the piece of cardboard is 12 in. by 24 in., what are the dimensions of the box of largest volume made in this way?

4. A rectangular box with square base and open top is to be made from 12 ft^2 of cardboard.   What is the maximum possible volume of such a box?

5. A cylindrical cup (open top) is to hold $\frac{1}{2}$ pint.   How should it be made so as to use the least amount of material?

6. A wire 24 in. long is cut in two, and then one part is bent into the shape of a circle and the other into the shape of a square.   How should it be cut if the sum of the areas of the circle and the square is to be a minimum? A maximum?

7. Of all the right circular cylinders that can be inscribed in a given right circular cone, show that the one of greatest volume has altitude $\frac{1}{3}$ that of the cone.

8. A rectangle has two of its vertices on the x-axis and the other two above the x-axis and on the graph of the parabola $y = 16 - x^2$.   Of all such possible rectangles, what are the dimensions of the one of maximum area?

9. A rectangle of perimeter p is rotated about one of its sides so as to form a cylinder.   Of all such possible rectangles, which generates a cylinder of maximum volume?

10. Find the dimensions of the right circular cylinder of maximum volume inscribed in a sphere of radius r.

11. Find the dimensions of the right circular cone of maximum volume inscribed in a sphere of radius r.

12. Find the point on the graph of the equation $y^2 = 4x$ which is nearest to the point (2,1).

13. A ladder is to reach over a fence 8 ft high to a wall 1 ft behind the fence. What is the length of the shortest ladder that can be used?

14. Find the rectangle of maximum area that can be inscribed in a semicircle of radius r.

15. Show that the greatest area of any rectangle inscribed in a triangle is $\frac{1}{2}$ that of the triangle.

16. A real estate office handles 80 apartment units.   When the rent of each unit is $60 per month, all units are occupied.   However, for each $2 increase in rent, one of the units becomes vacant.   Each occupied unit requires an average of $6 per month for service and repairs.   What rent should be charged to realize the most profit?

17. A man in a motor boat 4 miles from the nearest point P on the shore wishes to go to a point Q 10 miles from P along the straight shoreline. The motor boat can travel 18 miles/hr and a car, which can pick the man up at any point between P and Q, can travel 30 miles/hr.   At what point should the man land so as to reach Q in the least amount of time?

18. Three sides of a trapezoid have the same length a. Of all such possible trapezoids, show that the one of maximum area has its fourth side of length $2a$.

19. A Boston lodge has asked the railroad company to run a special train to New York for its members. The railroad company agrees to run the train if at least 200 people will go. The fare is to be $8 per person if 200 go, and will decrease by 1c for everybody for each person over 200 that goes (thus, if 250 people go, the fare will be $7.50). What number of passengers will give the railroad maximum revenue?

20. Show that (2,2) is the point on the graph of the equation $y = x^3 - 3x$ that is nearest the point (11,1).

8. Velocity and acceleration

The derivative is closely related to the rate of change of a function as defined below. Before discussing rates of change in general, let us consider the special case of the motion of a point on a straight line.

We shall assume for the present that L is a horizontal coordinate line with unit point to the right of the origin as in Figure 6.23. At the time t,

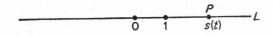

Figure 6.23

the expression $s(t)$ will designate the coordinate of the point P which is in motion on L. The function s so determined by the position of P on L is called the *position function* of the moving point P.

For example, if

$$s(t) = t^2 - 2t,$$

then at the time $t = 0$, the position is $s(0) = 0$ and the point P is at the origin. At the time $t = 1$, $s(1) = -1$ and P is one unit to the left of the origin. Since $s(2) = 0$, then P returns to the origin after two units of time. When $t = 3$, $s(3) = 3$ and the point P has moved 3 units to the right. When $t = 4$, the position of P will be given by $s(4) = 8$.

In this example, the point P moves from the position 0 to the position 8, a distance of 8 units, between time $t = 2$ and $t = 4$. Thus the point P moves 8 units of distance in 2 units of time. Average velocity is the ratio of distance traveled to time elapsed, so the average velocity of P from time $t = 2$ to $t = 4$ is $\frac{8}{2} = 4$ units of distance per unit of time. If, for example, distance is measured in feet and time in seconds, the average velocity of P from time $t = 2$ to time $t = 3$ is given by

$$\frac{s(3) - s(2)}{3 - 2} = 3 \text{ ft/sec}$$

More generally, if s is the position function of a moving point P, the *average velocity* of P from the time t to the time $t + h$ is

$$\frac{s(t + h) - s(t)}{h}.$$

Knowledge of the average velocity of a moving point P gives us little if any information about the motion of the point at a particular instant. We cannot conclude, for example, that a jet airplane did not break the sound barrier if its average velocity on a certain flight was 500 miles per hour, nor can we conclude that it did break the sound barrier. The average velocity does not describe the "momentary" or "instantaneous" character of the motion.

This need for knowledge of the instantaneous character of the motion of a point leads us to the following definition.

6.16 Definition. If s is the position function of a moving point P, the *velocity* of P *at the time* t is defined to be

$$\lim_{h \to 0} \frac{s(t + h) - s(t)}{h},$$

and is designated by $v(t)$.

Thus

$$v(t) = \lim_{h \to 0} \frac{s(t + h) - s(t)}{h}.$$

We do not append the condition "if this limit exists," since we are working in the realm of physical motion and it is to be assumed that any point P in motion has a velocity at any time t.

What we have done above with the position function of a moving point can be done in general with any function. If a function f is defined in an interval $[a,b]$, then $f(b) - f(a)$ is the *change* in f between a and b, and

$$\frac{f(b) - f(a)}{b - a}$$

is the average change in f over each unit of the interval $[a,b]$, that is, it is the *average rate of change* of f in $[a,b]$.

The *instantaneous rate of change* of f at a can then be defined as the limit of the average rate of change of f,

$$\lim_{h \to 0} \frac{f(a + h) - f(a)}{h},$$

if this limit exists. Since this limit is just the derivative of f at a, it follows that $f'(a)$ may be considered the instantaneous rate of change of f at a.

To return to the position function s, we recognize the limit in 6.16 to be the derivative of s, so that

$$v(t) = s'(t).$$

Thus s is increasing at t if $v(t) > 0$ and decreasing at t if $v(t) < 0$. To say that s is increasing is to say that the point P is moving to the right on L; and to say that s is decreasing is to say that P is moving to the left on L. When $v(t) = 0$, the point P is said to be (momentarily) *at rest*.

Thus we have:

1. *If $v(t) > 0$, then P is moving to the right.*
2. *If $v(t) < 0$, then P is moving to the left.*
3. *If $v(t) = 0$, then P is at rest.*

We are assuming that $v(t)$ exists for every time t, and hence $s'(t)$ always exists. Therefore the only critical numbers of s (called the critical times of the position function) are those for which $s'(t) = 0$, and we may make the following observation: *A point in motion on a straight line cannot change its direction without coming to rest.*

In the example above,

$$s(t) = t^2 - 2t,$$

and hence

$$v(t) = 2t - 2.$$

Since $v(0) = -2$, then P is moving to the left at time $t = 0$. When $t = 1$, $v(1) = 0$ and P is at rest. In fact, P is at rest at no other time, since the equation

$$v(t) = 2(t - 1) = 0$$

has the unique solution $t = 1$. Clearly $v(t) > 0$ (and P is moving to the right) if $t > 1$. The motion of P for $t \geq 0$ is indicated in Figure 6.24.

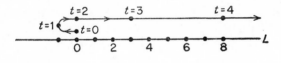

Figure 6.24

It is to be remembered that the point P always remains on the line L and that the figure is diagrammatic.

The *speed* of a moving point P at time t is defined to be

$$|v(t)|.$$

Thus the speed is the magnitude of the velocity, and it does not indicate the direction of motion.

Average acceleration is defined to be the average rate of change in velocity relative to time. Thus, if v is the velocity function of the moving point P, the *average acceleration* of P from time t to time $t + h$ is

$$\frac{v(t + h) - v(t)}{h}.$$

The acceleration of P at a given time is defined as follows.

6.17 Definition. If v is the velocity function of a moving point P, the *acceleration* of P *at the time* t is defined to be

$$\underset{h \to 0}{\text{limit}} \frac{v(t + h) - v(t)}{h},$$

and is designated by $a(t)$.

It follows that
$$a(t) = v'(t) = s''(t).$$
In the example above,

$$s(t) = t^2 - 2t, \quad v(t) = 2t - 2, \quad a(t) = 2.$$

If distance is measured in feet and time in seconds, the units of velocity are feet per second (ft/sec) and those of acceleration are feet per second per second (ft/sec²). Thus, in this example, the acceleration is a constant of 2 ft/sec².

The *second law of Newtonian mechanics* states that the force acting on an object is the product of the mass of the object and its acceleration. If m is the mass of the object P, moving along a straight line with position function s, then the force $F(t)$ acting on P at time t is given by the equation

$$F(t) = m \cdot a(t),$$
or
$$F(t) = m \cdot s''(t).$$

If at some time t, $a(t) = 0$, then also $F(t) = 0$ and no force is acting on P. In this event P can be said to be coasting.

If at time t_1 the point P is at rest $[v(t_1) = 0]$ and if $a(t_1) < 0$, then by the second derivative test [recalling that $a(t_1) = s''(t_1)$], $s(t_1)$ is a maximum value of s, i.e., $s(t) < s(t_1)$ for $t \neq t_1$ in some time interval (t_2, t_3) containing t. Then P must have approached the position $s(t_1)$ from the left, it must have come to rest at the position $s(t_1)$, and it must have reversed the direction of its motion.

A similar argument may be made if $v(t_1) = 0$ and $a(t_1) > 0$, in which case $s(t_1)$ is a minimum value of s. In either case, we may make the following statement.

If $v(t_1) = 0$ and $a(t_1) \neq 0$ then P must reverse its direction of motion at the position $s(t_1)$.

Example 1. Discuss the motion of the point P if its position at the time t on a coordinate line L is given by

$$s(t) = t^3 - 6t^2 + 20, \quad -2 \leq t \leq 6.$$

Solution: Since $v(t) = s'(t)$ and $a(t) = v'(t)$,

$$v(t) = 3t^2 - 12t, \quad a(t) = 6t - 12.$$

The point P will be at rest when

$$v(t) = 3t(t - 4) = 0,$$

that is, when $t = 0$ or $t = 4$. Thus 0 and 4 are the critical times of s. Since $a(0) < 0$ and $a(4) > 0$, point P changes its direction of motion at each critical time; and $s(0) = 20$ is a maximum value of s and $s(4) = -12$ is a minimum value of s.

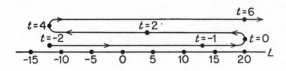

Figure 6.25

An indication of the motion of P can be obtained from the accompanying table of values and Figure 6.25.

t	$s(t)$	$v(t)$	$a(t)$
-2	-12	36	-24
-1	13	15	-18
0	20	0	-12
2	4	-12	0
4	-12	0	12
6	20	36	24

We give now a somewhat different type of problem involving rates of change of a function.

Example 2.   Water is running into the conical tank of Figure 6.26 at a constant rate of 2 cubic feet per minute (ft³/min).   How fast is the water rising in the tank at any instant?

Solution: At any time t min after the water starts running, let $h(t)$ be the depth of the water and $r(t)$ be the radius of the surface of the water in the tank (Figure 6.26).   Clearly $r(t) = h(t)/2$, and the volume $V(t)$ of the water in the tank is $2t$, $V(t) = 2t$.   By geometry,

$$V = \frac{1}{3}\pi r^2 h;$$

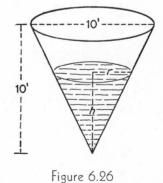

thus
$$2t = \frac{1}{3}\pi\left(\frac{h}{2}\right)^2 h,$$

and $24t = \pi h^3$,   or $h^3 = \dfrac{24}{\pi}t$.

Hence $h(t) = \left(2\sqrt[3]{\dfrac{3}{\pi}}\right)t^{1/3}$.

Figure 6.26

The rate of rise of the water is just the instantaneous rate of change of h, which is h' by our discussion above.   Thus

$$h'(t) = \frac{2}{3}\sqrt[3]{\frac{3}{\pi}}\,t^{-2/3} \text{ ft/min}$$

is the rate at which the water is rising in the tank t minutes after the water **starts**

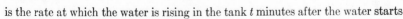

running.   Since $\sqrt[3]{3/\pi} = .98$ approx.,

$$h'(t) = \frac{.65}{\sqrt[3]{t^2}} \text{ approx.}$$

Thus, at $t = 8$, $\sqrt[3]{t^2} = 4$ and

$$h'(t) = .16 \text{ ft/min.}$$

■ ■ ■ EXERCISES

In each of the following exercises, the position function of a point moving on a straight line is given.   Discuss the motion of the point.

1. $s(t) = -16t^2 + 80t, \ 0 \le t \le 5$.
2. $s(t) = -16t^2 + 32t + 20, \ 0 \le t \le 4$.
3. $s(t) = t^2 - 8t + 4, \ -2 \le t \le 6$.
4. $s(t) = 12 + 6t + t^2, \ -6 \le t \le 0$.
5. $s(t) = t^3 - 3t$.   6. $s(t) = t^3 - 3t^2 - 24t$.
7. $s(t) = 2 + t - t^2 - t^3$.   8. $s(t) = t^4 - 4t^3$.
9. $s(t) = t^2 + \dfrac{16}{t}, \ t \ge 1$.   10. $s(t) = 4t + \dfrac{9}{t}, \ t \ge 1$.

11. Gas is being pumped into a balloon so that its volume is constantly increasing at the rate of 4 in.³/sec.   Find the rate of increase of the radius of the balloon at any time t seconds after the inflation begins.   Approximate this rate at $t = 8$.

12. A ladder 25 ft long is leaning against a wall, with the bottom of the ladder 7 ft from the base of the wall.   If the lower end is pulled away from the wall at the rate of 1 ft/sec, find the rate of descent of the upper end along the wall.   Approximate this rate of descent at the end of 8 sec.

13. Ship A is 60 miles due north of ship B at 10 A.M.   Ship A is sailing due east at 20 miles/hr, while ship B is sailing due north at 16 miles/hr.   Find the distance $d(t)$ between the ships t hours after 10 A.M.   Also find the rate of change of the distance between them.   At what time are the ships closest together?

14. A conical tank, full of water, is 12 ft high and 20 ft in diameter at the top. If the water is let out at the bottom at the rate of 4 ft³/min, find the rate of change of the depth of the water t minutes after the water starts running out.   Approximate this rate at $t = 10$ min.

15. A trough 9 ft long has as its cross section an isosceles right triangle with hypotenuse of length 2 ft along the top of the trough.   If water is pouring into the trough at the rate of 2 ft³/min, find the depth $h(t)$ of the water t minutes after the water is turned on.   Also find the rate at which the depth is increasing when $t = 2$.

9. *Antiderivatives*

Corresponding to each function f is its derived function f'. For example, if f is defined by

$$f(x) = x^3 - 6x + 12,$$

then f' is defined by

$$f'(x) = 3x^2 - 6.$$

We now ask the following question. Given a function g, does there exist a function f such that g is the derivative of f? If, for example, g is defined by

$$g(x) = 3x^2 - 6,$$

then g is the derivative of f defined by

$$f(x) = x^3 - 6x + 12.$$

The answer to this question is yes if g is a continuous function. The proof of this fact will come in Chapter 8 after the concept of the integral has been introduced. Here we shall be concerned only with formal properties of the antiderivative, defined as follows.

6.18 Definition. The function f is called an *antiderivative* of the function g if $f' = g$.

For example, if

$$g(x) = 6x^2,$$

then the function f_1 defined by

$$f_1(x) = 2x^3$$

is an antiderivative of g since

$$f_1'(x) = g(x).$$

It is equally true that the function f_2 defined by

$$f_2(x) = 2x^3 + 7$$

is an antiderivative of g, since

$$f_2'(x) = g(x).$$

It is clear that if f_1 is an antiderivative of g, and if

$$f_2(x) = f_1(x) + c, \quad c \text{ a real number,}$$

then $\qquad f_2'(x) = f_1'(x) = g(x)$

and f_2 also is an antiderivative of g. The converse of this statement is also true, as we shall now prove.

6.19 Theorem. If for the functions f_1 and f_2 there exists an interval $[a,b]$ such that

$$f_1'(x) = f_2'(x)$$

in $[a,b]$, then there exists a number c such that
$$f_1(x) = f_2(x) + c$$
in $[a,b]$.

Proof: Let the function F be the difference between f_1 and f_2,
$$F(x) = f_1(x) - f_2(x), \quad x \text{ in } [a,b].$$
By hypothesis,
$$F'(x) = 0, \quad x \text{ in } [a,b].$$
Hence, by the mean value theorem, for every x in $[a,b]$ there exists a number z in (a,x) such that
$$F(x) - F(a) = (x - a)F'(z) = 0.$$
Thus $F(x) = F(a)$ for every x in $[a,b]$, and
$$f_1(x) = f_2(x) + c, \quad x \text{ in } [a,b],$$
where $c = F(a)$.

If
$$f'(x) = 6x^2,$$
as in the example above, then
$$f(x) = 2x^3 + c$$
for some number c according to 6.19.

According to a previous differentiation formula,
$$D_x\left[\frac{a}{m+1} x^{m+1}\right] = ax^m,$$
m a rational number, $m \neq -1$, a any real number. Thus, if
$$g(x) = ax^m, \quad m \neq -1,$$
the function f defined by
$$f(x) = \frac{a}{m+1} x^{m+1}$$
is an antiderivative of g, since
$$D_x f(x) = g(x).$$
We state this as a formula:

If $f'(x) = ax^m$, then $f(x) = \dfrac{a}{m+1} x^{m+1} + c, \quad m \neq -1.$

If
$$g(x) = g_1(x) + g_2(x),$$
and if f_1 and f_2 are antiderivatives of g_1 and g_2, respectively, then f defined by
$$f(x) = f_1(x) + f_2(x)$$
is an antiderivative of g, since
$$D_x f(x) = D_x f_1(x) + D_x f_2(x) = g_1(x) + g_2(x) = g(x).$$

More generally, *an antiderivative of a sum of functions is the sum of anti-derivatives of the functions.*

Example 1. Find $f(x)$ if
$$f'(x) = 4x^3 - 2x^2 + 5x + 3.$$
Solution: Since
$$D_x\left(x^4 - \frac{2}{3}x^3 + \frac{5}{2}x^2 + 3x\right) = 4x^3 - 2x^2 + 5x + 3,$$
$$f(x) = x^4 - \frac{2}{3}x^3 + \frac{5}{2}x^2 + 3x + c$$
for some number c.

If
$$f'(x) = 4x - 3 \quad \text{and} \quad f(1) = 3,$$
then
$$f(x) = 2x^2 - 3x + c$$
for some number c. Since
$$f(1) = 2 - 3 + c = 3,$$
$c = 4$. Thus
$$f(x) = 2x^2 - 3x + 4,$$
and there is just one function f satisfying the given conditions.

The equation
$$f'(x) = 4x - 3$$
is an example of a *differential equation,* and the equation
$$f(1) = 3$$
is called a *boundary condition* of f. Given f' and a boundary condition on f, there is a unique antiderivative f of f' satisfying the given boundary condition. This function f is called the *solution* of the given differential equation.

Example 2. Solve the differential equation
$$f'(x) = x^2 + 5$$
with boundary condition
$$f(0) = -1.$$
Solution: Clearly
$$f(x) = \frac{1}{3}x^3 + 5x + c$$
for some number c. Since
$$f(0) = 0 + 0 + c = -1,$$
$c = -1$ and
$$f(x) = \frac{1}{3}x^3 + 5x - 1.$$

If s, v, and a are the respective position, velocity, and acceleration functions of some point P in motion on a coordinate line L, then s is an antiderivative of v and v is an antiderivative of a, since

$$s'(t) = v(t), \qquad v'(t) = a(t).$$

Hence given the velocity or acceleration function and some boundary conditions, called *initial conditions* if given for $t = 0$, it is possible to determine the position function.   This is illustrated below.

Example 3.   Find $s(t)$ if it is known that

$$a(t) = 6t - 2,$$

and $$v(0) = 3, \qquad s(0) = -1.$$

Solution: Since $a(t) = v'(t)$, $v'(t) = 6t - 2$, and

$$v(t) = 3t^2 - 2t + c_1,$$

for some number c_1.   However,

$$v(0) = 0 - 0 + c_1 = 3,$$

and $c_1 = 3$.   Thus

$$v(t) = 3t^2 - 2t + 3.$$

Again, $v(t) = s'(t) = 3t^2 - 2t + 3$, and

$$s(t) = t^3 - t^2 + 3t + c_2$$

for some number c_2.   Since

$$s(0) = c_2 = -1,$$

$c_2 = -1$ and

$$s(t) = t^3 - t^2 + 3t - 1.$$

An object P is pulled toward the earth by a *force of gravity*.   The *acceleration of gravity* due to this force is designated by g.   The number g varies with the distance of P from the center of the earth, but is essentially a constant over a small range of distances.   An approximate value of g is

$$g = 32 \text{ ft/sec}^2$$

if the object P is near sea level.

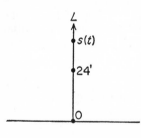

Figure 6.27

Example 4.   A ball is thrown directly upward from a point 24 ft above the ground with an initial velocity of 40 ft/sec.   Assuming no air resistance, how high will the ball rise and when will it return to the ground?

Solution: In Figure 6.27, the vertical line L indicates the path of the ball and the horizontal line represents the ground.   The units on L are feet.   If s is the position function of the ball,

$$s(0) = 24$$

by the assumption that the ball starts 24 ft above the ground.   Also,

$$v(0) = 40$$

since the initial velocity is 40 ft/sec.

Since L is directed upward whereas the force of gravity pulls the ball towards the earth, the velocity will decrease and therefore

$$a(t) = -32.$$

Since v is an antiderivative of a,

$$v(t) = -32t + c_1.$$

However, $v(0) = 40$, and therefore $c_1 = 40$ and

$$v(t) = -32t + 40.$$

Also, s is an antiderivative of v, so that

$$s(t) = -16t^2 + 40t + c_2.$$

Again, $s(0) = 24$, and $c_2 = 24$. Thus

$$s(t) = -16t^2 + 40t + 24.$$

The ball reaches its maximum height when $v(t) = 0$, i.e., when

$$-32t + 40 = 0$$

or, $$t = \frac{5}{4} \text{ sec.}$$

The actual maximum height is given by

$$s\left(\frac{5}{4}\right) = -16\left(\frac{5}{4}\right)^2 + 40\left(\frac{5}{4}\right) + 24 = 49 \text{ ft.}$$

The ball reaches the ground when $s(t) = 0$, i.e., when

$$-16t^2 + 40t + 24 = 0.$$

Since

$$-16t^2 + 40t + 24 = -8(2t + 1)(t - 3),$$

the ball reaches the ground when $t = 3$, that is, after 3 sec. The number $t = -\frac{1}{2}$ is not in the domain of s, since the ball was thrown at the time $t = 0$.

■ ■ ■ EXERCISES

In each of the following exercises, find an antiderivative of the given function.

1. $f(x) = 1 - 4x + 9x^2$.

2. $g(x) = 3 - 6x + 4x^3$.

3. $G(x) = 6x^2 - 3x + 5$.

4. $F(x) = 12x^2 - 8x + 7$.

5. $s(t) = t^3 + t^2 - 7t$.

6. $f(x) = 4x^5 - 3x^4 + 12x$.

7. $g(x) = 4x^4 - 3x^3 + x^2 + 2$.

8. $s(t) = t^5 - 5t$.

9. $f(y) = \frac{1}{3}y^3 - \frac{1}{2}y^2 + 3y$.

10. $g(x) = x\sqrt{x} + \sqrt{x} - 5$.

11. $F(x) = \frac{\sqrt{x}}{2} - \frac{2}{\sqrt{x}}$.

12. $f(z) = \frac{\sqrt[3]{z}}{3} - \frac{3}{\sqrt[3]{z}}$.

In each of the following exercises, find the solution of the given differential equation that satisfies the given boundary conditions.

13. $f'(x) = 8x - 3, f(0) = 3$.

14. $g'(z) = 6z - 5, g(1) = -4.$

15. $F'(x) = 4x^2 + 6x - 5, F(-3) = 7.$

16. $f'(y) = 8 - 6y - 3y^2, f(-1) = 6.$

17. $G'(x) = \sqrt{2} - 2x + x^2, G(\sqrt{2}) = 1.$

18. $F'(x) = \dfrac{1}{\sqrt{x}} - 2x, F(4) = -12.$

19. $s''(t) = 8, s'(2) = 7, s(-1) = -3.$

20. $f''(x) = \dfrac{1}{\sqrt{x}} - 10, f'(1) = 3, f(4) = 0.$

21. A ball is thrown directly upward from the ground with an initial velocity of 56 ft/sec. Assuming no air resistance, how high will the ball rise and when will it return to the ground?

22. An object slides down an inclined plane with an acceleration of 16 ft/sec². If the object is given an initial velocity of 4 ft/sec from the top of the inclined plane, find the position function of the object. If the plane is 60 ft long, when does the object reach the end of the plane?

23. A ball is thrown directly downward from a point 144 ft above the ground with enough initial velocity so that it reaches the ground in 2 sec. Neglecting air resistance, find the initial velocity.

24. A car is coasting along a level road at an initial speed of 30 ft/sec. If the car is retarded by friction at the rate of 2 ft/sec² (i.e., an acceleration of -2 ft/sec²), in how many seconds will the car stop? How far will it have coasted?

25. A ball rolls down an inclined plane 200 ft long with an acceleration of 8 ft/sec². Find the position function of the ball if it is given no initial velocity. How long does it take the ball to reach the end of the plane? What initial velocity must it be given to reach the end of the plane in 4 sec?

26. Starting from rest, with what constant acceleration must a car proceed to go 200 ft in 4 sec?

7

The conic sections and other algebraic curves

■ ■ ■ ■ ■ THE GRAPH OF an algebraic equation in x and y is called an algebraic curve. For example,

$$x^2 + 4y^2 - 8x + 8y + 16 = 0$$

is an algebraic equation in x and y. Its graph is an ellipse, as we shall show later in this chapter. In the discussion to follow, the methods of the calculus will be used whenever they apply. However, we will be primarily concerned with such properties of graphs as extent, position, and symmetry that are not closely related to derivatives or other similar topics of the calculus.

1. Position and symmetry

Given an equation in x and y, we can frequently make general statements about the position of the graph of this equation in the coordinate plane without actually sketching the graph. For example, we might be able to state that the graph is above the x-axis, or between two vertical lines, or in the first quadrant only, and so on.

If, for example, $P(x,y)$ is a point on the graph of the equation

$$xy = 4,$$

then x and y have the same sign. Hence P is in either

153

the first or the third quadrant, and the graph of the equation $xy = 4$ lies in these two quadrants.

On solving the equation

$$4x^2 + y^2 = 4$$

for y, we obtain

$$y = \pm 2\sqrt{1 - x^2}.$$

Now $1 - x^2 \geq 0$ if and only if $x^2 \leq 1$, and therefore y is not a real number if $x^2 > 1$. Since $x^2 \leq 1$ if and only if $-1 \leq x \leq 1$, we conclude that the graph of the given equation lies between the lines $x = -1$ and $x = 1$. On solving the given equation for x, we get

$$x = \pm \frac{1}{2}\sqrt{4 - y^2}.$$

Again, $4 - y^2 \geq 0$ if and only if $-2 \leq y \leq 2$, and the graph lies between the lines $y = -2$ and $y = 2$. Thus the graph must lie in the rectangle sketched in Figure 7.1.

The points of a graph on the x-axis are called the *x-intercepts* of the graph; those on the y-axis the *y-intercepts*. Since $x = \pm 1$ when $y = 0$ in the example above, $(1,0)$ and $(-1,0)$ are the x-intercepts of the graph. Also, $y = \pm 2$ when $x = 0$, and $(0,2)$ and $(0,-2)$ are the y-intercepts.

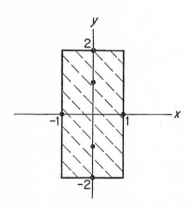

Figure 7.1

The graph of an equation is said to be *bounded* if the graph is completely contained in some rectangular region of the plane. For example, the graph of the equation $4x^2 + y^2 = 4$ discussed above is bounded since it is completely contained in the rectangle of Figure 7.1.

If for each point (x,y) on the graph of an equation the point $(x,-y)$ also is on the graph, then the graph is said to be *symmetric to the x-axis*, and the x-axis is called an *axis of symmetry* of the graph. Similarly, if $(-x,y)$ is on the graph whenever (x,y) is, the graph is said to be *symmetric to the y-axis*, and the y-axis is an axis of symmetry. Finally, the graph of an equation is *symmetric to the origin* if the point $(-x,-y)$ is on the graph whenever the point (x,y) is. In such a case, the origin is called a *center* of the graph.

If in an equation in x and y we replace each y by $-y$, then the graph of the resulting equation is the graph of the original equation reflected in the x-axis. Now if the original graph is symmetric to the x-axis, the graph is its own reflection in the x-axis, and conversely. Therefore the graph of an equation in x and y is symmetric to the x-axis if and only if the equation is unchanged (in the sense that its graph is unchanged) when y is replaced by $-y$ throughout the equation.

These remarks together with similar ones for symmetry to the y-axis and to the origin yield the following result.

7.1 Symmetry tests.   The graph of an equation in x and y has:

1. the x-axis as an axis of symmetry if the equation is unchanged when y is replaced by $-y$.
2. the y-axis as an axis of symmetry if the equation is unchanged when x is replaced by $-x$.
3. the origin as a center of symmetry if the equation is unchanged when x is replaced by $-x$ and y is replaced by $-y$.

If both coordinate axes are axes of symmetry of a graph, then the origin is a center of symmetry.   The converse of this statement need not be true.

If an equation contains y to even powers only, then its graph is necessarily symmetric to the x-axis; and if an equation contains x to even powers only, then its graph is necessarily symmetric to the y-axis.

Example 1.   Discuss and sketch the graph of the equation

$$4x^2 + y^2 = 4.$$

Solution: We have already observed that the graph is bounded, and has x-intercepts $(1,0)$ and $(-1,0)$ and y-intercepts $(0,2)$ and $(0,-2)$.   Since

$$4x^2 + (-y)^2 = 4$$

reduces to the original equation, the x-axis is an axis of symmetry of the graph.   Likewise, the graph is symmetric to the y-axis since

Figure 7.2

$$4(-x)^2 + y^2 = 4$$

reduces to the given equation.   Hence the origin is a center of the graph.   The graph is sketched in Figure 7.2 from the accompanying table of values.   It is an ellipse, as we shall prove later on in this chapter.

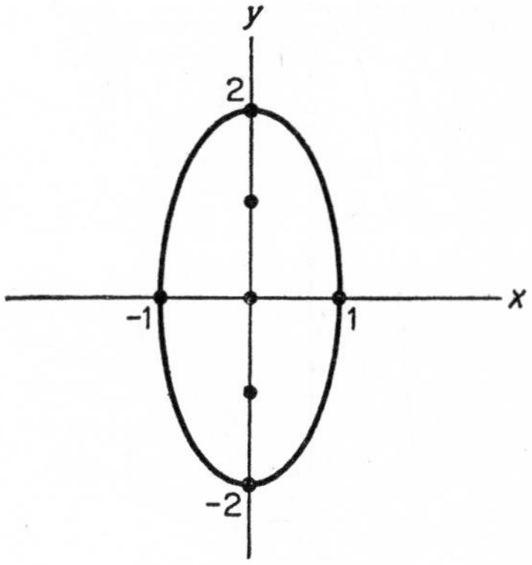

x	0	$\pm\frac{1}{2}$	$\pm\frac{3}{4}$	± 1
y	± 2	$\pm\sqrt{3}$	$\pm\dfrac{\sqrt{7}}{2}$	0

Example 2.   Discuss and sketch the graph of the equation

$$y = x^3.$$

Solution: If we replace x by $-x$ in this equation, we obtain the equation

$$y = (-x)^3 \quad \text{or} \quad y = -x^3$$

which is clearly different from the original equation. Thus the graph is not symmetric to the y-axis. It is not symmetric to the x-axis for a similar reason.

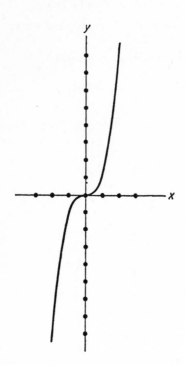

It is symmetric to the origin, since the equation

$$-y = (-x)^3$$

reduces to the given one. The graph lies in the first and third quadrants and is unbounded since for large values of $|x|$, $|y|$ is very large. Since

$$\frac{dy}{dx} = 3x^2, \qquad \frac{d^2y}{dx^2} = 6x,$$

it is evident that the graph has the x-axis as a tangent line at the origin, and is concave upward for $x > 0$ and concave downward for $x < 0$. The graph is sketched in Figure 7.3 from the accompanying table of values and its known symmetry to the origin.

x	0	$\frac{1}{2}$	1	2	3
y	0	$\frac{1}{8}$	1	8	27

Figure 7.3

Example 3. Discuss and sketch the graph of the equation

$$y^2 = 1 + x^3.$$

Solution: If we replace y by $-y$ in the given equation, we get the equation

$$(-y)^2 = 1 + x^3$$

which reduces to the original. Hence the graph is symmetric to the x-axis. It is not symmetric to either the y-axis or the origin. We can solve the equation for y, obtaining

$$y = \pm\sqrt{1 + x^3}.$$

The graph of the equation

$$y = \sqrt{1 + x^3}$$

is the upper half of the graph of the given equation; that of

$$y = -\sqrt{1 + x^3}$$

is the lower half of the original graph.

The graph of the equation

$$y = 1 + x^3$$

is just the graph of Example 2 moved up one unit, and is sketched in Figure

7.4.   If (x,y) is a point on this graph, then $(x,\sqrt{y})$ is a point on the graph of

$$y = \sqrt{1 + x^3}.$$

That is, for each abscissa x, the ordinate of the graph of $y = \sqrt{1 + x^3}$ is the

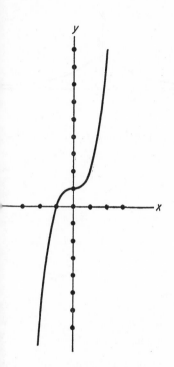

Figure 7.4

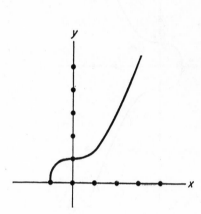

Figure 7.5

square root of the ordinate of the graph of $y = 1 + x^3$. Clearly, then, the graph of $y = \sqrt{1 + x^3}$ occurs only at the abscissas for which the graph of $y = 1 + x^3$ is above the x-axis; it is sketched in Figure 7.5.

Since

$$D_x\sqrt{1 + x^3} = \frac{3x^2}{2\sqrt{1 + x^3}},$$

The critical numbers of the function f defined by $f(x) = \sqrt{1 + x^3}$ are 0 and -1. It is easily verified that the graph of f (Figure 7.5) has a horizontal tangent line at $(0,1)$ and a vertical tangent line at $(-1,0)$.

The graph of the given equation will then be as sketched in Figure 7.6.

Example 4.   Sketch the graph of the equation

$$y = \frac{1}{1 + x^2}.$$

Solution: The equation has x appearing to even powers only; hence the graph is

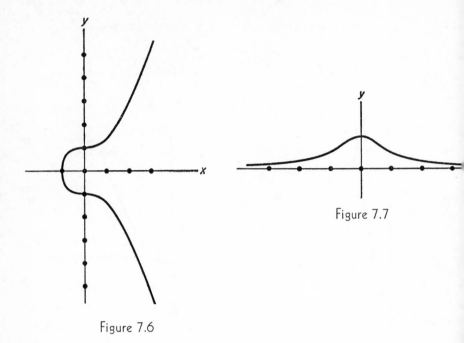

Figure 7.7

Figure 7.6

symmetric to the y-axis.   Since $1 + x^2 \geq 1$,

$$0 < y \leq 1$$

for every number x.   Thus the graph lies between the lines $y = 0$ and $y = 1$. Clearly $(0,1)$ is the maximum point on the graph.   It may be verified that $\left(\pm \dfrac{\sqrt{3}}{3}, \tfrac{3}{4} \right)$ are the points of inflection of the graph.   The graph, sketched in Figure 7.7, appears to be very close to the x-axis for large values of $|x|$.

■ ■ ■ EXERCISES

Discuss and sketch the graph of each of the following equations.

1. $y = 9 - 4x^2$.
2. $y = 1 - x^3$.
3. $y^2 = 9 - 4x^2$.
4. $y^2 = 1 - x^3$.
5. $y = x(x - 2)$.
6. $y = x - x^3$.
7. $y^2 = x(x - 2)$.
8. $y^2 = x - x^3$.
9. $y = x^3 - 2x^2$.
10. $y = x^4 - 4x^2$.
11. $y^2 = x^3 - 2x^2$.
12. $y^2 = x^4 - 4x^2$.
13. $y^2 + y^2x^2 = 1$.
14. $y + yx^2 = x^2$.
15. $y^3 = 1 + x^3$.
16. $y^2 + y^2x^2 = x^2$.
17. $y^2 = x^2 - 4$.
18. $y^3 = x^2 - 4$.
19. $y + yx^2 = x$.
20. $y^2 + y^2x^2 = x$.

21. Show that if a graph possesses any two of the properties of symmetry discussed above, then it must possess the third.

2. Horizontal asymptotes

The symbol ∞, introduced in Chapter 1, is useful in describing certain limiting values of functions.

7.2 Definition. For a function f,

$$\lim_{x \to \infty} f(x) = b$$

if for every number $\epsilon > 0$ there exists a number N such that

$$|f(x) - b| < \epsilon \quad \text{for every number } x > N.$$

Intuitively, the limit of $f(x)$ as x approaches ∞ is the number b (if such exists) that $f(x)$ is getting close to as x gets large.

We define

$$\lim_{x \to -\infty} f(x) = b$$

similarly. Thus, this limit holds if for every $\epsilon > 0$ there exists a number N such that $|f(x) - b| < \epsilon$ for every $x < N$. In words, this limit holds if $f(x)$ is close to b when x is small (i.e., large negatively).

A useful instance of such a limit is as follows:

7.3 $$\lim_{x \to \infty} \frac{1}{x^p} = 0, \quad \text{if } p > 0.$$

To prove 7.3, let there by given an $\epsilon > 0$. Then if $x > 0$,

$$\left| \frac{1}{x^p} - 0 \right| < \epsilon$$

if and only if $1/x^p < \epsilon$, or,

$$x^p > \frac{1}{\epsilon}.$$

In turn, $x^p > 1/\epsilon$ if and only if

$$x > \left(\frac{1}{\epsilon} \right)^{1/p}.$$

Thus, if we let

$$N = \left(\frac{1}{\epsilon} \right)^{1/p},$$

$1/x^p < \epsilon$ for every $x > N$, and 7.3 is proved.

Limit 7.3 also holds for x approaching $-\infty$ provided, of course, p is chosen so that x^p is real for negative values of x.

The ordinary limit theorems also hold for limits as x approaches $\pm\infty$. We shall not prove these, since their proofs are but slight modifications of those given in Chapter 4.

It is convenient to write

$$\lim_{x \to \infty} f(x) = \infty$$

if $f(x)$ is large when x is large; to be more precise, if for every number K (no matter how large) there exists a number N such that $f(x) > K$ for every $x > N$. The many variations of this limit involving $-\infty$ are defined analogously. Clearly

$$\lim_{x \to \infty} x^p = \infty, \quad \text{if } p > 0.$$

Example 1. Find

$$\lim_{x \to \infty} \frac{2 - x + 3x^2}{1 + x^2}.$$

Solution: In order to use 7.3, we divide numerator and denominator of the given expression by x^2, and then proceed as indicated below:

$$\lim_{x \to \infty} \frac{2 - x + 3x^2}{1 + x^2} = \lim_{x \to \infty} \frac{2/x^2 - 1/x + 3}{1/x^2 + 1}$$

$$= \frac{2 \lim\limits_{x \to \infty} 1/x^2 - \lim\limits_{x \to \infty} 1/x + \lim\limits_{x \to \infty} 3}{\lim\limits_{x \to \infty} 1/x^2 + \lim\limits_{x \to \infty} 1}$$

$$= \frac{3}{1} = 3.$$

Example 2. Find

$$\lim_{x \to -\infty} (\sqrt{x^2 + 1} + x).$$

Solution: Since

$$(\sqrt{x^2 + 1} + x)(\sqrt{x^2 + 1} - x) = 1,$$

we have for every $x < 0$, $\sqrt{x^2 + 1} = -x\sqrt{1 + 1/x^2}$ and

$$\sqrt{x^2 + 1} + x = \frac{1}{\sqrt{x^2 + 1} - x} = \frac{1}{x}\left(\frac{1}{-\sqrt{1 + \dfrac{1}{x^2}} - 1}\right).$$

Thus

$$\lim_{x \to -\infty} (\sqrt{x^2 + 1} + x) = \lim_{x \to -\infty} \frac{1}{x} \frac{1}{-\sqrt{1 + \lim\limits_{x \to -\infty} \dfrac{1}{x^2}} - 1}$$

$$= 0 \cdot -\frac{1}{2} = 0.$$

The existence of a limit involving ∞ for a function f tells us something about the graph of f far away from the origin. If

$$\lim_{x \to \infty} f(x) = b,$$

then $f(x)$ is close to b when x is large, and the graph of f gets close to the line $y = b$ when x gets large. Such a line $y = b$ is called an asymptote o the graph.   Thus, if either

$$\text{limit}_{x \to \infty} f(x) = b \quad \text{or} \quad \text{limit}_{x \to -\infty} f(x) = b,$$

the line $y = b$ is called a *horizontal asymptote* of the graph of f.

For example, the line $y = 0$ (the x-axis) is an asymptote of the graph of the equation

$$y = \frac{1}{1 + x^2}$$

sketched in Figure 7.7, since

$$\text{limit}_{x \to \pm\infty} \frac{1}{1 + x^2} = \text{limit}_{x \to \pm\infty} \frac{\frac{1}{x^2}}{\frac{1}{x^2} + 1} = \frac{0}{0 + 1} = 0.$$

Example 3.   Discuss and sketch the graph of the equation

$$y = \frac{4x^2}{x^2 + 1}.$$

Solution: The graph is symmetric to the y-axis, since x occurs to even powers only.
Since

$$0 \le \frac{x^2}{x^2 + 1} < 1,$$

$0 \le y < 4$ for every number x.   Thus the graph lies between the lines $y = 0$ and $y = 4$.
Since

$$\text{limit}_{x \to \pm\infty} \frac{4x^2}{x^2 + 1} = \text{limit}_{x \to \pm\infty} \frac{4}{1 + 1/x^2} = 4,$$

the line $y = 4$ is an asymptote of the graph of the given equation (i.e., of the graph of the function f defined by $f(x) = 4x^2/(x^2 + 1)$).

We may verify that

$$\frac{dy}{dx} = \frac{8x}{(x^2 + 1)^2}, \qquad \frac{d^2y}{dx^2} = \frac{8(1 - 3x^2)}{(x^2 + 1)^3},$$

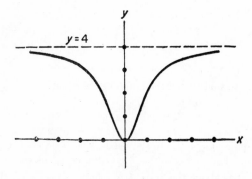

Figure 7.8

and therefore that (0,0) is a minimum point and $\left(\pm\dfrac{\sqrt{3}}{3},\tfrac{5}{4}\right)$ are the points of inflection of the graph.   The graph is sketched in Figure 7.8.

Example 4.   Discuss and sketch the graph of the equation

$$y = \frac{4x}{x^2 + 1}.$$

Solution: The graph is symmetric to the origin, since the equation

$$-y = \frac{4(-x)}{(-x)^2 + 1}$$

reduces to the original.   It is not symmetric to either axis.   Clearly the graph occurs in the first and third quadrants only.   Since

$$\lim_{x \to \pm\infty} \frac{4x}{x^2 + 1} = \lim_{x \to \pm\infty} \frac{4/x}{1 + 1/x^2} = 0,$$

the line $y = 0$ (i.e., the x-axis) is an asymptote.

The first and second derivatives are given by:

$$\frac{dy}{dx} = \frac{4(1 - x^2)}{(x^2 + 1)^2}, \qquad \frac{d^2y}{dx^2} = -\frac{8x(3 - x^2)}{(x^2 + 1)^2}.$$

From these we verify that (1,2) is a maximum point and $(-1,-2)$ is a minimum point on the graph, and that (0,0), $(\sqrt{3},\sqrt{3})$, and $(-\sqrt{3},-\sqrt{3})$ are points of inflection.   The graph is sketched in Figure 7.9.

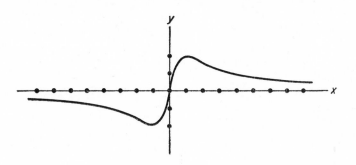

Figure 7.9

Example 5.   Discuss and sketch the graph of the equation

$$y^2 = \frac{4x}{x^2 + 1}.$$

Solution: The graph is symmetric to the x-axis, since y enters to even powers only in the equation.   For each point (x,y) on the graph of the previous example (Figure 7.9) that is above the x-axis, the point $(x,\sqrt{y})$ is on the graph of the present equation.   Thus the graph is in the first and fourth quadrants.   The part of the curve in the first quadrant is the graph of the function f, where

$$f(x) = \frac{2\sqrt{x}}{\sqrt{x^2 + 1}}.$$

Since

$$\operatorname*{limit}_{x \to \infty} f(x) = \operatorname*{limit}_{x \to \infty} \frac{\dfrac{2}{\sqrt{x}}}{\sqrt{1 + 1/x^2}} = 0,$$

the x-axis is an asymptote of this graph also. By taking square roots of ordinates of the previous graph, the graph of the given equation is sketched in Figure 7.10.

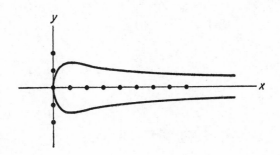

Figure 7.10

■ ■ ■ EXERCISES

Evaluate each of the following limits.

1. $\displaystyle\operatorname*{limit}_{x \to \infty} \frac{1 - 2x + x^2}{3 + x - 4x^2}.$

2. $\displaystyle\operatorname*{limit}_{x \to -\infty} \frac{x^3 - 1}{x^3 + 1}.$

3. $\displaystyle\operatorname*{limit}_{x \to -\infty} \frac{x - x^2}{1 + x^2 - 3x^3}.$

4. $\displaystyle\operatorname*{limit}_{x \to \infty} \frac{x^5 + 1}{x^4 + x^2 + 2}.$

5. $\displaystyle\operatorname*{limit}_{x \to \infty} \frac{x^2}{1 - x}.$

6. $\displaystyle\operatorname*{limit}_{x \to -\infty} \frac{x\sqrt{x}}{\sqrt{1 + 4x^3}}.$

7. $\displaystyle\operatorname*{limit}_{x \to \infty} (\sqrt{4 + x^2} - x).$

8. $\displaystyle\operatorname*{limit}_{x \to \infty} (\sqrt{2x^2 + 1} - \sqrt{2x}).$

Discuss and sketch the graph of each of the following equations.

9. $y = \dfrac{4}{4 + x^2}.$

10. $y = \dfrac{9x}{9 + x^2}.$

11. $y^2 = \dfrac{4}{4 + x^2}.$

12. $y^2 = \dfrac{9x}{9 + x^2}.$

13. $y = \dfrac{3}{x^2 + x + 1}.$

14. $y = \dfrac{1}{x^2 - x + 1}.$

15. $y = \dfrac{x^2 + x + 1}{x^2 + 1}.$

16. $y = \dfrac{x^2 + x}{x^2 + 1}.$

17. $y = \dfrac{x^4}{x^4 + 1}.$ 　　　　　　　　**18.** $y = \dfrac{x^3}{x^2 + 1}.$

19. $y^2 = \dfrac{x^4}{x^4 + 1}.$ 　　　　　　　**20.** $y^2 = \dfrac{x^3}{x^2 + 1}.$

21. Let $\quad f(x) = \dfrac{x^n}{x^2 + 1}$, n an integer.　Show that

(a) $\displaystyle\lim_{x \to \pm\infty} f(x) = 0 \quad$ if $\quad n < 2.$

(b) $\displaystyle\lim_{x \to \pm\infty} f(x) = 1 \quad$ if $\quad n = 2.$

(c) $\displaystyle\lim_{x \to \infty} f(x) = \infty \quad$ if $\quad n > 2.$

(d) $\displaystyle\lim_{x \to -\infty} f(x) = -\infty \quad$ if $\quad n > 2, \quad n$ an odd integer.

3. Vertical asymptotes

We write

$$\lim_{x \to 0^+} \frac{1}{x} = \infty$$

to indicate that as x approaches 0, $x > 0$, $1/x$ gets large; and

$$\lim_{x \to 0^-} \frac{1}{x} = -\infty$$

to indicate that as x approaches 0, $x < 0$, $1/x$ gets small (i.e., large negatively).　These are special cases of the following definition.

7.4 Definition.　For a function f,

$$\lim_{x \to a^+} f(x) = \infty$$

if for every number N there exists a number $\delta > 0$ such that

$$f(x) > N \text{ for every } x \text{ satisfying } 0 < x - a < \delta.$$

Also,

$$\lim_{x \to a^-} f(x) = \infty$$

if for every number N there exists a number $\delta > 0$ such that

$$f(x) > N \text{ for every } x \text{ satisfying } 0 < a - x < \delta.$$

Analogous definitions may be made for

$$\lim_{x \to a^+} f(x) = -\infty, \qquad \lim_{x \to a^-} f(x) = -\infty.$$

If

$$\lim_{x \to a^+} f(x) = \lim_{x \to a^-} f(x) = \infty,$$

then we write

$$\lim_{x \to a} f(x) = \infty,$$

and similarly for $-\infty$.

We may read $x \to a^+$ as "x approaches a from the right" and $x \to a^-$ as "x approaches a from the left."

Most of the infinite limits that we shall encounter are of the following type:

7.5
$$\lim_{x \to a^+} \frac{1}{(x-a)^p} = \infty, \quad p > 0.$$

Proof: Let N be an arbitrarily chosen (large) positive number. Then if $x - a > 0$,

$$\frac{1}{(x-a)^p} > N \quad \text{if and only if} \quad (x-a)^p < \frac{1}{N},$$

and

$$(x-a)^p < \frac{1}{N} \quad \text{if and only if} \quad x - a < \frac{1}{N^{1/p}}.$$

Thus, if $\delta = (1/N)^{1/p}$,

$$\frac{1}{(x-a)^p} > N \text{ for every } x \text{ satisfying } 0 < x - a < \delta.$$

This proves 7.5.

The limit 7.5 above evidently still holds for x approaching a from the left if $p = m/n > 0$ where m is an even integer and n is odd.

If p is an odd positive integer or the ratio of two odd positive integers, then $(x-a)^p < 0$ if $x < a$ and

$$\lim_{x \to a^-} \frac{1}{(x-a)^p} = -\infty$$

by a proof similar to that of 7.5.

Modified limit theorems hold for these infinite limits. We state without proof two of these that will be useful to us in the sequel.

7.6 If the function g is continuous at a and if

$$\lim_{x \to a^+} f(x) = \pm\infty,$$

then

(1)
$$\lim_{x \to a^+} [f(x) + g(x)] = \lim_{x \to a^+} f(x).$$

(2)
$$\lim_{x \to a^+} f(x)g(x) = \begin{cases} \lim\limits_{x \to a^+} f(x) & \text{if } g(a) > 0 \\ -\lim\limits_{x \to a^+} f(x) & \text{if } g(a) < 0 \end{cases},$$

and similarly for x approaching a from the left.

Example 1. Find $\displaystyle\lim_{x \to 1^+} \frac{1}{x^2 - x}$ and $\displaystyle\lim_{x \to 1^-} \frac{1}{x^2 - x}$.

Solution: We write

$$\frac{1}{x^2 - x} = \frac{1}{x} \cdot \frac{1}{x-1}.$$

Then, by 7.6, (2) with $f(x) = 1/(x - 1)$ and $g(x) = 1/x$,

$$\operatorname{limit}_{x\to 1^+} \frac{1}{x^2 - x} = \operatorname{limit}_{x\to 1^+} \frac{1}{x - 1} = \infty,$$

$$\operatorname{limit}_{x\to 1^-} \frac{1}{x^2 - x} = \operatorname{limit}_{x\to 1^-} \frac{1}{x - 1} = -\infty.$$

The graph of the equation

$$y = \frac{1}{x},$$

sketched in Figure 7.11, has the x-axis as an asymptote since

$$\operatorname{limit}_{x\to \pm\infty} \frac{1}{x} = 0.$$

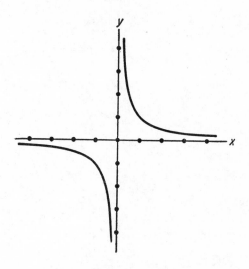

Figure 7.11

It is intuitively clear that the y-axis also is an asymptote, since

$$\operatorname{limit}_{x\to 0^+} \frac{1}{x} = \infty \quad \text{and} \quad \operatorname{limit}_{x\to 0^-} \frac{1}{x} = -\infty.$$

With this example in mind, let us call the line $x = a$ a *vertical asymptote* of the graph of a function f if either

$$\operatorname{limit}_{x\to a^+} f(x) = \pm\infty \quad \text{or} \quad \operatorname{limit}_{x\to a^-} f(x) = \pm\infty.$$

If $x = a$ is an asymptote of f, then necessarily f is discontinuous at a.

Example 2. Discuss and sketch the graph of the equation

$$y = \frac{x}{x^2 - 1}.$$

Solution: The graph is symmetric to the origin; (0,0) is the only x- or y-intercept. Since

$$\lim_{x \to \pm\infty} \frac{x}{x^2 - 1} = 0,$$

the x-axis is a horizontal asymptote. Now

$$\frac{x}{x^2 - 1} = x \cdot \frac{1}{x + 1} \cdot \frac{1}{x - 1},$$

and therefore [since $x/(x + 1) > 0$ if $x = 1$ and $x/(x - 1) > 0$ if $x = -1$],

$$\lim_{x \to 1^+} \frac{x}{x^2 - 1} = \lim_{x \to 1^+} \frac{1}{x - 1} = \infty,$$

$$\lim_{x \to 1^-} \frac{x}{x^2 - 1} = \lim_{x \to 1^-} \frac{1}{x - 1} = -\infty,$$

$$\lim_{x \to -1^+} \frac{x}{x^2 - 1} = \lim_{x \to -1^+} \frac{1}{x + 1} = \infty,$$

$$\lim_{x \to -1^-} \frac{x}{x^2 - 1} = \lim_{x \to -1^-} \frac{1}{x + 1} = -\infty.$$

From either of the first two limits, we conclude that $x = 1$ is a vertical asymptote; from either of the last two, that $x = -1$ is a vertical asymptote. Actually, these limits tell us more than that. The first one tells us that as x approaches 1 from the right, the graph approaches $+\infty$ (i.e., rises indefinitely); the second one that as x approaches 1 from the left, the graph approaches $-\infty$ (i.e., falls indefinitely); and so on.

We easily verify that

$$\frac{dy}{dx} = -\frac{x^2 + 1}{(x^2 - 1)^2}.$$

Clearly the graph has no maximum or minimum points. The graph is sketched in Figure 7.12 from the information above.

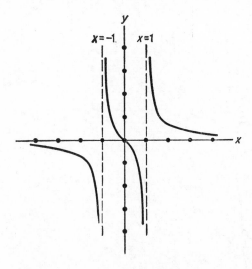

Figure 7.12

Example 3. Discuss and sketch the graph of the equation

$$y^2(x - 3)(x + 2) = 1.$$

Solution: The graph is symmetric to the x-axis, since y is squared. The equation of the upper half of the graph is

$$y = \frac{1}{\sqrt{(x - 3)(x + 2)}}.$$

In order for y to be a real number, we must have $(x - 3)(x + 2) > 0$. Such is the case if either $x < -2$ or $x > 3$, but not otherwise. Since

$$\lim_{x \to -2^-} \frac{1}{\sqrt{(x - 3)(x + 2)}} = \lim_{x \to 3^+} \frac{1}{\sqrt{(x - 3)(x + 2)}} = \infty,$$

the lines $x = -2$ and $x = 3$ are vertical asymptotes of the graph. Clearly the x-axis also is an asymptote. The graph is sketched in Figure 7.13.

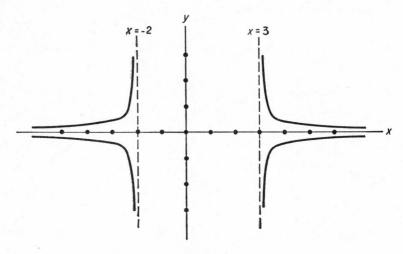

Figure 7.13

■ ■ ■ EXERCISES

1. If $f(x) = \dfrac{(x - 2)^2}{(x + 3)(x - 1)}$, show that for the graph of f:

(a) $(2,0)$ is the x-intercept; $(0, -\frac{4}{3})$ is the y-intercept.

(b) $y = 1$ is a horizontal asymptote.

(c) $x = -3$ and $x = 1$ are vertical asymptotes.

(d) $f(x) > 1$ if $x < -3$.

(e) $f(x) < 0$ if $-3 < x < 1$.

(f) $f(x) \geq 0$ if $x > 1$.

(g) $f(x) = 1$ if and only if $x = \frac{7}{6}$.

Sketch the graph of f.

2. Sketch the graph of the equation $y^2 = \dfrac{(x-2)^2}{(x+3)(x-1)}$.

3. If $f(x) = \dfrac{4x^3}{x^3+1}$, show that for the graph of f:

   (a) $(0,0)$ is the only intercept.
   (b) $y = 4$ is a horizontal asymptote.
   (c) $x = -1$ is a vertical asymptote.
   (d) The tangent line at the origin is horizontal.
   (e) $0 < f(x) < 4$ if $x > 0$.
   (f) $f(x) < 0$ if $-1 < x < 0$.
   (g) $f(x) > 4$ if $x < -1$.
   Sketch the graph of f.

4. Sketch the graph of the equation $y^2 = \dfrac{4x^3}{x^3+1}$.

Discuss and sketch the graph of each of the following equations.

5. $y(x-1) = 1$.   **6.** $y(x+3) = 4$.

7. $y^2(x-1) = 1$.   **8.** $y^2(x+3) = 4$.

9. $y = \dfrac{1}{x^2 - x}$.   **10.** $y = \dfrac{x+1}{x^2 - x}$.

11. $y^2 = \dfrac{1}{x^2 - x}$.   **12.** $y^2 = \dfrac{x+1}{x^2 - x}$.

13. $y = \dfrac{(x+1)^2}{2x - x^2}$.   **14.** $y = \dfrac{x^2}{-2x^2 + 3x - 1}$.

15. Sketch the graph of:

   (a) $y = \dfrac{x^2+1}{x^2}$.   (b) $x = \dfrac{y^2+1}{y^2}$.

16. Sketch the graph of:

   (a) $y = \dfrac{x}{x^3+1}$.   (b) $x = \dfrac{y}{y^3+1}$.

17. If p is an odd positive integer, prove that

$$\lim_{x \to a^-} \frac{1}{(x-a)^p} = -\infty.$$

18. If $\lim\limits_{x \to a^+} f(x) = \infty$ and $\lim\limits_{x \to a} g(x) = b > 0$, prove:

   (a) $\lim\limits_{x \to a^+} [f(x) + g(x)] = \infty$.   (b) $\lim\limits_{x \to a^+} f(x)g(x) = \infty$.

(Hint for (b): There exists some number $\delta_1 > 0$ such that $g(x) > b/2$ for every x satisfying $0 < x - a < \delta_1$. For every number N, there exists some number $\delta_2 > 0$ such that $f(x) > 2N/b$ for every x satisfying $0 < x - a < \delta_2$. If δ is the smaller of δ_1 and δ_2, then

$$f(x)g(x) > (2N/b)g(x) > N$$

for every x satisfying $0 < x - a < \delta$.)

4. The parabola

If a right circular cone of two nappes is cut by a plane, the curve of inter-section is called a *conic section*.   There are essentially three types of curves obtainable in this way, parabolas, ellipses, and hyperbolas.   We shall study these curves in this and the following sections.

A parabola may be defined as follows.

7.7 Definition.   A *parabola* is the locus of all points equidistant from a fixed point (the *focus*) and a fixed line (the *directrix*).

Let us determine an equation of a parabola; in other words, let us find an equation the graph of which is a parabola.   To this end, we let $F(p,0)$ be the focus and $x = -p$ be the directrix of a given parabola.   Thus $|2p|$ represents the distance between the focus and the directrix.

A point $P(x,y)$ in the plane is on the given parabola if and only if (Figure 7.14)

$$|PF| = |PA|,$$

that is, if and only if

$$\sqrt{(x - p)^2 + y^2} = \sqrt{(x + p)^2 + (y - y)^2}.$$

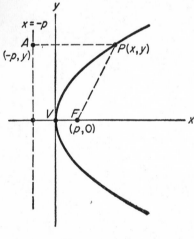

Figure 7.14

This equation is equivalent to the equation

$$(x - p)^2 + y^2 = (x + p)^2,$$

which reduces to

7.8 $y^2 = 4px.$

Thus 7.8 is the equation of a parabola with focus $(p,0)$ and directrix $x = -p.$

The point V midway between the focus and the directrix (Figure 7.14) is called the *vertex* of the parabola; the line on the vertex and the focus is called the *axis* of the parabola. Clearly the parabola is symmetric to its axis.   If $p > 0$, as in Figure 7.14, the parabola lies totally to the right of the y-axis, whereas, if $p < 0$, the parabola will be to the left of the y-axis.   In either case, the parabola opens up around the focus.

If we start with the point $(0,p)$ as the focus F and $y = -p$ as the directrix, then the equation of the parabola is

7.9 $x^2 = 4py,$

since we are just interchanging the roles of x and y in the two cases (Figure

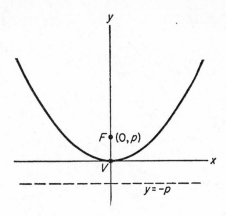

Figure 7.15

7.15). The axis of this parabola is the y-axis. If $p > 0$, the parabola opens as in Figure 7.15, whereas if $p < 0$ the parabola opens downward.

Example 1. Find the equation of the parabola with focus at $(-2,0)$ and directrix $x = 2$.

Solution: This is just 7.8 with $p = -2$. The equation therefore is

$$y^2 = -8x.$$

In sketching the parabola, it is convenient to draw in the chord of the parabola that is on the focus and perpendicular to the axis. This chord is called the *latus rectum* of the parabola. In the present example, AB is the latus rectum (Figure 7.16). Note that $|AB| = 8$.

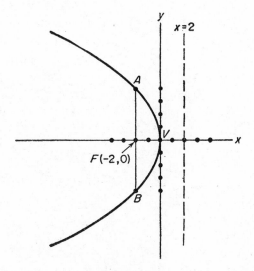

Figure 7.16

Example 2.   Discuss and sketch the graph of the equation

$$x^2 = 6y.$$

Solution: This equation has the form 7.9 with $4p = 6$, or

$$p = \frac{3}{2}.$$

Therefore the graph is a parabola with the y-axis as its axis, and with focus $(0,\frac{3}{2})$ and directrix $y = -\frac{3}{2}$. The parabola is sketched in Figure 7.17. The segment AB, of length 6, is its latus rectum.

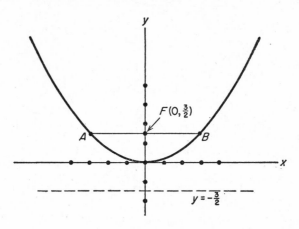

Figure 7.17

■ ■ ■ EXERCISES

Discuss and sketch the graph of each of the following equations.

1. $y^2 = 12x$.   2. $x^2 = -4y$.

3. $x^2 = y$.   4. $y^2 = 3x$.

5. $y^2 = -2x$.   6. $x^2 = 20y$.

7. $x^2 + 8y = 0$.   8. $4y^2 - x = 0$.

Find the equations of the parabolas satisfying the following conditions.

9. Focus $(4,0)$, directrix $x = -4$.

10. Focus $(-4,0)$, directrix $x = 4$.

11. Focus $(0,2)$, vertex $(0,0)$.

12. Vertex $(0,0)$, directrix $y = 3$.

13. Focus $(\frac{1}{2},0)$, vertex $(0,0)$.

14. Focus $(0,-\frac{1}{4})$, directrix $y = \frac{1}{4}$.

15. Focus $(0,0)$, directrix $x = -2$.   (*Hint:* Proceed as in the proof of 7.8.)

16. Focus $(0,0)$, directrix $y = -2p$.   (*Hint:* Use 7.7.)

17. Show that an equation of the tangent line to the parabola $y^2 = 4px$ at the point $P(x_1,y_1)$ is $y_1y = 2p(x + x_1)$.

18. Show that the tangent lines at the ends of the latus rectum of a parabola are perpendicular and intersect on the directrix.

19. Let L be the tangent line at an arbitrary point A on a parabola. If F is the focus of the parabola and B is the point of intersection of L and the directrix, prove that the lines AF and BF are perpendicular.

20. Let L be the tangent line at an arbitrary point A on the parabola $x^2 = 4py$. If F is the focus of the parabola and B is the point of intersection of L and the x-axis, prove that the lines AB and BF are perpendicular.

5. The ellipse

The second type of a conic section we shall discuss is the ellipse, of which the circle is a special case.

7.10 Definition. An *ellipse* is the locus of all points the sum of whose distances from two fixed points (the *foci*) is a constant.

An ellipse can be constructed from a loop of string in the following way. Place two thumbtacks (the foci) in the paper and loop the piece of string over them. Then pull the string taut with your pencil point P as in Figure 7.18. Now move the pencil, always keeping the string taut.

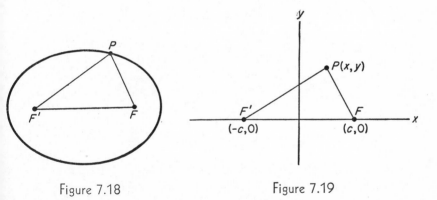

Figure 7.18   Figure 7.19

Since $|FP| + |F'P|$ is always a constant, the curve traced out will be an ellipse according to 7.10. If F and F' coincide, clearly the ellipse becomes a circle.

The equation of an ellipse in the coordinate plane can be determined by arguments similar to those for the parabola. Let the foci F and F' be on the x-axis equispaced from the origin. Thus F will have coordinates $(c,0)$ and F' coordinates $(-c,0)$. Let us designate the constant sum of the distances from a point P on the ellipse to the foci by $2a$. Evidently $a > c$. Thus, in Figure 7.19, the point $P(x,y)$ will be on the ellipse if and only if

$$|FP| + |F'P| = 2a,$$

that is, if and only if

$$\sqrt{(x-c)^2 + y^2} + \sqrt{(x+c)^2 + y^2} = 2a.$$

If this equation is rationalized by transposing one of the radicals and then squaring both sides, and similarly for one more step, it reduces to

$$\frac{x^2}{a^2} + \frac{y^2}{a^2 - c^2} = 1.$$

If we let

7.11 $b^2 = a^2 - c^2,$

the above equation becomes

7.12 $$\frac{x^2}{a^2} + \frac{y^2}{b^2} = 1.$$

We have proved that every point $P(x,y)$ on the given ellipse satisfies Equation 7.12. In order to prove that 7.12 is an equation of the ellipse,

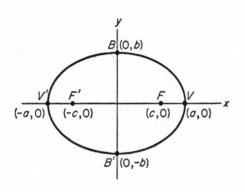

Figure 7.20

we must show conversely that every point $P(x,y)$ satisfying Equation 7.12 lies on the given ellipse. The proof of this fact is left as an exercise for the reader (Exercise 15 at the end of this section).

It is clear from Equation 7.12 that the ellipse under discussion is symmetric to both coordinate axes and to the origin. The origin is the *center* of the ellipse. If $y = 0$, then $x = \pm a$; if $x = 0$, $y = \pm b$ in 7.12. Thus the ellipse cuts the x-axis at $(\pm a, 0)$ and the y-axis at $(0, \pm b)$ as indicated in Figure 7.20. The points $V(a,0)$ and $V'(-a,0)$ are called the *vertices* of the ellipse, and the segment VV' is called the *major axis* of the ellipse. The segment BB' is called the *minor axis* of the ellipse. The major axis of the ellipse contains the foci and is of length $2a$, whereas the minor axis is of length $2b$. From 7.11 it is clear that $a > b$, and therefore the major axis of an ellipse is actually longer than the minor axis (unless the ellipse is a circle).

If the foci of an ellipse are on the y-axis and equispaced from the origin, and if $2a$ again designates the sum of the distances of the foci from each point on the ellipse, then the equation of the ellipse is just 7.12 with x and y interchanged, that is,

7.13 $$\frac{y^2}{a^2} + \frac{x^2}{b^2} = 1.$$

The vertices and major axis are now on the y-axis, as shown in **Figure** 7.21.

Example 1. Find the equation of the ellipse with foci $(\pm 3, 0)$ and vertices $(\pm 5, 0)$.

Solution: The ellipse has its center at the origin and its foci on the x-axis; therefore its equation is of the form 7.12. Since $c = 3$ and $a = 5$, we have (7.11)

$$b^2 = 5^2 - 3^2 = 16,$$

and $b = 4$. Thus the ellipse has equation

$$\frac{x^2}{25} + \frac{y^2}{16} = 1,$$

or $16x^2 + 25y^2 = 400.$

Example 2. Discuss the graph of the equation

$$4x^2 + y^2 = 4.$$

Solution: If we divide each member of this equation by 4, we get the equation

$$\frac{x^2}{1} + \frac{y^2}{4} = 1.$$

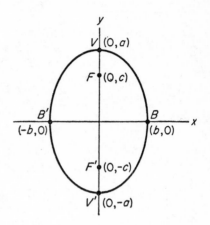

Figure 7.21

This equation is of the form 7.13 with $a^2 = 4$ and $b^2 = 1$. Thus the graph is an ellipse with major axis on the y-axis and minor axis on the x-axis. The vertices are $(0, \pm 2)$, and the ends of the minor axis are $(\pm 1, 0)$. Since

$$c^2 = a^2 - b^2 = 3,$$

$c = \sqrt{3}$ and the foci are the points $(0, \pm \sqrt{3})$.

■ ■ ■ EXERCISES

Discuss and sketch the graph of each of the following equations.

1. $x^2 + 4y^2 = 4.$
2. $25x^2 + 16y^2 = 400.$
3. $25x^2 + 9y^2 = 225.$
4. $4x^2 + 9y^2 = 16.$
5. $16x^2 + 25y^2 = 9.$
6. $x^2 + 2y^2 = 1.$
7. $4x^2 + y^2 = 1.$
8. $3x^2 + 4y^2 = 7.$

Find the equations of the ellipses satisfying the following conditions.

9. Foci $(\pm 4, 0)$, vertices $(\pm 5, 0)$.
10. Foci $(0, \pm 2)$, ends of minor axis $(\pm 1, 0)$.
11. Foci $(0, \pm \sqrt{21})$, end of minor axis $(2, 0)$.
12. Vertices $(\pm 6, 0)$, focus $(-3\sqrt{3}, 0)$.
13. Vertices $(0, \pm 3)$, passing through the point $(\frac{2}{3}, 2\sqrt{2})$.

14. Foci $(\pm\sqrt{5},0)$, passing through the point $(\tfrac{3}{2},\sqrt{3})$.

15. Prove that for every point $P(x,y)$ satisfying Equation 7.12,

$$|PF| + |PF'| = 2a$$

(notation of Figure 7.19). (*Hint:* Multiply each side of the equation $\sqrt{(x-c)^2 + y^2} + \sqrt{(x+c)^2 + y^2} = 2a$ by a, then replace a^2y^2 under each radical by $a^2b^2 - b^2x^2$. Using 7.11, the resulting equation reduces to $|a^2 - cx| + |a^2 + cx| = 2a^2$. But $x \le a$, etc.)

16. Show that the rectangle of maximum area inscribed in the ellipse with Equation 7.12 has area $2ab$.

17. Show that

$$\frac{x_1 x}{a^2} + \frac{y_1 y}{b^2} = 1$$

is an equation of the tangent line to the ellipse 7.12 at $P(x_1,y_1)$.

18. Define the latus rectum for an ellipse as for a parabola. Show that its length is $2b^2/a$.

19. A *diameter* of an ellipse is any chord through its center. Show that the minor axis is the shortest and the major axis is the longest diameter.

6. The hyperbola

The third type of a conic section is the hyperbola, defined as follows.

7.14 Definition. A *hyperbola* is the locus of all points the difference of whose distances from two fixed points (the *foci*) is a constant.

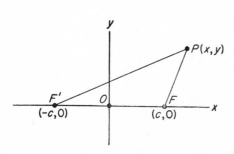

Figure 7.22

Let us determine the equation of a hyperbola just as we did that of the ellipse by placing the foci on the x-axis equispaced from the origin (Figure 7.22). The point O midway between the foci is called the *center* of the hyperbola. Again, as in the ellipse, we let the coordinates of the foci be $(\pm c,0)$, and we designate the difference of the distances of the foci from a point on the hyperbola by $2a$.

Thus the point $P(x,y)$ will be on the hyperbola if and only if (Figure 7.22)

$$|FP| - |F'P| = \pm 2a,$$

that is, if and only if

$$\sqrt{(x-c)^2 + y^2} - \sqrt{(x+c)^2 + y^2} = \pm 2a.$$

The plus or minus sign on the right side of the equation is necessitated by the fact that we allow either $|FP|$ or $|F'P|$ to be the larger number, and insist only that the larger number minus the smaller number be $2a$.

In order for the hyperbola to have some point P on it that is not on the x-axis, we must have $|F'F| + |FP| > |F'P|$ (i.e., the sum of the lengths of two sides of a triangle exceeds the length of the third side) and $|F'F| + |F'P| > |FP|$. Thus $|F'F| > |F'P| - |FP|$ and $|F'F| > |FP| - |F'P|$, and since $|F'F| = 2c$, $2c > 2a$ and $c > a$. So we insist henceforth that $c > a$.

If we rationalize the above equation of the hyperbola, we obtain the equation

$$\frac{x^2}{a^2} - \frac{y^2}{c^2 - a^2} = 1,$$

or, on letting

7.15 $$b^2 = c^2 - a^2,$$

we get

7.16 $$\frac{x^2}{a^2} - \frac{y^2}{b^2} = 1.$$

Every point on the hyperbola satisfies this equation. That, conversely, every point P satisfying Equation 7.16 is on the hyperbola is left as an exercise for the reader. Thus 7.16 is an equation of the given hyperbola.

It is evident from its equation that the hyperbola is symmetric to both axes and its center (the origin in this case). If $y = 0$, then $x = \pm a$, and the hyperbola cuts the x-axis at the points $V(a,0)$ and $V'(-a,0)$ called the *vertices* of the hyperbola. The hyperbola does not intersect the y-axis. The segment VV' connecting the vertices is called the *transverse axis* of the hyperbola.

Solving Equation 7.16 for y, we obtain

7.17 $$y = \pm \frac{b}{a} \sqrt{x^2 - a^2},$$

from which equation it is evident that the curve does not exist if $x^2 \leq a^2$. Thus the hyperbola has two branches, one to the right of $x = a$ and the other to the left of $x = -a$. It is sketched in Figure 7.23.

The hyperbola with Equation 7.16 has asymptotes, as we shall now show. It is intuitively clear that $\sqrt{x^2 - a^2}$ and x are approximately equal when x is a large positive number. Hence y, given by 7.17, should be approximately equal to

$$y = \pm \frac{b}{a} x.$$

To be more precise, let us prove that

$$\lim_{x \to \infty} \left(\frac{b}{a} x - \frac{b}{a} \sqrt{x^2 - a^2} \right) = 0,$$

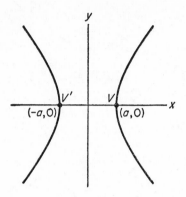

Figure 7.23

which will prove that the line $y = bx/a$ is an asymptote of the hyperbola. Since

$$(x - \sqrt{x^2 - a^2})(x + \sqrt{x^2 - a^2}) = a^2,$$

evidently

$$\lim_{x \to \infty} \frac{b}{a}(x - \sqrt{x^2 - a^2}) = \lim_{x \to \infty} \frac{ab}{x + \sqrt{x^2 - a^2}} = 0.$$

In a similar manner, the line

$$y = -\frac{b}{a}x$$

can be shown to be an asymptote of the graph of

$$y = -\frac{b}{a}\sqrt{x^2 - a^2}.$$

Thus the lines

$$y = \pm\frac{b}{a}x$$

are asymptotes of the hyperbola with Equation 7.16.

An easy way to construct the asymptotes of a hyperbola is shown in Figure 7.24. The asymptotes are just the diagonals of the dotted rectangle. Having drawn in the asymptotes, the hyperbola approaches these lines as indicated in the figure.

If we start with the foci of the hyperbola on the y-axis and equispaced from the origin, the equation of the hyperbola takes on the form

7.18 $$\frac{y^2}{a^2} - \frac{x^2}{b^2} = 1,$$

where, again, $b^2 = c^2 - a^2$. The vertices of this hyperbola have coordinates $(0, \pm a)$ and the transverse axis is along the y-axis. The asymptotes have equations

$$x = \pm\frac{b}{a}y.$$

The hyperbola with Equation 7.18 is sketched in Figure 7.25.

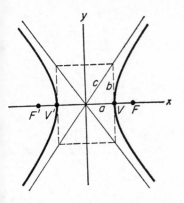

Figure 7.24

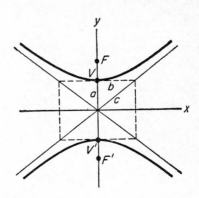

Figure 7.25

Example 1. Find the equation of the hyperbola with foci ($\pm 5,0$) and vertices ($\pm 4,0$).

Solution: The center of this hyperbola is the origin and the transverse axis is along the x-axis. Therefore its equation has the form 7.16. Clearly $c = 5$ and $a = 4$, so that

$$b^2 = c^2 - a^2 = 9.$$

Thus the equation is

$$\frac{x^2}{16} - \frac{y^2}{9} = 1,$$

or $$9x^2 - 16y^2 = 144.$$

The asymptotes of this hyperbola are the lines

$$y = \frac{3}{4}x \quad \text{and} \quad y = -\frac{3}{4}x.$$

Example 2. Discuss the graph of the equation

$$4x^2 - 5y^2 + 20 = 0.$$

Solution: If we divide each member of this equation by 20, we obtain the equation

$$\frac{y^2}{4} - \frac{x^2}{5} = 1.$$

This equation has the form 7.18 with $a^2 = 4$ and $b^2 = 5$. Thus

$$c^2 = a^2 + b^2 = 9,$$

and $a = 2$, $b = \sqrt{5}$, and $c = 3$. The transverse axis is along the y-axis, the vertices are the points ($0,\pm 2$), the foci the points ($0,\pm 3$), and the asymptotes the lines

$$x = \pm \frac{\sqrt{5}}{2} y.$$

■ ■ ■ EXERCISES

Discuss and sketch the graph of each of the following equations.

1. $x^2 - 4y^2 = 4$.

2. $25x^2 - 16y^2 = 400$.

3. $9x^2 - 16y^2 + 144 = 0$.

4. $16x^2 - 9y^2 + 144 = 0$.

5. $x^2 - y^2 = 4$.

6. $4x^2 - 4y^2 + 1 = 0$.

7. $4x^2 - 9y^2 + 16 = 0$.

8. $144x^2 - 25y^2 = 3600$.

Find the equations of the hyperbolas satisfying the following conditions.

9. Foci $(\pm 4,0)$, vertices $(\pm 2,0)$.

10. Foci $(0,\pm 13)$, vertices $(0,\pm 5)$.

11. Foci $(\pm 10,0)$, vertices $(\pm 6,0)$.

12. Foci $(0,\pm\sqrt{2})$, vertices $(0,\pm 1)$.

13. Vertices $(\pm 2,0)$, asymptotes $y = \pm 2x$.

14. Vertices $(0,\pm 4)$, asymptotes $y = \pm 2x/3$.

15. Prove that for every point $P(x,y)$ satisfying Equation 7.16,

$$|FP| - |F'P| = \pm 2a$$

(notation of Figure 7.22).   (*Hint:* See Exercise 15 of the previous section.)

16. Show that

$$\frac{x_1 x}{a^2} - \frac{y_1 y}{b^2} = 1$$

is an equation of the tangent line to the hyperbola 7.16 at the point $P(x_1,y_1)$.

17. If A and B are the points at which the tangent line to a hyperbola at any point P intersect the asymptotes, show that P is the mid-point of AB.

7. *Translation of axes*

If, in the coordinate plane with given x- and y-axis, new coordinate axes are chosen parallel to the given ones, then we shall say that there has been a *translation of axes* in the plane.   In Figure 7.26, the given x- and y-axes have been translated to the x'- and y'-axes with origin (h,k) relative to the given axes.   The positive numbers are assumed to be on the same side of the origin on the new axes as they were on the given axes.

A point P with coordinates (x,y) relative to the given coordinate axes will also have coordinates, say (x',y'), relative to the new axes.   These coordinates of P are related to each other by the equations

7.19 $x' = x - h, \qquad y' = y - k$

or

7.20 $x = x' + h, \qquad y = y' + k$.

To prove these, let the points O, A, B, O', A', and B' be selected as in

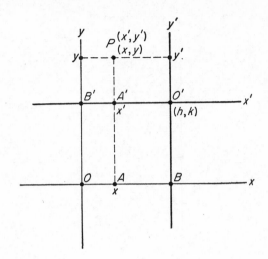

Figure 7.26

Figure 7.26. Then $x = \overline{OA}$, $x' = \overline{O'A'}$, $h = \overline{OB}$, and $k = \overline{OB'}$. Since

$$\overline{OB} = \overline{OA} + \overline{AB} = \overline{OA} + \overline{A'O'} = \overline{OA} - \overline{O'A'},$$

we have

$$h = x - x' \quad \text{or} \quad x' = x - h.$$

The other part of 7.19 is proved similarly, whereas 7.20 is just 7.19 written in a slightly different way.

From a given equation in x and y we may derive an equation in x' and y' simply by replacing x by $x' + h$ and y by $y' + k$ as in 7.20. The graph of the given equation relative to the x- and y-axes must coincide with the graph of the new equation (in x' and y') relative to the new x'- and y'-axes, since the point (x,y) satisfies the given equation if and only if (x',y') satisfies the new equation. We give an example now to illustrate these ideas.

Example 1.   Let the given coordinate axes be translated to the new origin (2,3). Find the equation relative to the new x'- and y'-axes of the graph of the equation

$$x^2 - 4x - 3y + 13 = 0$$

relative to the x- and y-axes.

Solution: The old and new coordinate axes are shown in Figure 7.27. A point P with coordinates (x',y') relative to the new coordinate axes has coordinates (x,y) relative to the old axes given by

$$x = x' + 2, \qquad y = y' + 3$$

according to 7.20. Upon replacing x by $x' + 2$, and y by $y' + 3$ in the given equation, we obtain the equation

$$(x' + 2)^2 - 4(x' + 2) - 3(y' + 3) + 13 = 0.$$

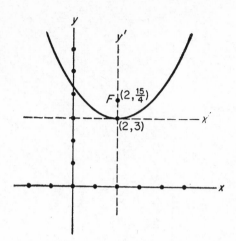

Figure 7.27

This simplifies to the equation

$$x'^2 = 3y'.$$

The graph of this equation relative to the x'- and y'-axes is a parabola with $p = \frac{3}{4}$. It is sketched in Figure 7.27. Thus the graph of the given equation relative to the x- and y-axes is a parabola with vertex the point $(2,3)$, focus the point $(2,\frac{15}{4})$, and directrix the line $y = \frac{9}{4}$.

This illustrates an important use of translation of axes, namely, to reduce an equation to a simpler form so as to facilitate the graphing of the given equation.

The second degree equation in x and y,

$$x^2 + y^2 + 2 = 0,$$

has no graph at all, since $x^2 \geq 0$, $y^2 \geq 0$, and $x^2 + y^2 + 2 > 0$ for every real number x and y. The equation

$$4(x - 2)^2 + 9(y + 3)^2 = 0$$

has a graph consisting of one point, namely, the point $(2,-3)$. The equation

$$y^2 - x^2 = 0$$

has as its graph the two straight lines $y = \pm x$. From these examples, it is evident that the graph of a second-degree equation in x and y might not exist, or might consist of just a point or of (one or two) straight lines. The graph of a second-degree equation of the form

7.21 $$A x^2 + C y^2 + Dx + Ey + F = 0,$$

if it exists and is not made up of just a point or straight lines, is necessarily one of the conic sections. A proper translation of axes will reduce the equation into a standard form of one of the conics as given in the previous sections. In Example 1, the second-degree equation reduced to the standard form of the equation of a parabola. More examples of the reduction of equations of the form 7.21 to standard forms are given below.

Example 2. Discuss the graph of the equation

$$9x^2 + 4y^2 - 18x + 16y - 11 = 0.$$

Solution: In order to determine the proper translation of axes to reduce this equation, let us complete the squares on the x and y terms as follows:

$$9(x^2 - 2x) + 4(y^2 + 4y) = 11,$$
$$9(x^2 - 2x + 1) + 4(y^2 + 4y + 4) = 11 + 9 + 16,$$
$$9(x - 1)^2 + 4(y + 2)^2 = 36,$$
$$\frac{(x - 1)^2}{4} + \frac{(y + 2)^2}{9} = 1.$$

If we let

$$x' = x - 1, \qquad y' = y + 2,$$

so that $h = 1$ and $k = -2$ in 7.19, the given equation reduces to the standard form of an ellipse (7.13)

$$\frac{x'^2}{4} + \frac{y'^2}{9} = 1.$$

Thus a translation of axes to the new origin $(1, -2)$ shows that the graph of the given equation is an ellipse with axes parallel to the coordinate axes. It is sketched in Figure 7.28.

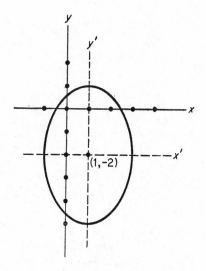

Figure 7.28

Example 3. Discuss the graph of the equation

$$x^2 - 4y^2 + 6x + 24y - 31 = 0.$$

Solution: We first complete the squares as follows:

$$(x^2 + 6x + 9) - 4(y^2 - 6y + 9) = 31 + 9 - 36,$$

$$(x + 3)^2 - 4(y - 3)^2 = 4,$$

$$\frac{(x + 3)^2}{4} - \frac{(y - 3)^2}{1} = 1.$$

Letting

$$x' = x + 3, \qquad y' = y - 3,$$

so that $h = -3$ and $k = 3$ in 7.19, the given equation reduces to the standard form of a hyperbola (7.16),

$$\frac{x'^2}{4} - \frac{y'^2}{1} = 1.$$

Hence a translation of axes to the new origin $(-3,3)$ shows that the graph of the given equation is a hyperbola. The graph is sketched in Figure 7.29.

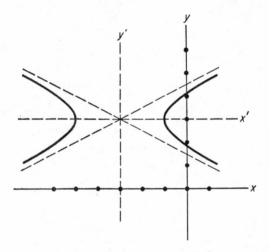

Figure 7.29

Example 4. Discuss the graph of the equation

$$y^2 - 12x + 6 = 0.$$

Solution: There is no need to complete squares in this example, since there is no linear y-term. Thus we have

$$y^2 = 12 \left(x - \frac{1}{2} \right),$$

or

$$y'^2 = 12x'$$

if we let

$$x' = x - \frac{1}{2} \quad \text{and} \quad y' = y.$$

Hence the graph is a parabola with vertex $(\frac{1}{2},0)$ as sketched in Figure 7.30.

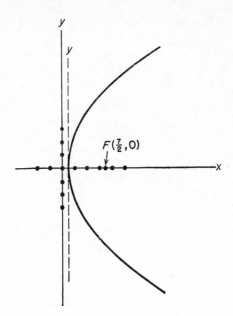

Figure 7.30

■ ■ ■ EXERCISES

Discuss and sketch the graph of each of the following equations.

1. $x^2 - 6x - 4y + 1 = 0.$ 2. $y^2 + 2y + 8x - 15 = 0.$

3. $x^2 + 9y^2 - 4x - 18y + 4 = 0.$

4. $2x^2 + 8y^2 - 8x - 16y + 9 = 0.$

5. $2x^2 + 3y^2 - 4x + 12y + 8 = 0.$

6. $4x^2 - y^2 - 24x - 4y + 36 = 0.$

7. $x^2 - y^2 + 4x - 4y + 1 = 0.$ 8. $x^2 + y^2 + 6x + 5 = 0.$

9. $y^2 + 8x - 6 = 0.$ 10. $x^2 + 2x - 2y + 2 = 0.$

11. $9x^2 - 4y^2 - 54x + 45 = 0.$ 12. $9x^2 - 25y^2 - 90x - 50y - 25 = 0.$

13. Find an equation of the parabola with vertex (h,k) and focus $(h+p,k)$.

14. Find an equation of the parabola with vertex (h,k) and focus $(h,k+p)$.

15. Find an equation of the ellipse with center (h,k), foci $(h\pm c,k)$, and vertices $(h\pm a,k)$.

16. Find an equation of the ellipse with center (h,k), foci $(h,k\pm c)$, and vertices $(h,k\pm a)$.

17. Find an equation of the hyperbola with center (h,k), foci $(h\pm c,k)$, and vertices $(h\pm a,k)$.

18. Find an equation of the hyperbola with center (h,k), foci $(h,k\pm c)$, and vertices $(h,k\pm a)$.

8. *Rotation of axes*

If, in the coordinate plane with given x- and y-axes, new coordinate axes are chosen having the same origin O as the given ones (Figure 7.31), then we shall say that there has been a rotation of axes in the plane. If θ is the angle from the positive half Ox of the x-axis to the positive half Ox'

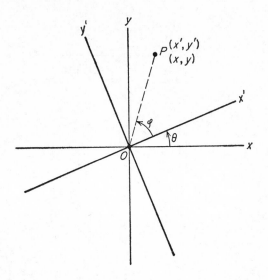

Figure 7.31

of the x'-axis, then we shall say that the new axes are formed by a rotation of axes through an angle θ.

Every point P in the plane now has two sets of coordinates, namely, (x,y) relative to the given axes and (x',y') relative to the new x'- and y'-axes. If ϕ is the angle from Ox' to OP, then by the definition of the trigonometric functions, $\sin \phi = y'/p$ and $\cos \phi = x'/p$, where $p = |OP|$. Thus

$$x' = p \cos \phi, \qquad y' = p \sin \phi.$$

The angle from Ox to OP is $\theta + \phi$, so for the same reason as above,

$$x = p \cos (\theta + \phi), \qquad y = p \sin (\theta + \phi).$$

These equations expand to the form

$$x = p \cos \theta \cos \phi - p \sin \theta \sin \phi$$

$$y = p \sin \theta \cos \phi + p \cos \theta \sin \phi$$

by use of the addition formulas of trigonometry. Replacing $p \cos \phi$ and $p \sin \phi$ by x' and y', respectively, we obtain

7.22
$$x = x' \cos \theta - y' \sin \theta$$

$$y = x' \sin \theta + y' \cos \theta.$$

These equations can be solved for x' and y' in the usual way, yielding

7.23
$$x' = x \cos \theta + y \sin \theta$$
$$y' = -x \sin \theta + y \cos \theta.$$

Equations 7.22 and 7.23 give the relationship between the original co-ordinates (x,y) of a point P and the new coordinates (x',y') of P after the axes have been rotated through an angle θ.

From a given equation in x and y we may derive an equation in x' and y' by use of 7.22. The graph of the given equation relative to the x- and y-axes must coincide with the graph of the new equation (in x' and y') relative to the x'- and y'-axes. We illustrate this process by an example.

Example 1. Let the given coordinate axes be rotated through an angle of 45°. Find the equation relative to the new x'- and y'-axes of the graph of the equation

$$y^2 - x^2 = 4$$

in the given coordinate system.

Solution: Since $\sin 45° = \cos 45° = \sqrt{2}/2$, **7.22** has the form

$$x = \frac{\sqrt{2}}{2} (x' - y'), \qquad y = \frac{\sqrt{2}}{2} (x' + y')$$

here. Thus the given equation becomes

$$\frac{2(x' + y')^2}{4} - \frac{2(x' - y')^2}{4} = 4,$$

or, upon simplification,

$$x'y' = 2.$$

The graph of the equation $x'y' = 2$ relative to the x'- and y'-axes coincides with

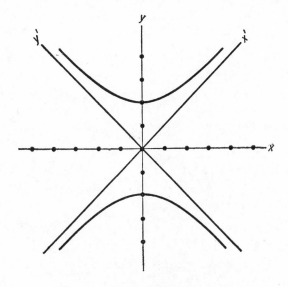

Figure 7.32

the graph of the equation $y^2 - x^2 = 4$ relative to the x- and y-axes, as is shown in Figure 7.32. We note that the new axes are just the asymptotes of the given hyperbola.

A rotation of axes may change an equation in x and y into an equation in x' and y' whose graph is known. Since the graph of this new equation relative to the x'- and y'-axes is the same as the graph of the given equation relative to the x- and y-axes, we also will know the graph of the given equation. An example of this is given now.

Example 2. Discuss the graph of the equation

$$x^2 - 2\sqrt{3}xy + 3y^2 - 16\sqrt{3}x - 16y = 0$$

by first rotating the axes through an angle of 30°.

Solution: We obtain from 7.22 with $\theta = 30°$

$$x = \frac{1}{2}(\sqrt{3}x' - y') \quad \text{and} \quad y = \frac{1}{2}(x' + \sqrt{3}y').$$

Substituting these values for x and y in the given equation, we get

$$\frac{(\sqrt{3}x' - y')^2}{4} - \frac{\sqrt{3}(\sqrt{3}x' - y')(x' + \sqrt{3}y')}{2} + \frac{3(x' + \sqrt{3}y')^2}{4}$$

$$- 8\sqrt{3}(\sqrt{3}x' - y') - 8(x' + \sqrt{3}y') = 0.$$

This may be simplified as follows:

$$(3x'^2 - 2\sqrt{3}x'y' + y'^2) - 2\sqrt{3}(\sqrt{3}x'^2 + 2x'y' - \sqrt{3}y'^2) + 3(x'^2 + 2\sqrt{3}x'y' + 3y'^2)$$

$$- (96x' - 32\sqrt{3}y') - (32x' + 32\sqrt{3}y') = 0,$$

or

$$16y'^2 - 128x' = 0,$$

or, finally,

$$y'^2 = 8x'.$$

We recognize this at once to be the equation of a parabola symmetric to the x'-axis. Its graph is sketched in Figure 7.33.

The process illustrated in this example may be done in general with any second-degree equation. That is, a proper rotation of axes will change the general second-degree equation

7.24 $$Ax^2 + Bxy + Cy^2 + Dx + Ey + F = 0$$

into a second-degree equation in x' and y' having no $x'y'$ term. Its graph can then be recognized from our previous work on the conic sections.

If we replace x and y in 7.24 by their values in terms of x' and y' given in 7.22, we obtain

$$A(x' \cos \theta - y' \sin \theta)^2 + B(x' \cos \theta - y' \sin \theta)(x' \sin \theta + y' \cos \theta)$$

$$+ C(x' \sin \theta + y' \cos \theta)^2 + D(x' \cos \theta - y' \sin \theta)$$

$$+ E(x' \sin \theta + y' \cos \theta) + F = 0.$$

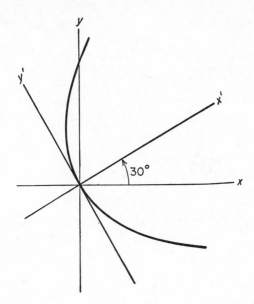

Figure 7.33

This equation has the form

7.25 $A'x'^2 + B'x'y' + C'y'^2 + D'x' + E'y' + F = 0,$

where one easily determines the coefficients of the various terms to be as follows:

$$A' = A \cos^2 \theta + B \sin \theta \cos \theta + C \sin^2 \theta,$$
$$B' = 2(C - A) \sin \theta \cos \theta + B(\cos^2 \theta - \sin^2 \theta),$$
$$C' = A \sin^2 \theta - B \sin \theta \cos \theta + C \cos^2 \theta,$$
$$D' = D \cos \theta + E \sin \theta,$$
$$E' = E \cos \theta - D \sin \theta.$$

Equation 7.25 will have no $x'y'$ term if we can select θ so that $B' = 0$, that is, so that

7.26 $2(C - A) \sin \theta \cos \theta + B(\cos^2 \theta - \sin^2 \theta) = 0.$

Since

$$2 \sin \theta \cos \theta = \sin 2\theta$$

and

$$\cos^2 \theta - \sin^2 \theta = \cos 2\theta,$$

this equation may be put in the form

$$(C - A) \sin 2\theta + B \cos 2\theta = 0,$$

or

7.27 $\cot 2\theta = \dfrac{A - C}{B}, \qquad \text{if } B \neq 0.$

If B had been equal to zero, no rotation would have been necessary. Thus a rotation through an angle θ satisfying 7.27 will eliminate the $x'y'$ term in 7.25. It is possible to solve 7.26 for $\tan \theta$, yielding

7.28 $\tan \theta = \dfrac{(C - A) \pm \sqrt{(C - A)^2 + B^2}}{B}, \quad B \neq 0.$

Either 7.27 or 7.28 can be used to obtain the angle of rotation θ.

Example 3. Discuss the graph of the equation

$$x^2 + 4xy - 2y^2 - 12 = 0.$$

Solution: We rotate the axes through an angle θ determined by Equation 7.28; then

$$\tan \theta = \frac{(-2 - 1) \pm \sqrt{(-2 - 1)^2 + 4^2}}{4},$$

and $\tan \theta = \frac{1}{2}$ or -2. Either angle will do, so we select an acute angle θ such that $\tan \theta = \frac{1}{2}$. Then $\sin \theta = 1/\sqrt{5}$, $\cos \theta = 2/\sqrt{5}$, and Equation 7.22 becomes

$$x = \frac{1}{\sqrt{5}}(2x' - y'), \qquad y = \frac{1}{\sqrt{5}}(x' + 2y').$$

A substitution of these equations in the original equation yields

$$\frac{(2x' - y')^2}{5} + \frac{4(2x' - y')(x' + 2y')}{5} - \frac{2(x' + 2y')^2}{5} - 12 = 0,$$

or, upon simplification,

$$2x'^2 - 3y'^2 - 12 = 0,$$

$$\frac{x'^2}{6} - \frac{y'^2}{4} = 1.$$

We recognize this as the equation of a hyperbola with transverse axis along the x'-axis. The angle of rotation θ is approximately $26°34'$.

■ ▨ ■ EXERCISES

Discuss and sketch the graph of each of the following equations.

1. $5x^2 + 4xy + 2y^2 - 6 = 0.$
2. $10x^2 + 6xy + 2y^2 - 11 = 0.$
3. $2x^2 - \sqrt{3}xy + y^2 - x + 2y - 6 = 0.$
4. $x^2 - xy + y^2 - 1 = 0.$
5. $3x^2 - 6xy - 5y^2 + 3 = 0.$
6. $4x^2 + 24xy - 3y^2 - 60 = 0.$
7. $5x^2 + 6xy - 3y^2 - 22x + 6y - 24 = 0.$
8. $9x^2 - 24xy + 16y^2 - 2x - 14y + 15 = 0.$

The definite integral

8

■ ■ ■ ■ ■   WE INTERRUPT OUR study of the derivative at this point to
lay a foundation for the other principal topic of the calculus, namely, the integral.   Before defining the integral,
we must state some further properties of the real number
system that will enter into this definition.

1. Upper and lower bounds of sets of real numbers

If a and b are real numbers and $a < b$, then the set of all
numbers between a and b has been called an interval and
has been designated by (a,b).   It will be convenient at
times in the work to follow to designate sets by letters
such as C, S, V, and so on.   For example, if C designates
the set of all rational numbers between 0 and 1, then the
number x is in C if and only if $0 < x < 1$ and $x = p/q$,
p and q integers with $q \neq 0$.

   If the square root process is applied in finding $\sqrt{2}$, we
get successively the numbers

$$1, \ 1.4, \ 1.41, \ 1.414, \ 1.4142, \cdots.$$

The collection S of numbers so obtained has the property
that if x is in S, then $x \leq \sqrt{2}$.   This illustrates part of
the following definition.

191

8.1 Definition. Let S be a set of real numbers. A number a is called
a *lower bound* of S if

$$a \leq x \quad \text{for every number } x \text{ in } S.$$

Similarly, a number b is called an *upper bound* of S if

$$b \geq x \quad \text{for every number } x \text{ in } S.$$

In the example just before 8.1, $\sqrt{2}$ is an upper bound of the set S since
$\sqrt{2} \geq x$ for every x in S. The number 1 is a lower bound of S since
$1 \leq x$ for every x in S. These are not the only upper and lower bounds
of S. Thus 2 is an upper bound and 0 is a lower bound of S.

As another example, let Q designate the set of all positive real numbers,
so that the number x is in Q if and only if $x > 0$. The set Q has -3 as a
lower bound, since $-3 \leq x$ for every positive number x. It is equally
true that -2, $-\frac{1}{2}$, and 0 are lower bounds of Q. A lower bound (or an
upper bound), when it exists, is never unique.

The set Q of all positive real numbers has no upper bound. If, on the
contrary, a were an upper bound of Q, then a would have to be a positive
number. However, the positive number $a + 1$ is greater than a. Hence
it clearly is not true that $a \geq x$ for every positive real number x. Thus a
is not an upper bound of Q, and it follows that Q has no upper bound.

The interval (a,b) is by definition the set of all numbers x such that
$a < x < b$. Clearly a is a lower bound and b is an upper bound of the
interval (a,b). Each number c less than a also is a lower bound of (a,b)
and each number d greater than b also is an upper bound of (a,b). If
the number c is in the interval (a,b), then so are the numbers $(a + c)/2$
and $(c + b)/2$, and

$$a < \frac{(a + c)}{2} < c < \frac{(c + b)}{2} < b.$$

Evidently c is neither a lower bound [since $(a + c)/2 < c$] nor an upper
bound [since $c < (b + c)/2$] of the interval (a,b). Thus, of all possible
lower bounds of (a,b), the greatest one is a. Similarly, b is the least of all
the upper bounds of (a,b).

8.2 Definition. Let S be a set of real numbers. A lower bound a of S
is called the *greatest lower bound* of S if no lower bound of S is greater than
a. An upper bound b of S is called the *least upper bound* of S if no upper
bound of S is less than b.

For example, of all the possible lower bounds of the set Q, of all positive
real numbers, 0 is the greatest lower bound. The set Q has no upper
bound, and therefore cannot have a least upper bound.

As another example, the interval $(-1,3)$ has -1 as its greatest lower
bound and 3 as its least upper bound.

An important property of the system of real numbers is as follows:

8.3 The completeness property. Every set S of real numbers that has a lower bound has a greatest lower bound, and every set S that has an upper bound has a least upper bound.

This is not a theorem to be proved; it is, rather, a defining property of the real number system. Together with the elementary algebraic and order properties discussed in the first chapter, Property 8.3 completely characterizes the system of real numbers.

We may use Property 8.3 to prove that the set I of positive integers has no upper bound. If, on the contrary, I has an upper bound, then I has a least upper bound b. Since $x \le b$ for every positive integer x, and since $x + 1$ is a positive integer whenever x is, $x + 1 \le b$ also. Hence $x \le b - 1$ for every positive integer x, and the set I has an upper bound $b - 1$ that is less than the least upper bound b of I. This contradiction shows that I can have no upper bound.

If the set S has least upper bound b, and if c is a number such that $c < b$, then necessarily there exists some number s in the set S such that $c < s \le b$. For if no such s existed, then c would be an upper bound of S less than the least upper bound. Similarly, if the set S has a greatest lower bound a and if $c > a$, then there exists some number s in S such that $c > s \ge a$.

■ ■ ■ EXERCISES

1. If S is a set of real numbers and b is a number such that (1) b is an upper bound of S, and (2) for every upper bound b' of S the relation $b \le b'$ holds, then b is a least upper bound (l.u.b.) of S. Prove that b is unique. (*Hint:* Assume that b and c are least upper bounds of S. Show that $b \le c$ and $c \le b$ both hold.) State a similar theorem for greatest lower bound (g.l.b.).

2. It is shown in the text that a is the g.l.b. and b is the l.u.b. of the open interval (a,b). Prove that a is the g.l.b. and b is the l.u.b. of the closed interval $[a,b]$ also.

3. Give examples of sets which contain their l.u.b. and which do not, and similarly for g.l.b.

4. If a set S contains a greatest element b, prove that b is the l.u.b. of S. State and prove a similar result for g.l.b.

5. Prove that every set consisting of a finite number $a_1, a_2 \cdots, a_n$ of real numbers contains its l.u.b. and g.l.b.

6. If $c > 0$ and S is the set of all multiples $c, 2c, 3c, \cdots, nc, \cdots$ of c, prove that S has no upper bound, and hence no l.u.b.

7. Use the preceding exercise to prove the *Archimedean Principle:* Let c and d be any numbers with $c > 0$. Then there exists some positive integer n such that $nc > d$. Illustrate this principle in case:
   (a) $c = 2$, $d = 131$; (b) $c = 10^{-6}$, $d = 10^6$.

8. Let S be the set consisting of the rational numbers $1/2$, $2/3$, $3/4$, $4/5$ $\cdots$, $n/(n+1)$, $\cdots$. Prove that 1 is the l.u.b. of S. (*Hint:* If $0 < c$ < 1, use Exercise 7 to show that there exists a positive integer m such that $c < m/(m+1)$.)

9. Let the set S consist of the reciprocals of all positive integers: 1, $1/2$, $1/3$ $1/4$, $\cdots$, $1/n$, $\cdots$. Prove that 0 is the g.l.b. of S. (*Hint:* If $c > 0$ use Exercise 7 to prove that there exists a positive integer n such that $c > 1/n$.)

10. Prove that if a and b are any positive real numbers with $a < b$, then there exists some rational number r between a and b, $a < r < b$. (*Hint* Select a positive integer n such that $na > 1$ and $n(b - a) > 1$. Then select a positive integer m such that $m > na$ and $m - 1 \leq na$. Show that $a < m/n < b$.)

11. Let S be the set of all rational numbers less than a given real number b Use Exercise 10 to prove that b is the l.u.b. of S.

12. If the number $a > 1$, then show that the set of all powers of a, a, a^2, a^3 $\cdots$, a^n, $\cdots$, has no upper bound. Hence prove that if $b > 0$, then $a^{-n} < b$ for some integer $n > 0$.

2. *Area of a region under a curve*

Associated with each rectangle is a number called the "area" that in some way measures the size of the rectangle. This area is defined to be the product of the length and the width of the rectangle. A triangle also has an area, defined to be half the product of the lengths of the base and the altitude. Since any polygon can be subdivided into triangles, as indicated in Figure 8.1, the area of a polygon can be defined to be the sum

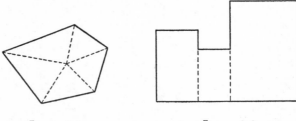

Figure 8.1   Figure 8.2

of the areas of the triangles into which it is subdivided. It can be proved that the area so obtained is the same no matter how the polygon is divided up into triangles. Those polygons which are made up of rectangles are of special importance in the work to follow. They will be called *rectangular polygons* (Figure 8.2). The area of a rectangular polygon is just the sum of the areas of the rectangles into which it is subdivided.

If a region of the plane has a curved boundary, then it is not clear how one goes about defining its area. Actually, it is not even clear that every bounded region of the plane has an area. In this section, we shall investigate the problem of finding the areas of certain regions with curved boundaries.

Let f be a function that is continuous and nonnegative (i.e., $f(x) \geq 0$) in an interval $[a,b]$. We shall call the region R (Figure 8.3) in the co-

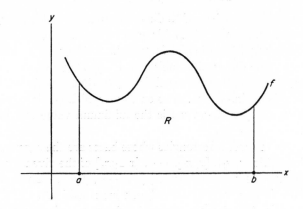

Figure 8.3

ordinate plane bounded by the graph of f, the lines $x = a$ and $x = b$, and the x-axis, *the region under the graph of f from a to b.*

We wish to associate with this region R a number A to be called the area of R. The area A we assign to R should be consistent with the area of a polygon in the following sense: the area of R should be a number no less than the area of a polygon contained in R and no more than the area of a polygon completely containing R. We shall see in a later section that there is only one number A which has this property.

Before discussing the problem of finding the area of R, let us define what is meant by a partition of the interval $[a,b]$. By a partition of $[a,b]$ we mean a subdivision of $[a,b]$ into smaller intervals. If x_0, x_1, x_2, x_3, x_4, x_5

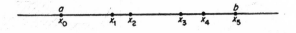

Figure 8.4

are distinct numbers in the interval $[a,b]$, with $x_0 = a$ and $x_5 = b$, as indicated geometrically in Figure 8.4, then $[a,b]$ is partitioned into five subintervals by these numbers, namely

$$[x_0,x_1], \ [x_1,x_2], \ [x_2,x_3], \ [x_3,x_4], \ [x_4,x_5].$$

We shall use the notation $[x_0, x_1, x_2, x_3, x_4, x_5]$ to designate this partition. More generally, if $x_0 = a$ and $x_n = b$, and

$$x_0 < x_1 < x_2 < \cdots < x_{n-1} < x_n,$$

then

$$[x_0, x_1, \cdots, x_{n-1}, x_n]$$

designates the partition of $[a,b]$ into the n subintervals

$$[x_0, x_1], [x_1, x_2], \cdots, [x_{n-1}, x_n].$$

Returning to the problem of finding the area of R, let $[x_0, x_1, \cdots, x_n]$ be any partition of $[a,b]$. Since f is continuous in $[a,b]$ by assumption, we can select a number u_1 in the first subinterval $[x_0, x_1]$ so that $f(u_1)$ is the minimum value of f in this subinterval (by 6.2); and we can select a number u_2 in the second subinterval $[x_1, x_2]$ so that $f(u_2)$ is the minimum value of f in this subinterval; and so on to u_n, which is selected in the nth subinterval $[x_{n-1}, x_n]$ so that $f(u_n)$ is the minimum value of f in this last subinterval.

Next, let us construct n rectangles whose bases are the segments defined by the subintervals $[x_0, x_1], [x_1, x_2], \cdots, [x_{n-1}, x_n]$ of the given partition and whose respective heights are $f(u_1), f(u_2), \cdots, f(u_n)$. These rectangles taken together form a rectangular polygon inscribed in R.

This process is illustrated in Figure 8.5 for a partition $[x_0, x_1, x_2, x_3, x_4, x_5]$ of $[a,b]$ into 5 subintervals. In this example note that $u_2 = x_1$, $u_3 = x_3$, and $u_4 = x_4$, whereas u_1 and u_5 are interior to the first and fifth subintervals, respectively. The area of the rectangular polygon inscribed under the graph of f from a to b in Figure 8.5 is

$$f(u_1)(x_1 - x_0) + f(u_2)(x_2 - x_1) + f(u_3)(x_3 - x_2)$$
$$+ f(u_4)(x_4 - x_3) + f(u_5)(x_5 - x_4).$$

In general, the area S of the rectangular polygon defined by the partition $[x_0, x_1, \cdots, x_{n-1}, x_n]$ of $[a,b]$ is given by

$$S = f(u_1)(x_1 - x_0) + f(u_2)(x_2 - x_1) + \cdots + f(u_n)(x_n - x_{n-1}).$$

Since this rectangular polygon is completely contained in the given region

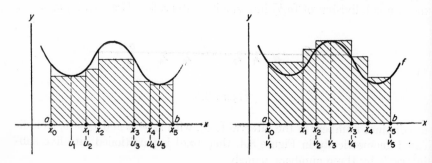

Figure 8.5   Figure 8.6

R, S cannot exceed the area A of R.   Thus, if I is the set of all areas S of rectangular polygons inscribed under the graph of f from a to b, the area A of the region R (if it exists) must be an *upper bound* of the set I.

In a similar way, we can associate with the partition $[x_0, x_1, \cdots, x_{n-1}, x_n]$ of $[a,b]$ a rectangular polygon circumscribed about R.   Thus, choose v_1 so that $f(v_1)$ is the maximum value of f in $[x_0, x_1]$; choose v_2 so that $f(v_2)$ is the maximum value of f in $[x_1, x_2]$; and finally choose v_n so that $f(v_n)$ is the maximum value of f in $[x_{n-1}, x_n]$.

The same partition of $[a,b]$ used in Figure 8.5 is used in Figure 8.6 to illustrate the rectangular polygon circumscribed about the region R.   The area of this polygon is

$$f(v_1)(x_1 - x_0) + f(v_2)(x_2 - x_1) + f(v_3)(x_3 - x_2)$$
$$+ f(v_4)(x_4 - x_3) + f(v_5)(x_5 - x_4).$$

More generally, the area T of the rectangular polygon associated with the partition $[x_0, x_1, \cdots, x_{n-1}, x_n]$ and circumscribed about the region R is given by

$$T = f(v_1)(x_1 - x_0) + f(v_2)(x_2 - x_1) + \cdots + f(v_n)(x_n - x_{n-1}).$$

Since the rectangular polygon of area T completely contains the region R, the area A of R cannot exceed T.   If J is the set of all areas T of rectangular polygons circumscribed about the graph of f from a to b, the area A of the region R under the graph of f from a to b (if it exists) must be a *lower bound* of the set J.

It is clear that for each number S in I and T in J,

$$S \leq T,$$

since each rectangular polygon inscribed in the region R (and of area S) is contained in every rectangular polygon circumscribed about the region R (and of area T).   Thus every number of the set I is a lower bound of the set J and every number of the set J is an upper bound of the set I.   Hence, by the completeness property, the set I has a least upper bound A_1, and the set J has a greatest lower bound A_2.   Since each T in J is an upper bound of I, whereas A_1 is the least upper bound, $A_1 \leq T$ for every T in J. Therefore A_1 is a lower bound of J.   Since A_2 is the greatest lower bound of J, necessarily

$$A_1 \leq A_2.$$

We have already decided that the area A of the region R under consideration (Figure 8.3) must be an upper bound of the set I and a lower bound of the set J.   In view of the choice of A_1 and A_2 as the least upper bound of I and the greatest lower bound of J, respectively, we have

$$A_1 \leq A \leq A_2.$$

If it happens that $A_1 = A_2$, then we may say that the region R has one (and only one) area $A = A_1 = A_2$.   We shall establish later on in this chapter that if the function f is continuous in the interval $[a,b]$, such as has been considered in this section, it is actually the case that $A_1 = A_2$. Thus, for a function f continuous in the interval $[a,b]$, the area under the graph of f from a to b may be defined to be the common least upper bound of I and greatest lower bound of J.

The next section is concerned with essentially the same ideas as this, but from a nongeometric standpoint, i.e., one which removes the restriction that the function f should be nonnegative in $[a,b]$.

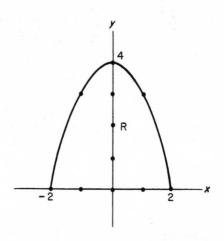

Figure 8.7

Example 1. If $f(x) = 4 - x^2$, let R be the region under the graph of f from -2 to 2 (Figure 8.7).

(a) Compute S and T for the partition $[-2,-1/2,1,2]$ of $[-2,2]$.
(b) Compute S and T for the partition of $[-2,2]$ into 8 subintervals of equal length.

Solution: (a) The function f is increasing in $[-2,0]$ and decreasing in $[0,2]$. Thus $f(-2)$ is the minimum value of f in $[-2,-1/2]$, $f(1)$ is the minimum value of f in $[-1/2,1]$, and $f(2)$ is the minimum value of f in $[1,2]$. Hence

$$S = f(-2)(-\tfrac{1}{2} + 2) + f(1)(1 + \tfrac{1}{2}) + f(2)(2 - 1) = \tfrac{9}{2}.$$

In a similar way, we find

$$T = f(-\tfrac{1}{2})(-\tfrac{1}{2} + 2) + f(0)(1 + \tfrac{1}{2}) + f(1)(2 - 1) = \tfrac{11\frac{7}{8}}{}.$$

(b) The partition of $[-2,2]$ into 8 equal subintervals is $[-2,-3/2,-1,-1/2, 0,1/2,1,3/2,2]$. For this partition,

$$S = \tfrac{1}{2}f(-2) + \tfrac{1}{2}f(-\tfrac{3}{2}) + \tfrac{1}{2}f(-1) + \tfrac{1}{2}f(-\tfrac{1}{2}) + \tfrac{1}{2}f(\tfrac{1}{2}) + \tfrac{1}{2}f(1) + \tfrac{1}{2}f(\tfrac{3}{2}) + \tfrac{1}{2}f(2) = \tfrac{17}{2}.$$

$$T = \tfrac{1}{2}[f(-\tfrac{3}{2}) + f(-1) + f(-\tfrac{1}{2}) + f(0) + f(0) + f(\tfrac{1}{2}) + f(\tfrac{3}{2})] = S + f(0) = \tfrac{25}{2}.$$

Example 2. Let $f(x) = x^2$ and R be the region under the graph of f from a to b, where $0 \le a < b$. Find S and T for the partition $[x_0,x_1,\cdots,x_{n-1},x_n]$ of $[a,b]$, and show that $S < (b^3 - a^3)/3 < T$.

Solution: Since f is increasing in $[a,b]$, the minimum value of f is assumed at the left-hand endpoint and the maximum value at the right-hand endpoint of any subinterval of $[a,b]$.   Thus

$$S = x_0^2(x_1 - x_0) + x_1^2(x_2 - x_1) + \cdots + x_{n-2}^2(x_{n-1} - x_{n-2}) + x_{n-1}^2(x_n - x_{n-1}),$$

$$T = x_1^2(x_1 - x_0) + x_2^2(x_2 - x_1) + \cdots + x_{n-1}^2(x_{n-1} - x_{n-2}) + x_n^2(x_n - x_{n-1}).$$

Since $0 \le x_0 < x_1$, we have $x_0^2 \le x_0 x_1 < x_1^2$.   Thus

$$x_0^2 + x_0^2 + x_0^2 < x_0^2 + x_0 x_1 + x_1^2 < x_1^2 + x_1^2 + x_1^2,$$

or

$$x_0^2 < \frac{x_0^2 + x_0 x_1 + x_1^2}{3} < x_1^2.$$

In a similar way, we may show that for each integer $i = 1, 2, \cdots, n$,

$$x_{i-1}^2 < \frac{x_{i-1}^2 + x_{i-1}x_i + x_i^2}{3} < x_i^2.$$

Since

$$(x_{i-1}^2 + x_{i-1}x_i + x_i^2)(x_i - x_{i-1}) = x_i^3 - x_{i-1}^3,$$

we also have

$$x_{i-1}^2(x_i - x_{i-1}) < \frac{x_i^3 - x_{i-1}^3}{3} < x_i^2(x_i - x_{i-1})$$

for each integer $i = 1, 2, \cdots, n$.   If we add up the corresponding members of the n inequalities

$$x_0^2(x_1 - x_0) < \frac{x_1^3 - x_0^3}{3} < x_1^2(x_1 - x_0),$$

$$x_1^2(x_2 - x_1) < \frac{x_2^3 - x_1^3}{3} < x_2^2(x_2 - x_1),$$

. . . .

. . . .

$$x_{n-2}^2(x_{n-1} - x_{n-2}) < \frac{x_{n-1}^3 - x_{n-2}^3}{3} < x_{n-1}^2(x_{n-1} - x_{n-2}),$$

$$x_{n-1}^2(x_n - x_{n-1}) < \frac{x_n^3 - x_{n-1}^3}{3} < x_n^2(x_n - x_{n-1}),$$

we obtain

$$S < \tfrac{1}{3}(x_1^3 - x_0^3 + x_2^3 - x_1^3 + \cdots + x_{n-1}^3 - x_{n-2}^3 + x_n^3 - x_{n-1}^3) < T.$$

The terms of the inner member of the inequality cancel out in pairs except for $-x_0^3$ and x_n^3, leaving

$$S < \frac{x_n^3 - x_0^3}{3} < T.$$

If we recall that $a = x_0$ and $b = x_n$, we have shown that $S < (b^3 - a^3)/3 < T$ as desired.

■ ■ ■ EXERCISES

1. If $f(x) = x^2$, then f is increasing in the interval $[2,4]$.
   Sketch the region R under the graph of f from 2 to 4.

(a) Compute the areas S and T of rectangular polygons, inscribed in R and circumscribed about R, associated with the partition $[2,\frac{5}{2},3,\frac{7}{2},4]$ of $[2,4]$.

(b) Compute S and T for the partition of $[2,4]$ into 8 subintervals of equal length.

2. If $f(x) = x^3$, let R be the region under the graph of f from 1 to 2. Sketch the region R.

(a) Compute S and T for the partition $[1,2]$ of $[1,2]$.

(b) Compute S and T for the partition $[1,\frac{3}{2},2]$ of $[1,2]$.

(c) Compute S and T for the partition of $[1,2]$ into 4 subintervals of equal length.

3. If $f(x) = 1 - x^3$, let R be the region bounded by the graph of f and the coordinate axes. Sketch the region R.

(a) Compute S and T for the partition $[0,\frac{1}{2},1]$ of $[0,1]$.

(b) Compute S and T for the partition of $[0,1]$ into 8 subintervals of equal length.

4. If $f(x) = 1/x$, let R be the region under the graph of f from $\frac{1}{2}$ to 2. Sketch the region R (use a large unit segment).

(a) Compute S and T for the partition of $[\frac{1}{2},2]$ into 6 subintervals of equal length.

(b) Compute S and T for the partition of $[\frac{1}{2},2]$ into 12 subintervals of equal length.

5. If $f(x) = 1/x^2$, let R be the region under the graph of f from 1 to 4. Sketch the region R (use a large unit segment).

(a) Compute S and T for the partition $[1,2,3,4]$ of $[1,4]$.

(b) Compute S and T for the partition of $[1,4]$ into 6 subintervals of equal length.

6. If $f(x) = b$, a positive constant, and R is the region under the graph of f from 0 to a, then R is a rectangle. Show that S and T equal the area of R for every partition of $[0,a]$.

7. Let $f(x) = x$ and R be the trapezoid under the graph of f from a to b, $0 < a < b$. Find S and T for the partition $[x_0,x_1,\cdots,x_{n-1},x_n]$ of $[a,b]$, and show that $S < (b^2 - a^2)/2 < T$. (*Hint:* Follow Example 2. Note that $(b^2 - a^2)/2$ is the area of the trapezoid.)

8. Let $f(x) = x^3$ and R be the region under the graph of f from a to b, where $0 \le a < b$. By the methods of Example 2, show that for any inscribed rectangular polygon of area S and any circumscribed rectangular polygon of area T, $S < (b^4 - a^4)/4 < T$. (*Hint:* For any numbers p and q, where $0 \le p < q$, $p^3 < (p^3 + p^2q + pq^2 + q^3)/4 < q^3$. Also, $(q - p)\cdot(p^3 + p^2q + pq^2 + q^3) = q^4 - p^4$.) Taking $(b^4 - a^4)/4$ as the area of R, what does this give for the area of R in Exercise 2?

9. Let $f(x) = 1/x^2$ and R be the region under the graph of f from a to b, where $0 < a < b$, and let $[x_0,x_1,\cdots,x_{n-1},x_n]$ be a partition of $[a,b]$.

(a) Write down the sums S and T associated with this partition.

(b) Show that for each integer i between 1 and n,

$$\frac{1}{x_i^2} < \frac{1}{x_i x_{i-1}} < \frac{1}{x_{i-1}^2},$$

and hence that

$$\frac{1}{x_i^2}(x_i - x_{i-1}) < \frac{1}{x_{i-1}} - \frac{1}{x_i} < \frac{1}{x_{i-1}^2}(x_i - x_{i-1}).$$

Then show that

$$S < \frac{1}{a} - \frac{1}{b} < T.$$

(c) Since $1/a - 1/b$ is an upper bound of the set I of all S and a lower bound of the set J of all T, it might be called the area of R. What does this give for the area of R in Exercise 5 above?

10. Let $f(x) = 1/x^3$ and R be the region under the graph of f from a to b, where $0 < a < b$, and let $[x_0,x_1,\cdots,x_{n-1},x_n]$ be a partition of $[a,b]$.
   (a) Write down the sums S and T associated with this partition.
   (b) Using methods similar to those of the preceding problem, show that

$$S < \frac{1}{2}\left(\frac{1}{a^2} - \frac{1}{b^2}\right) < T.$$

   (c) What would you say the area of the region under the graph of f from $\frac{1}{2}$ to 2 is?

3. Upper and lower integrals

We have previously defined a partition of an interval $[a,b]$ to be a division of $[a,b]$ into subintervals

$$[x_0,x_1], \quad [x_1,x_2], \quad \cdots, \quad [x_{n-1},x_n]$$

where

$$a = x_0 < x_1 < x_2 < \cdots < x_{n-1} < x_n = b.$$

This partition of $[a,b]$ is designated $[x_0,x_1, \cdots ,x_{n-1},x_n]$. For convenience, we shall also use italic letters such as p and q to designate partitions of intervals.

Let f be a function that is continuous in an interval $[a,b]$, and let

$$p = [x_0, x_1, \cdots , x_{n-1}, x_n]$$

be a partition of $[a,b]$ into n subintervals. Select a number u_1 in the first subinterval $[x_0,x_1]$ of p so that $f(u_1)$ is the minimum value of f in $[x_0,x_1]$; select a number u_2 in the second subinterval $[x_1,x_2]$ of p so that $f(u_2)$ is the minimum value of f in $[x_1,x_2]$; and so on, finally selecting a number u_n in the last subinterval $[x_{n-1},x_n]$ of p so that $f(u_n)$ is the minimum value of f in $[x_{n-1},x_n]$. Thus the continuity of f in $[a,b]$ allows us to choose $u_1, u_2, \cdots ,$ u_n such that:

$$x_0 \leq u_1 \leq x_1 \quad \text{and} \quad f(u_1) \leq f(x) \quad \text{for every } x \text{ in } [x_0,x_1];$$

$$x_1 \leq u_2 \leq x_2 \quad \text{and} \quad f(u_2) \leq f(x) \quad \text{for every } x \text{ in } [x_1,x_2];$$

. . . .

$$x_{n-1} \leq u_n \leq x_n \quad \text{and} \quad f(u_n) \leq f(x) \quad \text{for every } x \text{ in } [x_{n-1},x_n].$$

We now define the *lower sum* S_p of f relative to the partition p of $[a,b]$ to be

8.4 $\quad S_p = f(u_1)(x_1 - x_0) + f(u_2)(x_2 - x_1) + \cdots + f(u_n)(x_n - x_{n-1}).$

The geometric meaning of S_p for a nonnegative function f is illustrated in Figure 8.5 where S_p is the area of a rectangular polygon inscribed under the graph of f from a to b.

Similarly, there is associated with each partition $p = [x_0, x_1, \cdots, x_{n-1}, x_n]$ of $[a,b]$ the *upper sum* T_p of f defined by

8.5 $\quad T_p = f(v_1)(x_1 - x_0) + f(v_2)(x_2 - x_1) + \cdots + f(v_n)(x_n - x_{n-1}).$

The numbers $v_1, v_2, \cdots, v_n$ are chosen, respectively, in the subintervals $[x_0, x_1], [x_1, x_2], \cdots, [x_{n-1}, x_n]$ of p so that $f(v_1), f(v_2), \cdots, f(v_n)$ are the maximum values of f over these subintervals.

Thus

$$x_0 \leq v_1 \leq x_1 \quad \text{and} \quad f(v_1) \geq f(x) \quad \text{for every } x \text{ in } [x_0, x_1];$$
$$x_1 \leq v_2 \leq x_2 \quad \text{and} \quad f(v_2) \geq f(x) \quad \text{for every } x \text{ in } [x_1, x_2];$$
$$\cdots \cdots \cdots \cdots \cdots \cdots \cdots \cdots \cdots \cdots$$
$$x_{n-1} \leq v_n \leq x_n \quad \text{and} \quad f(v_n) \geq f(x) \quad \text{for every } x \text{ in } [x_{n-1}, x_n].$$

If f is nonnegative, T_p is the area of a rectangular polygon circumscribed over the graph of f from a to b as illustrated in Figure 8.6.

Since $f(u_1) \leq f(v_1)$, $f(u_2) \leq f(v_2)$, and so on, each term of S_p is less than or equal to the corresponding term of T_p, and therefore

$$S_p \leq T_p.$$

If a number u is chosen in $[a,b]$ so that $f(u)$ is the minimum value of f in $[a,b]$, then $f(u) \leq f(u_1)$, $f(u) \leq f(u_2)$, $\cdots$, $f(u) \leq f(u_n)$ since $f(u_1)$, $f(u_2)$, $\cdots$, $f(u_n)$ are minimum values of f in subintervals of $[a,b]$ whereas $f(u)$ is the minimum value of f in the whole interval $[a,b]$. Hence, by 8.4,

$$S_p \geq f(u)(x_1 - x_0) + f(u)(x_2 - x_1) + \cdots + f(u)(x_n - x_{n-1}).$$

Factoring $f(u)$ from each term of the right side of this inequality, and observing that

$$(x_1 - x_0) + (x_2 - x_1) + \cdots + (x_n - x_{n-1}) = x_n - x_0 = b - a,$$

we obtain the inequality

$$S_p \geq f(u)(b - a).$$

Similarly, if $f(v)$ is the maximum value of f in $[a,b]$ we may prove that

$$T_p \leq f(v)(b - a).$$

We collect these facts in the following theorem.

8.6 Theorem. If $f(u)$ and $f(v)$ are, respectively, the minimum and maximum values of the function f in the interval $[a,b]$, then the lower sum

S_p and the upper sum T_p of f relative to each partition p of $[a,b]$ satisfy the inequality

$$f(u)(b - a) \leq S_p \leq T_p \leq f(v)(b - a).$$

Let U designate the set of all lower sums of f over $[a,b]$, obtained from every possible partition p of $[a,b]$. Each number S_p in the set U is less than or equal to the number $f(v)(b - a)$ by the theorem above. In other words, $f(v)(b - a)$ is an *upper bound* of the set U. Since the set U has an upper bound, U has a *least upper bound* by the completeness property of the real number system.

Similarly, if V designates the set of all upper sums of f over $[a,b]$, then V has a lower bound $f(u)(b - a)$ by the previous theorem. Therefore the set V has a *greatest lower bound*, and we are able to make the following definition.

8.7 Definition. Let the function f be continuous in the interval $[a,b]$. The *lower integral* of f from a to b, designated by

$$\underline{\int_a^b} f$$

is defined to be the least upper bound of the set U of all lower sums of f over $[a,b]$. The *upper integral* of f from a to b, designated by

$$\overline{\int_a^b} f$$

is defined to be the greatest lower bound of the set V of all upper sums of f over $[a,b]$.

A consequence of this definition is that

$$S_p \leq \underline{\int_a^b} f \quad \text{and} \quad T_p \geq \overline{\int_a^b} f$$

for every partition p of $[a,b]$.

If $f(u)$ and $f(v)$ are the minimum and maximum values, respectively, of the function f in the interval $[a,b]$, then we have as an easy corollary of 8.6 that

8.8 $$f(u)(b - a) \leq \underline{\int_a^b} f \leq f(v)(b - a),$$

and similarly for the upper integral.

Although the lower and upper integrals of a function f from a to b are not defined by 8.7 if $b = a$, it is convenient to define these integrals to be zero, i.e.,

$$\underline{\int_a^a} f = 0, \qquad \overline{\int_a^a} f = 0.$$

We certainly suspect from their definitions that the lower integral of f from a to b cannot exceed the upper integral. While this is true, the proof is rather involved and is put off to the next section.

Example 1. If $f(x) = 1/(x^2 + 1)$ and $p = [-1,0,1,3/2,3]$, find S_p and T_p.

Solution: The function f is increasing in the interval $[-1,0]$ and decreasing in the interval $[0,3]$. With this in mind, we have

$$S_p = f(-1)(0 + 1) + f(1)(1 - 0) + f(\tfrac{3}{2})(\tfrac{3}{2} - 1) + f(3)(3 - \tfrac{3}{2})$$
$$= \tfrac{1}{2} + \tfrac{1}{2} + \tfrac{2}{13} + \tfrac{3}{20} \doteq 1.30.$$
$$T_p = f(0)(0 + 1) + f(0)(1 - 0) + f(1)(\tfrac{3}{2} - 1) + f(\tfrac{3}{2})(3 - \tfrac{3}{2})$$
$$= 1 + 1 + \tfrac{1}{4} + \tfrac{6}{13} \doteq 2.71.$$

Example 2. Let $f(x) = x^2$ and $0 \le a < b$. It is shown in Example 2 of the preceding section that

$$S_p < \frac{b^3 - a^3}{3} < T_p$$

for every partition p of $[a,b]$. Prove that

$$\underline{\int_a^b} f = \overline{\int_a^b} f = \frac{b^3 - a^3}{3}.$$

Solution: Since $(b^3 - a^3)/3$ is an upper bound of the set U of all lower sums of f over $[a,b]$, the least upper bound of the set U is less than or equal to $(b^3 - a^3)/3$; that is

$$\underline{\int_a^b} f \le \frac{b^3 - a^3}{3}.$$

Similarly,

$$\frac{b^3 - a^3}{3} \le \overline{\int_a^b} f.$$

Thus, the inequality

(1) $$S_p \le \underline{\int_a^b} f \le \frac{b^3 - a^3}{3} \le \overline{\int_a^b} f \le T_p$$

holds for every partition p of $[a,b]$.

If we select p as the regular partition of $[a,b]$ into n subintervals (see the exercises below) and let $h = (b - a)/n$, then

$$S_p = h(x_0^2 + x_1^2 + \cdots + x_{n-2}^2 + x_{n-1}^2),$$
$$T_p = h(x_1^2 + x_2^2 + \cdots + x_{n-1}^2 + x_n^2),$$

and

$$T_p - S_p = h(x_n^2 - x_0^2) = \frac{(b - a)(b^2 - a^2)}{n}.$$

Can $\underline{\int_a^b} f \ne \overline{\int_a^b} f$? If these were unequal, then

$$d = \overline{\int_a^b} f - \underline{\int_a^b} f > 0.$$

Select the integer n so that

$$nd > (b - a)(b^2 - a^2).$$

For this integer n, the regular partition p of $[a,b]$ into n subintervals is such that

(2) $$T_p - S_p = \frac{(b-a)(b^2-a^2)}{n} < d.$$

However, by (1) above,

(3) $$T_p - S_p \geq \int_a^b f - \int_{\underline{a}}^b f = d.$$

Since (2) and (3) are contradictory, our assumption that the lower and upper integrals are unequal is wrong. Thus they are equal, and by (1) they must equal $(b^3 - a^3)/3$.

■ ■ ■ EXERCISES

Find S_p and T_p for each of the following functions and partitions p. (You may approximate your answers to two decimal places.)

1. $f(x) = 1 - x^2$, $p = [0,\frac{1}{2},1,\frac{3}{2},2]$.
2. $f(x) = 1 - x^2$, $p = [0,\frac{1}{4},\frac{3}{4},1,\frac{7}{4},2]$.
3. $f(x) = 2x^2$, $p = [-1,-\frac{1}{2},0,\frac{1}{2},1]$.
4. $f(x) = 2x^2$, $p = [-1,-\frac{5}{8},\frac{1}{8},\frac{1}{2},\frac{3}{4},1]$.
5. $f(x) = x^3$, $p = [-2,-\frac{5}{3},-\frac{4}{3},-1,-\frac{2}{3},-\frac{1}{3},0]$.
6. $f(x) = x^3$, $p = [-2,-\frac{3}{2},-\frac{5}{4},-1,-\frac{1}{2},-\frac{1}{4},0]$.
7. $f(x) = 1/x$, $p = [-4,-3,-2,-1]$.
8. $f(x) = 1/x$, $p = [-4,-\frac{7}{2},-\frac{13}{4},-3,-\frac{5}{2},-\frac{3}{2},-1]$.
9. $f(x) = 1/x^2$, $p = [1,\frac{3}{2},2,\frac{5}{2},3,\frac{7}{2},4]$.
10. $f(x) = 1/x^2$, $p = [1,\frac{5}{4},\frac{7}{4},\frac{9}{4},3,\frac{13}{4},4]$.

A partition $p = [x_0,x_1,\cdots,x_{n-1},x_n]$ of $[a,b]$ is called *regular* if each subinterval of p has the same length, i.e., $x_1 - x_0 = x_2 - x_1 = \cdots = x_n - x_{n-1}$. The length of each subinterval of p is $(b-a)/n$.

11. Let f be continuous and increasing in the interval $[a,b]$ and let p be the regular partition of $[a,b]$ into n subintervals. Show that if $h = (b-a)/n$, then

$$S_p = h[f(a) + f(a+h) + f(a+2h) + \cdots + f(a+(n-1)h)],$$
$$T_p = h[f(a+h) + f(a+2h) + \cdots + f(a+nh)].$$

Then prove that

$$T_p - S_p = h[f(b) - f(a)].$$

12. Let f be continuous and decreasing in the interval $[a,b]$ and let p be the regular partition of $[a,b]$ into n subintervals. Find S_p and T_p, and show that $T_p - S_p = h[f(a) - f(b)]$ where $h = (b-a)/n$.

13. If $f(x) = x$, then it is shown in Exercise 7 of Section 2 that

$$S_p < (b^2 - a^2)/2 < T_p$$

for every partition p of $[a,b]$.   Prove that

$$\int_{\underline{a}}^{b} f = \int_{a}^{\overline{b}} f = \frac{b^2 - a^2}{2}.$$

14. Let $f(x) = x^3$ and $0 \leq a < b$ as in Exercise 8 of Section 2.   It may be shown, as indicated there, that $S_p < (b^4 - a^4)/4 < T_p$ for every partition p of $[a,b]$.   Prove that

$$\int_{\underline{a}}^{b} f = \int_{a}^{\overline{b}} f = \frac{b^4 - a^4}{4}.$$

15. Let $f(x) = 1/x^2$ and $0 < a < b$ as in Exercise 9 of Section 2.   It may be shown, as indicated there, that $S_p < 1/a - 1/b < T_p$ for every partition p of $[a,b]$.   Prove that

$$\int_{\underline{a}}^{b} f = \int_{a}^{\overline{b}} f = \frac{1}{a} - \frac{1}{b}.$$

16. Let $f(x) = 1/x^3$ and $0 < a < b$ as in Exercise 10 of Section 2.   Prove that

$$\int_{\underline{a}}^{b} f = \int_{a}^{\overline{b}} f = \frac{1}{2}\left(\frac{1}{a^2} - \frac{1}{b^2}\right).$$

17. Write out the proof of 8.8.

18. If the functions f and g are continuous in $[a,b]$ and if $f(x) \leq g(x)$ for every x in $[a,b]$, prove that

$$\int_{\underline{a}}^{b} f \leq \int_{\underline{a}}^{b} g,$$

and similarly for the upper integral.

4. Equality of the upper and lower integrals

This section will be devoted to the proof that the upper and lower integrals of a continuous function f are equal.

Given a partition p of $[a,b]$, we may further partition the subintervals of p, thereby obtaining a *refinement* of p.   For example, if

$$p = [1, 2, 3, 4], \qquad q = [1, \tfrac{3}{2}, 2, \tfrac{7}{3}, 3, \tfrac{13}{4}, \tfrac{15}{4}, 4],$$

then q is a refinement of p.

Let $p = [x_0, x_1, \cdots, x_n]$ be a partition of $[a,b]$ and q be a refinement of p that has exactly one more subinterval than p.   Thus, one of the subintervals of p is partitioned into two subintervals in q and the remaining subintervals of p and q are the same.   For convenience, let $[x_0, x_1]$, the first subinterval of p, be partitioned into two subintervals, say $[x_0, x]$ and $[x, x_1]$, in q.   Hence $q = [x_0, x, x_1, \cdots, x_n]$ has $n + 1$ subintervals.

By definition,

$$S_p = f(u_1)(x_1 - x_0) + f(u_2)(x_2 - x_1) + \cdots + f(u_n)(x_n - x_{n-1}),$$

$$S_q = f(u')(x - x_0) + f(u'')(x_1 - x) + f(u_2)(x_2 - x_1) + \cdots + f(u_n)(x_n - x_{n-1}),$$

where each u_i, u', and u'' is chosen as usual.   The last $n - 1$ terms in S_p and S_q are identical, and therefore

$$S_q - S_p = f(u')(x - x_0) + f(u'')(x_1 - x) - f(u_1)(x_1 - x_0).$$

Since $f(u')$ is the least value of f in $[x_0,x]$ and $f(u'')$ is the least value of f in $[x,x_1]$, whereas $f(u_1)$ is the least value of f in the whole interval $[x_0,x_1]$, evidently $f(u') \geq f(u_1)$ and $f(u'') \geq f(u_1)$.   Hence

$$S_q - S_p \geq f(u_1)(x - x_0) + f(u_1)(x_1 - x) - f(u_1)(x_1 - x_0) = 0,$$

and $S_q \geq S_p$.   Thus, if q is a refinement of p containing exactly one more subinterval, necessarily $S_q \geq S_p$.

Every refinement q of a partition p of $[a,b]$ can be arrived at by a sequence of partitions

$$p, p_1, p_2, \cdots, p_{k-1}, q,$$

where p_1 is a refinement of p having one more subinterval, p_2 is a refinement of p_1 having one more subinterval, and so on, with q a refinement of p_{k-1} having one more subinterval.   If p has n subintervals, then q has $n + k$ subintervals.   By the results of the previous paragraph,

$$S_p \leq S_{p_1} \leq S_{p_2} \leq \cdots \leq S_{p_{k-1}} \leq S_q.$$

Thus, if q is any refinement of p, necessarily $S_p \leq S_q$.

By a similar argument, it may be shown that if q is a refinement of the partition p, then $T_q \leq T_p$.   We collect these results in the following theorem.

8.9 Theorem.   Let the function f be continuous in the interval $[a,b]$ and let p and q be partitions of $[a,b]$.   If q is a refinement of p, then

$$S_p \leq S_q, \qquad T_q \leq T_p.$$

Given two partitions p and q of an interval $[a,b]$, then it is clear that there exists a common refinement r of p and q.   Thus, if $p = [x_0,x_1, \cdots ,x_n]$ and $q = [y_0,y_1, \cdots ,y_m]$, we select r so that each of the x_i and y_i occurs in r. For example, if

$$p = [1,2,3,4,5], \qquad q = [1,\tfrac{3}{2},\tfrac{9}{4},\tfrac{5}{2},4,5],$$

then

$$r = [1,\tfrac{3}{2},2,\tfrac{9}{4},\tfrac{5}{2},3,4,5]$$

is a refinement of both p and q.

Let us prove the following theorem.

8.10 Theorem.   Let the function f be continuous in the interval $[a,b]$ and let p and q be partitions of $[a,b]$.   Then

$$S_p \leq T_q.$$

Proof: Let r be a common refinement of p and q. By 8.9, $S_p \leq S_r$ and $T_r \leq T_q$. Since $S_r \leq T_r$ by 8.6, we have $S_p \leq S_r \leq T_r \leq T_q$. This proves the theorem.

An immediate consequence of this theorem is that each upper sum T_q is an upper bound of the set U of all lower sums of f over $[a,b]$. Hence

$$\underline{\int_a^b} f \leq T_q,$$

since the lower integral of f is the *least* upper bound of U. Thus the lower integral is a lower bound of the set V of all upper sums of f over $[a,b]$, and since the upper integral is the *greatest* lower bound of V, necessarily the lower integral is less than or equal to the upper integral. This proves the following theorem.

8.11 Theorem. If the function f is continuous in the interval $[a,b]$, then

$$\underline{\int_a^b} f \leq \overline{\int_a^b} f.$$

Our final argument that the lower and upper integrals actually are equal depends on the following theorem which we will not prove until later (14.1).

8.12 Theorem. If the function f is continuous in the closed interval $[a,b]$, then for every number $\epsilon > 0$ there exists a partition $p = [x_0, x_1, \cdots, x_n]$ of $[a,b]$ such that for each i,

$$f(v_i) - f(u_i) < \epsilon, \qquad i = 1, 2, \cdots, n,$$

where $f(v_i)$ is the maximum value and $f(u_i)$ is the minimum value of f in the ith subinterval $[x_{i-1}, x_i]$ of p.

Geometrically, this theorem states that for every grating of equispaced lines parallel to the x-axis, no matter how close together the lines are, we can find a finite set of lines parallel to the y-axis between a and b such that the graph of f between two consecutive lines of this set lies between two consecutive lines of the grating (Figure 8.8). The number ϵ is the distance between consecutive lines of the grating.

8.13 Theorem. If the function f is continuous in the closed interval $[a,b]$, then

$$\underline{\int_a^b} f = \overline{\int_a^b} f.$$

Proof: For every number $\epsilon > 0$, $\epsilon/(b-a) > 0$ also and, according to the previous theorem, there exists a partition $p = [x_0, x_1, \cdots, x_n]$ of $[a,b]$ such that for each i,

$$f(v_i) - f(u_i) < \frac{\epsilon}{b-a}, \quad i = 1, 2, \cdots, n,$$

where $f(v_i)$ is the maximum value and $f(u_i)$ is the minimum value of f in

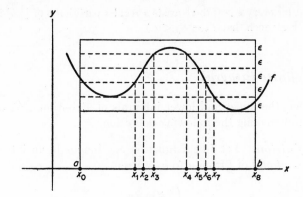

Figure 8.8

the ith subinterval $[x_{i-1}, x_i]$ of p.   Since

$$T_p - S_p = [f(v_1) - f(u_1)](x_1 - x_0) + [f(v_2) - f(u_2)](x_2 - x_1)$$
$$+ \cdots + [f(v_n) - f(u_n)](x_n - x_{n-1}),$$

we have

$$T_p - S_p < \frac{\epsilon}{b-a}(x_1 - x_0) + \frac{\epsilon}{b-a}(x_2 - x_1) + \cdots + \frac{\epsilon}{b-a}(x_n - x_{n-1}).$$

If we factor $\epsilon/(b-a)$ from each term of the right side of this inequality, we get (since $x_0 = a$ and $x_n = b$)

$$\frac{\epsilon}{b-a}(x_1 - x_0 + x_2 - x_1 + \cdots + x_n - x_{n-1}) = \frac{\epsilon}{b-a}(x_n - x_0) = \epsilon.$$

Thus, for every $\epsilon > 0$, there exists a partition p of $[a,b]$ such that

$$0 \le T_p - S_p < \epsilon.$$

since

$$\overline{\int_a^b} f \le T_p, \qquad S_p \le \underline{\int_a^b} f,$$

we have, using 8.11,

$$0 \le \overline{\int_a^b} f - \underline{\int_a^b} f \le T_p - S_p < \epsilon.$$

The difference of the upper and lower integrals, being less than every positive number ϵ, must equal zero.   This proves the theorem.

■ ■ ■ EXERCISE

1. If the function f is continuous and increasing (or decreasing) in the interval $[a,b]$, prove that the upper integral and the lower integral are equal without using Theorem 8.12.   (*Hint:* Use Exercises 11 and 12 of Section 3 to prove

that for every $\epsilon > 0$ there exists a regular partition p of $[a,b]$ into n sub-intervals such that $T_p - S_p < \epsilon$.)

5. The definite integral

The fact that the upper and lower integrals of a continuous function are equal suggests making the following definition.

8.14 Definition. Let f be a function continuous in an interval $[a,b]$. The *definite integral* of f from a to b, written

$$\int_a^b f(x)\ dx,$$

is the common value of the lower and upper integrals of f from a to b.

Thus, by definition,

$$\int_a^b f(x)\ dx = \underline{\int_a^b} f = \overline{\int_a^b} f.$$

While it would be mathematically correct to write the definite integral in the notation

$$\int_a^b f$$

without any x's, we shall bow to convention and use the notation for the integral given in the definition. The x's play no essential role in this definition. Thus

$$\int_a^b f(x)\ dx = \int_a^b f(u)\ du = \int_a^b f(z)\ dz,$$

and so on. By definition,

$$\int_a^a f(x)\ dx = 0.$$

It is convenient to define

$$\int_a^b f(x)\ dx = -\int_b^a f(x)\ dx$$

in case $b < a$. We had always assumed previously that $a \leq b$ in the definite integral $\int_a^b f(x)\ dx$.

Areas are additive, that is, if a polygon is made up of two smaller polygons, then the area of the larger polygon is the sum of the areas of the smaller polygons. Let us now prove that the definite integral also is additive, that is, that the integral of f from a to b plus the integral of f from b to c is the integral of f from a to c.

8.15 Theorem. If the function f is continuous in a closed interval containing the three numbers a, b, and c, then

$$\int_a^b f(x)\ dx + \int_b^c f(x)\ dx = \int_a^c f(x)\ dx.$$

Proof: Let us assume that $a < b < c$.

For each partition $r = [x_0, x_1, \cdots, x_n]$ of $[a,c]$, let r' be the refinement of r formed by dividing the subinterval $[x_{i-1}, x_i]$ of r containing b into two subintervals $[x_{i-1}, b]$ and $[b, x_i]$. If $b = x_i$ for some i, take $r' = r$. In either case,

$$S_r \leq S_{r'}$$

by 8.9. The partition r' of $[a,c]$ is made up of a partition $p = [x_0, x_1, \cdots, b]$ of $[a,b]$ and a partition $q = [b, x_i, \cdots, x_n]$ of $[b,c]$. Hence

$$S_{r'} = S_p + S_q.$$

According to the definition of the (lower) integral,

$$S_p \leq \int_a^b f(x)\ dx, \qquad S_q \leq \int_b^c f(x)\ dx.$$

Hence

$$S_r \leq \int_a^b f(x)\ dx + \int_b^c f(x)\ dx$$

for each partition r of $[a,c]$, and the right side of this inequality is an upper bound of the set of all lower sums of f over $[a,c]$. Therefore, by the very definition of the (lower) integral,

$$(1) \qquad \int_a^c f(x)\ dx \leq \int_a^b f(x)\ dx + \int_b^c f(x)\ dx.$$

In turn, using (upper) integral arguments like those of the previous paragraph with $T_r \geq T_{r'} = T_p + T_q$, we get

$$(2) \qquad \int_a^c f(x)\ dx \geq \int_a^b f(x)\ dx + \int_b^c f(x)\ dx.$$

Inequalities (1) and (2) together prove the theorem when $a < b < c$.

We may use this result to prove the theorem for any other ordering of a, b, and c. For example, if $c < b < a$, then we have shown that

$$\int_c^b f(x)\ dx + \int_b^a f(x)\ dx = \int_c^a f(x)\ dx.$$

But $\quad \displaystyle\int_c^b f(x)\ dx = -\int_b^c f(x)\ dx, \qquad \int_b^a f(x)\ dx = -\int_a^b f(x)\ dx,$

and $\qquad \displaystyle\int_c^a f(x)\ dx = -\int_a^c f(x)\ dx.$

Thus

$$-\int_b^c f(x)\ dx - \int_a^b f(x)\ dx = -\int_a^c f(x)\ dx,$$

or

$$\int_a^b f(x)\ dx + \int_b^c f(x)\ dx = \int_a^c f(x)\ dx.$$

■ ■ ■ EXERCISES

1. Write out the last part of the proof of Theorem 8.15, starting with $T_r \geq T_p + T_q$.

2. Using the fact that Theorem 8.15 is valid if $a < b < c$, show that the theorem is correct if:

(a) $a < c < b$.   (b) $b < a < c$.

(c) $b < c < a$.   (d) $c < a < b$.

(e) $a = b$.

3. We have shown in previous sets of exercises that:

(1) $\displaystyle\int_a^b x \, dx = \frac{1}{2} (b^2 - a^2).$ (2) $\displaystyle\int_a^b x^2 \, dx = \frac{1}{3} (b^3 - a^3).$

(3) $\displaystyle\int_a^b \frac{1}{x^2} \, dx = -\left(\frac{1}{b} - \frac{1}{a}\right).$ (4) $\displaystyle\int_a^b \frac{1}{x^3} \, dx = -\frac{1}{2}\left(\frac{1}{b^2} - \frac{1}{a^2}\right).$

What do these suggest for the value of

$$\int_a^b x^n \, dx,$$

n a positive or negative integer?

6. The fundamental theorem of the calculus

The concepts of the derivative and the integral were well known before the time of Newton and Leibniz. However, the great English physicist and mathematician Isaac Newton (1642–1727) and the great German mathematician and philosopher Gottfried Wilhelm Leibniz (1646–1716) were the first to see the intimate relationship between the derivative and the integral, now known as the fundamental theorem of the calculus. Because of this insight, gained independently of each other, they are usually given credit for the discovery of the calculus.

The fundamental theorem of the calculus, in modern terminology, states that the evaluation of a definite integral of a function f is equivalent to the evaluation of an antiderivative of f. We recall that the function F is an antiderivative of f if $F' = f$.

8.16 Fundamental theorem of the calculus. If f is a function continuous in a closed interval, then:

(1) The function f has antiderivatives in this interval.

(2) If F is any antiderivative of f, and a and b are numbers in the given interval,

$$\int_a^b f(x) \, dx = F(b) - F(a).$$

Proof: We first assume that $a < b$ and define the function G as follows:

$$G(x) = \int_a^x f(x) \, dx, \quad a \leq x \leq b.$$

Let us prove that G is an antiderivative of f, that is, that
$$D_x G(x) = f(x), \quad a \le x \le b.$$
By definition,
$$D_x G(x) = \lim_{h \to 0} \frac{G(x+h) - G(x)}{h}$$
$$= \lim_{h \to 0} \frac{\int_a^{x+h} f(x)\, dx - \int_a^x f(x)\, dx}{h}.$$

By the additivity of the integral,
$$\int_a^x f(x)\, dx + \int_x^{x+h} f(x)\, dx = \int_a^{x+h} f(x)\, dx.$$
Thus
$$D_x G(x) = \lim_{h \to 0} \frac{\int_x^{x+h} f(x)\, dx}{h}.$$

If $h > 0$, let $f(u)$ and $f(v)$ be the minimum and maximum values of f, respectively, in the interval $[x, x + h]$. Then, by Theorem 8.8,
$$hf(u) \le \int_x^{x+h} f(x)\, dx \le hf(v),$$
and therefore
$$f(u) \le \frac{\int_x^{x+h} f(x)\, dx}{h} \le f(v).$$

Even if $h < 0$, the above inequality is true, as may be easily verified.

Since f is continuous at x, for every $\epsilon > 0$ there exists an h such that
$$f(x) - \epsilon < f(u) \le \frac{\int_x^{x+h} f(x)\, dx}{h} \le f(v) < f(x) + \epsilon.$$

From this inequality we deduce that
$$D_x G(x) = \lim_{h \to 0} \frac{\int_x^{x+h} f(x)\, dx}{h} = f(x).$$

This proves part (1) of the theorem.

To prove part (2), let us again assume that $a < b$, and let F be any antiderivative of f in $[a, b]$, so that
$$D_x F(x) = f(x), \quad a \le x \le b.$$

Since G also is an antiderivative of f, there is a constant c such that (6.22)
$$F(x) - G(x) = c.$$

Evidently $G(a) = 0$, and therefore
$$F(a) = c.$$

Thus $F(b) - G(b) = c = F(a)$ and $G(b) = F(b) - F(a)$, that is,

$$G(b) = \int_a^b f(x)\,dx = F(b) - F(a).$$

This proves part (2) of the theorem if $a < b$. We leave it for the reader to verify the theorem if $b \le a$.

It is convenient to introduce the notation

$$F(x) \Big|_a^b = F(b) - F(a).$$

According to part (2) of the fundamental theorem of the calculus,

$$\int_a^b f(x)\,dx = F(x) \Big|_a^b,$$

where F is any antiderivative of f.

The process of finding the integral of a function is called *integration*. The fundamental theorem of the calculus allows us to give general integration formulas corresponding to the differentiation formulas. Thus, corresponding to the power differentiation formula (5.15) is the following power integration formula.

8.17 $$\int_a^b x^r\,dx = \frac{x^{r+1}}{r+1}\Big|_a^b, \quad r \ne -1.$$

If we consider the functions f and F defined by

$$f(x) = x^r, \qquad F(x) = \frac{x^{r+1}}{r+1},$$

then $D_x F(x) = x^r$, that is, F is an antiderivative of f. In view of the fundamental theorem of the calculus, this proves 8.17.

If r is a negative rational number in 8.17, then x^r is undefined at $x = 0$. Since the definite integral of f from a to b is defined only if f is continuous in the interval $[a,b]$, a and b must both be positive or both be negative in case $r < 0$.

Example 1. Find $\int_2^4 x^2\,dx.$

Solution: By 8.17,

$$\int_2^4 x^2\,dx = \frac{x^3}{3}\Big|_2^4 = \frac{1}{3}(64 - 8) = \frac{56}{3}.$$

Example 2. Find $\int_1^4 \sqrt{x}\,dx.$

Solution: Since $\sqrt{x} = x^{1/2}$, we have by 8.17,

$$\int_1^4 x^{1/2}\,dx = \frac{x^{3/2}}{\frac{3}{2}}\Big|_1^4 = \frac{2}{3}(4^{3/2} - 1^{3/2}) = \frac{14}{3}.$$

Example 3. Find $\int_{-1/2}^{-1} \frac{1}{x^3}\,dx.$

Solution: Since $1/x^3 = x^{-3}$, we have by 8.17,

$$\int_{-1/2}^{-1} x^{-3}\, dx = \frac{x^{-2}}{-2}\Big|_{-1/2}^{-1} = -\frac{1}{2}\left(\frac{1}{(-1)^2} - \frac{1}{(-\frac{1}{2})^2}\right) = \frac{3}{2}.$$

If the function F is an antiderivative of f, then for any number c, $D_x[cF(x)] = cD_xF(x) = c[f(x)]$ and we conclude that cF is an antiderivative of cf, i.e.,

8.18
$$\int_a^b c[f(x)]\, dx = c\int_a^b f(x)\, dx.$$

Also, if the functions F and G are respective antiderivatives of f and g, then $F + G$ is an antiderivative of $f + g$, since

$$D_x[F(x) + G(x)] = D_xF(x) + D_xG(x) = f(x) + g(x).$$

This proves the following integration formula.

8.19
$$\int_a^b [f(x) + g(x)]\, dx = \int_a^b f(x)\, dx + \int_a^b g(x)\, dx.$$

Thus, just as with the derivative, *the definite integral of a sum of functions is the sum of the definite integrals of the functions.*

Example 4.   Find
$$\int_{-1}^{1} (x^2 + 2x - 3)\, dx.$$

Solution:

$$\int_{-1}^{1} (x^2 + 2x - 3)\, dx = \left(\frac{1}{3}x^3 + x^2 - 3x\right)\Big|_{-1}^{1}$$

$$= \left(\frac{1}{3} + 1 - 3\right) - \left(-\frac{1}{3} + 1 + 3\right) = -\frac{16}{3}.$$

Example 5.   Find
$$\int_0^{-2} (15u^4 - 12u^3 + 3u^2 + 6u + 1)\, du.$$

Solution:

$$\int_0^{-2} (15u^4 - 12u^3 + 3u^2 + 6u + 1)\, du = (3u^5 - 3u^4 + u^3 + 3u^2 + u)\Big|_0^{-2}$$

$$= [3(-2)^5 - 3(-2)^4 + (-2)^3 + 3(-2)^2 + (-2)] - [0] = -142.$$

Example 6.   Find
$$\int_1^{2} \frac{x^2 + 2}{x^2}\, dx.$$

Solution: We note that

$$\frac{x^2 + 2}{x^2} = \frac{x^2}{x^2} + \frac{2}{x^2} = 1 + 2x^{-2}.$$

Therefore

$$\int_1^{2} \frac{x^2 + 2}{x^2}\, dx = \int_1^{2} (1 + 2x^{-2})\, dx = (x - 2x^{-1})\Big|_1^{2}$$

$$= \left(2 - \frac{2}{2}\right) - \left(1 - \frac{2}{1}\right) = 2.$$

Example 7. Find

$$\int_{-1}^{0} (t+3)^2 \, dt.$$

Solution: Since

$$(t+3)^2 = t^2 + 6t + 9,$$

we have

$$\int_{-1}^{0} (t+3)^2 \, dt = \int_{-1}^{0} (t^2 + 6t + 9) \, dt = \left(\frac{1}{3} t^3 + 3t^2 + 9t \right) \bigg|_{-1}^{0}$$

$$= [0] - \left[-\frac{1}{3} + 3 - 9 \right] = \frac{19}{3}.$$

■ ■ ■ EXERCISES

Evaluate the following integrals.

1. $\int_{0}^{2} x^3 \, dx.$

2. $\int_{-1}^{1} (x+1) \, dx.$

3. $\int_{1}^{4} (u^2 - 2u + 3) \, du.$

4. $\int_{0}^{5} (-3u^2 + 2u + 5) \, du.$

5. $\int_{-5}^{-1} (t^2 + 1) \, dt.$

6. $\int_{0}^{1} (\sqrt{x} + 1)^2 \, dx.$

7. $\int_{4}^{1} x(\sqrt{x} - 3) \, dx.$

8. $\int_{-1}^{-8} z(\sqrt[3]{z} - 2z) \, dz.$

9. $\int_{4}^{9} \left(\sqrt{x} - \frac{1}{\sqrt{x}} \right) dx.$

10. $\int_{1}^{2} \frac{x^2 - 3x + 4}{\sqrt{x}} \, dx.$

11. $\int_{1}^{2} \frac{\sqrt{u} - 1}{u^2} \, du.$

12. $\int_{1}^{5} \frac{1}{\sqrt{5t}} \, dt.$

13. $\int_{-3}^{-1} \frac{z^2 - 1}{z^5} \, dz.$

14. $\int_{-2}^{-1} \frac{3 - x + x^2}{x^4} \, dx.$

15. $\int_{3}^{6} \sqrt{x - 2} \, dx.$

16. $\int_{0}^{1} \frac{1}{\sqrt{x+1}} \, dx.$

17. Show that $D_x \sqrt{2x+1} = 1/\sqrt{2x+1}.$ Then find $\int_{0}^{4} \frac{1}{\sqrt{2x+1}} \, dx.$

18. Show that $D_x(x^2+1)^{10} = 20x(x^2+1)^9.$ Then find $\int_{0}^{1} 20x(x^2+1)^9 \, dx.$

19. Show that $D_x(3x-2)^{-1} = -3(3x-2)^{-2}.$ Then find $\int_{1}^{2} \frac{1}{(3x-2)^2} \, dx.$

20. Show that $D_x \sqrt{1+2x^2} = 2x/\sqrt{1+2x^2}.$ Then find $\int_{0}^{2} \frac{x}{\sqrt{1+2x^2}} \, dx.$

7. *The intermediate value theorems*

The fundamental theorem of the calculus, relating the integral of a continuous function to the derivative of another function, may be used to establish some so-called intermediate value theorems. For example, if

$$f(x) = x^2 - \sqrt{1 + x},$$

then $f(0) = -1$ and $f(3) = 7$. According to one of the following theorems, there must exist some number z between 0 and 3 such that $f(z) = 2$, where 2 was selected (at random) as a number between -1 and 7.

We recall from Theorem 6.9 that if a function F has a nonzero derivative at every number in an interval $[a,b]$, so that F has no critical numbers in $[a,b]$, then necessarily $F'(x) > 0$ in $[a,b]$ or $F'(x) < 0$ in $[a,b]$. Therefore, if F is a function having a derivative at every number in an interval $[a,b]$, and if $F'(a)$ and $F'(b)$ have different signs, necessarily $F'(c) = 0$ for some number c in (a,b) (i.e., F has a critical number in (a,b)). Actually, we can prove the following slightly stronger result.

8.20 Theorem. If the function F and its derivative F' exist in an interval $[a,b]$ and if w is a number between $F'(a)$ and $F'(b)$, then there exists a number z in $[a,b]$ such that $F'(z) = w$.

Proof: Let us assume $F'(a) < w < F'(b)$. If the function G is defined by

$$G(x) = F(x) - wx,$$

then $G'(x) = F'(x) - w$, and, in particular,

$$G'(a) = F'(a) - w < 0, \qquad G'(b) = F'(b) - w > 0.$$

Hence, by our remarks above,

$$G'(z) = 0$$

for some z in (a,b). Thus $F'(z) - w = 0$ and $F'(z) = w$ as desired.

A similar proof holds if $F'(b) < w < F'(a)$. If $w = F'(a)$, then we need only select $z = a$; and, similarly, if $w = F'(b)$, select $z = b$.

Using the fundamental theorem of the calculus, we establish the following intermediate value theorem.

8.21 Theorem. If the function f is continuous in the interval $[a,b]$ and if w is a number between $f(a)$ and $f(b)$, then there exists a number z in $[a,b]$ such that $f(z) = w$.

Proof: According to the fundamental theorem of the calculus, the function f has an antiderivative F in $[a,b]$. Since $F'(x) = f(x)$ in $[a,b]$, $F'(z) = f(z) = w$ for some z in $[a,b]$ by 8.20. This proves the theorem.

If $f(u)$ is the minimum and $f(v)$ the maximum value of the continuous function f in $[a,b]$, then

$$f(u)(b - a) \leq \int_a^b f(x)\, dx \leq f(v)(b - a)$$

by 8.8 and 8.13.   Hence

$$f(u) \leq \frac{1}{b-a} \int_a^b f(x)\, dx \leq f(v).$$

By the preceding theorem, there is a number z between u and v, and there-fore in the interval $[a,b]$, such that

$$f(z) = \frac{1}{b-a} \int_a^b f(x)\, dx.$$

This establishes the following intermediate value theorem for the integral.

   8.22 Theorem.   If the function f is continuous in the interval $[a,b]$, then there exists a number z in $[a,b]$ such that

$$\int_a^b f(x)\, dx = f(z)(b-a).$$

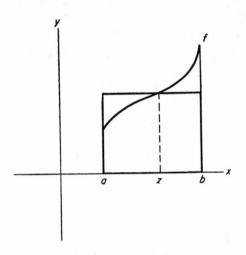

Figure 8.9

   This theorem has the simple geometric interpretation indicated in Figure 8.9; there is a rectangle with base of length $b - a$ and altitude $f(z)$ having the same area as the region under the graph of f from a to b.

■ ■ ■ EXERCISES

   1. Prove 8.22 directly from the mean value theorem (6.11).   (Hint: Let $F(x) = \displaystyle\int_a^x f(x)\, dx$ in the mean value theorem.)

   2. If the functions f and g are continuous in $[a,b]$ and if $f(x) \leq g(x)$ in $[a,b]$, prove that

$$\int_a^b f(x)\ dx \le \int_a^b g(x)\ dx.$$

(Hint: Use 8.22 to prove that $\int_a^b [g(x) - f(x)]\ dx \ge 0$.)

3. If the function f is continuous in $[a,b]$, prove that

$$-\int_a^b |f(x)|\ dx \le \int_a^b f(x)\ dx \le \int_a^b |f(x)|\ dx,$$

i.e., $\left| \int_a^b f(x)\ dx \right| \le \int_a^b |f(x)|\ dx.$

4. Let f be continuous in $[0,1]$, and let $0 \le f(x) \le 1$ for every x in $[0,1]$. Prove that there is a number z in $[0,1]$ such that $f(z) = z$. [If $f(0) = 0$ or $f(1) = 1$, the theorem is true. If $f(0) > 0$ and $f(1) < 1$, consider $g(x) = f(x) - x$.]

5. Assuming the existence of integral powers of a number only, prove that every positive number w has a unique nth root, n any positive integer. (Hint: There exist integers p and q such that $p > w$ and $q > 1/w$. Since $p \ge 1$, $p^2 \ge p > w$, and in general $p^n > w$. Similarly, $q^n > 1/w$. If $f(x) = x^n$, then $f(1/q) < w < f(p)$, etc.)

8. *Change of variable*

Integrals that cannot be evaluated directly from known formulas may sometimes be evaluated after a so-called "change of variable." A formula for this transformation follows directly from the chain rule.

By the chain rule,

$$D_x F(g(x)) = F'(g(x))g'(x).$$

Therefore

$$\int_a^b F'(g(x))g'(x)\ dx = F(g(x)) \Big|_a^b.$$

Since

$$F(g(x)) \Big|_a^b = F(g(b)) - F(g(a)) = F(u) \Big|_{g(a)}^{g(b)}$$

and

$$\int_{g(a)}^{g(b)} F'(u)\ du = F(u) \Big|_{g(a)}^{g(b)},$$

the formula above may be written in the form

$$\int_a^b F'(g(x))g'(x)\ dx = \int_{g(a)}^{g(b)} F'(u)\ du.$$

Finally, letting $f = F'$, we have proved the following useful formula, called the *change of variable* integration formula.

8.23 $$\int_a^b f(g(x))g'(x)\ dx = \int_{g(a)}^{g(b)} f(u)\ du.$$

We may remember 8.23 in the following way. We "change variables" in the given integral (the left side of 8.23) by letting

$$u = g(x),$$

and then by formally letting du be the derivative of g times dx,

$$du = g'(x)\, dx.$$

Then if a and b are thought of as x-limits of integration, the u-limits are $g(a)$ and $g(b)$.

Example 1.   Find $\displaystyle\int_0^1 2x(x^2 + 1)^3\, dx.$

Solution: Let $u = x^2 + 1$, so that $du = 2x\, dx$.   Since $u = 1$ when $x = 0$, and $u = 2$ when $x = 1$, we have by 8.23,

$$\int_0^1 2x(x^2 + 1)^3\, dx = \int_1^2 u^3\, du = \left.\frac{u^4}{4}\right|_1^2 = \frac{15}{4}.$$

A fact worth remembering in using 8.23 is that

$$\int_a^b f(x)\, dx = \frac{1}{c}\int_a^b c[f(x)]\, dx$$

for any nonzero constant c.   This is a direct consequence of 8.18.   According to this equation, we may supply a constant factor to an *integrand* (the quantity under the integral sign) merely by multiplying the integral by the reciprocal of the constant.   How this fact is used in evaluating an integral is illustrated below.

Example 2.   Find

$$\int_1^3 x\sqrt{x^2 - 1}\, dx.$$

Solution: We change variables by letting

$$u = x^2 - 1, \qquad du = 2x\, dx.$$

If we supply a factor of 2 in the integrand and multiply the integral by $\frac{1}{2}$, we have

$$\int_1^3 x\sqrt{x^2 - 1}\, dx = \frac{1}{2}\int_1^3 \sqrt{x^2 - 1}\,(2x\, dx)$$

$$= \frac{1}{2}\int_0^8 u^{1/2}\, du = \frac{1}{2}\left.\left(\frac{2}{3}u^{3/2}\right)\right|_0^8$$

$$= \frac{1}{3}(8^{3/2} - 0^{3/2}) = \frac{16\sqrt{2}}{3}.$$

A slight change in the integral of Example 2 makes it nonintegrable by the present methods.   Thus, we cannot evaluate

$$\int_1^3 \sqrt{x^2 - 1}\, dx.$$

by use of 8.23.   If we proceed as before and let

$$u = x^2 - 1, \qquad du = 2x\,dx,$$

then

$$u^{1/2}\,du = \sqrt{x^2 - 1}\,(2x\,dx)$$

We can supply a factor of 2 in the integrand, but we cannot supply an x. This integral will be evaluated later by other methods.

Example 3.   Find

$$\int_0^2 \frac{x^2}{(x^3 + 1)^2}\,dx.$$

Solution: We let

$$u = x^3 + 1, \qquad du = 3x^2\,dx.$$

If $x = 0$, $u = 1$; if $x = 2$, $u = 9$.   Thus

$$\int_0^2 \frac{x^2}{(x^3 + 1)^2}\,dx = \frac{1}{3}\int_0^2 \frac{3x^2}{(x^3 + 1)^2}\,dx$$

$$= \frac{1}{3}\int_1^9 \frac{1}{u^2}\,du = \frac{1}{3}\int_1^9 u^{-2}\,du = -\frac{1}{3}u^{-1}\Big|_1^9 = \frac{8}{27}.$$

■ ■ ■ EXERCISES

Evaluate the following integrals.

1. $\int_0^3 \sqrt{x + 1}\,dx.$

2. $\int_0^4 2\sqrt{2x + 1}\,dx.$

3. $\int_{-1}^1 \frac{2x}{(4 + x^2)^2}\,dx.$

4. $\int_{-1}^2 9x^2(1 + 3x^3)^2\,dx.$

5. $\int_0^{-5} \sqrt{1 - 3u}\,du.$

6. $\int_0^2 \frac{1}{\sqrt{4u + 1}}\,du.$

7. $\int_0^1 y\sqrt{1 - y^2}\,dy.$

8. $\int_{-1}^{-2} 3z\sqrt[3]{z^2 + 1}\,dz.$

9. $\int_0^{-1} \frac{x}{\sqrt{1 + 8x^2}}\,dx.$

10. $\int_{-3}^{-1} \frac{1}{(4x - 1)^2}\,dx.$

11. $\int_{-3}^{-1} \frac{1}{(2 - 3t)^3}\,dt.$

12. $\int_1^2 \frac{t^2}{(1 + t^3)^2}\,dt.$

13. $\int_{-1}^1 u(1 - u^2)^5\,du.$

14. $\int_1^2 \frac{1}{x^2}\sqrt{1 - \frac{1}{x}}\,dx.$

15. $\int_1^4 \frac{\sqrt{1 + \sqrt{x}}}{\sqrt{x}}\,dx.$

16. $\int_0^1 \sqrt{u}\sqrt{1 + u\sqrt{u}}\,du.$

9. *Areas by integration*

An intuitive discussion of areas was given in the second section of this
chapter.   Let the region R of a coordinate plane be bounded by the graph
of the nonnegative and continuous function f, by the lines $x = a$ and
$x = b$, and by the x-axis, as indicated in Figure 8.10.   We raised the

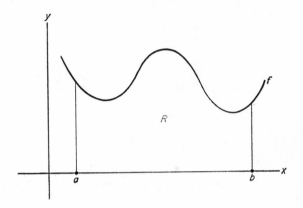

Figure 8.10

question in the previous section whether or not is is possible to assign an
area to the region R that is consistent with the ordinary rectangular area.

If the area A we assign to R is to be no less than the area of each polygon
inscribed in R, then A must be an upper bound of the set I of all the areas
of rectangular polygons inscribed in R.   The least upper bound of I therefore cannot exceed A:

$$\underline{\int_a^b} f \le A.$$

Similarly, A must be a lower bound of the set J of all the areas of rectangular polygons circumscribed about R; hence

$$A \le \overline{\int_a^b} f.$$

However, the upper and lower integrals of a continuous function are equal
by Theorem 8.13, and their common value is the definite integral of f
from a to b.

These facts suggest defining the area of R as follows.

8.24 Definition.   If f is a nonnegative, continuous function in an interval $[a,b]$, then the *area of the region under the graph of f from a to b is
defined to be*

$$\int_a^b f(x)\,dx.$$

If the function f is continuous and nonpositive in the interval $[a,b]$, so that the graph of f lies below the x-axis between $x = a$ and $x = b$ as in Figure 8.11, then the function g defined by

$$g(x) = -f(x)$$

is continuous and nonnegative in $[a,b]$ and has the graph of Figure 8.12. The region R in Figure 8.11 should have the same area as the region S in Figure 8.12.

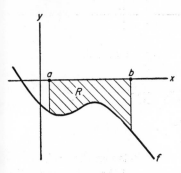

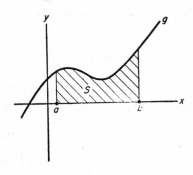

Figure 8.11   Figure 8.12

The area A of S, and therefore of R, is given by

$$A = \int_a^b g(x)\, dx$$

according to definition. Since $g(x) = -f(x)$, also

$$A = \int_a^b -f(x)\, dx = -\int_a^b f(x)\, dx.$$

We conclude that *if the function f is continuous and nonpositive in an interval $[a,b]$, the area A of the region over the graph of f from a to b is given by*

$$A = -\int_a^b f(x)\, dx.$$

If the functions f and g are continuous in $[a,b]$ and if

$$f(x) \geq g(x) \quad \text{for every } x \text{ in } [a,b],$$

then there is a region R of the coordinate plane whose boundaries are the graph of f, the graph of g, and the lines $x = a$ and $x = b$. (See Figure 8.13.)

Let us choose a number k less than the minimum value of g in $[a,b]$. Then $g(x) - k > 0$ for every x in $[a,b]$, and, since $f(x) \geq g(x)$, $f(x) - k > 0$ for every x in $[a,b]$. Hence the functions $\bar{f}$ and $\bar{g}$ defined by

$$\bar{f}(x) = f(x) - k, \qquad \bar{g}(x) = g(x) - k,$$

are continuous and positive in $[a,b]$. If k is chosen as in Figure 8.13, then the graphs of $\bar{f}$ and $\bar{g}$ are given in Figure 8.14.

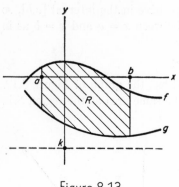

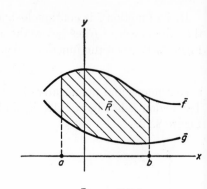

Figure 8.13   Figure 8.14

The area of the region $\overline{R}$ between the graphs of $\overline{f}$ and $\overline{g}$ will be the same as the area of R. However, the area A of $\overline{R}$ clearly should be defined to be

$$A = \int_a^b \overline{f}(x) \, dx - \int_a^b \overline{g}(x) \, dx,$$

that is, A should be defined to be the difference between the area of the region under the graph of $\overline{f}$ from a to b and the area of the region under the graph of $\overline{g}$ from a to b.

Now

$$\int_a^b \overline{f}(x) \, dx - \int_a^b \overline{g}(x) \, dx = \int_a^b [\overline{f}(x) - \overline{g}(x)] \, dx,$$

$$= \int_a^b \{[f(x) - k] - [g(x) - k]\} \, dx,$$

$$= \int_a^b [f(x) - g(x)] \, dx,$$

and therefore we have the following definition.

If f and g are continuous functions in $[a,b]$ and if $f(x) \geq g(x)$ for every x in $[a,b]$, then the area A of the region between the graphs of f and g from a to b is given by the formula

$$A = \int_a^b [f(x) - g(x)] \, dx.$$

Example 1. If

$$f(x) = x^2,$$

find the area of the region R under the graph of f from 0 to 2.

Solution: The region R is indicated in Figure 8.15. The area A of R is given by

$$A = \int_0^2 x^2 \, dx = \frac{x^3}{3}\bigg|_0^2 = \frac{8}{3}.$$

Example 2. If

$$g(x) = \sqrt[3]{x},$$

find the area of the region R under the graph of g from 1 to 8.

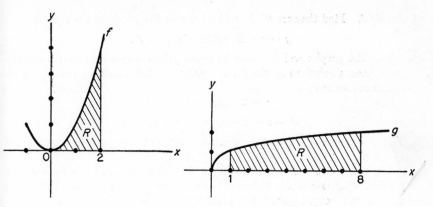

Figure 8.15   Figure 8.16

Solution: The region R, indicated in Figure 8.16, has area

$$A = \int_1^8 \sqrt[3]{x}\, dx = \int_1^8 x^{1/3}\, dx = \frac{3}{4} x^{4/3} \Big|_1^8$$

$$= \frac{3}{4}\left(8^{4/3} - 1^{4/3}\right) = \frac{45}{4}.$$

Example 3. Find the area of the region over the graph of f between -1 and 2 if

$$f(x) = x^3 - 3x - 3.$$

Solution: The graph of f has a maximum point at $(-1,-1)$ and a minimum point at $(1,-5)$ as sketched in Figure 8.17. The area A of the shaded region R is given by

$$A = -\int_{-1}^2 (x^3 - 3x - 3)\, dx = -\left(\frac{x^4}{4} - 3\frac{x^2}{2} - 3x\right)\Big|_{-1}^2 = \frac{39}{4}.$$

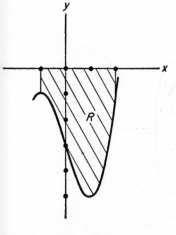

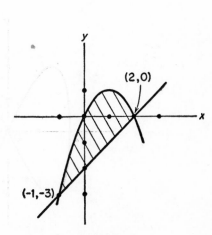

Figure 8.17   Figure 8.18

Example 4. Find the area of the region between the graphs of the equations

$$y = x - 2 \quad \text{and} \quad y = 2x - x^2.$$

Solution: The graphs will intersect in those points whose coordinates are the simultaneous solutions of the given equations. Eliminating y between these equations, we have

$$x - 2 = 2x - x^2,$$

or $$x^2 - x - 2 = (x - 2)(x + 1) = 0.$$

Thus $x = 2$ or $x = -1$, and the common points of the two graphs are $(2,0)$ and $(-1,-3)$.

The graph of $y = x - 2$ is a straight line. The graph of $y = 2x - x^2$ is a parabola that is concave downward and has its vertex at $(1,1)$. The region whose area is sought is shaded in Figure 8.18. This area is given by

$$A = \int_{-1}^{2} [(2x - x^2) - (x - 2)] \, dx = \int_{-1}^{2} (-x^2 + x + 2) \, dx$$

$$= \left(-\frac{1}{3} x^3 + \frac{1}{2} x^2 + 2x \right) \bigg|_{-1}^{2} = \frac{9}{2}.$$

Example 5. Find the area of the region bounded by one loop of the graph of the equation

$$y^2 = 4x^2 - x^4.$$

Solution: The graph is symmetric to both axes. Since

$$y = \pm x\sqrt{4 - x^2},$$

it is clear that the total graph lies between $x = -2$ and $x = 2$. The point $(\sqrt{2},2)$ is a maximum point on the graph. We can plot a few points and sketch the rest of the curve by symmetry as indicated in Figure 8.19.

Let us find the area of the shaded region R bounded by the loop between $x = 0$ and $x = 2$. The equation of the top half of this loop is

$$y = x\sqrt{4 - x^2},$$

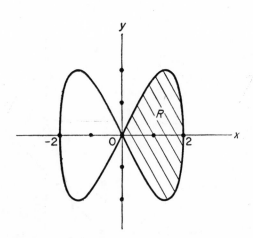

Figure 8.19

whereas that of the lower half is

$$y = -x\sqrt{4 - x^2}.$$

Thus the area of R is given by

$$A = \int_0^2 [(x\sqrt{4 - x^2}) - (-x\sqrt{4 - x^2})]\, dx$$

$$= \int_0^2 2x\sqrt{4 - x^2}\, dx.$$

In order to evaluate this integral, we let

$$u = 4 - x^2, \qquad du = -2x\, dx.$$

Then $u = 4$ when $x = 0$, and $u = 0$ when $x = 2$. Hence

$$A = \int_0^2 2x\sqrt{4 - x^2}\, dx$$

$$= -\int_4^0 u^{1/2}\, du = -\frac{2}{3} u^{3/2} \Big|_4^0 = \frac{16}{3}.$$

■ ■ ■ EXERCISES

Find the area of the region bounded by the graphs of the following equations.
Sketch each region.

1. $y = x^3$, $y = 0$, $x = 1$, $x = 3$.
2. $y = 9 - x^2$, $y = 0$, $x = -2$, $x = 1$.
3. $y = \sqrt{x}$, $y = -\sqrt{x}$, $x = 4$.
4. $y = \sqrt{x + 4}$, $y = 0$, $x = 0$.
5. $y = x^2 - 4$, $y = 4 - x^2$.
6. $y = \sqrt[3]{x^2}$, $y = 0$, $x = 8$.
7. $y = x^2$, $y = 1$.
8. $4y = x^2$, $x - 4y + 2 = 0$.
9. $x^2 y = 4$, $3x + y - 7 = 0$.
10. $y = x(x - 2)^2$, $y = 0$.
11. $y^2 = 4x$, $x = 1$.
12. $y = x^3 - x$, $y = 0$, in fourth quadrant.
13. $y = x^2 - 4x + 1$, $x + y - 5 = 0$.
14. $y = 3 - 2x - x^2$, $x + y - 1 = 0$.
15. $y^2(4 - x^2) = x^2$, $x = 1$.
16. $y = (x - 1)/\sqrt{x^2 - 2x + 4}$, $x = 0$, $y = 0$.

9

The definite integral
as a limit of a sum

■ ■ ■ ■ ■   THE INTEGRAL AS WELL AS the derivative can be expressed
in terms of limits, as we shall show in the present chapter.
However, the integral is a limit of a special kind of function
called a sequence.   Thus, we start off this chapter with a
discussion of sequences and their limits, and then apply
this knowledge to the study of the integral.

1. Sequences

Certain functions, called sequences, are of particular in-
terest in mathematics.

9.1 Definition.   A *sequence* is a function having as its
domain the set of positive integers.

In order to define any function, we must somehow describe the correspondence that associates with each number in the domain of the function a number in its range.
This may be done by means of a table (cf. Example 3,
p. 49), an equation (cf. Example 1, p. 48), or a combination of a table and an equation (cf. Example 4, p. 49).

The customary way to define a sequence a is to list in
order the values of a at the successive positive integers as
indicated below.

$$a(1), \ a(2), \ a(3), \ \cdots \ .$$

The dots are used to suggest that the "table" is an infinite one. A further convention is to use subscripts rather than the usual functional notation. Thus, the sequence above will be written

$$a_1, a_2, a_3, \cdots .$$

The numbers a_1, a_2, a_3, and so on, are called the *elements* of the sequence a, a_k being the kth element.

In essence, a sequence is just an unending succession of numbers described by some rule of formation. The following are examples of sequences:

(1) $\dfrac{2}{1}, \dfrac{2}{2}, \dfrac{2}{3}, \dfrac{2}{4}, \cdots$; $\qquad\qquad a_n = \dfrac{2}{n}.$

(2) $1^2, 2^2, 3^2, 4^2, \cdots$; $\qquad\qquad a_n = n^2.$

(3) $-1, -2, -3, -4, \cdots$; $\qquad a_n = -n.$

(4) $2, 4, 6, 8, \cdots$; $\qquad\qquad\quad a_n = 2n.$

(5) $1, \sqrt{2}, \sqrt{3}, \sqrt{4}, \cdots$; $\qquad a_n = \sqrt{n}.$

(6) $2, 2, 2, 2, \cdots$; $\qquad\qquad\quad a_n = 2.$

(7) $-2, 2, -2, 2, \cdots$; $\qquad\quad a_n = (-1)^n 2.$

(8) $\dfrac{1}{2}, \dfrac{2}{3}, \dfrac{3}{4}, \dfrac{4}{5}, \cdots$; $\qquad\qquad a_n = \dfrac{n}{n+1}.$

(9) $-\dfrac{1}{2}, \dfrac{1}{4}, -\dfrac{1}{8}, \dfrac{1}{16}, \cdots$; $\qquad a_n = \left(-\dfrac{1}{2}\right)^n.$

(10) $2, \dfrac{5}{2}, \dfrac{8}{3}, \dfrac{11}{4}, \cdots$; $\qquad\qquad a_n = 3 - \dfrac{1}{n}.$

In each of the examples above, we have displayed the nth element so as to give the general rule of formation of the sequence. For example, in (1), knowing that $a_n = 2/n$, we find

$$a_1 = \frac{2}{1},\ a_2 = \frac{2}{2},\ a_3 = \frac{2}{3},\ a_4 = \frac{2}{4},\ a_5 = \frac{2}{5},$$

and so on. Thus the 32nd element of the sequence is $a_{32} = 2/32 = 1/16$. In most of the examples above, we could guess the rule of formation used just by looking at the first few elements of the sequence. However, given that a sequence starts out as follows,

$$5, 7, 7, 3, \cdots ,$$

we would not be able to continue it without some clue as to how the first four elements were chosen. The rule we used in forming this sequence was to let a_n be the nth digit in the decimal expansion of $\sqrt{3}/3$,

$$\frac{\sqrt{3}}{3} = .577350 \cdots .$$

It is important to distinguish between a sequence and the *set of elements of the sequence.* For example, the set of elements of sequence (5) above is the set of square roots of all the positive integers. An entirely different sequence is the following:

$$1, \sqrt{2}, 1, \sqrt{3}, 1, \sqrt{4}, \cdots ; \qquad a_n = \begin{cases} 1, & n \text{ odd} \\ \sqrt{\dfrac{n}{2}} + 1, & n \text{ even} \end{cases}$$

Although these two sequences are different, they consist of the same set of elements. In other words, the ranges of the two sequences are the same. The set of elements in sequence (7) above consists of two elements, -2 and 2.

The nth element $2/n$ of sequence (1) above is close to zero if n is large. For this reason, we shall say that the limit of sequence (1) is zero.

The limit of sequence (6) is 2, since the nth element is equal to 2 (and hence close to 2) when n is large.

Since the nth element of sequence (10) above is $3 - 1/n$, evidently the nth element is close to 3 when n is large. Thus the limit of this sequence is 3 according to the definition of the limit of a sequence that follows.

9.2 Definition. The sequence

$$a_1, a_2, \cdots, a_n, \cdots$$

has limit L if for every number $\epsilon > 0$ there exists a number N such that

$$|a_n - L| < \epsilon \text{ for every integer } n > N.$$

If the sequence with nth element a_n has limit L, then we shall write

$$\lim_{n \to \infty} a_n = L.$$

It should be noted that the definition of the limit of a sequence is almost word for word the same as the definition of

$$\lim_{x \to \infty} f(x)$$

given in 7.2. Hence we can expect the methods used in Chapter 7 for infinite limits of functions to carry over to limits of sequences.

Let us use 9.2 to prove that sequence (10) above has limit 3, that is, that

$$\lim_{n \to \infty} \left(3 - \frac{1}{n} \right) = 3.$$

We must show that for every number $\epsilon > 0$ there exists a number N such that

$$\left| 3 - \frac{1}{n} - 3 \right| < \epsilon \quad \text{for every integer } n > N.$$

Since $|3 - 1/n - 3| = 1/n$ and

$$\frac{1}{n} < \epsilon \quad \text{for every integer } n > \frac{1}{\epsilon},$$

we need only select $N = 1/\epsilon$ to obtain the desired conclusion.

Of the ten examples of sequences listed at the beginning of this section, it is intuitively clear that (2), (3), (4), (5), and (7) do not have limits. Each of the other sequences has a limit.

The sequence

$$\frac{k}{1^p}, \frac{k}{2^p}, \frac{k}{3^p}, \cdots, \frac{k}{n^p}, \cdots$$

has the limit 0 for any real number k and any positive rational number p, that is,

9.3 $$\lim_{n \to \infty} \frac{k}{n^p} = 0, \quad p > 0.$$

We shall not prove 9.3, since its proof is almost identical with that of 7.3. As a consequence of 9.3, each of the following sequences has 0 as its limit:

$$1, \frac{1}{2}, \frac{1}{3}, \frac{1}{4}, \cdots, \frac{1}{n}, \cdots .$$

$$-2, \frac{-2}{\sqrt{2}}, \frac{-2}{\sqrt{3}}, \frac{-2}{\sqrt{4}}, \cdots, \frac{-2}{\sqrt{n}}, \cdots .$$

$$3, \frac{3}{2^2}, \frac{3}{3^2}, \frac{3}{4^2}, \cdots, \frac{3}{n^2}, \cdots .$$

Limits of sequences have many of the properties of limits of functions as given in Chapter 4. Before stating these properties, we observe that from the sequences

$$a_1, a_2, \cdots, a_n, \cdots ,$$

$$b_1, b_2, \cdots, b_n, \cdots ,$$

we can form many new sequences; for example,

$$a_1 + b_1, a_2 + b_2, \cdots, a_n + b_n, \cdots ,$$

$$a_1 b_1, a_2 b_2, \cdots, a_n b_n, \cdots ,$$

$$\frac{a_1}{b_1}, \frac{a_2}{b_2}, \cdots, \frac{a_n}{b_n}, \cdots \quad \text{(if each } b_n \neq 0\text{)},$$

$$|a_1|, |a_2|, \cdots, |a_n|, \cdots ,$$

and so on.

The constant sequence $c, c, \cdots, c, \cdots$ has c as its limit; that is,

9.4 $$\lim_{n \to \infty} c = c.$$

If

$$\lim_{n \to \infty} a_n = A, \quad \lim_{n \to \infty} b_n = B,$$

then

9.5 $$\lim_{n \to \infty} (a_n \pm b_n) = A \pm B,$$

9.6 $$\lim_{n \to \infty} a_n b_n = AB,$$

9.7 $$\text{limit}_{n\to\infty} \frac{a_n}{b_n} = \frac{A}{B}, \quad b_n \neq 0, \quad B \neq 0.$$

The proofs of these limit theorems, being similar to the corresponding ones for functions, will be omitted.

Some useful limit theorems of a slightly different nature are as follows:

9.8 If $a_n \leq c_n \leq b_n$ for each integer n and if

$$\text{limit}_{n\to\infty} a_n = \text{limit}_{n\to\infty} b_n = A, \quad \text{then } \text{limit}_{n\to\infty} c_n = A.$$

9.9 If $\text{limit}_{n\to\infty} a_n = A$, then $\text{limit}_{n\to\infty} |a_n| = |A|$.

9.10 If $\text{limit}_{n\to\infty} |a_n| = 0$, then $\text{limit}_{n\to\infty} a_n = 0$.

Proof of 9.8: For every number $\epsilon > 0$, there must exist some number N such that

$$|a_n - A| < \epsilon, \quad |b_n - A| < \epsilon \quad \text{for every integer } n > N.$$

Hence

$$-\epsilon < a_n - A < \epsilon, \quad -\epsilon < b_n - A < \epsilon \quad \text{for every integer } n > N.$$

Since $a_n - A \leq c_n - A \leq b_n - A$, we have

$$-\epsilon < a_n - A \leq c_n - A \leq b_n - A < \epsilon,$$

or $$-\epsilon < c_n - A < \epsilon \quad \text{for every integer } n > N.$$

This proves 9.8.

The proofs of 9.9 and 9.10 are left for the reader to supply.

With the aid of the above limit theorems, it is possible to evaluate directly the limits of many sequences as illustrated below.

Example 1. Find $\text{limit}_{n\to\infty} \dfrac{n}{n+1}$.

Solution: Since

$$\frac{n}{n+1} = \frac{1}{1 + \dfrac{1}{n}},$$

the given sequence is the quotient of two sequences having nth terms 1 and $1 + 1/n$, respectively. Thus, by 9.7,

$$\text{limit}_{n\to\infty} \frac{n}{n+1} = \text{limit}_{n\to\infty} \frac{1}{1 + 1/n}$$

$$= \frac{\text{limit}_{n\to\infty} 1}{\text{limit}_{n\to\infty} (1 + 1/n)}.$$

However, $$\text{limit}_{n\to\infty} \left(1 + \frac{1}{n}\right) = \text{limit}_{n\to\infty} 1 + \text{limit}_{n\to\infty} \frac{1}{n} = 1$$

by 9.5, 9.4, and 9.3. We conclude that

$$\lim_{n \to \infty} \frac{n}{n + 1} = 1.$$

Example 2. Find $\displaystyle\lim_{n \to \infty} \frac{1 - 2n + 3n^2}{5n^2}$.

Solution: We note that

$$\frac{1 - 2n + 3n^2}{5n^2} = \frac{\frac{1}{5}}{n^2} - \frac{\frac{2}{5}}{n} + \frac{3}{5}.$$

Hence

$$\lim_{n \to \infty} \frac{1 - 2n + 3n^2}{5n^2} = \lim_{n \to \infty} \frac{\frac{1}{5}}{n^2} - \lim_{n \to \infty} \frac{\frac{2}{5}}{n} + \lim_{n \to \infty} \frac{3}{5}$$

$$= 0 - 0 + \frac{3}{5} = \frac{3}{5}.$$

Example 3. Find $\displaystyle\lim_{n \to \infty} \frac{5n}{n^2 + 1}$.

Solution: We again change $5n/(n^2 + 1)$ into a form containing powers of $1/n$:

$$\frac{5n}{n^2 + 1} = \frac{5/n}{1 + 1/n^2}.$$

Hence

$$\lim_{n \to \infty} \frac{5n}{n^2 + 1} = \frac{\lim_{n \to \infty} (5/n)}{\lim_{n \to \infty} 1 + \lim_{n \to \infty} (1/n^2)} = \frac{0}{1 + 0} = 0.$$

■ ■ ■ EXERCISES

In each of the following, the nth element a_n of a sequence is given. Write down the first five numbers of the sequence, and then find $\lim_{n \to \infty} a_n$, if it exists. (You may use any of the limit theorems.)

1. $a_n = \dfrac{3}{n}$.

2. $a_n = 1 - \dfrac{2}{n}$.

3. $a_n = \dfrac{2n}{n + 3}$.

4. $a_n = \dfrac{1 - 2n}{1 + n}$.

5. $a_n = \dfrac{(-1)^n}{n^2}$.

6. $a_n = \dfrac{(-1)^{n+1}(n + 1)}{2n}$.

7. $a_n = \dfrac{n^2 - 2}{n^2 + 2}$.

8. $a_n = \dfrac{n^3 - 1}{n^3 + 1}$.

9. $a_n = \dfrac{2n}{n + 1} - \dfrac{n + 1}{2n}$.

10. $a_n = \dfrac{n^2}{2n + 1} - \dfrac{n^2}{2n - 1}$.

11. $a_n = \dfrac{n^3}{n^2 + 2} - \dfrac{n^3}{n^2 - 2}$.

12. $a_n = \dfrac{n^2 + 5n - 2}{2n^2}$.

13. Prove that $\displaystyle\lim_{n \to \infty} \frac{1}{\sqrt{n^2 + 1}} = 0$. (*Hint:* $n^2 < n^2 + 1$, and therefore $1/n > 1/\sqrt{n^2 + 1} > 0$. Now use 9.8.)

14. If $\underset{n\to\infty}{\text{limit}}\ a_n = L$, use 9.2 only to prove that:

    (a) $\underset{n\to\infty}{\text{limit}}\ (-a_n) = -L.$ (b) $\underset{n\to\infty}{\text{limit}}\ ca_n = cL.$

15. If $\underset{n\to\infty}{\text{limit}}\ a_n = 0$, use 9.2 only to prove that

$$\underset{n\to\infty}{\text{limit}}\ (a_n)^2 = 0.$$

16. Prove 9.5. (*Hint:* Look at the proof of 4.15.)

17. Using 9.2 only, prove that if $\underset{n\to\infty}{\text{limit}}\ a_n = L$, then $\underset{n\to\infty}{\text{limit}}\ (a_n - L)^2 = 0$. (*Hint:* Look at the proof of 4.6.)

18. Use the preceding exercise to prove that if $\underset{n\to\infty}{\text{limit}}\ a_n = L$, then

$$\underset{n\to\infty}{\text{limit}}\ (a_n)^2 = L^2.$$

19. Prove 9.6. (*Hint:* Use the preceding exercise; look at the proof of 4.16.)

20. Prove that if $\underset{x\to\infty}{\text{limit}}\ a_n = L$ and $L > 0$, then there exists a number N such that $a_n > 0$ for every $n > N$. State the corresponding theorem if $L < 0$.

21. Prove 9.9. (*Hint:* Use the preceding exercise.)

22. Prove 9.10.

2. Riemann sums

Let f be a function continuous in an interval $[a,b]$, and let

$$p = [x_0, x_1, \cdots, x_{m-1}, x_m], \quad x_0 = a, \quad x_m = b,$$

be a partition of $[a,b]$. The lower and upper sums of f relative to p are given by

$$S_p = f(u_1)(x_1 - x_0) + f(u_2)(x_2 - x_1) + \cdots + f(u_m)(x_m - x_{m-1})$$

and

$$T_p = f(v_1)(x_1 - x_0) + f(v_2)(x_2 - x_1) + \cdots + f(v_m)(x_m - x_{m-1}),$$

respectively, where $f(u_i)$ is the minimum value and $f(v_i)$ is the maximum value of f in $[x_{i-1}, x_i]$ for each integer i. Each of these sums is an example of a Riemann sum of f over $[a,b]$.

A *Riemann* sum* of f over $[a,b]$ is any sum of the form

$$R_p = f(z_1)(x_1 - x_0) + f(z_2)(x_2 - x_1) + \cdots + f(z_m)(x_m - x_{m-1}),$$

related to a partition $p = [x_0, x_1, \cdots, x_{m-1}, x_m]$ of $[a,b]$, where z_1 is any number in $[x_0, x_1]$, z_2 in $[x_1, x_2]$, $\cdots$, and z_m in $[x_{m-1}, x_m]$:

$$x_0 \leq z_1 \leq x_1,\ x_1 \leq z_2 \leq x_2,\ \cdots,\ x_{m-1} \leq z_m \leq x_m.$$

Since

$$f(u_i) \leq f(z_i) \leq f(v_i)$$

---

* Riemann was a famous German mathematician of the 19th century. In his paper of 1850 on the foundations of analysis, we find for the first time a careful definition of the integral as a limit of a sum.

for each integer i, clearly

9.11 $S_p \leq R_p \leq T_p$

for each partition p of $[a,b]$ and each Riemann sum R_p defined on p.

The basic theorem we wish to prove expresses the definite integral of f from a to b as a limit of a sequence of Riemann sums of f over $[a,b]$. Before stating this important theorem, we define the concept of the norm of a partition.

If $p = [x_0, x_1, \cdots, x_{m-1}, x_m]$ is a partition of the interval $[a,b]$, the *norm* of p is defined to be the largest of the numbers

$$x_1 - x_0, \quad x_2 - x_1, \quad \cdots, x_{m-1} - x_{m-2}, \quad x_m - x_{m-1}.$$

We shall designate the norm of p by $|p|$. Thus, for a partition p, $|p|$ is the length of the largest subinterval of p. By definition,

$$|p| \geq x_i - x_{i-1} \quad \text{for each positive integer } i,$$

with equality holding for some i.

9.12 Theorem. Let f be a function continuous in a closed interval $[a,b]$, and let $p_1, p_2, \cdots, p_n, \cdots$ be a sequence of partitions of $[a,b]$ for which

$$\lim_{n \to \infty} |p_n| = 0.$$

Then if $R_1, R_2, \cdots, R_n, \cdots$ is any sequence of Riemann sums of f associated with the given sequence of partitions,

$$\lim_{n \to \infty} R_n = \int_a^b f(x)\, dx.$$

Proof: For every number $\epsilon > 0$, $\epsilon/2(b-a) > 0$ and, by Theorem 8.12 there exists a partition $p = [x_0, x_1, \cdots, x_k]$ of $[a,b]$ such that

$$f(v_i) - f(u_i) < \frac{\epsilon}{2(b-a)}, \quad i = 1, 2, \cdots, k,$$

where $f(u_i)$ is the minimum value and $f(v_i)$ is the maximum value of f in the ith subinterval $[x_{i-1}, x_i]$ of p. Let d designate the length of the *shortest* subinterval of p; thus d is the smallest of the numbers $x_1 - x_0, x_2 - x_1, \cdots, x_k - x_{k-1}$.

By assumption,

$$\lim_{n \to \infty} |p_n| = 0,$$

and therefore corresponding to the positive number d there must exist a number N such that

$$|p_n| < d \quad \text{for every integer } n > N.$$

Hence, if $n > N$, the length of the *longest* subinterval of p_n is less than d; therefore, the length of every subinterval of p_n is less than the length of the shortest subinterval of p. Consequently, no subinterval of p_n can completely contain a subinterval of p. Thus, each subinterval of p_n intersects at most two subintervals of p (if a subinterval of p_n intersected three subintervals of p, it would have to contain one of the three completely).

If $n > N$ and $p_n = [x_0', x_1', \cdots, x_m']$, let $f(u_i')$ be the minimum value and $f(v_i')$ be the maximum value of f in the ith subinterval $[x_{i-1}', x_i']$. If u_i' and v_i' are in the same subinterval of p, then necessarily

(1)
$$f(v_i') - f(u_i') < \frac{\epsilon}{2(b-a)}.$$

If u_i' and v_i' are in different subintervals of p, they must be in two consecutive subintervals of p, say u_i' in $[x_{j-1}, x_j]$ and v_i' in $[x_j, x_{j+1}]$, since the subinterval $[x_{i-1}', x_i']$ intersects at most two subintervals of p. Now u_i' and x_j are in the same subinterval of p, and therefore

$$f(x_j) - f(u_i') < \frac{\epsilon}{2(b-a)};$$

and v_i' and x_j are in the next subinterval of p, so

$$f(v_i') - f(x_j) < \frac{\epsilon}{2(b-a)}.$$

On adding these inequalities, we get

$$[f(x_j) - f(u_i')] + [f(v_i') - f(x_j)] < \frac{\epsilon}{2(b-a)} + \frac{\epsilon}{2(b-a)},$$

or

(2)
$$f(v_i') - f(u_i') < \frac{\epsilon}{b-a}.$$

For either case (1) or case (2), we can state that

(3)
$$f(v_i') - f(u_i') < \frac{\epsilon}{b-a}$$

for each integer i, $i = 1, 2, \cdots, m$.

Let S_n designate the lower sum and T_n the upper sum of f relative to the partition p_n. If $n > N$ and $p_n = [x_0', x_1', \cdots, x_m']$, then

$$T_n - S_n = [f(v_1') - f(u_1')](x_1' - x_0') + [f(v_2') - f(u_2')](x_2' - x_1') \\ + \cdots + [f(v_m') - f(u_m')](x_m' - x_{m-1}')$$

and, using (3) above,

$$T_n - S_n < \frac{\epsilon}{b-a}(x_1' - x_0' + x_2' - x_1' + \cdots + x_m' - x_{m-1}'),$$

or (see the proof of 8.13)

$$T_n - S_n < \epsilon.$$

Thus, for every number $\epsilon > 0$, there exists a number N such that

(4)
$$T_n - S_n < \epsilon \quad \text{for every integer } n > N.$$

Since

$$S_n \leq \int_a^b f(x)\,dx \leq T_n,$$

we have by (4),

$$0 \le \int_a^b f(x)\, dx - S_n \le T_n - S_n < \epsilon \quad \text{for every } n > N.$$

Thus
$$\lim_{n \to \infty} S_n = \int_a^b f(x)\, dx,$$

and, by a similar argument,

$$\lim_{n \to \infty} T_n = \int_a^b f(x)\, dx.$$

Since
$$S_n \le R_n \le T_n,$$

we have by 9.8 that

$$\lim_{n \to \infty} R_n = \int_a^b f(x)\, dx.$$

This proves Theorem 9.12.

3. The sigma and delta notations

A sum of n terms such as $a_1 + a_2 + \cdots + a_n$ is designated by

$$\sum_{i=1}^n a_i$$

in the handy *sigma notation*; that is,

$$\sum_{i=1}^n a_i = a_1 + a_2 + \cdots + a_n.$$

Some examples of the use of the sigma notation are given below.

$$\sum_{i=1}^n i = 1 + 2 + \cdots + n.$$

$$\sum_{j=2}^m j^2 = 2^2 + 3^2 + \cdots + m^2.$$

$$\sum_{i=1}^n c = c + c + \cdots + c = nc.$$

$$\sum_{k=3}^6 k(k-2) = 3 \cdot 1 + 4 \cdot 2 + 5 \cdot 3 + 6 \cdot 4 = 50.$$

$$\sum_{i=0}^5 \frac{i-1}{i+1} = \frac{-1}{1} + \frac{0}{2} + \frac{1}{3} + \frac{2}{4} + \frac{3}{5} + \frac{4}{6} = 1.1.$$

We list a few useful summation formulas for future reference. These may be proved by mathematical induction.

9.12
$$\sum_{i=1}^{n} i = \frac{n(n+1)}{2}.$$

9.13
$$\sum_{i=1}^{n} i^2 = \frac{n(n+1)(2n+1)}{6}.$$

9.14
$$\sum_{i=1}^{n} i^3 = \left[\frac{n(n+1)}{2}\right]^2.$$

If $p = [x_0,x_1, \cdots ,x_m]$ is a partition of $[a,b]$, the *delta notation* is useful in describing the lengths of the subintervals of p as follows:

$$\Delta x_1 = x_1 - x_0, \quad \Delta x_2 = x_2 - x_1, \quad \cdots , \quad \Delta x_m = x_m - x_{m-1}.$$

The Greek letter delta, Δ, is used in mathematics to indicate a difference; thus Δx_1 is the difference between x_1 and x_0, Δx_2 between x_2 and x_1, and so on.

In terms of the sigma and delta notations, a Riemann sum such as

$$R_p = f(z_1)(x_1 - x_0) + f(z_2)(x_2 - x_1) + \cdots + f(z_m)(x_m - x_{m-1})$$

associated with a partition $p = [x_0,x_1, \cdots ,x_m]$ of $[a,b]$ can be written in the form

$$R_p = \sum_{i=1}^{m} f(z_i)\, \Delta x_i.$$

We may write the conclusion of Theorem 9.12 in a shortened form as follows.   Let each partition

$$p_n = [x_{n0},x_{n1}, \cdots ,x_{nk_n}];$$

thus the first of the two subscripts on x_{ni} indicates that the number is in the nth partition p_n, whereas the second subscript indicates the subinterval of p_n in which x_{ni} is contained.   That is, $[x_{ni-1},x_{ni}]$ is the ith subinterval of the nth partition p_n.   The number k_n is the number of subintervals of p_n. If

$$\Delta x_{ni} = x_{ni} - x_{ni-1},$$

then

$$R_n = \sum_{i=1}^{k_n} f(z_{ni})\, \Delta x_{ni}$$

where z_{ni} is a number in $[x_{ni-1},x_{ni}]$.   Hence, if $\lim_{n\to\infty} |p_n| = 0$,

$$\int_a^b f(x)\, dx = \lim_{n\to\infty} \sum_{i=1}^{k_n} f(z_{ni})\, \Delta x_{ni},$$

according to 9.12.

The partitions

$$r_1 = [a,b], \qquad\qquad\qquad \Delta x_1 = b - a,$$

$$r_2 = [a,a + \Delta x_2,b], \qquad\qquad \Delta x_2 = \frac{b - a}{2},$$

$$r_3 = [a, a + \Delta x_3, a + 2\Delta x_3, b], \qquad \Delta x_3 = \frac{b - a}{3},$$

. . . .

$$r_n = [a, a + \Delta x_n, a + 2\Delta x_n, \cdots, a + (n - 1)\Delta x_n, b], \qquad \Delta x_n = \frac{b - a}{n},$$

. . . .

are called the *regular partitions* of $[a,b]$. The regular partitions have sub-intervals of equal length. Thus the norm of r_n is Δx_n, the length of each subinterval of r_n. Since

$$\lim_{n \to \infty} \Delta x_n = \lim_{n \to \infty} \frac{b - a}{n} = 0,$$

the sequence $r_1, r_2, \cdots, r_n, \cdots$ of regular partitions may be used in Theorem 9.12, in which case the conclusion is

9.16
$$\int_a^b f(x) \, dx = \lim_{n \to \infty} \sum_{i=1}^{n} f(z_{ni}) \, \Delta x_n,$$

where z_{ni} is a number in the ith subinterval of r_n.

Example. Find $\int_0^2 x^2 \, dx$ by use of 9.16.

Solution: The nth regular partition r_n is given by:

$$r_n = [0, \Delta x_n, 2\Delta x_n, \cdots, n\Delta x_n], \qquad \Delta x_n = \frac{2}{n}.$$

If $f(x) = x^2$, then the function f is increasing in $[0,2]$, and

$$S_n = \sum_{i=1}^{n} f((i-1)\Delta x_n) \, \Delta x_n = \sum_{i=1}^{n} (i - 1)^2 \, (\Delta x_n)^3.$$

The constant $(\Delta x_n)^3 = 8/n^3$ may be factored from each term of this last sum, yielding

$$S_n = \frac{8}{n^3} \sum_{i=1}^{n} (i - 1)^2.$$

Now

$$\sum_{i=1}^{n} (i - 1)^2 = 0^2 + 1^2 + \cdots + (n - 1)^2 = \sum_{i=1}^{n-1} i^2;$$

thus, using 9.14,

$$S_n = \frac{8}{n^3} \sum_{i=1}^{n-1} i^2 = \frac{8}{n^3} \frac{(n - 1)n(2n - 1)}{6},$$

or, simplifying,

$$S_n = \frac{4}{3}\left(2 - \frac{3}{n} + \frac{1}{n^2}\right).$$

By 9.16,

$$\int_0^2 x^2 \, dx = \lim_{n \to \infty} \sum_{i=1}^{n} (i-1)^2 (\Delta x_n)^3$$

$$= \lim_{n \to \infty} \frac{4}{3} \left(2 - \frac{3}{n} + \frac{1}{n^2} \right) = \frac{8}{3}.$$

This result naturally checks with that obtained using the fundamental theorem of the calculus:

$$\int_0^2 x^2 \, dx = \frac{x^3}{3} \bigg|_0^2 = \frac{8}{3}.$$

■ ■ ■ EXERCISES

1. Show that $\displaystyle\sum_{i=1}^{n} (a_i + b_i) = \sum_{i=1}^{n} a_i + \sum_{j=1}^{n} b_i.$

2. Show that $\displaystyle\sum_{i=1}^{n} c a_i = c \sum_{i=1}^{n} a_i.$

Use Exercises 1 and 2 and Formulas 9.13–9.15 to evaluate the following sums.

3. $\displaystyle\sum_{i=1}^{8} (i^2 - 2i).$ **4.** $\displaystyle\sum_{i=1}^{10} (3i^2 - 4i + 1).$

5. $\displaystyle\sum_{j=1}^{7} (4j^2 - 5j + 3).$ **6.** $\displaystyle\sum_{k=1}^{12} \frac{3k+1}{5}.$

7. $\displaystyle\sum_{k=1}^{n} (2k - 1).$ **8.** $\displaystyle\sum_{i=1}^{n} (2i - 1)^2.$

9. $\displaystyle\sum_{i=1}^{n} (2i - 1)^3.$ **10.** $\displaystyle\sum_{j=1}^{n} (3j - 2)^2.$

Find the lower sum S_n and the upper sum T_n relative to the regular partition r_n for each of the following functions over the indicated interval. Then find either $\lim_{n \to \infty} S_n$ or $\lim_{n \to \infty} T_n$, and check your answer by integration.

11. $f(x) = x$, [0,4].   **12.** $f(x) = -2x$, [0,3].
13. $g(x) = 2x^2$, [0,2].   **14.** $g(x) = 3x^2 + 1$, [0,2].
15. $F(x) = x + x^2$, [0,3].   **16.** $f(x) = 2x + x^2$, [0,2].
17. $f(x) = x^2 - 7x + 2$, [1,3].   **18.** $g(x) = 3 - 2x + x^2$, [−1,1].
19. $g(x) = x^3$, [0,2].   **20.** $F(x) = 1 - x^3$, [0,1].

Find the Riemann sum R_n relative to the regular partition r_n, with z_{ni} (9.16) taken as the mid-point of the ith subinterval of r_n, for each of the following functions over the indicated interval. Then find $\lim_{n \to \infty} R_n$, and check your answer by integration.

21. $f(x) = x$, $[0,4]$.   **22.** $f(x) = -2x$, $[0,3]$.
23. $g(x) = x^2$, $[0,3]$.   **24.** $g(x) = 1 - x^2$, $[1,3]$.
25. $F(x) = x^3$, $[0,2]$.   **26.** $f(x) = 1 - x^3$, $[0,1]$.

4. Solids of revolution, the disc method

If the semicircle in Figure 9.1 is revolved about the x-axis, the region bounded by the semicircle and the x-axis will sweep out a sphere. Similarly, the triangular region in Figure 9.2 will sweep out a right circular

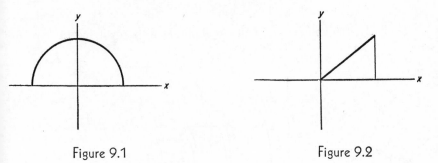

Figure 9.1   Figure 9.2

cone if it is revolved about the x-axis. Because of the way in which the sphere and the cone can be generated, they are called solids of revolution. It is the aim of this section to show how the volume of a solid of revolution can be defined and computed.

The simplest solid of revolution is the circular cylinder, generated by revolving a rectangle about a side. If H and R designate the lengths of the sides of the rectangle, and if the rectangle is rotated about a side of length H (Figure 9.3), then the area of a circular base of the cylinder is πR^2 and the altitude (or thickness) of the cylinder is H. We define the volume of this cylinder to be $\pi R^2 H$, that is, the area of the base times the altitude.

The volume of a composite of circular cylinders (or *discs*) as in Figure 9.4 is the sum of the volumes of the component cylinders. This is also a solid of revolution, generated by rotating a rectangular polygon about a line (Figure 9.5).

Let f be a function which is continuous and non-negative in an interval $[a,b]$. If the region under the graph of f from a to b is revolved about the x-axis, it will sweep out a solid of revolution as indicated in **Figure 9.6.** We wish to assign to this solid a number V, its volume.

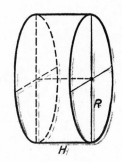

Figure 9.3

With this in mind, let $p = [x_0, x_1, \cdots, x_m]$ be a partition of $[a,b]$. Inscribe a rectangular polygon under the graph of f from a to b in the usual way (Figure 9.7). If $f(u_i)$ is the least value of f in the subinterval $[x_{i-1}, x_i]$, then the volume $\underline{V}_p$ of the solid obtained by revolving the inscribed rectangular polygon about the x-axis is given by

$$\underline{V}_p = \sum_{i=1}^{m} \pi \cdot f^2(u_i) \, \Delta x_i,$$

since the ith cylinder of this solid has radius $f(u_i)$ and thickness Δx_i. This solid made up of cylinders is completely contained in the given solid of revolution, and therefore we must have

$$\underline{V}_p \leq V.$$

Similarly, the volume $\overline{V}_p$ of the solid obtained by revolving the circum-

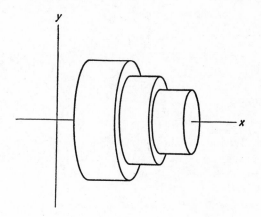

Figure 9.4

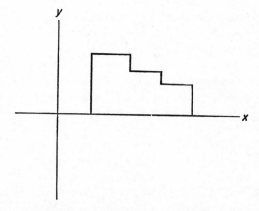

Figure 9.5

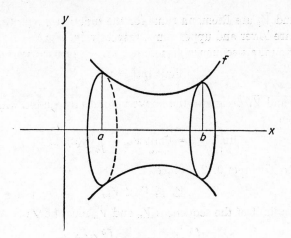

Figure 9.6

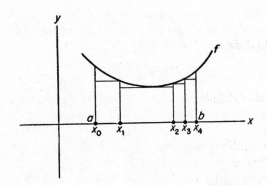

Figure 9.7

scribed rectangular polygon about the x-axis is given by

$$\overline{V}_p = \sum_{i=1}^{m} \pi \cdot f^2(v_i) \, \Delta x_i,$$

where $f(v_i)$ is the maximum value of f in $[x_{i-1}, x_i]$. Clearly

$$\overline{V}_p \geq V.$$

The sums $\underline{V}_p$ and $\overline{V}_p$ above have the appearance of Riemann sums, but not for the function f. However, if

$$g(x) = \pi \cdot f^2(x),$$

then the function g is continuous in $[a,b]$ and

$$\underline{V}_p = \sum_{i=1}^{m} g(u_i) \, \Delta x_i, \qquad \overline{V}_p = \sum_{i=1}^{m} g(v_i) \, \Delta x_i.$$

Thus $\underline{V}_p$ and $\overline{V}_p$ are Riemann sums for the function g over $[a,b]$. (Actually, they are lower and upper sums, respectively, of g.)

Now if we take a sequence $p_1, p_2, \cdots, p_n, \cdots$ of partitions of $[a,b]$ with

$$\lim_{n \to \infty} |p_n| = 0,$$

and let $\underline{V}_n$ and $\overline{V}_n$ designate the above volumes associated with the partition p_n, then

$$\lim_{n \to \infty} \underline{V}_n = \lim_{n \to \infty} \overline{V}_n = \int_a^b g(x)\, dx$$

according to Theorem 9.12. Since

$$\underline{V}_n \le V < \overline{V}_n,$$

the common limit of the sequences $\underline{V}_n$ and $\overline{V}_n$ must be V:

$$V = \int_a^b g(x)\, dx = \pi \int_a^b f^2(x)\, dx.$$

We are therefore led to the following definition.

If f is continuous and nonnegative in the interval $[a,b]$, the volume V of the solid of revolution generated by revolving the region under the graph of f from a to b about the x-axis is given by

9.17 $$V = \pi \int_a^b f^2(x)\, dx.$$

This method of defining a volume of revolution is often called the "disc method," since discs are inscribed in and circumscribed about the solid of revolution.

Even if the continuous function f is negative in the interval $[a,b]$, the above definition of the volume of revolution still holds. The solid of revolution generated by revolving the region bounded by the graph of f, the x-axis, and the lines $x = a$ and $x = b$, is just the same as that gen-

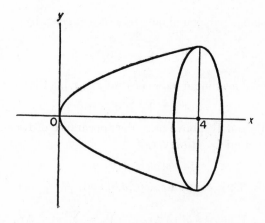

Figure 9.8

erated by revolving the region under the graph of $|f|$ from a to b about the x-axis.   Thus,

$$V = \pi \int_a^b |f(x)|^2 \, dx = \pi \int_a^b f^2(x) \, dx.$$

Example 1.   Find the volume of the solid generated by rotating about the x-axis the region under the graph of f from 0 to 4, if

$$f(x) = \sqrt{x}.$$

Solution: The solid of revolution whose volume we seek is sketched in Figure 9.8. Its volume is given by

$$V = \pi \int_0^4 (\sqrt{x})^2 \, dx = \pi \int_0^4 x \, dx = \frac{\pi x^2}{2} \bigg|_0^4 = 8\pi.$$

Example 2.   Derive the formula for the volume of a right circular cone of altitude h which has a base of radius r.

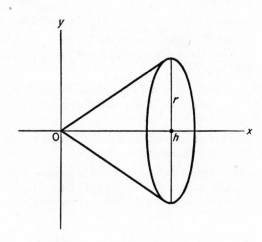

Figure 9.9

Solution: The cone is obtained by revolving the right triangle of Figure 9.9 about the x-axis.   The line of the figure has equation

$$y = \frac{r}{h} x.$$

Thus, if

$$f(x) = \frac{r}{h} x,$$

The cone is generated by revolving about the x-axis the region under the graph of f from 0 to h.   Hence the volume V of the cone is given by

$$V = \pi \int_0^h \left(\frac{r}{h} x\right)^2 \, dx = \frac{\pi r^2}{h^2} \int_0^h x^2 \, dx = \frac{\pi r^2 x^3}{3 h^2} \bigg|_0^h = \frac{1}{3} \pi r^2 h.$$

■ ■ ■ EXERCISES

In each of the following exercises, the graphs of the given equations bound a region of the plane. Find the volume of the solid obtained by rotating each region about the x-axis. Sketch the solid.

1. $y = x^2, y = 0, x = 2.$ 2. $y = 2x^2, y = 0, x = 3.$

3. $y = \sqrt{4 + x}, x = 0, y = 0.$ 4. $y = 4 - x^2, y = 0.$

5. $y = \dfrac{1}{x}, x = 1, x = 3, y = 0.$ 6. $y = \sqrt{9 - x}, x = 0, y = 0.$

7. $y = x^2 - x, y = 0.$

8. $y = \dfrac{4}{x + 1}, x = -5, x = -2, y = 0.$

9. $y = \dfrac{1}{(x - 1)^3}, x = -1, x = 0, y = 0.$

10. $y = \sqrt[3]{x}, x = 0, x = 8, y = 0.$

11. Find the volume of a sphere of radius r by the methods of this section.

12. Find the volume of a frustum of a cone by the methods of this section. Take the radius of the upper base to be r, of the lower base to be R, and the altitude to be h.

13. Let a sphere of radius r be cut by a plane, thereby forming a segment of the sphere of height h. Prove that the volume of the segment is $\pi h^2(r - h/3)$.

14. Find the volume of an ellipsoid of revolution formed by rotating an ellipse about its major axis; its minor axis.

15. Find the volume of a parabolic disc formed by rotating the region bounded by a parabola and its latus rectum about the latus rectum. Let p be the distance between the focus and the vertex of the parabola.

5. A product formula

If the functions f and g are continuous in a closed interval, then so is their product. Thus the definite integral

$$\int_a^b f(x)g(x)\, dx$$

exists, and if $p_1, p_2, \cdots, p_n, \cdots$ is a sequence of partitions of $[a,b]$ such that $\underset{n \to \infty}{\text{limit}}\, |p_n| = 0$, we have by 9.12 that

$$\int_a^b f(x)g(x)\, dx = \underset{n \to \infty}{\text{limit}} \sum_{i=1}^{k_n} f(z_{ni})g(z_{ni})\, \Delta x_{ni},$$

where z_{ni} is a number in the subinterval $[x_{ni-1}, x_{ni}]$ of p_n.

In the solution of some physical problems, it is necessary to evaluate a limit of the form

$$\operatorname*{limit}_{n\to\infty} \sum_{i=1}^{k_n} f(w_{ni})g(z_{ni})\, \Delta x_{ni},$$

where the numbers w_{ni} and z_{ni} are in the interval $[x_{ni-1}, x_{ni}]$. Since f and g are evaluated at possibly different numbers in each subinterval $[x_{ni-1}, x_{ni}]$, it is not evident that this limit is again a definite integral. However it is according to the following theorem.

9.18 Theorem. Let the functions f and g be continuous in a closed interval $[a,b]$ and let $p_1, p_2, \cdots, p_n, \cdots$ be a sequence of partitions of $[a,b]$, $p_n = [x_{n0}, x_{n1}, \cdots, x_{nk_n}]$, such that

$$\operatorname*{limit}_{n\to\infty} |p_n| = 0.$$

If w_{ni} and z_{ni} are numbers in the interval $[x_{ni-1}, x_{ni}]$, then

$$\operatorname*{limit}_{n\to\infty} \sum_{i=1}^{k_n} f(w_{ni})g(z_{ni})\, \Delta x_{ni} = \int_a^b f(x)g(x)\, dx.$$

Proof: Let M be a number such that $|f(x)| \le M$ in $[a,b]$. If

$$P_n = \left| \sum_{i=1}^{k_n} f(w_{ni})g(z_{ni})\, \Delta x_{ni} - \sum_{i=1}^{k_n} f(w_{ni})g(w_{ni})\, \Delta x_{ni} \right|$$

then

$$P_n = \left| \sum_{i=1}^{k_n} f(w_{ni})[g(z_{ni}) - g(w_{ni})]\, \Delta x_{ni} \right|.$$

Since the absolute value of a sum of terms is less than or equal to the sum of the absolute values of the terms,

$$0 \le P_n \le \sum_{i=1}^{k_n} \left| f(w_{ni})[g(z_{ni}) - g(w_{ni})]\, \Delta x_{ni} \right|$$

and

$$0 \le P_n \le \sum_{i=1}^{k_n} |f(w_{ni})||g(z_{ni}) - g(w_{ni})| \Delta x_{ni}.$$

Hence, since each $|f(w_{ni})| \le M$,

$$0 \le P_n \le M \sum_{i=1}^{k_n} |g(z_{ni}) - g(w_{ni})| \Delta x_{ni}.$$

If $g(u_{ni})$ and $g(v_{ni})$ are, respectively, the minimum and maximum values of g in $[x_{ni-1}, x_{ni}]$, then

$$g(u_{ni}) \le g(z_{ni}) \le g(v_{ni}), \qquad g(u_{ni}) \le g(w_{ni}) \le g(v_{ni}).$$

The inequalities above may be combined to yield

$$-[g(v_{ni}) - g(u_{ni})] \le g(z_{ni}) - g(w_{ni}) \le g(v_{ni}) - g(u_{ni}),$$

or

$$|g(z_{ni}) - g(w_{ni})| \le g(v_{ni}) - g(u_{ni}).$$

Therefore

$$0 \le P_n \le M \sum_{i=1}^{k_n} [g(v_{ni}) - g(u_{ni})] \, \Delta x_{ni},$$

or
$$0 \le P_n \le M \left[\sum_{i=1}^{k_n} g(v_{ni}) \, \Delta x_{ni} - \sum_{i=1}^{k_n} g(u_{ni}) \, \Delta x_{ni} \right].$$

Since

$$\lim_{n \to \infty} \sum_{i=1}^{k_n} g(v_{ni}) \, \Delta x_{ni} = \lim_{n \to \infty} \sum_{i=1}^{k_n} g(u_{ni}) \, \Delta x_{ni} = \int_a^b g(x) \, dx,$$

we conclude that

$$\lim_{n \to \infty} P_n = 0.$$

The theorem now follows from 9.10.

6. Solids of revolution, the shell method

Another approach to the problem of defining the volume of a solid of revolution is the so-called "shell method" described below. We recall that the volume of a solid of revolution was approximated by a sum of volumes of discs in a previous section.

If a rectangle is revolved about a line parallel to one of its sides and not intersecting the rectangle, then the solid generated is a cylindrical shell (Figure 9.10). If r is the inner radius and R is the outer radius of this shell, and if h is its altitude, then the volume V of the shell is the difference between the volumes of two cylinders:

$$V = \pi R^2 h - \pi r^2 h = \pi(R^2 - r^2)h.$$

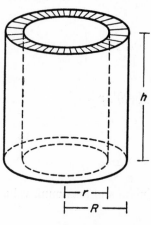

Figure 9.10

Let f be a function continuous and non-negative in the interval $[a,b]$, where $0 \le a < b$. We wish to define the volume of the solid obtained by revolving about *the y-axis* the region under the graph of f from a to b.

We start off by inscribing a rectangular polygon under the graph of f from a to b. If this polygon is rotated about the y-axis, it sweeps out a solid composed of cylindrical shells (Figure 9.11). This solid is completely contained in the solid whose volume we desire. If $p = [x_0, x_1, \cdots, x_m]$ is the given partition of $[a,b]$, the volume $\underline{V}_p$ of the solid made up of cylindrical shells is given by

$$\underline{V}_p = \sum_{i=1}^{m} \pi(x_i^2 - x_{i-1}^2)f(u_i),$$

where, as usual, $f(u_i)$ is the least value of f in $[x_{i-1}, x_i]$.

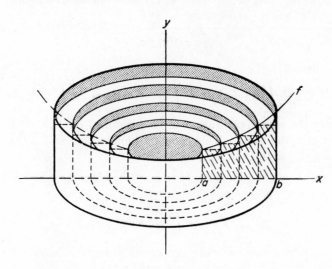

Figure 9.11

If we circumscribe a rectangular polygon over the graph of f from a to b and revolve this polygon about the y-axis, the generated solid has volume

$$\overline{V}_p = \sum_{i=1}^{m} \pi(x_i^2 - x_{i-1}^2)f(v_i),$$

where $f(v_i)$ is the greatest value of f in $[x_{i-1}, x_i]$. The solid so formed completely contains the solid of revolution whose volume we desire.

Therefore, if the volume of the solid obtained by revolving about the y-axis the region under the graph of f from a to b is V,

$$\underline{V}_p \le V \le \overline{V}_p.$$

We can write $\underline{V}_p$ in the form

$$\underline{V}_p = \sum_{i=1}^{m} \pi(x_i + x_{i-1})f(u_i)(x_i - x_{i-1}),$$

and therefore in the form

(1) $$\underline{V}_p = \sum_{i=1}^{m} \pi x_i \cdot f(u_i)\,\Delta x_i + \sum_{i=1}^{m} \pi x_{i-1} \cdot f(u_i)\,\Delta x_i.$$

Each of these sums has the form

$$\sum_{i=1}^{m} f(u_i)g(z_i)\,\Delta x_i, \qquad \text{where } g(x) = \pi x.$$

If we take a sequence of partitions $p_1, p_2, \cdots, p_n, \cdots$ such that

$$\lim_{n \to \infty} |p_n| = 0,$$

then the limit of each of the sums in (1) as n approaches infinity exists by Theorem 9.18 and has the value

$$\int_a^b \pi x f(x) \, dx.$$

Therefore, from (1),

$$\lim_{n \to \infty} \underline{V}_{p_n} = \int_a^b \pi x \cdot f(x) \, dx + \int_a^b \pi x \cdot f(x) \, dx = 2\pi \int_a^b x f(x) \, dx.$$

Evidently the same operations can be performed on $\overline{V}_p$, and the final limit is exactly the same. This common limit of $\underline{V}_{p_n}$ and $\overline{V}_{p_n}$ as n approaches infinity is the volume V.

The volume V of the solid obtained by revolving about the y-axis the region under the graph of f from a to b is given by

9.19 $V = 2\pi \int_a^b x f(x) \, dx.$

Example 1. Find the volume of the solid generated by rotating about the y-axis the region bounded by the x-axis, $x = 2$, and the graph of $y = x^2$.

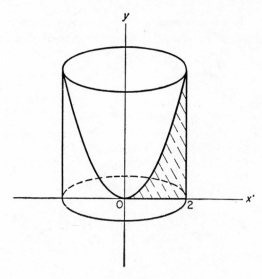

Figure 9.12

Solution: The solid in question is a hollowed-out cylinder, as sketched in Figure 9.12. The region under the graph of f from 0 to 2, where

$$f(x) = x^2,$$

is the one rotated about the y-axis.　Hence, by 9.19,

$$V = 2\pi \int_0^2 x \cdot x^2 \, dx = 2\pi \int_0^2 x^3 \, dx = 2\pi \left. \frac{x^4}{4} \right|_0^2 = 8\pi.$$

Example 2.　Find the volume of a sphere of radius r.

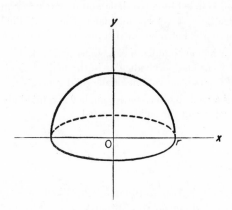

Figure 9.13

Solution: A hemisphere of radius r can be generated by rotating the quarter circle of radius r (Figure 9.13) about the y-axis.　Hence the volume of the hemisphere is given by

$$V = 2\pi \int_0^r x\sqrt{r^2 - x^2} \, dx.$$

If we let

$$u = r^2 - x^2, \qquad du = -2x \, dx,$$

then

$$V = -\pi \int_{r^2}^0 u^{1/2} \, du = -\frac{2}{3} \pi u^{3/2} \Big|_{r^2}^0 = \frac{2}{3} \pi r^3.$$

Thus the volume of the sphere is $4\pi r^3/3$.

■ ■ ■ EXERCISES

In each of the following exercises, the graphs of the given equations bound a region of the plane.　Use the shell method to find the volume of the solid obtained by rotating each region about the y-axis.　Sketch the solid

1. $y = \sqrt{x}$, $x = 4$, $y = 0$.　　　　2. $y = x$, $x = 4$, $y = 0$.

3. $y = x^3$, $x = 2$, $y = 0$.　　　　4. $y = x\sqrt{x}$, $x = 4$, $y = 0$.

5. $y^3 = x$, $x = 8$, $y = 0$.　　　　6. $y^2 = 4x$, $x = 1$.

7. $y = \dfrac{1}{x}$, $x = 1$, $x = 4$, $y = 0$.　　8. $y = \dfrac{1}{\sqrt{x}}$, $x = 1$, $x = 4$, $y = 0$.

9. $x^2 - y^2 = 1$, $x = 3$.　　　　10. $x^2 + 4y^2 = 4$, $x = 1$, $x = 2$.

11. A hole of radius R is drilled through the center of a sphere of radius r. Find the volume of the solid remaining.

12. The region bounded by the hyperbola $x^2/a^2 - y^2/b^2 = 1$ and the line through a focus perpendicular to the transverse axis is rotated about the y-axis. Find the volume of the solid generated.

13. The region bounded by a parabola and its latus rectum is rotated about a line through its vertex perpendicular to the axis. Find the volume of the solid generated. Let p be the distance between the focus and the vertex.

14. The smaller region bounded by an ellipse and its latus rectum (i.e., the line through a focus and perpendicular to the major axis) is rotated about the minor axis. Find the volume of the solid generated.

15. A sector of a circle having central angle θ is rotated about one of its sides. Find the volume of the solid generated.

7. *Work*

If a constant force of F lb is applied to an object in moving it a distance of d ft, then the *work* done on the object has magnitude W defined by

$$W = Fd.$$

If the unit of force is pounds and the unit of distance is feet, then the unit of work is foot-pounds. Other possible units of work are inch-pounds, foot-tons, etc.

Example 1. An object of weight 110 lb is lifted (at a constant velocity) a distance of 23 ft. Find the amount of work done on the object.

Solution: A force of 110 lb is needed to lift the object; therefore the amount of work done on the object in lifting it 23 ft is given by

$$W = 110 \cdot 23 = 2530 \text{ ft-lb.}$$

The calculus comes into play when we wish to define the work done on an object by a variable force. Let us assume that an object A is being moved along a coordinate line L (Fig. 9.14), and that a force of $F(x)$ units

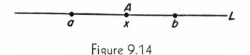

Figure 9.14

is being applied to A when A is at the point with coordinate x on L. We assume that the object A moves from a to b and that the force function F so defined is continuous in the interval $[a,b]$.

In order to define the amount of work done on the object A as it moves from a to b, we select a partition $p = [x_0, x_1, \cdots, x_m]$ of $[a,b]$. In each subinterval $[x_{i-1}, x_i]$ of p, let $F(u_i)$ be the minimum and $F(v_i)$ be the maximum value of the force F.   It is reasonable to assume that the amount W_i of work done on A as it moves from x_{i-1} to x_i is between the minimum value of the force times the distance Δx_i and the maximum value of the force times Δx_i:

$$(1) \qquad\qquad F(u_i)\,\Delta x_i \le W_i \le F(v_i)\,\Delta x_i.$$

Since the total amount W of work done on A as it moves from a to b is just the sum of the W_i,

$$W = \sum_{i=1}^{m} W_i,$$

we obtain from (1) that

$$(2) \qquad\qquad \sum_{i=1}^{m} F(u_i)\,\Delta x_i \le W \le \sum_{i=1}^{m} F(v_i)\,\Delta x_i.$$

The inequality (2) holds for every partition p of $[a,b]$. If we take a sequence of partitions $p_1, p_2, \cdots, p_n, \cdots$ with norms of limit zero, then the limit of each sum in (2) as n approaches infinity is equal to

$$\int_a^b F(x)\,dx$$

according to Theorem 9.11.   Their common limit must be W.   This leads us to the following definition.

The amount W of work done on an object in moving it from a to b along a coordinate line is given by

9.20 $$\qquad\qquad W = \int_a^b F(x)\,dx,$$

where $F(x)$ is the force applied to the object at position x.

Example 2.   Find the amount of work done in stretching a spring from its natural length of 6 in. to double that length if a force of 20 lb is needed to hold the spring at double its natural length.

Solution: The force $F(x)$ required to hold a spring extended (within its elastic limit) x units beyond its natural length is given by

$$F(x) = kx, \quad k \text{ a constant,}$$

according to *Hooke's law*.   We are given that $F(6) = 20$; therefore

$$20 = k \cdot 6, \quad \text{and} \quad k = \frac{10}{3}.$$

Thus

$$F(x) = \frac{10}{3}\,x$$

for this particular spring.

The amount W of work done in stretching the spring from its natural length ($x = 0$) to double its natural length ($x = 6$) is given by

$$W = \int_0^6 \frac{10}{3}\,x\,dx = \frac{5}{3}\,x^2 \Big|_0^6 = 60 \text{ in.-lb.}$$

If we wish to find the amount of work done in stretching this spring from a position already 2 in. extended to a position 4 in. extended, we evaluate the integral

$$\int_{2}^{4} \frac{10}{3} x \, dx = 20 \text{ in.-lb};$$

and so on.

Example 3. Find the amount W of work done in removing all the water at the top from a vertical cylindrical tank 4 ft in diameter and 6 ft high.

Solution: Let us think of the water as being pushed out of the tank by a piston starting out from the bottom of the tank (Figure 9.15). The force $F(x)$ on the piston after it has moved a distance of x ft is just the weight of the water remaining in the tank, that is,

$$F(x) = \pi \cdot 2^2 \cdot (6 - x) \cdot k,$$

where $k = 62.5$ lb, the weight of a cubic foot of water. Hence

$$W = \int_{0}^{6} 4\pi k(6 - x) \, dx = 4\pi k \left(6x - \frac{x^2}{2} \right) \Big|_{0}^{6}$$

$$= 72\pi k = 14{,}140 \text{ ft-lb (approx.)}.$$

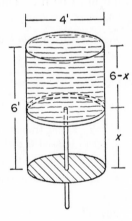

Figure 9.15

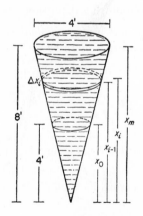

Figure 9.16

Example 4. Water is to be pumped out of the conical tank in Figure 9.16 to a point 10 ft above the top of the tank. Find the amount of work required to pump out 4 ft of water.

Solution: Let us think of the mass of water in the tank as cut up into m disc-shaped pieces. One such piece is shown in Figure 9.16. The weight M_i of this piece satisfies the inequality

$$62.5\pi r_{i-1}^2 \, \Delta x_i \leq M_i \leq 62.5\pi r_i^2 \, \Delta x_i.$$

This slice must be lifted a distance between $10 + (8 - x_i)$ and $10 + (8 - x_{i-1})$

ft.   Hence the work W_i done in emptying the water from this slice satisfies the inequality

$$62.5\pi r_{i-1}^2(18 - x_i)\,\Delta x_i \leq W_i \leq 62.5\pi r_i^2(18 - x_{i-1})\,\Delta x_i.$$

The total work W done in emptying the tank therefore satisfies the inequality

(1) $$\sum_{i=1}^{m} 62.5\pi r_{i-1}^2(18 - x_i)\,\Delta x_i \leq W \leq \sum_{i=1}^{m} 62.5\pi r_i^2(18 - x_{i-1})\,\Delta x_i.$$

It is evident by similar triangles that

$$\frac{r_i}{x_i} = \frac{2}{8}, \quad \text{or} \quad r_i = \frac{x_i}{4}.$$

If we take a sequence of partitions $p_1, p_2, \cdots, p_n, \cdots$ of $[4,8]$ with norms having limit zero, each partition p_n of the sequence leads to an inequality of the form (1).   Taking the limit of each sum in (1) as n approaches infinity, we obtain the same value

$$\int_4^8 62.5\pi \left(\frac{x}{4}\right)^2 (18 - x)\,dx$$

according to Theorem 9.18.   Thus

$$W = \frac{62.5\pi}{16} \int_4^8 (18x^2 - x^3)\,dx$$

$$= \frac{125\pi}{32}\left(6x^3 - \frac{x^4}{4}\right)\Big|_4^8$$

$$= 6750\pi \text{ ft-lb.}$$

■ ■ ■ EXERCISES

1. Find the work done in stretching a spring from its natural length of 12 in. to a length of 18 in. if a force of 4 lb is needed to hold the spring extended 1 in.

2. A spring of natural length 5 in. requires a force of 9 oz to hold it at a length of 7 in.   Find the work done in stretching the spring from a length of 7 in. to a length of 10 in.

3. A vertical cylindrical tank 6 ft in diameter and 10 ft high is half full of water.   Find the amount of work done in pumping all the water out at the top of the tank.

4. A vertical cylindrical tank 6 ft in diameter and 10 ft high is full of water. Find the amount of work done in pumping half the water out at the top of the tank.

5. According to Newton's law of universal gravitation, two objects of weights W_1 and W_2 lb are attracted to each other by a force of kW_1W_2/x^2 lb, where x ft is the distance between the objects and k is a constant.   Find the work done in separating the objects from a distance of a ft to a distance of b ft apart.

6. A certain chain, 100 ft long and weighing 4 lb/ft, is being wound up in a windlass situated on the 6th floor of a building under construction. Find the amount of work required to wind up the chain. (*Hint:* The force $F(x)$ required to hold the chain when x ft of the chain remains to be wound is $4x$ lb.)

7. Do the preceding exercise in case there is a 500-lb weight hanging from the end of the chain.

8. Water is being pumped into the conical tank of Example 4 above (Figure 9.16) at the bottom. Find the amount of work required to fill the tank.

9. Water is being pumped into the cylindrical tank of Example 3 above (Figure 9.15) at the bottom. Find the amount of work required to fill the tank half full.

10. A tank has the shape of a paraboloid of revolution. The radius of the circular top is 4 ft and its depth is 10 ft. If the tank is full of water, find the work required to empty the water from the tank at a point 5 ft above the top of the tank. (*Hint:* If the parabola has its vertex at the origin, its equation is $y = kx^2$ for some determinable number k. Then "slice" the water into discs as in Example 4 above.)

8. Approximations

If no antiderivative of f is known, then we cannot evaluate

$$\int_a^b f(x)\, dx$$

by use of the fundamental theorem. However, it still is possible to approximate the value of this integral as closely as we desire. One way of approximating the value of an integral will be given in this section; better methods will be given in a later chapter.

Let the function f be continuous in a closed interval $[a,b]$, and let $p_1, p_2, \cdots, p_n, \cdots$ be any sequence of partitions of $[a,b]$ for which

$$\lim_{n \to \infty} |p_n| = 0.$$

If $R_1, R_2, \cdots, R_n, \cdots$ is any sequence of Riemann sums associated with the given sequence of partitions,

$$\lim_{n \to \infty} R_n = \int_a^b f(x)\, dx.$$

Hence, for every $\epsilon > 0$ there exists a number N such that

$$\left| \int_a^b f(x)\, dx - R_n \right| < \epsilon \quad \text{for each } n > N.$$

That is to say, every R_n, $n > N$, is an approximation within ϵ of the integral in question.

In an actual example, we can take as our sequence of partitions of $[a,b]$

the sequence of regular partitions $r_1, r_2, \cdots, r_n, \cdots$. If

$$S_1, S_2, \cdots, S_n, \cdots \quad \text{and} \quad T_1, T_2, \cdots, T_n, \cdots$$

are the sequences of lower and upper sums relative to the regular partitions, then for each integer n,

$$S_n \leq \int_a^b f(x)\, dx \leq T_n, \qquad \underset{n \to \infty}{\text{limit}}\ S_n = \int_a^b f(x)\, dx = \underset{n \to \infty}{\text{limit}}\ T_n.$$

Thus S_n and T_n are approximations of the integral, with the goodness of the approximation increasing with the size of n. Since the integral is between S_n and T_n, S_n (or T_n) is an approximation of $\int_a^b f(x)\, dx$ with an error of at most $T_n - S_n$. Also, $(S_n + T_n)/2$ is an approximation of the integral correct to within $(T_n - S_n)/2$.

Example 1. Approximate $\displaystyle \int_1^3 \frac{1}{x}\, dx$.

Solution: The function f defined by

$$f(x) = \frac{1}{x}$$

is continuous in the interval $[1,3]$. We do not as yet know the antiderivative of f, so the integral cannot be evaluated in the usual manner. The function f is decreasing in the interval $[1,3]$.

The regular partitions of $[1,3]$ are

$$r_1 = [1,3],\ r_2 = [1,2,3],\ r_3 = [1,\tfrac{5}{3},\tfrac{7}{3},3],$$

and, in general,

$$r_n = [1,\ 1 + \Delta x_n,\ 1 + 2\,\Delta x_n,\ \cdots,\ 1 + (n-1)\,\Delta x_n,\ 3],\ \Delta x_n = \frac{2}{n}.$$

The maximum and minimum values of f in any subinterval $[x_{i-1}, x_i]$ are $f(x_{i-1})$ and $f(x_i)$, respectively. Thus

$$S_1 = f(3)\cdot 2 = \frac{2}{3} = .67 \text{ (approx.)}$$

$$S_2 = f(2)\cdot 1 + f(3)\cdot 1 = \frac{5}{6} = .83$$

$$S_3 = f\left(\frac{5}{3}\right)\cdot\frac{2}{3} + f\left(\frac{7}{3}\right)\cdot\frac{2}{3} + f(3)\cdot\frac{2}{3} = .91$$

and

$$T_1 = f(1)\cdot 2 = 2$$

$$T_2 = f(1)\cdot 1 + f(2)\cdot 1 = 1.5$$

$$T_3 = f(1)\cdot\frac{2}{3} + f\left(\frac{5}{3}\right)\cdot\frac{2}{3} + f\left(\frac{7}{3}\right)\cdot\frac{2}{3} = 1.35,$$

and so on. If we take the arithmetic average of S_3 and T_3, namely,

$$\frac{1}{2}\,(.91 + 1.35) = 1.13,$$

then we can assert that 1.13 is an approximation of the integral correct to within

$$\frac{1}{2}(T_3 - S_3) = .22$$

units.   Actually, 1.13 differs from the correct value of the integral by less than .04 unit.

A more accurate approximation of the given integral can be found by computing additional S_n and T_n.

The averaging of S_n and T_n above to approximate the integral suggests the following so-called *trapezoidal* rule: if $r_n = [x_0, x_1, \cdots, x_n]$ is the regular partition of $[a,b]$, then

9.21 $\quad \displaystyle\int_a^b f(x)\,dx \doteq \frac{b-a}{2n}[f(x_0) + 2f(x_1) + \cdots + 2f(x_{n-1}) + f(x_n)],$

where the symbol $\doteq$ means "approximately equal."

The right side of 9.21 is just the arithmetic average of two Riemann sums of f relative to the partition r_n.   Thus, if

$$R_1 = \sum_{i=1}^{n} f(x_{i-1})\,\Delta x_n, \quad R_2 = \sum_{i=1}^{n} f(x_i)\,\Delta x_n, \quad \Delta x_n = \frac{b-a}{n},$$

then

$$\frac{R_1 + R_2}{2} = \frac{\Delta x_n}{2}\left[\sum_{i=1}^{n} f(x_{i-1}) + \sum_{i=1}^{n} f(x_i)\right]$$

$$= \frac{b-a}{2n}\,[f(x_0) + 2f(x_1) + \cdots + 2f(x_{n-1}) + f(x_n)].$$

If the graph of f is above the x-axis between $x = a$ and $x = b$, then the right side of 9.21 is just the sum of the areas of n trapezoids, each of thick-

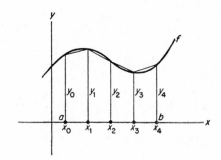

Figure 9.17

ness Δx_n, as indicated in Figure 9.17.   Thus, if $n = 4$ as in the figure, the sum S of the areas of the 4 trapezoids is given by

$$S = \frac{y_0 + y_1}{2}\,\Delta x + \frac{y_1 + y_2}{2}\,\Delta x + \frac{y_2 + y_3}{2}\,\Delta x + \frac{y_3 + y_4}{2}\,\Delta x,$$

where $y_i = f(x_i)$ and $\Delta x = (b - a)/4$. We may reduce S to the form

$$S = \frac{b - a}{8} (y_0 + 2y_1 + 2y_2 + 2y_3 + y_4),$$

which is just the right side of 9.21 if $n = 4$.

Example 2. Use the trapezoidal rule to approximate the area of the region under the graph of the equation

$$y = \sqrt{x^2 + 1}$$

between $x = 0$ and $x = 3$.

Solution: The area in question is given by the integral

$$\int_0^3 \sqrt{x^2 + 1}\, dx,$$

an integral that cannot be evaluated exactly by any of our previous methods. If we let

$$f(x) = \sqrt{x^2 + 1}$$

and $n = 6$, then the partition r_6 of $[0,3]$ is given by

$$r_6 = [0,\tfrac{1}{2},1,\tfrac{3}{2},2,\tfrac{5}{2},3].$$

The accompanying table of values of f is approximated

x	0	.5	1	1.5	2	2.5	3
$f(x)$	1	1.12	1.41	1.80	2.24	2.69	3.16

to two decimal places of accuracy. If we let $n = 6$ in Formula 9.21, we get

$$\int_0^3 \sqrt{x^2 + 1}\, dx \doteq \frac{1}{4} [1 + 2.24 + 2.82 + 3.60 + 4.48 + 5.38 + 3.16],$$

or

$$\int_0^3 \sqrt{x^2 + 1}\, dx \doteq 5.67.$$

All that we can say about the accuracy of this result is that it is correct within $(T_6 - S_6)/2 = .54$. Actually, the result is much more accurate than that, since it may be shown that the correct result is 5.65 to two decimal places of accuracy.

■ ■ ■ EXERCISES

Use the trapezoidal rule to approximate each of the following integrals, taking the suggested value of n.

1. $\int_1^3 \frac{1}{x}\, dx$, $n = 8$.

2. $\int_{-4}^{-1} \frac{1}{x}\, dx$, $n = 6$.

3. $4 \int_0^1 \sqrt{1 - x^2}\, dx$, $n = 4$.

4. $\int_0^1 \frac{4}{1 + x^2}\, dx$, $n = 4$.

5. $\int_{-1}^{1} \dfrac{2}{1 + x^2}\, dx, \ n = 8.$ **6.** $\int_{-3}^{0} \dfrac{1}{1 - 2x}\, dx, \ n = 6.$

7. $\int_{-4}^{-1} \dfrac{x}{3x + 1}\, dx, \ n = 6.$ **8.** $\int_{2}^{4} \dfrac{x}{1 - x^3}\, dx, \ n = 4.$

9. Prove that the right side of 9.21 is just $(S_n + T_n)/2$ if the function f is increasing (or decreasing) from a to b.

10

Differentiation of transcendental functions

■ ■ ■ ■ ■ WHILE THE THEORY of the derivative and the integral developed in the previous chapters holds for any continuous function, the examples illustrating the theory were drawn from the set of algebraic functions.

We shall enlarge our set of functions in the present chapter to include the elementary transcendental functions. Thus our new set of functions will include the algebraic, exponential, logarithmic, trigonometric, and inverse trigonometric functions.

1. Exponential functions

Rational powers of a positive number are defined in terms of integral powers and roots of a number. Thus, if $a > 0$ and m and n are integers with $n > 0$,

$$a^{m/n} = \sqrt[n]{a^m} = (\sqrt[n]{a})^m.$$

We shall show in this section that irrational powers of a positive number, such as, for example,

$$3^{\sqrt{2}}, \qquad (1 + \sqrt[3]{2})^\pi,$$

can also be defined in a meaningful way.

261

In order to define

$$a^x, \quad a > 1,$$

for any real number x, let S be the set of all numbers

$$a^r, \quad r \le x, \quad r \text{ a rational number.}$$

If we select an integer $n \ge x$, then for each rational number r such that $r \le x$, also $r \le n$. Since $a > 1$, $a^r \le a^n$ if $r \le n$. Therefore for each number a^r in the set S, $a^r \le a^n$ and the set S has a^n as an upper bound. Hence the set S has a least upper bound by the completeness property of the real number system (8.3), and we may make the following definition.

10.1 Definition. Let a and x be real numbers with $a > 0$.

(1) If $a > 1$, a^x is the least upper bound of the set S of all numbers a^r where $r \le x$, r a rational number.

(2) If $a = 1$, $a^x = 1$.

(3) If $a < 1$, so that $1/a > 1$, then $a^x = 1/(1/a)^x$.

If $a > 1$ and x is a *rational number*, then a^x is the least upper bound of the set S and a^x is defined as previously, and similarly if $0 \le a \le 1$.

Since a^x is defined for every real number x, a function is associated with each positive number a in the obvious way.

10.2 Definition. If $a > 0$, the *exponential function* f with base a is defined by

$$f(x) = a^x.$$

The elementary properties of exponential functions, usually called the *laws of exponents*, are contained in the following theorem stated here without proof.

10.3 Theorem. If a and b are positive numbers, then for any numbers x and y:

(1) $a^x a^y = a^{x+y}$. $\qquad\qquad$ (2) $\dfrac{a^x}{a^y} = a^{x-y}$.

(3) $a^x b^x = (ab)^x$. $\qquad\qquad$ (4) $\dfrac{a^x}{b^x} = \left(\dfrac{a}{b}\right)^x$.

(5) $(a^x)^y = a^{xy}$. $\qquad\qquad$ (6) $a^x > 0$.

(7) If $a \ne 1$, $a^x = a^y$ if and only if $x = y$.

(8) If $a > 1$, $a^x > a^y$ if and only if $x > y$.

(9) If $a < 1$, $a^x > a^y$ if and only if $x < y$.

Example. Sketch the graph of f if

$$f(x) = 2^x.$$

Solution: Since the base 2 is greater than 1,

$$2^x > 2^y$$

if $x > y$ according to (8) above. Thus the graph of f is rising everywhere. By (6) above, the graph lies above the x-axis. The graph is sketched in Figure 10.1 with the aid of the accompanying table of values.

x	0	1	2	3	4	-1	-2	-3
2^x	1	2	4	8	16	$\frac{1}{2}$	$\frac{1}{4}$	$\frac{1}{8}$

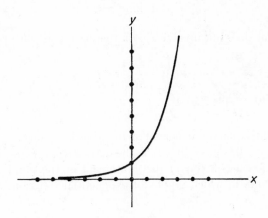

Figure 10.1

■ ■ ■ EXERCISES

Sketch the graph of each of the following functions.

1. $f(x) = 3^x$.

2. $f(x) = \left(\frac{1}{2}\right)^x$.

3. $g(x) = \left(\frac{1}{3}\right)^x$.

4. $F(x) = 1^x$.

5. $F(x) = 2^{x^2}$.

6. $g(x) = 2^{-x^2}$.

7. $f(x) = 3^{1-x}$.

8. $f(x) = 2^{x/2}$.

9. Use the laws of exponents to show that if $0 < a < b$, then:
   (a) $a^x < b^x$ if $x > 0$.
   (b) $a^x > b^x$ if $x < 0$.

2. Derivative of the exponential function—intuitive discussion

If $a > 1$, then the exponential function

$$f(x) = a^x$$

is increasing in the interval $(-\infty, \infty)$. The graph of f appears to have a tangent line at each point (Figure 10.1), and each tangent has a positive slope. Thus, it is intuitively clear that the function f has a derivative at each number x. This derivative is given by

$$f'(x) = \lim_{h \to 0} \frac{a^{x+h} - a^x}{h}$$

$$= \lim_{h \to 0} \frac{a^x(a^h - 1)}{h}$$

$$= a^x \lim_{h \to 0} \frac{a^h - 1}{h}.$$

The latter limit does not involve x, and therefore it is some positive number k_a,

$$\lim_{h \to 0} \frac{a^h - 1}{h} = k_a,$$

depending on a. Thus

$$D_x a^x = k_a \cdot a^x,$$

and the derivative of the exponential function is a constant times itself.

By setting $x = 0$, we see that k_a is the derivative of f at 0. Thus, k_a is the slope of the tangent line at the y-intercept of the graph. It is clear from Figure 10.2, in which graphs of exponential functions are sketched

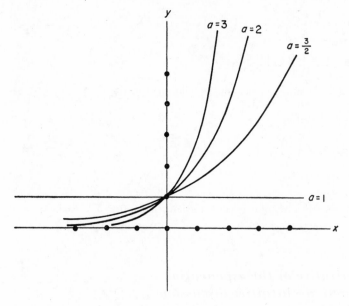

Figure 10.2

for several values of a, that $k_1 = 0$ (i.e., the line $y = 1$ has slope 0) and as a increases so does k_a. It would appear that by properly choosing a, k_a can be made any prescribed positive number.

Perhaps the most useful value of k_a is 1, in which case $D_x a^x = a^x$. The number a for which $k_a = 1$ is usually designated by e, so that $k = 1$ and $D_x e^x = e^x$. What is the number e?

Since

$$\lim_{h \to 0} \frac{e^h - 1}{h} = 1,$$

we have

$$\frac{e^h - 1}{h} \doteq 1$$

($\doteq$ means "is approximately equal to") if $h \doteq 0$. Thus,

$$e^h - 1 \doteq h,$$

$$e^h \doteq 1 + h,$$

and we may expect that

$$e \doteq (1 + h)^{1/h} \quad \text{if} \quad h \doteq 0.$$

Hence it seems plausible that

$$e = \lim_{h \to 0} (1 + h)^{1/h},$$

although we have by no means proved that this is so.

If we let h take on successive values from the sequence

$$1, \frac{1}{2}, \frac{1}{3}, \cdots, \frac{1}{n}, \cdots,$$

then perhaps

$$e = \lim_{n \to \infty} \left(1 + \frac{1}{n}\right)^n.$$

That this limit actually has the desired properties of the number e will be shown in the following sections.

3. The number e

Let us consider the sequences

$$s_1, s_2, \cdots, s_n, \cdots$$

$$t_1, t_2, \cdots, t_n, \cdots,$$

where

$$s_n = \left(1 + \frac{1}{n}\right)^n, \quad t_n = \left(1 + \frac{1}{n}\right)^{n+1}.$$

Thus,

$$s_1 = (1 + 1)^1 = 2, \quad s_2 = \left(1 + \frac{1}{2}\right)^2 = \frac{9}{4}, \quad s_3 = \left(1 + \frac{1}{3}\right)^3 = \frac{64}{27},$$

and so on; and

$$t_1 = (1 + 1)^2 = 4, \quad t_2 = \left(1 + \frac{1}{2}\right)^3 = \frac{27}{8}, \quad t_3 = \left(1 + \frac{1}{3}\right)^4 = \frac{256}{81},$$

and so on.   The reader may easily verify that $s_1 < s_2 < s_3$ and $t_1 > t_2 > t_3$. That such inequalities hold in general is proved in the following theorem.

10.4 Theorem.   If s_n and t_n are as defined above, then:

(1) $s_1 < s_2 < s_3 < \cdots < s_n < s_{n+1} < \cdots$.
(2) $t_1 > t_2 > t_3 > \cdots > t_n > t_{n+1} > \cdots$.
(3) $s_n < t_m$ for any positive integers m and n.

Proof: It may be proved that if $a > -1$ and $a \neq 0$, then*

(A) $(1 + a)^k > 1 + ka$ for every integer $k > 1$.

We shall have proved part (1) when we have shown that $s_{n+1}/s_n > 1$ for every positive integer n.   Clearly

$$\frac{s_{n+1}}{s_n} = \frac{(1 + 1/(n + 1))^{n+1}}{(1 + 1/n)^n} = \left(1 + \frac{1}{n}\right)\left(\frac{1 + 1/(n + 1)}{1 + 1/n}\right)^{n+1}$$

$$= \frac{n + 1}{n}\left[\frac{n^2 + 2n}{(n + 1)^2}\right]^{n+1} = \frac{n + 1}{n}\left[1 - \frac{1}{(n + 1)^2}\right]^{n+1}.$$

Using inequality (A) with $a = -1/(n + 1)^2$ and $k = n + 1$, we have

$$\left[1 - \frac{1}{(n + 1)^2}\right]^{n+1} > 1 - \frac{n + 1}{(n + 1)^2} = \frac{n}{n + 1}.$$

Hence

$$\frac{s_{n+1}}{s_n} > \frac{n + 1}{n} \cdot \frac{n}{n + 1} = 1,$$

and part (1) is proved.

Part (2) may be established in a similar fashion by showing that $t_n/t_{n+1} > 1$ for every positive integer n.   We leave this as an exercise.

To prove part (3), we first note that

$$t_n = \left(1 + \frac{1}{n}\right)^{n+1} = \left(1 + \frac{1}{n}\right) s_n,$$

and therefore that

(B) $t_n > s_n$

for every n, since $(1 + 1/n) > 1$.   If $m < n$, then $t_m > t_n$ by (2).   Thus

(C) $t_m > s_n$ if $m < n$.

If $m > n$, then $s_m > s_n$ and $t_m > s_m > s_n$, that is,

(D) $t_m > s_n$ if $m > n$.

The three statements (B), (C), and (D) constitute a proof of part (3). This completes the proof of the theorem.

The set S of all numbers s_n has each of the numbers t_m as an upper bound according to part (3) of the preceding theorem.   Therefore S has a least upper bound.

* See Exercise 32, p. 135.

10.5 Definition. The number e is the least upper bound of the set of all numbers

$$\left(1 + \frac{1}{n}\right)^n, \quad n \text{ a positive integer.}$$

Since e is the least upper bound of the set of all s_n, and in turn each t_n is an upper bound of this set, it follows that $e \geq s_n$ and $e \leq t_n$ for every integer $n > 0$. From the inequality $e \leq t_n$ we derive

$$e \leq \left(1 + \frac{1}{n}\right) s_n,$$

and

$$\frac{e}{1 + 1/n} \leq s_n.$$

Thus

$$\frac{e}{1 + 1/n} \leq s_n \leq e$$

for every integer $n > 0$ and, since

$$\lim_{n \to \infty} \frac{e}{1 + 1/n} = e,$$

we finally have (by 9.8)

$$\lim_{n \to \infty} \left(1 + \frac{1}{n}\right)^n = e.$$

The fact that $s_n \leq e \leq t_m$ for every integer m and n yields (letting $m = n - 1$)

$$\left(1 + \frac{1}{n}\right)^n \leq e \leq \left(1 + \frac{1}{n-1}\right)^n,$$

or

10.6 $1 + \dfrac{1}{n} \leq e^{1/n} \leq 1 + \dfrac{1}{n-1}$ for each integer $n > 1$.

We shall have need for this inequality in the next section.

It may be shown by more advanced methods than now at our disposal that e is an irrational number. A rational approximation of e to nine decimal places is 2.718281828. Efficient techniques for approximating e to any desired degree of accuracy will be developed in Chapter 14.

■ ■ ■ EXERCISES

1. Make a table of s_n and t_n for $n = 1, 2, 3, 4, 5$.
2. Prove part (2) of Theorem 10.4.
3. If e' designates the greatest lower bound of the set of all t_n, show that $s_n \leq e \leq e' \leq t_n$ for every n. Use the fact that $t_n - s_n = s_n/n$ to prove that $e = e'$.
4. Prove that $\lim_{n \to \infty} t_n = e$.

4. The derivative of e^x

We shall now prove that the number e has the property conjectured in Section 2, namely that $D_x e^x = e^x$. This means that we must prove that

10.7
$$\underset{h \to 0}{\text{limit}} \frac{e^h - 1}{h} = 1.$$

Proof: Since we are interested in the value of $(e^h - 1)/h$ only when h is close to zero, we may as well restrict h to satisfy the inequality

$$-\frac{1}{2} < h < \frac{1}{2}, \quad h \neq 0.$$

First, let us consider $0 < h < \frac{1}{2}$. Then $1/h > 2$, and there exists an integer $m > 1$ such that

(1)
$$m \leq \frac{1}{h} < m + 1, \quad \text{or} \quad \frac{1}{m+1} < h \leq \frac{1}{m}.$$

Since $e > 1$,

(2)
$$e^{1/(m+1)} < e^h \leq e^{1/m}.$$

On combining 10.6 with (2) above, we obtain

$$1 + \frac{1}{m+1} \leq e^{1/(m+1)} < e^h \leq e^{1/m} \leq 1 + \frac{1}{m-1},$$

or

(3)
$$1 + \frac{1}{m+1} < e^h \leq 1 + \frac{1}{m-1}.$$

From (1), $hm \leq 1$, $hm + h \leq 1 + h$, and

$$\frac{h}{1+h} \leq \frac{1}{m+1}.$$

Also, from (1), $1 < hm + h$, $1 - 2h < hm - h$, and

$$\frac{1}{m-1} < \frac{h}{1-2h}.$$

Thus

$$1 + \frac{h}{1+h} \leq 1 + \frac{1}{m+1} < e^h \leq 1 + \frac{1}{m-1} < 1 + \frac{h}{1-2h},$$

or

(4)
$$\frac{1+2h}{1+h} < e^h < \frac{1-h}{1-2h}.$$

Each member of (4) is a positive number. Therefore we may take reciprocals of each member to get

$$\frac{1+h}{1+2h} > e^{-h} > \frac{1-2h}{1-h}.$$

If we let $k = -h$ and reverse the direction of the above inequality, we obtain,

(5) $$\frac{1+2k}{1+k} < e^k < \frac{1-k}{1-2k}, \quad -\frac{1}{2} < k < 0.$$

Note that (4) and (5) are the same, that is, (4) holds for negative as well as positive values of h.

On subtracting 1 from each member of (4), we get

$$\frac{h}{1+h} < e^h - 1 < \frac{h}{1-2h}.$$

Hence, on dividing by h, we obtain

$$\frac{1}{1+h} < \frac{e^h-1}{h} < \frac{1}{1-2h}, \quad 0 < h < \frac{1}{2},$$

$$\frac{1}{1+h} > \frac{e^h-1}{h} > \frac{1}{1-2h}, \quad -\frac{1}{2} < h < 0.$$

Since

$$\lim_{h \to 0} \frac{1}{1+h} = \lim_{h \to 0} \frac{1}{1-2h} = 1,$$

we have immediately that

$$\lim_{h \to 0} \frac{e^h - 1}{h} = 1.$$

This completes the proof of 10.7.

Returning to the first sentence of this paragraph, we now have the following differentiation formula.

10.8 $$D_x e^x = e^x.$$

Thus we have found a function, the exponential function with base e, that is its own derivative!

We recall the chain rule (5.11) for differentiating the composite of two functions:

$$D_x f(g(x)) = f'(g(x))g'(x).$$

If we let $f(x) = e^x$ in this formula, then $f(g(x)) = e^{g(x)}$ and we obtain the following more general form of 10.8.

10.9 $$D_x e^{g(x)} = e^{g(x)} D_x g(x).$$

Since a differentiable function is necessarily continuous (4.28), we also have the following corollary of 10.8.

10.10 Theorem. If $f(x) = e^x$, the function f is continuous at every number x.

Example 1. Find $D_x e^{ax}$.

Solution: By 10.9, with $g(x) = ax$, we have

$$D_x e^{ax} = e^{ax} D_x ax = a e^{ax}.$$

Example 2. Find $D_x(e^{3x} - 5e^{2x} + e^{-x})$.

Solution: By 10.9, or Example 1 above,

$$D_x(e^{3x} - 5e^{2x} + e^{-x}) = 3e^{3x} - 10e^{2x} - e^{-x}.$$

Example 3. Find $D_x e^{x^2+1}$.

Solution: Using 10.9 with $g(x) = x^2 + 1$, we get

$$D_x e^{x^2+1} = e^{x^2+1} D_x(x^2 + 1) = 2xe^{x^2+1}.$$

■ ■ ■ EXERCISES

Differentiate each of the following:

1. $e^{ax} + e^{-ax}$.

2. $(1 + e^x)^2$.

3. $(1 + e^{3x})^3$.

4. xe^{4x}.

5. $\dfrac{x}{1 + e^{2x}}$.

6. $\sqrt{1 + e^x}$.

7. $x^2 e^{x^2}$.

8. $\dfrac{e^x - 1}{e^x + 1}$.

9. $e^{2x}(9x^2 + 6x - 2)$.

10. $e^{-x}\sqrt{e^{2x} + 1}$.

11. $\dfrac{e^{-3x}}{x^2 + 1}$.

12. $e^{\sqrt{x^2+1}}$.

13. $\dfrac{e^x}{\sqrt{e^{2x} - 1}}$, $x > 0$.

14. $\dfrac{x^2 - x}{e^{2x} + 1}$.

The hyperbolic sine of x, written sinh x, and the other hyperbolic functions are defined as follows:

$$\sinh x = \frac{e^x - e^{-x}}{2}, \quad \cosh x = \frac{e^x + e^{-x}}{2}, \quad \tanh x = \frac{\sinh x}{\cosh x}.$$

Find:

15. $-\sinh^2 x + \cosh^2 x$.

16. $D_x \sinh x$.

17. $D_x \cosh x$.

18. $D_x \tanh x$.

19. Verify that sinh $(x + y)$ = sinh x cosh y + cosh x sinh y.

20. Verify that cosh x + sinh $x = e^x$, and hence that

$$(\cosh x + \sinh x)^n = \cosh nx + \sinh nx.$$

21. Find $\displaystyle\int_0^2 e^x \, dx$.

22. Find $\displaystyle\int_0^2 xe^{x^2} \, dx$.

23. Find $\displaystyle\int_{-1}^1 e^{-x} \, dx$.

24. Find $\displaystyle\int_0^1 \sinh x \, dx$.

Find the maximum points, minimum points, and points of inflection of the graph of each of the following functions, and sketch each graph:

25. $f(x) = xe^x$.

26. $g(x) = x^2 e^x$.

27. $F(x) = xe^{-x}$.

28. $G(x) = x^2 e^{-x}$.

29. $g(x) = e^{-x^2}$.

30. $f(x) = \sinh x$.

31. $f(x) = \cosh x$.

32. $g(x) = \tanh x$.

5. *Natural logarithms*

Given a positive number x, there exists some integer n such that $e^n > x$. This is so since the set of all integral powers of e has no upper bound (see Exercise 12, p. 194).   If the integer m is chosen so that $e^m > 1/x$, then $e^{-m} < x$.   Hence, given a number $x > 0$, there exist integers m and n such that

$$e^{-m} < x < e^n.$$

Since the exponential function is continuous, we may use the intermediate value theorem (8.21) to conclude that a number y exists such that

$$e^y = x.$$

The number y is unique by one of the laws of exponents.   Thus we may make the following definition.

   10.11 Definition.   For each positive number x, the unique number y such that

$$x = e^y$$

is called the *natural logarithm* of x, and we write

$$y = \log_e x \quad \text{or} \quad y = \ln x.$$

From this definition, we have immediately that for every number x,

10.12
$$e^{\ln x} = x, \quad x > 0.$$
$$\ln e^x = x.$$

   Corresponding to the laws of exponents are the following *laws of logarithms*.

   10.13 Theorem.   If x and y are positive numbers, then:

(1) $\ln x \cdot y = \ln x + \ln y.$

(2) $\ln \dfrac{x}{y} = \ln x - \ln y.$

(3) $\ln x^c = c \ln x.$

(4) $\ln x = \ln y$ if and only if $x = y.$

(5) $\ln x < \ln y$ if and only if $x < y.$

   Proof: To prove (1), we have by 10.12 that

$$x = e^{\ln x}, \quad y = e^{\ln y}, \quad xy = e^{\ln xy}.$$

Hence

$$xy = e^{\ln x}e^{\ln y} = e^{\ln x + \ln y}, \quad xy = e^{\ln xy},$$

and therefore by 10.3(7),

$$\ln xy = \ln x + \ln y.$$

   To prove (3), we have

$$x = e^{\ln x}, \quad x^c = (e^{\ln x})^c = e^{c \ln x}.$$

However,
$$x^c = e^{\ln x^c}$$
also. Thus
$$e^{\ln x^c} = e^{c \ln x},$$
and
$$\ln x^c = c \ln x.$$

The proofs of the remaining parts of 10.13 will be left as exercises for the reader.

Example. Sketch the graph of the natural logarithmic function, that is, of the equation

$$y = \ln x.$$

Solution: The graph occurs to the right of the y-axis, since $\ln x$ is defined only for $x > 0$. Also, the graph is always rising because of property 10.13(5). Since $e^0 = 1$, $\ln 1 = 0$ and the graph crosses the x-axis at $(1,0)$. The graph is sketched in Figure 10.3 from the accompanying table of values.

x	e^{-2}	e^{-1}	1	e	e^2	e^3
y	-2	-1	0	1	2	3

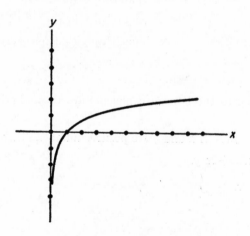

Figure 10.3

■ ■ ■ EXERCISES

1. Make a table of values for $\ln x$ with x taking on the following values:

$$e,\ e^2,\ e^3,\ e^4,\ 1/e,\ 1/e^2,\ 1/e^3,\ \sqrt{e},\ 1/\sqrt[3]{e}.$$

2. Make a table of values for $\ln x$ with x taking on the following values:

$$10,\ 4,\ \tfrac{5}{2},\ .5,\ .2,\ .1,\ .25,\ .01,\ .001,\ .0001,$$

given that $\ln 2 \doteq .693$, $\ln 5 \doteq 1.609$. (*Hint:* $\ln 20 = \ln (2^2 \cdot 5) = \ln 2^2 + \ln 5 = 2 \ln 2 + \ln 5 \doteq 2.995$, etc.)

3. Solve each of the following equations:
   (a) ln $x = 0$.   (b) ln $x = 1$.
   (c) ln $x = -1$.   (d) ln $x = -3$.
   (e) ln $(x - 2) = 3$.   (f) ln $(5 - x^2) = -2$.

4. Solve each of the following inequalities:
   (a) ln $x > 2$.   (b) ln $x < -3$.
   (c) ln $|x| < -1$.   (d) ln $(x + 2) < 0$.

Sketch the graph of each of the following equations:

5. $y = \ln(-x)$, $x < 0$.   6. $y = \ln|x|$, $x \neq 0$.
7. $y = \ln(1 + x)$, $x > -1$.   8. $y = \ln(1 - x)$, $x < 1$.

9. Prove 10.14, parts (2), (4), and (5). (*Hint:* Refer to the corresponding laws of exponents.)

10. Prove that there exists a unique number u such that $e^u + u = 0$.

11. Prove that there exists a unique number u such that ln $u + u = 0$.

12. Prove that limit $r^n = 0$ if $0 < |r| < 1$. (*Hint:* For every $\epsilon > 0$, $|r^n| < \epsilon$
    $\underset{n \to \infty}{}$
    if and only if $n \ln|r| < \ln \epsilon$, or $n > \ln \epsilon/\ln|r|$, etc.)

13. Find the maximum and minimum values of f if $f(x) = e^{2x} - 6e^x + 4x$.

6. The derivative of ln x

If the natural logarithmic function has a derivative, then it may be found from the equation

10.14 $e^{\ln x} = x,$ $x > 0,$

by implicit differentiation. Thus,

$$D_x e^{\ln x} = D_x x = 1,$$

and, by 10.9,

$$e^{\ln x} D_x \ln x = x D_x \ln x = 1.$$

Hence

10.15 $D_x \ln x = \dfrac{1}{x}.$

Formula 10.15 is correct provided that the natural logarithmic function has a derivative. There is a function F such that

$$F'(x) = \frac{1}{x},$$

namely that defined by

$$F(x) = \int_1^x \frac{1}{x}\, dx.$$

Evidently

$$F(1) = \int_1^1 \frac{1}{x}\, dx = 0.$$

Let us show that

$$F(x) = \ln x, \qquad x > 0,$$

which will prove that the natural logarithmic function is differentiable and will establish 10.15.

By the chain rule,

$$D_y F(e^y) = F'(e^y)D_y e^y = \frac{1}{e^y} e^y = 1.$$

Therefore

$$F(e^y) = y + C$$

for some constant C. Since

$$F(e^0) = F(1) = 0,$$

$0 = 0 + C$ and $C = 0$. Hence, for each number y,

$$F(e^y) = y.$$

Letting $y = \ln x$, we finally obtain (by 10.14)

$$F(x) = \ln x.$$

If g is a differentiable function and if $f(x) = \ln x$, then by the chain rule

$$D_x f(g(x)) = f'(g(x))g'(x) = \frac{1}{g(x)} \cdot g'(x).$$

This proves the following generalization of 10.15.

10.16 $$D_x \ln g(x) = \frac{D_x g(x)}{g(x)}, \quad g(x) > 0.$$

If $x \neq 0$, then $D_x|x| = |x|/x$ and therefore, by 10.16,

$$D_x \ln |x| = \frac{1}{|x|} \cdot \frac{|x|}{x} = \frac{1}{x}.$$

Hence, by the chain rule again,

10.17 $$D_x \ln |g(x)| = \frac{D_x g(x)}{g(x)}, \quad g(x) \neq 0.$$

Example 1.   Find $D_x \ln (x^2 - 2x + 3)$.

Solution: It is easily verified that $x^2 - 2x + 3 > 0$ for every number x.   By 10.16,

$$D_x \ln (x^2 - 2x + 3) = \frac{2x - 2}{x^2 - 2x + 3}.$$

Example 2.   Find $D_x \ln |x^3 + 1|$.

Solution: If $x \neq -1$, we have by 10.17

$$D_x \ln |x^3 + 1| = \frac{3x^2}{x^3 + 1}.$$

Example 3.   Find $D_x \ln \sqrt{\dfrac{x^2 + 1}{x^2 - 1}}$.

Solution: Clearly the domain of the function being differentiated is the set of all numbers x such that $|x| > 1$. Before differentiating, we algebraically simplify the given function as follows:

$$\ln \sqrt{\frac{x^2+1}{x^2-1}} = \ln \left(\frac{x^2+1}{x^2-1}\right)^{1/2} = \frac{1}{2}\ln\left(\frac{x^2+1}{x^2-1}\right)$$

$$= \frac{1}{2}\left[\ln(x^2+1) - \ln(x^2-1)\right].$$

Therefore

$$D_x \ln \sqrt{\frac{x^2+1}{x^2-1}} = \frac{1}{2}\left[D_x \ln(x^2+1) - D_x \ln(x^2-1)\right]$$

$$= \frac{1}{2}\left[\frac{2x}{x^2+1} - \frac{2x}{x^2-1}\right] = \frac{-2x}{x^4-1}.$$

The derivative of an exponential function with base other than e can be found by changing the function to the base e as illustrated below.

Example 4. If $g(x) = 10^x$, find $g'(x)$.

Solution: By 10.12,

$$10 = e^{\ln 10},$$

and therefore

$$g(x) = 10^x = e^{x \ln 10}.$$

Hence, by 10.9,

$$g'(x) = e^{x \ln 10} D_x(x \ln 10) = 10^x \ln 10.$$

▪ ▪ ▪ EXERCISES

Differentiate the following:

1. $\ln(x+1)$.
2. $\ln(x^2+1)$.
3. $(x+1)\ln|x^2-1|$.
4. $\ln\sqrt{x^4+4}$.
5. $\dfrac{x^2}{\ln x}$.
6. $e^x \ln x$.
7. $\ln(e^x+1)$.
8. $\ln\sqrt{e^x+1}$.
9. $\dfrac{\ln x}{x}$.
10. $\dfrac{4}{\ln x}$.
11. 2^x.
12. $(1+e)^x$.
13. $\ln|x+\sqrt{x^2+1}|$.
14. $x^2 \ln|1-2x|$.
15. $\dfrac{e^{3x}}{\ln(e^{3x}+1)}$.
16. $(\sqrt{3})^x$.
17. x^x. (*Hint:* $x = e^{\ln x}$, so $x^x = e^{x \ln x}$.)
18. $(x+1)^x$.
19. $(x^2+1)^x$.
20. $\ln(\ln x)$.

Find the maximum points, minimum points, and points of inflection of the graph of each of the following equations, and sketch each graph.

21. $y = x \ln x$.   **22.** $y = x^2 \ln x$.

23. $y = x - \ln x$.   **24.** $y = x^2 + 2 \ln x$.

25. Prove that $D_x a^{g(x)} = (\ln a)a^{g(x)} D_x g(x)$.

7. Logarithms to a base other than e

If x and a are positive numbers with $a \neq 1$, then

10.18 $x = e^{\ln x} = e^{(\ln a)(\ln x)/(\ln a)} = a^{(\ln x)/(\ln a)}$.

Thus, for each number $x > 0$, there exists a (unique) number y such that $x = a^y$, and we can make the following definition.

10.19 Definition. Let a be a positive number unequal to one. For each positive number x, the unique number y such that

$$x = a^y$$

is called the *logarithm of x to the base a*, and we write

$$y = \log_a x.$$

As in the case of the natural logarithm, we have that for every number x,

10.20
$$a^{\log_a x} = x, \quad x > 0.$$
$$\log_a a^x = x.$$

It is clear also that the laws of logarithms, stated in 10.13 for the base e, hold for any base a.

A useful relationship between logarithms to the base a and natural logarithms is as follows.

10.21 $$\log_a x = \frac{\ln x}{\ln a} = (\log_a e) \ln x.$$

Proof: By 10.18 and 10.20, we have

$$x = a^{\log_a x} = a^{\frac{\ln x}{\ln a}}.$$

This proves the first part of 10.21. Letting $x = e$ in this first part,

$$\log_a e = \frac{\ln e}{\ln a} = \frac{1}{\ln a},$$

and the second part is established.

We may use 10.21 to differentiate the logarithmic function with the base a. Thus

$$D_x \log_a x = (\log_a e) D_x \ln x = \frac{\log_a e}{x}.$$

The analogue of 10.17 then becomes,

10.22 $$D_x \log_a |g(x)| = (\log_a e) \frac{D_x g(x)}{g(x)}, \quad g(x) \neq 0.$$

Example. Find $D_x \log_{10} |3x + 1|$.

Solution: By 10.22,

$$D_x \log_{10} |3x + 1| = (\log_{10} e) \frac{3}{3x + 1} = \frac{3 \log_{10} e}{3x + 1}.$$

We recall that a function f defined by an equation of the form

$$f(x) = x^r$$

is called a *power function.* In view of the results of the present chapter, this is a well-defined function even if r is an irrational number, in which case the domain of f is the set of all positive numbers.

The derivative of f in case r is rational is given by the familiar formula

$$D_x x^r = rx^{r-1}.$$

Let us prove that this formula is valid even if r is an irrational number. Thus, since

$$x^r = e^{r \ln x},$$

we have

$$D_x x^r = e^{r \ln x} D_x (r \ln x) = x^r \cdot \frac{r}{x} = rx^{r-1}.$$

■ ■ ■ EXERCISES

Differentiate the following:

1. $\log_2 |5 - 2x|$.

2. $\log_{10} (x^2 + 2)$.

3. $x^2 \log_{10} (3 + 2x^2)$.

4. $\dfrac{\log_{10} x}{x}$.

5. $(\ln x + 1)^\pi$.

6. $\left(\dfrac{x}{x^2 + 1}\right)^e$.

7. $(1 + \sqrt{x})^{1+e}$.

8. $(1 + e)^{1+\sqrt{x}}$.

9. 2^{2x}.

10. e^{ex}.

8. *Exponential laws of growth and decay*

It sometimes happens that the rate of change of the amount of a given substance at any time is proportional to the amount of the substance present at that time. The first example that comes to mind is the decomposition of a radioactive substance, the rate of decomposition being proportional to the amount of radioactive substance present. The growth of a culture of bacteria obeys this same law under ideal conditions.

In order to give a mathematical analysis of this phenomenon, let $f(t) > 0$ be the amount of a substance present at time t. Then to say that the rate of change of f at time t is proportional to $f(t)$ is to say that

10.23 $$f'(t) = kf(t)$$

for some constant k and every time t in some interval. This differential equation may be solved for f as follows.

We first put 10.23 in the form

$$\frac{f'(t)}{f(t)} = k,$$

and then integrate as follows:

$$\int_0^t \frac{f'(t)}{f(t)}\, dt = \int_0^t k\, dt,$$

(changing variables by letting $u = f(t)$, $du = f'(t)\, dt$)

$$\int_{f(0)}^{f(t)} \frac{1}{u}\, du = \int_0^t k\, dt,$$

$$\ln u \Big|_{f(0)}^{f(t)} = kt \Big|_0^t,$$

$$\ln f(t) - \ln f(0) = kt.$$

$$\ln \frac{f(t)}{f(0)} = kt,$$

$$\frac{f(t)}{f(0)} = e^{kt},$$

$$f(t) = f(0)e^{kt}.$$

According to this equation, the amount $f(t)$ present at time t equals the initial amount $f(0)$ (at time $t = 0$) times e^{kt}. The constant k depends on the substance in question, and can be found if sufficient data are given. It is permissible to express the equation above in the form

10.24 $$f(t) = f(0)a^{ct}$$

using any base a we wish. Evidently $c = k \log_a e$.

Example 1. The half-life of radium is approximately 1600 years (i.e., a given amount of radium will be half gone after 1600 years). Starting with 150 milligrams of pure radium, find the amount left after t years. After how many years is only 30 milligrams left?

Solution: Using 10.24 with $a = 2$, and the unit of time a year, we have

$$f(t) = 150 \cdot 2^{ct}.$$

Since $f(1600) = 75$,

$$75 = 150 \cdot 2^{1600c},$$

$$\frac{1}{2} = 2^{1600c}.$$

Thus $1600c = -1$ and $c = -1/1600$. It is evident now that the base 2 was chosen so as to make the evaluation of c easy. We have proved that the amount

$f(t)$ of radium left after t years is given by

$$f(t) = 150 \cdot 2^{-t/1600}.$$

The solution of the equation

$$30 = 150 \cdot 2^{-t/1600},$$

or

$$\frac{1}{5} = 2^{-t/1600},$$

will give the number t of years that must elapse before only 30 milligrams is left. We solve this equation by logarithms, obtaining

$$t = (1600 \log 5)/\log 2 \doteq 3715 \text{ years.}$$

This is an example of an exponential law of decay. The following example is an exponential law of growth.

Example 2. The number of bacteria in a culture was 1000 at a certain instant and 8000 two hours later. Assuming ideal conditions for growth, how many bacteria are there after t hours?

Solution: The number $f(t)$ of bacteria after t hours is given by (using $a = 8$ in 10.24)

$$f(t) = 1000 \cdot 8^{ct}.$$

It is given that $f(2) = 8000$; thus

$$8000 = 1000 \cdot 8^{2c}$$
$$8 = 8^{2c}$$

and $2c = 1$. Hence

$$f(t) = 1000 \cdot 8^{t/2}.$$

After 5 hours, for example,

$$f(5) = 1000 \cdot 8^{5/2} = 64000\sqrt{8} \doteq 180,000.$$

■ ■ ■ EXERCISES

1. The radioactive element polonium has a half-life of 140 days. Starting with 10 milligrams of polonium, how much is left after t days? Approximately how much is left after 1 year?

2. Under normal conditions, the rate of change of population is considered to be proportional to the population at any time. If a town has a population of 20,000 in 1940 and 25,000 in 1950, what population is expected in 1965?

3. A culture of bacteria has a population of 10,000 initially and 50,000 an hour and a half later. Assuming ideal conditions for growth, find the time required to get a culture of 200,000 bacteria.

4. Assuming the ideal gas law, it may be shown that the rate of change of atmospheric pressure at any height is proportional to the pressure there. If the barometer reads 30 inches at sea level and 24 inches at 6,000 ft above sea level, find the barometric reading 10,000 ft above sea level.

5. Assuming that the retardation of a boat in still water is proportional to its speed, find the speed t seconds after the motor was shut off if the boat had

a speed of 20 mi/hr at that instant and a speed of 10 mi/hr 20 seconds later. What was the speed of the boat 35 seconds after the motor was shut off, and how far did it travel in those 35 seconds?

6. Sugar, in solution, decomposes into other substances at a rate proportional to the amount still unchanged. If 30 lb of sugar reduces to 10 lb in 4 hr, when will 95% of the sugar be decomposed?

A function y satisfies the differential equation $y' = ky$. Find $y = y(x)$ if the following initial conditions hold:

7. $y(0) = 1$, $y(1) = e^2$.

8. $y(0) = 1$, $y(1) = e^{-2}$.

9. $y(0) = 100$, $y(1) = 200$.

10. $y(0) = 100$, $y(1) = 50$.

11. Find $y(5)$ in Exercise 9.

12. Find $y(5)$ in Exercise 10.

9. Arc length of a circle and radian measure

Let AOB be an angle generated by a counterclockwise rotation of OA to OB, a rotation of less than a quarter of a revolution (Figure 10.4). We wish

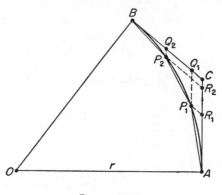

Figure 10.4

to assign to the arc $\overarc{AB}$ of the circle of radius r a real number s which is the length of $\overarc{AB}$.*

With this aim in mind, let points $P_1, P_2, \cdots, P_n$ be chosen in order between A and B on arc $\overarc{AB}$. The broken line

$$AP_1P_2 \cdots P_nB$$

is called an *inscripture* of arc $\overarc{AB}$. In Figure 10.4, for example, we have an inscripture of arc $\overarc{AB}$ with two intermediate points P_1 and P_2.

Each inscripture $I = AP_1P_2 \cdots P_nB$ of AB has *length* $|I|$ given by

$$|I| = |AP_1| + |P_1P_2| + \cdots + |P_nB|.$$

* See Chapter 15 for a general treatment of arc length.

The inscripture I of Figure 10.4, for example, has length
$$|I| = |AP_1| + |P_1P_2| + |P_2B|.$$

In Figure 10.4, C is the point of intersection of the tangent lines to the circle at A and B. The lines P_1R_1 and P_2R_2 are parallel to BC, and the lines P_1Q_1 and P_2Q_2 are parallel to AC. In triangle AP_1R_1, it is clear that $|AP_1| < |P_1R_1| + |AR_1|$. But $|P_1R_1| = |Q_1C|$, and therefore

(1) $$|AP_1| < |Q_1C| + |AR_1|.$$

Similarly,

(2) $$|P_1P_2| < |Q_1Q_2| + |R_1R_2|,$$

and

(3) $$|P_2B| < |Q_2B| + |R_2C|.$$

Adding (1), (2), and (3), we have
$$|AP_1| + |P_1P_2| + |P_2B| < |BC| + |AC|.$$

Thus the length of the inscripture AP_1P_2B is less than $|AC| + |BC|$.

In a similar fashion, we can prove that the length $|I|$ of each inscripture I of $\overarc{AB}$ satisfies the inequality
$$|I| < |AC| + |BC|.$$

Hence the set of all lengths of inscriptures of the arc $\overarc{AB}$ has an upper bound (namely, $|AC| + |BC|$) and therefore has a least upper bound. A slight modification of the arguments above will show that for every arc $\overarc{AB}$ of the circle, whether or not it is less than a quarter of the circle, the set of all lengths of inscriptures has an upper bound.

10.25 Definition. The *length s* of an arc $\overarc{AB}$ of a circle is the least upper bound of the set of all lengths of inscriptures of $\overarc{AB}$.

Since s is the least upper bound of a set having $|AC| + |BC|$ as an upper bound (Figure 10.4), we have

$$s \leq |AC| + |BC|.$$

10.26 Definition. Let AOB be a central angle of a circle of radius 1 having initial side OA and terminal side OB (Figure 10.5). The *radian measure* of angle AOB is the distance θ traveled on the unit circle by the point A under the rotation of the angle. The number θ is positive if the rotation is counterclockwise; otherwise θ is negative.

The circumference of a unit circle is 2π. Thus the semicircle has length π, and π must be the radian measure of a straight angle. The comparison between degree and radian measure of an angle therefore is given by

$$180° \sim \pi \text{ radians},$$

where the symbol $\sim$ is used to indicate that the given numbers measure the same angle.   Clearly a right angle has radian measure $\pi/2$, and hence

$$90° \sim \frac{\pi}{2} \text{ radians.}$$

Similarly,

$$45° \sim \frac{\pi}{4} \text{ radians,} \quad 60° \sim \frac{\pi}{3} \text{ radians,}$$

and so on.

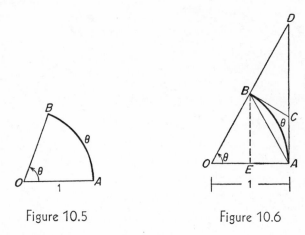

Figure 10.5   Figure 10.6

10. *Some trigonometric limits*

In this section, we will compare the radian measure of an angle with trigonometric functions of the angle.   This comparison will yield some fundamental trigonometric limits.

Let AOB be a central angle of a unit circle and let θ be the radian measure
of angle AOB.   We assume that

$$0 < \theta < \frac{\pi}{2}.$$

Also let AC and BC be tangent lines to the circle, and let D be the point
of intersection of lines AC and OB as shown in Figure 10.6.

By definition, $\theta \le |AC| + |BC|$.   Since BCD is a right triangle,
$|BC| < |CD|$.   Therefore $|AC| + |BC| < |AC| + |CD|$, and

$$\theta < |AD|.$$

In right triangle OAD,

$$\tan \theta = \frac{|AD|}{|OA|} = |AD|.$$

This gives us a comparison between θ and $\tan \theta$, namely,

10.27 $\theta < \tan \theta \quad \text{if } 0 < \theta < \frac{\pi}{2}.$

We recall that $\tan \theta = \sin \theta / \cos \theta$. Thus 10.27 may be put in the form $< \sin \theta / \cos \theta$ or, on multiplying throughout by $(\cos \theta)/\theta$,

10.28 $$\cos \theta < \frac{\sin \theta}{\theta} \quad \text{if } 0 < \theta < \frac{\pi}{2}.$$

Since the segment AB (Figure 10.6) is an inscripture of arc AB, $|AB| < \theta$. Using the law of cosines in triangle OAB, we have

$$|AB|^2 = 1^2 + 1^2 - 2 \cos \theta.$$

Thus $2 - 2 \cos \theta = |AB|^2 < \theta^2$, or

10.29 $$1 - \frac{\theta^2}{2} < \cos \theta \quad \text{if } 0 < \theta < \frac{\pi}{2}.$$

In triangle OEB of Figure 10.6,

$$\sin \theta = \frac{|EB|}{|OB|} = |EB|.$$

Clearly $|EB| < |AB| < \theta$, and therefore

10.30 $$\sin \theta < \theta \quad \text{if } 0 < \theta < \frac{\pi}{2}.$$

An alternative form of 10.30,

10.31 $$\frac{\sin \theta}{\theta} < 1 \quad \text{if } 0 < \theta < \frac{\pi}{2},$$

will be useful in the proof of the following important limit:

10.32 $$\lim_{\theta \to 0} \frac{\sin \theta}{\theta} = 1.$$

Proof: We easily get from 10.28–10.31 that

(1) $$1 - \frac{\theta^2}{2} < \frac{\sin \theta}{\theta} < 1 \quad \text{if } 0 < \theta < \frac{\pi}{2}.$$

If θ is a negative number such that

$$-\frac{\pi}{2} < \theta < 0,$$

then $$0 < -\theta < \frac{\pi}{2}$$

and, from (1),

(2) $$1 - \frac{(-\theta)^2}{2} < \frac{\sin (-\theta)}{-\theta} < 1 \quad \text{if } -\frac{\pi}{2} < \theta < 0.$$

However,

$$\frac{\sin (-\theta)}{-\theta} = \frac{-\sin \theta}{-\theta} = \frac{\sin \theta}{\theta},$$

and therefore (2) may be written in the form

(3) $$1 - \frac{\theta^2}{2} < \frac{\sin \theta}{\theta} < 1 \quad \text{if } -\frac{\pi}{2} < \theta < 0.$$

On combining (1) and (3), we obtain

(4) $$1 - \frac{\theta^2}{2} < \frac{\sin \theta}{\theta} < 1 \quad \text{if } -\frac{\pi}{2} < \theta < \frac{\pi}{2}, \quad \theta \neq 0.$$

Since

$$\lim_{\theta \to 0} \left(1 - \frac{\theta^2}{2}\right) = 1,$$

the desired limit follows from (4). This proves 10.32.

We establish as corollaries of 10.32 that the sine and cosine function are continuous at 0, that is,

10.33 $$\lim_{\theta \to 0} \sin \theta = 0,$$

and

10.34 $$\lim_{\theta \to 0} \cos \theta = 1.$$

The first of these is proved as follows,

$$\lim_{\theta \to 0} \sin \theta = \lim_{\theta \to 0} \frac{\sin \theta}{\theta} \theta = 1 \cdot 0 = 0,$$

while the second one is a consequence of the first one:

$$\lim_{\theta \to 0} \cos \theta = \lim_{\theta \to 0} \sqrt{1 - \sin^2 \theta} = 1.$$

The final limit we shall prove is given below,

10.35 $$\lim_{\theta \to 0} \frac{1 - \cos \theta}{\theta} = 0.$$

Proof: Since $\sin^2 \theta = 1 - \cos^2 \theta$,

$$\frac{1 - \cos \theta}{\theta} = \frac{\sin^2 \theta}{\theta(1 + \cos \theta)}.$$

Thus

$$\lim_{\theta \to 0} \frac{1 - \cos \theta}{\theta} = \lim_{\theta \to 0} \frac{\sin \theta}{\theta} \cdot \frac{\sin \theta}{1 + \cos \theta} = 1 \cdot \frac{0}{2} = 0.$$

■ ■ ■ EXERCISES

1. Make tables of values of $\sin x$, $\cos x$, and $\tan x$ for the following values of x

$$-\pi, \ -\frac{2\pi}{3}, \ -\frac{\pi}{2}, \ -\frac{\pi}{3}, \ -\frac{\pi}{4}, \ -\frac{\pi}{6}, \ 0, \ \frac{\pi}{6}, \ \frac{\pi}{4}, \ \frac{\pi}{3}, \ \frac{\pi}{2}, \ \frac{2\pi}{3}, \ \frac{3\pi}{4}, \ \frac{5\pi}{6}, \ \pi.$$

Sketch the graphs of the following equations for $-2\pi \leq x \leq 2\pi$.

2. $y = \sin x$.   3. $y = \cos x$.

4. $y = \tan x$.   5. $y = \sec x$.

Solve the following equations for θ, $-2\pi \leq \theta \leq 2\pi$:

6. $\sin \theta = 0$.   7. $\cos \theta = 0$.

8. $\sin 2\theta = 1$.

9. $\cos \theta = -\dfrac{1}{2}$.

10. $\sec \theta = -2$.

11. $\sin \theta = \dfrac{\sqrt{3}}{2}$.

12. $\csc \theta = \dfrac{2}{\sqrt{3}}$.

13. $\sin\left(\theta + \dfrac{\pi}{2}\right) = \dfrac{\sqrt{2}}{2}$.

Solve the following inequalities for θ, $-2\pi < \theta < 2\pi$.

14. $|\sin \theta| < \dfrac{1}{2}$.

15. $|\cos \theta| < \dfrac{\sqrt{2}}{2}$.

16. Prove that $\displaystyle\lim_{\theta\to0} \dfrac{1 - \cos \theta}{\theta^2} = \dfrac{1}{2}$. **17.** Find $\displaystyle\lim_{\theta\to0} \dfrac{\tan \theta}{\theta}$.

1. Derivatives of the trigonometric functions

We established in the previous section that

$$\lim_{h\to0} \frac{\sin h}{h} = 1, \quad \lim_{h\to0} \frac{1 - \cos h}{h} = 0.$$

With the aid of these limits we easily prove the following differentiation formulas.

10.36 $\qquad\qquad D_x \sin x = \cos x.$

10.37 $\qquad\qquad D_x \cos x = -\sin x.$

Proof of 10.36: By the definition of the derivative,

$$D_x \sin x = \lim_{h\to0} \frac{\sin (x + h) - \sin x}{h}.$$

Therefore, by one of the addition formulas of trigonometry and the above limits,

$$D_x \sin x = \lim_{h\to0} \frac{\sin x \cos h + \cos x \sin h - \sin x}{h},$$

$$= \lim_{h\to0} \left(-\sin x \frac{1 - \cos h}{h} + \cos x \frac{\sin h}{h}\right)$$

$$= -\sin x \cdot 0 + \cos x \cdot 1$$

$$= \cos x.$$

The proof of 10.37 follows the same pattern and is left as an exercise. Since

$$\tan x = \frac{\sin x}{\cos x},$$

$$D_x \tan x = \frac{\cos x\, D_x \sin x - \sin x\, D_x \cos x}{\cos^2 x}$$

$$= \frac{\cos^2 x + \sin^2 x}{\cos^2 x} = \frac{1}{\cos^2 x} = \sec^2 x.$$

Thus we have

10.38 $D_x \tan x = \sec^2 x.$

Similarly, one may prove that

10.39 $D_x \cot x = -\csc^2 x.$

The derivative of the cosecant function may be derived from the identity

$$\csc x = \frac{1}{\sin x} = (\sin x)^{-1}.$$

Thus $D_x \csc x = D_x (\sin x)^{-1} = -(\sin x)^{-2} \cos x$

$$= -\frac{1}{\sin x} \cdot \frac{\cos x}{\sin x} = -\csc x \cot x.$$

This proves

10.40 $D_x \csc x = -\csc x \cot x.$

In a similar way, we may prove that

10.41 $D_x \sec x = \sec x \tan x.$

The chain rule along with the above differentiation formulas yields the following general formulas.

10.42 $D_x \sin g(x) = \cos g(x)\, D_x g(x).$

10.43 $D_x \cos g(x) = -\sin g(x)\, D_x g(x).$

10.44 $D_x \tan g(x) = \sec^2 g(x)\, D_x g(x).$

10.45 $D_x \cot g(x) = -\csc^2 g(x)\, D_x g(x).$

10.46 $D_x \sec g(x) = \sec g(x) \tan g(x)\, D_x g(x).$

10.47 $D_x \csc g(x) = -\csc g(x) \cot g(x)\, D_x g(x).$

Example 1.   Find: (a) $D_x \sin ax.$ (b) $D_x (\sec 2x + \tan 2x).$

Solution: (a) By 10.42,

$$D_x \sin ax = \cos ax\, D_x(ax) = a \cos ax.$$

(b) By 10.44 and 10.46,

$$\begin{aligned} D_x (\sec 2x + \tan 2x) &= D_x \sec 2x + D_x \tan 2x \\ &= \sec 2x \tan 2x\, D_x\, 2x + \sec^2 2x\, D_x\, 2x \\ &= 2 \sec 2x \tan 2x + 2 \sec^2 2x. \end{aligned}$$

Example 2.   Find $D_x \ln |\sin x|.$

Solution: By 10.17,

$$D_x \ln |\sin x| = \frac{D_x \sin x}{\sin x}.$$

Therefore

$$D_x \ln |\sin x| = \frac{\cos x}{\sin x} = \cot x.$$

Example 3.   Find $f'(x)$ if $f(x) = e^{-x} \sin 3x$.

Solution: By the product differentiation formula,

$$f'(x) = e^{-x} D_x \sin 3x + \sin 3x \, D_x \, e^{-x}$$
$$= e^{-x}(3 \cos 3x) + \sin 3x(-e^{-x})$$
$$= e^{-x}(3 \cos 3x - \sin 3x).$$

Example 4.   Find $g'(x)$ if $g(x) = 2 \cos \dfrac{x}{2} - 6 \cos^3 \dfrac{x}{2}$.

Solution: We have

$$g'(x) = -2 \sin \frac{x}{2} D_x \frac{x}{2} - 6 \left(3 \cos^2 \frac{x}{2} D_x \cos \frac{x}{2} \right)$$

$$= -\sin \frac{x}{2} - 18 \left(\cos^2 \frac{x}{2} \right) \left(-\frac{1}{2} \sin \frac{x}{2} \right)$$

$$= \left(\sin \frac{x}{2} \right) \left(-1 + 9 \cos^2 \frac{x}{2} \right).$$

■ ■ ■   EXERCISES

Differentiate the following:

1. $2 \sin x \cos x$.

2. $\tan 4x$.

3. $\dfrac{\sin 2x}{1 + \cos 2x}$.

4. $\dfrac{\sec 3x}{1 + \tan 3x}$.

5. $\tan^3 \dfrac{x}{2}$.

6. $3 \sin^2 \dfrac{x}{3}$.

7. $\sec^2 x \tan^2 x$.

8. $\sin^3 x \cos^2 x$.

9. $\dfrac{\cot 2x - 1}{\csc 2x}$.

10. $(\csc 3x - \cot 3x)^2$.

11. $\ln |\sec x + \tan x|$.

12. $\ln |\csc x - \cot x|$.

13. $e^{2x} \cos 2x$.

14. $e^{ax}(a \sin bx - b \cos bx)$.

15. $x \sin x + \cos x$.

16. $x \sin \dfrac{1}{x}$.

17. $\sqrt{1 - \tan^2 2x}$.

18. $\tan \sqrt{x}$.

19. $\sec x^3$.

20. $x^2 \cot x^2$.

Find $\dfrac{dy}{dx}$ and $\dfrac{d^2y}{dx^2}$ if:

21. $y = \csc^3 2x$.

22. $y = \dfrac{1 - \sin x}{1 + \sin x}$.

23. $y = \tan x \sec^2 x$.

24. $y = x^2 \tan^2 2x$.

25. $y = x^2 \sin \dfrac{1}{x}$.

26. $y = \csc 2x^3$.

27. $y = \cos^2 2x - \sin^2 2x.$ **28.** $y = \sin x + \sin x \cos x.$

Find $\dfrac{dy}{dx}$ if:

29. $x = \sin y.$ **30.** $x = \tan y.$

31. $x = \sec y.$ **32.** $e^x \sin 2y = x + y.$

33. $\cos(x + y) = y \sin x.$ **34.** $\tan(x^2 + y) = 4 + \cot y.$

Find the extrema of the following functions and sketch their graphs for $0 \leq x \leq 2\pi$:

35. $f(x) = \sin x + \cos x.$ **36.** $g(x) = 2 \cos x + \cos 2x.$

37. $F(x) = \sin^2 x + \cos x.$ **38.** $f(x) = \tan x - 2x.$

39. $g(x) = 2 \sec x - \tan x.$ **40.** $F(x) = \sec x + 2 \cos x.$

If the position function of a point moving on a line has the form $s(t) = a \sin bt$ [or $s(t) = a \cos bt$], then the motion of the point is called *simple harmonic motion*. Describe the motion of a point, giving its velocity and acceleration, if

41. $s(t) = 4 \sin t.$ **42.** $s(t) = 2 \cos 2t.$

43. $s(t) = 3 \cos \pi t.$ **44.** $s(t) = \sin \dfrac{\pi t}{2}.$

45. A point P is moving along a circle of radius r with a constant angular velocity of b radians/sec. Show that the projection of P on a fixed diameter of the circle is moving in simple harmonic motion.

12. Inverse trigonometric functions

The sine function is a continuous function with values ranging between -1 and 1. Hence by Theorem 8.21, to each y between -1 and 1 there corresponds some number x such that

$$y = \sin x.$$

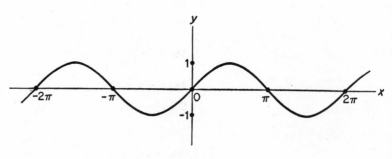

Figure 10.7

That the number x is not unique is evident from the graph of the sine function in Figure 10.7. Thus there is a number x in each of the intervals $\cdots$, $[-3\pi/2, -\pi/2]$, $[-\pi/2, \pi/2]$, $[\pi/2, 3\pi/2]$, $\cdots$ such that $y = \sin x.$

The equation

$$x = e^y$$

defines a function, namely,

$$y = \ln x.$$

We might expect, in a similar way, that the equation

$$x = \sin y$$

defines some function. It is clear from the graph of this equation (Figure 10.8) that to each number x in the interval $[-1,1]$ there correspond many numbers y such that $x = \sin y$. Thus, if this equation is to define a function, we must in some way limit ourselves to one choice of y for each x.

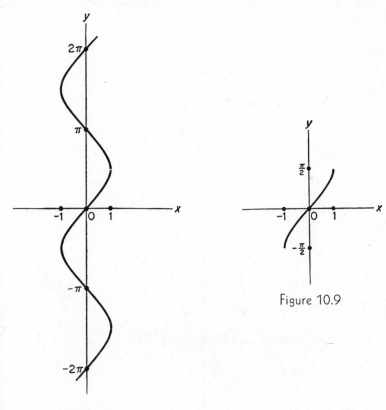

Figure 10.9

Figure 10.8

This suggests taking just a part of the graph of the equation $x = \sin y$, say that part between $y = -\pi/2$ and $y = \pi/2$ as sketched in Figure 10.9, so that to each x in the interval $[-1,1]$ there is precisely one point (x,y) on this piece of the graph. Thus we make the following definition.

10.48 Definition.   The *inverse sine function*, designated $\sin^{-1}$, is de
fined by:

$$\sin^{-1} x = y, \quad -1 \le x \le 1,$$

if and only if

$$x = \sin y \quad \text{and} \quad -\frac{\pi}{2} \le y \le \frac{\pi}{2}.$$

By definition, the domain of the inverse sine function is the interva
$[-1,1]$ and its range is the interval $[-\pi/2,\pi/2]$.   Its graph is given i·
Figure 10.9.

Because of the possible confusion between the two totally different con
cepts of

$$\sin^{-1} x, \quad (\sin x)^{-1},$$

we shall sometimes call the inverse sine function the *arcsine* function
and write

$$\text{arcsin } x$$

for $\sin^{-1} x$.   By definition,

$$\sin (\sin^{-1} x) = \sin (\arcsin x) = x, \quad -1 \le x \le 1,$$

10.49

$$\sin^{-1} (\sin x) = \arcsin (\sin x) = x, \quad -\frac{\pi}{2} \le x \le \frac{\pi}{2}.$$

The other inverse trigonometric functions may be defined similarly.   Let
us carry through the definition of one other such function, namely, the
inverse tangent.

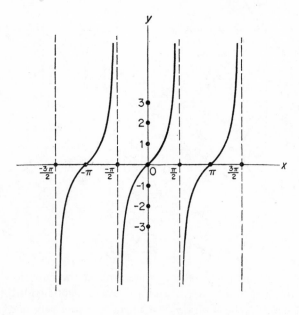

Figure 10.10

The tangent function is continuous at every number other than an odd multiple of $\pi/2$.   The lines

$$\cdots, \quad x = -\frac{3\pi}{2}, \quad x = -\frac{\pi}{2}, \quad x = \frac{\pi}{2}, \quad x = \frac{3\pi}{2}, \quad \cdots$$

are vertical asymptotes of the graph of the tangent function, as indicated in Figure 10.10.

Corresponding to each number x, there are many numbers y such that

$$\tan y = x.$$

However, if we restrict y to be in the interval $(-\pi/2, \pi/2)$, then to each number x there corresponds precisely one number y such that $\tan y = x$, and we may make the following definition.

10.50 Definition.   The *inverse tangent function*, designated $\tan^{-1}$, is defined by:

$$\tan^{-1} x = y$$

if and only if

$$x = \tan y \quad \text{and} \quad -\frac{\pi}{2} < y < \frac{\pi}{2}.$$

By definition, the domain of the inverse tangent function is the set of all real numbers and its range is the open interval $(-\pi/2, \pi/2)$.   Its graph is

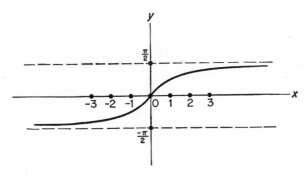

Figure 10.11

sketched in Figure 10.11.   Again, we shall sometimes call the inverse tangent function the *arctangent*.   By definition,

$$\tan (\tan^{-1} x) = \tan (\arctan x) = x,$$

10.51

$$\tan^{-1} (\tan x) = \arctan (\tan x) = x, \quad -\frac{\pi}{2} < x < \frac{\pi}{2}.$$

■ ■ ■ EXERCISES

Find:

1. $\sin^{-1} \dfrac{1}{2}$.

2. $\tan^{-1} 1$.

3. $\sin^{-1} \dfrac{\sqrt{2}}{2}$.

4. $\tan^{-1} -\dfrac{1}{\sqrt{3}}$.

5. $\arctan -1$.

6. $\arcsin -\dfrac{\sqrt{3}}{2}$.

7. $\arcsin 1$.

8. $\arctan \sqrt{3}$.

9. $\tan^{-1} -\sqrt{3}$.

10. $\sin^{-1} -\dfrac{1}{\sqrt{2}}$.

11. $\sin^{-1} -1$.

12. $\tan^{-1} \dfrac{1}{\sqrt{3}}$.

13. $\arcsin 0$.

14. $\arctan 0$.

15. $\sin (\arctan 1)$.

16. $\tan^{-1} \left(\sin \dfrac{\pi}{2} \right)$.

17. $\tan \left(\sin^{-1} \dfrac{\sqrt{3}}{2} \right)$.

18. $\sin (\tan^{-1} -\sqrt{3})$.

19. $\tan^{-1} (\sin 0)$.

20. $\sin \left(\tan^{-1} \dfrac{1}{\sqrt{3}} \right)$.

13. Derivatives of inverse trigonometric functions

Since

$$y = \sin^{-1} x$$

if and only if

$$\sin y = x, \qquad -\frac{\pi}{2} \le y \le \frac{\pi}{2},$$

implicit differentiation may be used to find the derivative of the inverse sine function, if indeed the inverse sine function has a derivative. By implicit differentiation of the equation above, we have

$$\cos y \, \frac{dy}{dx} = 1,$$

and

$$D_x \sin^{-1} x = \frac{dy}{dx} = \frac{1}{\cos y}, \qquad -\frac{\pi}{2} < y < \frac{\pi}{2}.$$

Since $\cos y > 0$ if $-\pi/2 < y < \pi/2$,

$$\cos y = \sqrt{1 - \sin^2 y} = \sqrt{1 - x^2}.$$

Hence, if the inverse sine function has a derivative, it is given by

10.52 $\qquad D_x \sin^{-1} x = \dfrac{1}{\sqrt{1 - x^2}}, \qquad -1 < x < 1.$

The proof that the inverse sine function has a derivative is similar to the corresponding proof for the logarithmic function (10.15). Thus, the function F defined by

$$F(x) = \int_0^x \frac{1}{\sqrt{1 - x^2}} \, dx$$

has the derivative

$$F'(x) = \frac{1}{\sqrt{1-x^2}}.$$

Let us prove that

$$F(x) = \sin^{-1} x, \qquad -1 < x < 1,$$

which will prove that the inverse sine function is differentiable and will establish 10.52.

According to the chain rule,

$$D_y F(\sin y) = F'(\sin y) \cos y = \frac{1}{\sqrt{1 - \sin^2 y}} \cos y = 1.$$

Hence

$$F(\sin y) = y + C$$

for some constant C. Since $F(\sin 0) = F(0) = 0 = 0 + C$, clearly $C = 0$ and

$$F(\sin y) = y.$$

Letting $y = \sin^{-1} x$, we have $\sin y = x$ and

$$F(x) = \sin^{-1} x.$$

If the inverse tangent function has a derivative, then it may be found by differentiating implicitly the equation

$$\tan y = x, \qquad -\frac{\pi}{2} < y < \frac{\pi}{2}.$$

Thus,

$$\sec^2 y \frac{dy}{dx} = 1,$$

and

$$D_x \tan^{-1} x = \frac{dy}{dx} = \frac{1}{\sec^2 y}.$$

Since $\sec^2 y = 1 + \tan^2 y = 1 + x^2$, we have

10.53
$$D_x \tan^{-1} x = \frac{1}{1 + x^2}.$$

The proof that the inverse tangent function has a derivative is omitted, since it is entirely similar to that given above for the inverse sine function.

The other inverse trigonometric functions may be differentiated in a similar fashion. An interesting feature of the derivatives of $\sin^{-1}$ and $\tan^{-1}$ given above is that they are algebraic functions. This might lead us to speculate that all the derivatives of the inverse trigonometric functions are algebraic functions, which is actually the case.

We write the derivatives of three of the inverse trigonometric functions below in the usual general form. The proof of the derivative of $\sec^{-1}$ is left as an exercise.

10.54
$$D_x \sin^{-1} g(x) = \frac{D_x g(x)}{\sqrt{1 - g^2(x)}}.$$

10.55 $$D_x \tan^{-1} g(x) = \frac{D_x g(x)}{1 + g^2(x)}.$$

10.56 $$D_x \sec^{-1} g(x) = \frac{D_x g(x)}{g(x)\sqrt{g^2(x) - 1}}.$$

Example 1. Find $D_x \sin^{-1} 5x$.

Solution: By 10.54, with $g(x) = 5x$,

$$D_x \sin^{-1} 5x = \frac{5}{\sqrt{1 - 25x^2}}.$$

Example 2. Find $D_x \sec^{-1} x^2$.

Solution: By 10.56, with $g(x) = x^2$,

$$D_x \sec^{-1} x^2 = \frac{2x}{x^2\sqrt{x^4 - 1}} = \frac{2}{x\sqrt{x^4 - 1}}.$$

■ ■ ■ EXERCISES

1. Define the inverse cosine function with the equation $\cos y = x, 0 \le y \le \pi$. Sketch its graph and find its derivative.

2. Define the inverse cotangent function with the equation $\cot y = x$, $0 < y < \pi$. Sketch its graph and find its derivative.

3. Define the inverse secant function with the equation $\sec y = x$, where either $0 \le y < \pi/2$ or $\pi \le y < 3\pi/2$. Sketch its graph and verify Formula 10.56.

4. How would you define the function $\csc^{-1}$? Sketch its graph and find its derivative.

Differentiate the following:

5. $\sin^{-1} 2x$.

6. $\tan^{-1} (x + 1)$.

7. $\sec^{-1} 4x$.

8. $\sin^{-1} e^x$.

9. $(1 + \arcsin 3x)^2$.

10. $\arctan \dfrac{1}{x}$.

11. $\dfrac{\arctan e^{2x}}{e^{2x}}$.

12. $2x \arctan x - \ln (1 + x^2)$.

13. $x \sin^{-1} x + \sqrt{1 - x^2}$.

14. $\operatorname{arcsec} \sqrt{x^2 - 1}$.

15. $\tan^{-1} \sqrt{x^2 - 1}$.

16. $\sin^{-1} \sqrt{1 - x^2}$.

17. $\sec^{-1} \sqrt{x}$.

18. $\sqrt{\sin^{-1} 3x}$.

19. $\ln \arctan x$.

20. $\sqrt{1 - x^2} + \arcsin x$.

21. $\arcsin x - x\sqrt{1 - x^2}$.

22. $\tan^{-1} \dfrac{1 + 2x}{2 - x}$.

23. $2x^3 \tan^{-1} x + \ln (1 + x^2) - x^2$.

24. $\sec \dfrac{1}{x}$.

25. Prove that $\tan^{-1} \dfrac{x + 1}{x - 1} + \tan^{-1} x = c$, a constant, and find c. (*Hint:* Use 6.19.)

26. Prove that $\sec^{-1} x = \dfrac{\pi}{2} - \sin^{-1} \dfrac{1}{x}$ for every $x \geq 1$.

27. Show that if $\ln (x^2 + y^2) + 2 \tan^{-1} \dfrac{x}{y} = 0$, then $\dfrac{dy}{dx} = \dfrac{x + y}{x - y}$.

28. Show that if $y = \sin (a \tan^{-1} x)$, then

$$(1 + x^2)^2 \frac{d^2y}{dx^2} + 2x(1 + x^2) \frac{dy}{dx} + a^2 y = 0.$$

29. Show that if $y = \sin (a \sin^{-1} x)$, then

$$(1 - x^2) \frac{d^2y}{dx^2} - x \frac{dy}{dx} + a^2 y = 0.$$

14. The inverse of a function

If f is an increasing function, so that

$$f(u) < f(v) \quad \text{if and only if } u < v,$$

u and v in the domain of f, then another function g may be defined from f as follows:

$$g(x) = y \quad \text{if and only if } x = f(y).$$

The domain of g is the range of f.   Evidently

$$g(f(y)) = y, \qquad f(g(x)) = x,$$

for every y in the domain of f and x in the domain of g.   The function g is called the *inverse function* of f.   It is convenient to designate the inverse function of f by f^{-1}.

A decreasing function has an inverse function defined in the same way. We give now some examples of inverse functions.

Example 1.   Find the inverse of f, if

$$f(x) = \sqrt{x}, \quad x \geq 0.$$

Solution: The function f is increasing.   Its inverse function f^{-1} is such that:

$$f^{-1}(f(x)) = x, \quad x \geq 0$$

i.e., such that

$$f^{-1}(\sqrt{x}) = x.$$

Thus $f^{-1}(y) = y^2$, $y \geq 0$, and we may say that the inverse function f^{-1} of f is defined by

$$f^{-1}(x) = x^2, \quad x \geq 0.$$

Example 2.   Find the inverse of g, if

$$g(x) = e^x.$$

Solution: The inverse g^{-1} of g is given by

$$g^{-1}(x) = \ln x, \quad x > 0,$$

since

$$g^{-1}(g(x)) = \ln e^x = x, \qquad g(g^{-1}(x)) = e^{\ln x} = x,$$

by 10.12.

Example 3. Find the inverse of F, where

$$F(x) = \sin x, \quad -\frac{\pi}{2} \le x \le \frac{\pi}{2}.$$

Solution: The inverse F^{-1} of F is the inverse sine function,

$$F^{-1}(x) = \sin^{-1} x,$$

according to 10.49.

Let f be an increasing function with inverse function f^{-1}, and let x_1 and x_2 be in the domain of f^{-1} with $x_1 < x_2$. Then

$$x_1 = f(y_1), \qquad x_2 = f(y_2)$$

for some numbers y_1 and y_2 in the domain of f. By assumption,

$$f(y_1) < f(y_2) \quad \text{and therefore} \quad y_1 < y_2.$$

Since $y_1 = f^{-1}(f(y_1)) = f^{-1}(x_1)$ and $y_2 = f^{-1}(x_2)$, we have that $f^{-1}(x_1) < f^{-1}(x_2)$. Thus

$$f^{-1}(x_1) < f^{-1}(x_2) \quad \text{if and only if } x_1 < x_2,$$

and we have proved that the *inverse function of an increasing function is an increasing function.*

The inverse function f^{-1} of an increasing function f, being itself an increasing function, also has an inverse function. It is easily demonstrated that the inverse of f^{-1} is again f. Thus f and f^{-1} are inverses of each other.

If the increasing function f is continuous in a closed interval $[a,b]$, then for every number y satisfying

$$f(a) < y < f(b),$$

there exists a number x in $[a,b]$ such that

$$y = f(x)$$

according to Theorem 8.21. Thus it is clear that the inverse function f^{-1} of f is defined at every number in the interval $[f(a),f(b)]$. Actually, the function f^{-1} is also continuous in $[f(a),f(b)]$ according to the following theorem.

10.57 Theorem. If the increasing function f is continuous in the closed interval $[a,b]$, then its inverse function f^{-1} is continuous in the closed interval $[f(a),f(b)]$.

Proof: Let c be in the open interval (a,b), so that $f(c)$ is in the open interval $(f(a),f(b))$. In order to prove that f^{-1} is continuous at $f(c)$, we must show that for every number $\epsilon > 0$, there exists some number $\delta > 0$ such that

$$f^{-1}(f(c)) - \epsilon < f^{-1}(y) < f^{-1}(f(c)) + \epsilon$$

for every y satisfying

$$f(c) - \delta < y < f(c) + \delta.$$

Since f and f^{-1} are inverse functions,

$$f^{-1}(f(c)) = c.$$

Let us select ϵ small enough so that both $c - \epsilon$ and $c + \epsilon$ are in the interval $[a,b]$. Now
$$c - \epsilon < f^{-1}(y) < c + \epsilon$$
if and only if
$$f(c - \epsilon) < y < f(c + \epsilon).$$
Let us select δ as the smaller of the two numbers
$$f(c) - f(c - \epsilon), \qquad f(c + \epsilon) - f(c).$$
Then
$$f(c - \epsilon) \leq f(c) - \delta, \qquad f(c) + \delta \leq f(c + \epsilon),$$
and every number y satisfying the inequality
$$f(c) - \delta < y < f(c) + \delta$$
also satisfies the inequality
$$f(c - \epsilon) < y < f(c + \epsilon).$$
In turn, for each y satisfying the above inequality,
$$c - \epsilon < f^{-1}(y) < c + \epsilon.$$
Thus $f^{-1}(f(c)) - \epsilon < f^{-1}(y) < f^{-1}(f(c)) + \epsilon$ for every y satisfying $f(c) - \delta < y < f(c) + \delta$, and the function f^{-1} is continuous at $f(c)$.

A modification of the argument above proves that f^{-1} is also continuous at the numbers $f(a)$ and $f(b)$.

The inverse of a function is differentiable if the function is according to the following theorem.

10.58 Theorem. If f and g are inverse functions and if $f'(g(x))$ exists and is nonzero, then
$$g'(x) = \frac{1}{f'(g(x))}.$$

Proof: Let c be chosen in the domain of g so that $f'(g(c))$ exists and is nonzero. By definition,
$$g'(c) = \underset{x \to c}{\text{limit}} \; \frac{g(x) - g(c)}{x - c}.$$
We introduce the new function F defined as follows:
$$F(y) = \frac{y - g(c)}{f(y) - f(g(c))}, \quad y \neq g(c),$$
$$F(g(c)) = \frac{1}{f'(g(c))}.$$
The domain of F is the same as that of f. Since
$$\underset{y \to g(c)}{\text{limit}} \; \frac{f(y) - f(g(c))}{y - g(c)} = f'(g(c)),$$
evidently
$$\underset{y \to g(c)}{\text{limit}} \; F(y) = \frac{1}{f'(g(c))}.$$
Thus the function F is continuous at $g(c)$.

We may now use Theorem 4.20 to draw the desired conclusion. Thus

$$\lim_{x \to c} F(g(x)) = F(g(c)) = \frac{1}{f'(g(c))}$$

according to 4.20, whereas

$$F(g(x)) = \frac{g(x) - g(c)}{x - c}$$

by the definition of the function F. Hence

$$\lim_{x \to c} \frac{g(x) - g(c)}{x - c} = \frac{1}{f'(g(c))},$$

and the theorem is proved.

The results of this section on increasing functions also hold for decreasing functions.

■ ■ ■ EXERCISES

Find the inverse of each of the following functions, and give its domain:

1. $f(x) = \sqrt[3]{x}$.

2. $g(x) = x^2, x \leq 0$.

3. $F(x) = \tan x, -\dfrac{\pi}{2} < x < \dfrac{\pi}{2}$.

4. $f(x) = \log_a x, x > 0$.

5. $f(x) = x + 2$.

6. $F(x) = 3 - x$.

7. $g(x) = 2x$.

8. $f(x) = 2 - 3x$.

9. $F(x) = a^x$.

10. $g(x) = e^{3x}$.

11. Show that the hyperbolic sine (p. 270) is an increasing function, and hence that it has an inverse function $\sinh^{-1}$. Thus, $y = \sinh^{-1} x$ if and only if $x = \sinh y$. Find the domain of $\sinh^{-1}$, and prove that $\sinh^{-1} x = \ln(x + \sqrt{x^2 + 1})$. [*Hint:* Solve $x = \sinh y = (e^y - e^{-y})/2$ for y.]

12. Show that the hyperbolic tangent (p. 270) is an increasing function, and hence that it has an inverse function $\tanh^{-1}$. Find the domain of $\tanh^{-1}$, and prove that

$$\tanh^{-1} x = \frac{1}{2} \ln\left(\frac{1 + x}{1 - x}\right), \qquad\qquad |x| < 1.$$

13. Show that the hyperbolic cosine (p. 270) is a decreasing function if $x < 0$ and an increasing function if $x > 0$. If $f(x) = \cosh x, x \geq 0$, prove that $f^{-1}(x) = \ln(x + \sqrt{x^2 - 1}), x \geq 1$: if $f(x) = \cosh x, x \leq 0$, prove that $f^{-1}(x) = -\ln(x + \sqrt{x^2 - 1}), x \geq 1$.

14. For the function $\sinh^{-1}$ defined in Exercise 11, show that $D_x \sinh^{-1} x = 1/\sqrt{x^2 + 1}$.

15. For the function $\tanh^{-1}$ defined in Exercise 12, show that $D_x \tanh^{-1} x = 1/(1 - x^2)$.

16. If f^{-1} is an inverse of the function cosh, defined in Exercise 13, show that $D_x f^{-1}(x) = \pm 1/\sqrt{x^2 - 1}$.

15. *Partial differentiation*

If, corresponding to each pair of numbers x,y of some set of pairs of numbers there is one and only one number $f(x,y)$, then f is called a *function of two variables*. Functions of three or more variables are defined analogously. A detailed discussion of functions of two or more variables will be given in Chapters 17, 18, and 19. We will just briefly discuss derivatives of such functions in the present chapter.

There are two (partial) derivatives of a function of two variables, as defined below:

$$f_x(x,y) = \lim_{h\to 0} \frac{f(x + h,y) - f(x,y)}{h},$$

$$f_y(x,y) = \lim_{k\to 0} \frac{f(x,y + k) - f(x,y)}{k},$$

provided these limits exist. The numbers $f_x(x,y)$ and $f_y(x,y)$ are called the (first) *partial derivatives* of f with respect to x and y, respectively.

Many different notations are in general usage for partial derivatives. Thus, if

$$z = f(x,y),$$

other notations for $f_x(x,y)$ are

$$\frac{\partial z}{\partial x}, \quad \frac{\partial f}{\partial x}, \quad \frac{\partial}{\partial x}f(x,y), \quad f_x,$$

and similarly for $f_y(x,y)$.

The definition of $f_x(x,y)$ is just the usual definition of the derivative of a function (of one variable) if we consider y a constant, and, similarly, $f_y(x,y)$ is the usual derivative if we consider x a constant.

For example, if

$$f(x,y) = 5x^2 + 3xy - 7y^2,$$

then $\qquad f_x(x,y) = 10x + 3y, \qquad f_y(x,y) = 3x - 14y.$

If

$$g(x,y) = y \sin (x - y),$$

then $\qquad \dfrac{\partial g}{\partial x} = y \cos (x - y) \cdot \dfrac{\partial}{\partial x} (x - y) = y \cos (x - y),$

$\dfrac{\partial g}{\partial y} = \sin (x - y) + y \cos (x - y) \cdot \dfrac{\partial}{\partial y} (x - y)$

$$= \sin (x - y) - y \cos (x - y).$$

A function f of two variables has four second partial derivatives defined as follows:

$$f_{xx} = \frac{\partial^2 f}{\partial x^2} = \frac{\partial}{\partial x} \frac{\partial f}{\partial x}.$$

$$f_{yy} = \frac{\partial^2 f}{\partial y^2} = \frac{\partial}{\partial y} \frac{\partial f}{\partial y}.$$

$$f_{xy} = \frac{\partial^2 f}{\partial y\, \partial x} = \frac{\partial}{\partial y} \frac{\partial f}{\partial x}.$$

$$f_{yx} = \frac{\partial^2 f}{\partial x\, \partial y} = \frac{\partial}{\partial x} \frac{\partial f}{\partial y}.$$

Example 1. If $f(x,y) = 3ye^{x^2}$, find the four second partial derivatives of f.

Solution: The first partial derivatives of f are

$$f_x(x,y) = 6xye^{x^2}, \qquad f_y(x,y) = 3e^{x^2}.$$

Hence

$$f_{xx}(x,y) = \frac{\partial}{\partial x} f_x(x,y) = 12x^2 y e^{x^2} + 6y e^{x^2}$$

$$f_{yy}(x,y) = \frac{\partial}{\partial y} f_y(x,y) = 0$$

$$f_{xy}(x,y) = \frac{\partial}{\partial y} f_x(x,y) = 6x e^{x^2}$$

$$f_{yx}(x,y) = \frac{\partial}{\partial x} f_y(x,y) = 6x e^{x^2}.$$

Note that in this example $f_{xy}(x,y) = f_{yx}(x,y)$. Under certain conditions (see Chapter 18), and for most functions considered in this text, the two "crossed partials" will be identical.

Example 2. Verify that if $z = xy^3 - 5xy + 7y^2$, then $\dfrac{\partial^2 z}{\partial y\, \partial x} = \dfrac{\partial^2 z}{\partial x\, \partial y}$.

Solution: The first partials are as follows:

$$\frac{\partial z}{\partial x} = y^3 - 5y, \qquad \frac{\partial z}{\partial y} = 3xy^2 - 5x + 14y.$$

Hence

$$\frac{\partial^2 z}{\partial y\, \partial x} = \frac{\partial}{\partial y}\,(y^3 - 5y) = 3y^2 - 5,$$

and

$$\frac{\partial^2 z}{\partial x\, \partial y} = \frac{\partial}{\partial x}\,(3xy^2 - 5x + 14y) = 3y^2 - 5.$$

Example 3. Show that if $u(x,y) = \cos(x+y) + \sin(x-y)$, then

$$u_{xx} = u_{yy}.$$

Solution: Since

$$u_x = -\sin(x+y) + \cos(x-y),$$

then

$$u_{xx} = -\cos(x+y) - \sin(x-y).$$

Since

$$u_y = -\sin(x+y) - \cos(x-y),$$

then

$$u_{yy} = -\cos(x+y) - \sin(x-y).$$

It follows that $u_{xx} = u_{yy}$.

■ ■ ■ EXERCISES

Find $\dfrac{\partial f}{\partial x}, \dfrac{\partial f}{\partial y}, \dfrac{\partial^2 f}{\partial x\, \partial y}, \dfrac{\partial^2 f}{\partial y\, \partial x}$ for each of the following functions:

1. $f(x,y) = x^3 + y^3 + 3xy.$

2. $f(x,y) = (x^3 - 2y)^2 + xy.$

3. $f(x,y) = \dfrac{x - y}{x + y}.$

4. $f(x,y) = \sin (2x + 3y).$

5. $f(x,y) = e^{-x^2 - y^2}.$

6. $f(x,y) = x \sin^{-1} y + y \sin^{-1} x.$

7. $f(x,y) = \dfrac{\sin xy}{x} - e^{-y} + xy.$

8. $f(x,y) = \dfrac{e^{xy}}{x^2 - y^2}.$

9. $f(x,y) = x^2 \ln y^2.$

10. $f(x,y) = e^{3x} \ln (x^2 y).$

11. $f(x,y) = \tan^{-1} (x + y).$

12. $f(x,y) = x \tan (x + 2y).$

13. If $f(x,y) = \dfrac{e^{x^2 + y^2}}{x^2 + y^2}$, show that $yf_x - xf_y = 0.$

14. If $f(x,y) = y^2 + \tan (ye^{1/x})$, show that $x^2 f_x + yf_y = 2y^2.$

15. If $g(x,y) = xe^{y/x}$, show that $xg_x + yg_y = g.$

16. If $z = \cos (x^2 + y^2)$, show that $y \dfrac{\partial z}{\partial x} - x \dfrac{\partial z}{\partial y} = 0.$

17. If $F(x,y) = \sqrt{x^2 - y^2} \sin^{-1} \dfrac{y}{x}$, show that $xF_x + yF_y = F.$

18. If $z = \arctan \dfrac{x}{y}$, show that $\dfrac{\partial^2 z}{\partial x^2} + \dfrac{\partial^2 z}{\partial y^2} = 0.$

19. If $f(x,y) = x \ln \dfrac{y}{x}$, show that $f_{yx} = f_{xy}$ and that

$$x^2 f_{xx} + 2xy f_{xy} + y^2 f_{yy} = 0.$$

20. If $g(x,y) = \ln \sqrt{x^2 + y^2}$, show that $g_{xx} + g_{yy} = 0.$

11

Elementary formal integration

■ ■ ■ ■ ■ ALL THE NECESSARY techniques for differentiating the algebraic and the elementary transcendental functions are now at our disposal. With these at hand, we proceed to the development of some integration techniques in this and the next chapter.

1. The indefinite integral

The notation

$$\int f(x) \, dx$$

is used to designate an antiderivative of f. This integral without limits is called an *indefinite integral* of the function f.

To be more precise, if the function F is an antiderivative of f over an interval $[a,b]$, so that

$$f(x) = F'(x), \qquad a \le x \le b,$$

then the indefinite integral of f, being an antiderivative, has the form

$$\int f(x) \, dx = F(x) + C, \qquad a \le x \le b,$$

for some constant C by 6.19. The interval $[a,b]$ over which the indefinite integral of f is taken will not be explicitly stated in the work to follow.　Any interval in which the integrand f is continuous will suffice.

According to this definition of the indefinite integral, the operations of differentiation and integration are inverses of each other in the sense that

$$D_x \int f(x)\, dx = f(x), \qquad \int D_x f(x)\, dx = f(x) + C.$$

The following two formulas are given here without proof.　They were proved for definite integrals in 8.18 and 8.19.

11.1　　　$\int [f(x) \pm g(x)]\, dx = \int f(x)\, dx \pm \int g(x)\, dx.$

11.2　　　$\int c[f(x)]\, dx = c \int f(x)\, dx.$

2. The power formulas

Any power function can be integrated by one of the following formulas.

11.3　　　$\int x^r\, dx = \dfrac{x^{r+1}}{r+1} + C, \quad r \neq -1.$

11.4　　　$\int x^{-1}\, dx = \ln |x| + C.$

The proof of 11.3 rests on the fact that if $r \neq -1$,

$$D_x \frac{x^{r+1}}{r+1} = x^r,$$

and, similarly, the proof of 11.4 rests on the fact that $D_x \ln |x| = 1/x$. Since

$$D_x(ax+b)^{r+1} = a(r+1)(ax+b)^r$$

and　　　　$D_x \ln |ax+b| = a(ax+b)^{-1},$

we may write down the following more general forms of 11.3 and 11.4: If $a \neq 0$,

11.5　　　$\int (ax+b)^r\, dx = \dfrac{(ax+b)^{r+1}}{a(r+1)} + C, \quad r \neq -1.$

11.6　　　$\int (ax+b)^{-1}\, dx = \dfrac{1}{a} \ln |ax+b| + C.$

With the help of the above four power integration formulas, any integral of the form (p a polynomial function)

$$\int \frac{p(x)}{x^r}\, dx \quad \text{or} \quad \int \frac{p(x)}{ax+b}\, dx$$

can be evaluated.　We illustrate this fact below with several examples.

Example 1.　Find　$\int (x^4 - 3x^3 + x^2 - 5)\, dx.$

Solution: We have

$$\int (x^4 - 3x^3 + x^2 - 5)\, dx = \int x^4\, dx - 3 \int x^3\, dx + \int x^2\, dx - \int 5\, dx$$

$$= \frac{x^5}{5} - \frac{3x^4}{4} + \frac{x^3}{3} - 5x + C.$$

Example 2. Find $\displaystyle\int \frac{x^2 - x + 3}{x}\, dx.$

Solution: Since

$$\frac{x^2 - x + 3}{x} = x - 1 + \frac{3}{x} = x - 1 + 3x^{-1},$$

we have

$$\int \frac{x^2 - x + 3}{x}\, dx = \int x\, dx - \int dx + 3 \int x^{-1}\, dx$$

$$= \frac{x^2}{2} - x + 3 \ln |x| + C.$$

Example 3. Find $\displaystyle\int \frac{x^2 + 1}{\sqrt{x}}\, dx.$

Solution: We have

$$\frac{x^2 + 1}{\sqrt{x}} = (x^2 + 1)x^{-1/2} = x^{3/2} + x^{-1/2},$$

and therefore

$$\int \frac{x^2 + 1}{\sqrt{x}}\, dx = \int x^{3/2}\, dx + \int x^{-1/2}\, dx = \frac{2x^{5/2}}{5} + 2x^{1/2} + C.$$

Example 4. Find $\displaystyle\int \frac{4x^2 + 2x - 1}{2x + 3}\, dx.$

Solution: By long division,

$$\frac{4x^2 + 2x - 1}{2x + 3} = 2x - 2 + \frac{5}{2x + 3}.$$

Hence

$$\int \frac{4x^2 + 2x - 1}{2x + 3}\, dx = \int (2x - 2)\, dx + 5 \int (2x + 3)^{-1}\, dx$$

$$= x^2 - 2x + \frac{5}{2} \ln |2x + 3| + C.$$

Example 5. Find $\displaystyle\int_0^2 \frac{1}{\sqrt[3]{3x + 2}}\, dx.$

Solution: Using 11.5, we have

$$\int_0^2 \frac{1}{\sqrt[3]{3x + 2}}\, dx = \int_0^2 (3x + 2)^{-1/3}\, dx$$

$$= \frac{(3x + 2)^{2/3}}{2} \Big|_0^2 = \frac{8^{2/3} - 2^{2/3}}{2} = 2 - \frac{\sqrt[3]{4}}{2}.$$

■ ■ ■ EXERCISES

Find:

1. $\int (x^3 - x + 5)\, dx.$

2. $\int \left(\dfrac{1}{x^3} - \dfrac{1}{x} + 5 \right) dx.$

3. $\int (3x + 2)^{5/2}\, dx.$

4. $\int_{-2}^{-5} \dfrac{1}{3x + 2}\, dx.$

5. $\int_0^1 \dfrac{1}{(3x + 2)^2}\, ax.$

6. $\int (2x^{1/3} - x^{-1/3})\, dx.$

7. $\int \dfrac{x^2 + 2x - 1}{\sqrt{x}}\, dx.$

8. $\int_1^4 \sqrt{x}(5x + 6)\, dx.$

9. $\int \dfrac{x - 1}{x + 1}\, dx.$

10. $\int \dfrac{3x + 2}{2x - 1}\, dx.$

11. $\int (x^2 + 2)^2\, dx.$

12. $\int_{-1}^0 (2x + 1)^6\, dx.$

13. $\int_{-3}^{-1} \dfrac{x^3 - x + 4}{x^2}\, dx.$

14. $\int \dfrac{1 - 7x + x^3}{x^4}\, dx.$

15. $\int \left(\sqrt{x} + \dfrac{1}{\sqrt{x}} \right)^2 dx.$

16. $\int \left(2x - \dfrac{1}{2x} \right)^2 dx.$

17. $\int_0^{-1} \dfrac{x^2 - 1}{x + 2}\, dx.$

18. $\int \dfrac{1 + x^2}{1 + 2x}\, dx.$

19. $\int (x - 1)(2x + 1)\, dx.$

20. $\int \sqrt[3]{(4x + 3)^2}\, dx.$

21. $\int \dfrac{4}{(x + 4)^3}\, dx.$

22. $\int \dfrac{12x^2}{1 + 2x}\, dx.$

23. $\int_{-1}^0 (3x + 1)^9\, dx.$

24. $\int \dfrac{2x^2 - 6x + 7}{2\sqrt{x}}\, dx.$

25. $\displaystyle \lim_{x \to \infty} \int_0^x \dfrac{1}{(2t + 1)^2}\, dt.$

26. $\displaystyle \lim_{x \to \infty} \int_1^x \dfrac{1}{t\sqrt{t}}\, dt.$

3. Change of variable

Integrals that cannot be evaluated directly from known formulas may sometimes be evaluated after a so-called "change of variable." This was done for definite integrals in Section 8 of Chapter 8. Formula 8.23, the change of variable formula for definite integrals, has the form

11.7
$$\int f(g(x))g'(x)\, dx = \int f(u)\, du \Big|_{u = g(x)}$$

for indefinite integrals. After the integration has been performed in the right-hand member of 11.7, the vertical bar followed by $u = g(x)$ indicates that u is to be replaced by $g(x)$. As was pointed out in Chapter 8, an easy way to remember 11.7 is that in the left-hand integral we let

$$u = g(x), \qquad du = g'(x)\, dx.$$

Some examples of the usefulness of 11.7 are given below.

Example 1. Find $\displaystyle\int (3x - 5)^6\, dx.$

Solution: This integral could be found by 11.5 as well as by 11.7. Let

$$u = 3x - 5, \qquad du = (D_x u)\, dx = 3\, dx.$$

Then

$$\int (3x - 5)^6\, dx = \frac{1}{3} \int (3x - 5)^6\, 3\, dx$$

$$= \frac{1}{3} \int u^6\, du \,\Big|_{u\,=\,3x\,-\,5}$$

$$= \frac{u^7}{21}\,\Big|_{u\,=\,3x\,-\,5} + C = \frac{(3x - 5)^7}{21} + C.$$

Example 2. Find $\displaystyle\int \frac{x}{\sqrt{1 + x^2}}\, dx.$

Solution: If we let $u = 1 + x^2$, then $du = 2x\, dx$. Hence

$$\int \frac{x}{\sqrt{1 + x^2}}\, dx = \frac{1}{2} \int (1 + x^2)^{-1/2}(2x)\, dx$$

$$= \frac{1}{2} \int u^{-1/2}\, du \,\Big|_{u\,=\,1\,+\,x^2}$$

$$= \frac{1}{2}\,(2u^{1/2})\,\Big|_{u\,=\,1\,+\,x^2} + C = \sqrt{1 + x^2} + C.$$

Example 3. Find $\displaystyle\int \frac{e^x}{1 + e^x}\, dx.$

Solution: If we let $u = 1 + e^x$, then $du = e^x\, dx$, and

$$\int \frac{e^x}{1 + e^x}\, dx = \int \frac{du}{u}\,\Big|_{u\,=\,1\,+\,e^x}$$

$$= \ln |u|\,\Big|_{u\,=\,1\,+\,e^x} + C = \ln (1 + e^x) + C.$$

Example 4. Find $\displaystyle\int \frac{\sin x}{(\cos x + 1)^2}\, dx.$

Solution: If we let $u = \cos x + 1$, then $du = -\sin x\, dx$.   Hence

$$\int \frac{\sin x}{(\cos x + 1)^2}\, dx = -\int \frac{-\sin x}{(\cos x + 1)^2}\, dx$$

$$= -\int u^{-2}\, du \,\Big|_{u\, =\, \cos x\, +\, 1}$$

$$= u^{-1}\,\Big|_{u\, =\, \cos x\, +\, 1} + C = \frac{1}{\cos x + 1} + C.$$

■ ■ ■ EXERCISES

Find:

1. $\displaystyle \int \frac{x^3}{(x^4 + 1)^3}\, dx.$

2. $\displaystyle \int \sqrt{2x + 3}\, dx.$

3. $\displaystyle \int \frac{x + 1}{x^2 + 2x + 3}\, dx.$

4. $\displaystyle \int \frac{x^4}{\sqrt{x^5 + 2}}\, dx.$

5. $\displaystyle \int \sin x \cos x\, dx.$

6. $\displaystyle \int \tan x \sec^2 x\, dx.$

7. $\displaystyle \int \frac{\ln |x|}{x}\, dx.$

8. $\displaystyle \int \sin^4 x \cos x\, dx.$

9. $\displaystyle \int \tan^3 x \sec^2 x\, dx.$

10. $\displaystyle \int \frac{e^x - e^{-x}}{e^x + e^{-x}}\, dx.$

11. $\displaystyle \int \frac{x^2}{x^3 + 2}\, dx.$

12. $\displaystyle \int \frac{\arcsin x}{\sqrt{1 - x^2}}\, dx.$

13. $\displaystyle \int \frac{\sqrt{\arctan x}}{1 + x^2}\, dx.$

14. $\displaystyle \int \frac{\sin x}{1 - \cos x}\, dx.$

15. $\displaystyle \int \frac{1}{1 - x}\, dx.$

16. $\displaystyle \int \frac{x}{(x^2 - 4)^{3/2}}\, dx.$

17. $\displaystyle \int \frac{e^{-x}}{(e^{-x} + 2)^2}\, dx.$

18. $\displaystyle \int \frac{\sec x \tan x}{\sqrt{1 + \sec x}}\, dx.$

19. $\displaystyle \int \frac{\sec x \tan x}{1 - 2 \sec x}\, dx.$

20. $\displaystyle \int e^x \sqrt{5 + e^x}\, dx.$

21. $\displaystyle \int \frac{\cos x}{\sin^3 x}\, dx.$

22. $\displaystyle \int \frac{1}{\sqrt[3]{x}\,(1 + \sqrt[3]{x^2})}\, dx.$

23. $\displaystyle \int \frac{x \ln (1 + x^2)}{1 + x^2}\, dx.$

24. $\displaystyle \int \tan x \sec^3 x\, dx.$

25. $\displaystyle \int \frac{1}{x^3}\left(\frac{1 - x^2}{x^2}\right)^{10} dx.$

26. $\displaystyle \int \frac{\sin x}{\sqrt[3]{\cos x}}\, dx.$

4. *Elementary trigonometric formulas*

The trigonometric functions were differentiated in the preceding chapter. Let us now integrate each of these functions.

Since $D_x \cos x = -\sin x$, we have $D_x(-\cos x) = \sin x$ and

11.8 $$\int \sin x \, dx = -\cos x + C.$$

Similarly, since $D_x \sin x = \cos x$, we have

11.9 $$\int \cos x \, dx = \sin x + C.$$

The tangent function can be integrated as follows:

$$\int \tan x \, dx = \int \frac{\sin x}{\cos x} \, dx$$

$$= -\int \frac{-\sin x}{\cos x} \, dx = -\int \frac{du}{u}\bigg|_{u=\cos x} = -\ln|\cos x| + C.$$

Since $\ln(1/A) = -\ln A$ for each number $A > 0$,

$$\ln|\sec x| = -\ln|\cos x|,$$

and we have proved the following integration formula:

11.10 $$\int \tan x \, dx = \ln|\sec x| + C.$$

One may prove similarly that

11.11 $$\int \cot x \, dx = \ln|\sin x| + C.$$

The integration of the secant function proceeds as follows:

$$\int \sec x \, dx = \int \frac{\sec x (\sec x + \tan x)}{\sec x + \tan x} \, dx$$

$$= \int \frac{\sec^2 x + \sec x \tan x}{\sec x + \tan x} \, dx$$

$$= \int \frac{du}{u}\bigg|_{u=\sec x + \tan x}$$

$$= \ln|\sec x + \tan x| + C.$$

Therefore

11.12 $$\int \sec x \, dx = \ln|\sec x + \tan x| + C.$$

We prove similarly that

11.13 $$\int \csc x \, dx = \ln|\csc x - \cot x| + C.$$

Other integration formulas that follow immediately from the trigonometric differentiation formulas are given below.

11.14 $\displaystyle\int \sec^2 x \, dx = \tan x + C.$

11.15 $\displaystyle\int \csc^2 x \, dx = -\cot x + C.$

11.16 $\displaystyle\int \sec x \tan x \, dx = \sec x + C.$

11.17 $\displaystyle\int \csc x \cot x \, dx = -\csc x + C.$

With these integration formulas and the change of variable formula, we are able to integrate many rather complicated functions.

Example 1. Find $\displaystyle\int \sin 5x \, dx.$

Solution: If $u = 5x$, then $du = 5 \, dx$. Hence

$$\int \sin 5x \, dx = \frac{1}{5} \int (\sin 5x) 5 \, dx$$

$$= \frac{1}{5} \int \sin u \, du \Big|_{u = 5x}$$

$$= -\frac{1}{5} \cos 5x + C.$$

Example 2. Find $\displaystyle\int \sin^3 2x \cos 2x \, dx.$

Solution: If $u = \sin 2x$, then $du = 2 \cos 2x \, dx$, and

$$\int \sin^3 2x \cos 2x \, dx = \frac{1}{2} \int \sin^3 2x (2 \cos 2x) \, dx$$

$$= \frac{1}{2} \int u^3 \, du \Big|_{u = \sin 2x}$$

$$= \frac{1}{8} u^4 \Big|_{u = \sin 2x} + C$$

$$= \frac{1}{8} \sin^4 2x + C.$$

Example 3. Find $\displaystyle\int \sec (7x - 1) \tan (7x - 1) \, dx.$

Solution: If $u = 7x - 1$, then $du = 7 \, dx$. Hence

$$\int \sec (7x - 1) \tan (7x - 1) \, dx = \frac{1}{7} \int \sec u \tan u \, du \Big|_{u = 7x - 1}$$

$$= \frac{1}{7} \sec u \Big|_{u\,=\,7x\,-\,1} + C$$

$$= \frac{1}{7} \sec (7x - 1) + C.$$

Example 4. Find $\int \sec^2 x \tan^2 x \, dx$.

Solution: Let $u = \tan x$, so that $du = \sec^2 x \, dx$. Then

$$\int \sec^2 x \tan^2 x \, dx = \int u^2 \, du \Big|_{u\,=\,\tan x}$$

$$= \frac{1}{3} u^3 \Big|_{u\,=\,\tan x} + C = \frac{1}{3} \tan^3 x + C.$$

Example 5. Find $\int e^x \tan (1 + e^x) \, dx$.

Solution: Let $u = 1 + e^x$, so that $du = e^x \, dx$. Then

$$\int e^x \tan (1 + e^x) \, dx = \int \tan u \, du \Big|_{u\,=\,1\,+\,e^x}$$

$$= \ln |\sec u| \Big|_{u\,=\,1\,+\,e^x} + C = \ln |\sec (1 + e^x)| + C.$$

■ ■ ■ EXERCISES

Find:

1. $\int \cos 4x \, dx$.

2. $\int \sec^2 \frac{x}{2} \, dx$.

3. $\int x \sin 3x^2 \, dx$.

4. $\int e^x \sin e^x \, dx$.

5. $\int \tan (1 - 2x) \, dx$.

6. $\int \csc 4x \, dx$.

7. $\int \sec^2 \frac{3x}{2} \, dx$.

8. $\int x \cos (2x^2 + 1) \, dx$.

9. $\int \cot \frac{x}{2} \, dx$.

10. $\int \csc^2 (2x + 1) \, dx$.

11. $\int \frac{\cos 2x}{\sqrt{\sin 2x}} \, dx$.

12. $\int \frac{1 - 2 \cos x}{\sin^2 x} \, dx$.

13. $\int \sec^2 3x \tan^5 3x \, dx$.

14. $\int \sin \frac{x}{2} \cos \frac{x}{2} \, dx$.

15. $\int \sin 2x \cos^4 2x \, dx$.

16. $\int x \sec^2 x^2 \tan^3 x^2 \, dx$.

17. $\int x^2 \csc^2 x^3 \, dx.$

18. $\int e^x \cot (1 - e^x) \, dx.$

19. $\int \dfrac{\sec x}{\csc x} \, dx.$

20. $\int \left(\dfrac{4}{\cos^2 x} + \dfrac{7}{x} \right) dx.$

21. $\int \dfrac{1}{x} \sin (\ln |x|) \, dx.$

22. $\int \tan x \ln |\sec x| \, dx.$

23. $\int \dfrac{\cos 2x}{(1 + \sin 2x)^3} \, dx.$

24. $\int \sin \dfrac{x}{2} \left(1 - \cos \dfrac{x}{2} \right)^4 dx.$

25. $\int (\sec x + \tan x)^2 \, dx.$

26. $\int \dfrac{1 + \cos x}{x + \sin x} \, dx.$

27. $\int \dfrac{1}{1 + \cos x} \, dx.$

28. $\int \dfrac{1}{1 - \cos x} \, dx.$

29. $\int \dfrac{1}{\sec x - \tan x} \, dx.$

30. $\int \dfrac{1}{\sec x + \tan x} \, dx.$

31. Derive Formula 11.11.

32. Derive Formula 11.13. Prove that an alternate form of 11.13 is

$$\int \csc x \, dx = -\ln |\csc x + \cot x| + C.$$

33. According to a trigonometric identity, $\sin 2x = 2 \sin x \cos x$. However,

$$\int \sin 2x \, dx = -\frac{1}{2} \cos 2x + C,$$

whereas

$$\int 2 \sin x \cos x \, dx = \sin^2 x + C.$$

Explain the difference in answers.

34. We may integrate $\int \sec^2 x \tan x \, dx$ in two ways, namely,

$$\int \sec^2 x \tan x \, dx = \frac{1}{2} \tan^2 x + C,$$

$$\int \sec x (\sec x \tan x) \, dx = \frac{1}{2} \sec^2 x + C.$$

Explain the difference in answers.

5. Further trigonometric integration

Using the preceding integration formulas and certain trigonometric identities, we are able to find other trigonometric integrals.

For example, the identity

$$\tan^2 x = \sec^2 x - 1$$

allows us to find the integral of the square of the tangent function:

$$\int \tan^2 x \, dx = \int (\sec^2 x - 1) \, dx = \tan x - x + C.$$

The integrals

$$\int \tan^n x \, dx, \quad \int \sec^n x \, dx, \quad n \text{ an even positive integer,}$$

can be evaluated in a similar fashion.   For example,

$$\int \sec^4 x \, dx = \int \sec^2 x \sec^2 x \, dx$$

$$= \int (1 + \tan^2 x) \sec^2 x \, dx$$

$$= \int \sec^2 x \, dx + \int \tan^2 x \sec^2 x \, dx$$

$$= \tan x + \frac{1}{3} \tan^3 x + C.$$

Thus $\int \tan^4 x \, dx = \int (\sec^2 x - 1)^2 \, dx$

$$= \int (\sec^4 x - 2 \sec^2 x + 1) \, dx$$

$$= \left(\tan x + \frac{1}{3} \tan^3 x \right) - 2 \tan x + x + C$$

$$= \frac{1}{3} \tan^3 x - \tan x + x + C.$$

More generally, it is possible to evaluate any integral of the form

$$\int \tan^n x \sec^m x \, dx,$$

m an even positive integer, by keeping a factor $\sec^2 x$ in the integrand and changing the rest of the secants into tangents.

If n is an odd positive integer in the integral above, the integration can be carried out for any number m by keeping a factor $\sec x \tan x$ in the integrand and changing the remaining tangents to secants.   For example,

$$\int \sec^5 x \tan^3 x \, dx = \int \sec^4 x \tan^2 x \, (\sec x \tan x) \, dx$$

$$= \int \sec^4 x \, (\sec^2 x - 1)(\sec x \tan x) \, dx$$

$$= \int (\sec^6 x - \sec^4 x)(\sec x \tan x) \, dx$$

$$= \int (u^6 - u^4) \, du \, \Big|_{u \,=\, \sec x}$$

$$= \frac{1}{7} \sec^7 x - \frac{1}{5} \sec^5 x + C.$$

The identity

$$\sin^2 x + \cos^2 x = 1$$

allows us to evaluate any integral of the form

$$\int \sin^n x \cos^m x \, dx, \quad n \text{ or } m \text{ a positive odd integer.}$$

If $n = 1$ or $m = 1$, the integration is immediate. For example,

$$\int \sin x \cos^5 x \, dx = -\int u^5 \, du \Bigg|_{u \,=\, \cos x} = -\frac{1}{6} \cos^6 x + C.$$

The general case is amply illustrated by the following example.

$$\int \sin^{1/2} x \cos^3 x \, dx = \int \sin^{1/2} x \cos^2 x \cos x \, dx$$

$$= \int (\sin^{1/2} x)(1 - \sin^2 x) \cos x \, dx$$

$$= \int (\sin^{1/2} x - \sin^{5/2} x) \cos x \, dx$$

$$= \int (u^{1/2} - u^{5/2}) \, du \Bigg|_{u \,=\, \sin x}$$

$$= \frac{2}{3} \sin^{3/2} x - \frac{2}{7} \sin^{7/2} x + C.$$

The trigonometric identities

$$\sin^2 x = \frac{1 - \cos 2x}{2}, \qquad \cos^2 x = \frac{1 + \cos 2x}{2}$$

may be used to reduce an integral of the form

$$\int \sin^n x \cos^m x \, dx, \quad m \text{ and } n \text{ even positive integers,}$$

to one of the previous integrals.

For example,

$$\int \sin^2 x \, dx = \int \frac{1 - \cos 2x}{2} \, dx$$

$$= \frac{1}{2} \left(\int dx - \int \cos 2x \, dx \right)$$

$$= \frac{1}{2} \left(x - \frac{1}{2} \sin 2x \right) + C.$$

As another example,

$$\int \sin^2 x \cos^2 x \, dx = \int \frac{1 - \cos 2x}{2} \cdot \frac{1 + \cos 2x}{2} \, dx$$

$$= \frac{1}{4} \int \left(1 - \cos^2 2x \right) dx$$

$$= \frac{1}{4} \int \sin^2 2x \; dx$$

$$= \frac{1}{8} \int (1 - \cos 4x) \; dx$$

$$= \frac{1}{8} \left(x - \frac{1}{4} \sin 4x \right) + C.$$

The trigonometric identity

$$\sin x \cos y = \frac{1}{2} \left[\sin (x + y) + \sin (x - y) \right]$$

may be used to evaluate an integral such as

$$\int \sin 7x \cos 3x \; dx.$$

Thus

$$\int \sin 7x \cos 3x \; dx = \frac{1}{2} \left(\int \sin 10x \; dx + \int \sin 4x \; dx \right)$$

$$= -\frac{1}{20} \cos 10x - \frac{1}{8} \cos 4x + C.$$

Similar identities may be used to evaluate such integrals as

$$\int \sin 4x \sin x \; dx \quad \text{and} \quad \int \cos \frac{x}{2} \cos \frac{x}{3} \; dx.$$

■ ■ ■ EXERCISES

Find:

1. $\int \sin^3 2x \; dx.$

2. $\int \tan^2 2x \sec^4 2x \; dx.$

3. $\int \tan \frac{x}{2} \sec^3 \frac{x}{2} \; dx.$

4. $\int \cos^2 5x \; dx.$

5. $\int \cos^4 x \; dx.$

6. $\int \frac{\tan^3 x}{\sec x} \; dx.$

7. $\int \tan^4 3x \; dx.$

8. $\int \frac{\sin^3 x}{\cos x} \; dx.$

9. $\int \csc^4 2x \; dx.$

10. $\int \cot^4 x \csc^4 x \; dx.$

11. $\int \tan^3 3x \sec^3 3x \; dx.$

12. $\int \sin^4 \frac{x}{2} \; dx.$

13. $\int \sqrt{\sin x} \cos^3 x \; dx.$

14. $\int \sin^3 x \cos^{3/2} x \; dx.$

15. $\int \tan^{3/2} x \sec^4 x \, dx.$ **16.** $\int \cos^3 \frac{x}{4} \, dx.$

17. $\int \sin x \cos 3x \, dx.$ **18.** $\int \sin 4x \sin 2x \, dx.$

19. $\int \cos 3x \cos 2x \, dx.$ **20.** $\int \sin x \sin 3x \sin 5x \, dx.$

21. Verify that for any positive integer n, $\int_0^\pi \sin^2 nx \, dx = \frac{\pi}{2}.$

22. Verify that for any positive integer n,

$$\int_0^{\pi/n} \sin nx \cos nx \, dx = 0.$$

23. (a) Verify that for any positive integers m and n, with $m \neq n$, and any real numbers a and b,

$$\int_0^{2\pi} \sin (mx + a) \cos (nx + b) \, dx = 0.$$

    (b) If $m = n$, find the value of the above integral. Under what conditions on a and b does it equal zero?

6. Exponential integrals

Since $D_x e^x = e^x$, we have

11.18 $$\int e^x \, dx = e^x + C.$$

The integral

$$\int e^{ax+b} \, dx, \quad a \neq 0.$$

may be evaluated by letting

$$u = ax + b, \qquad du = a \, dx.$$

Then

$$\int e^{ax+b} \, dx = \frac{1}{a} \int e^u \, du \Bigg|_{u = ax + b}$$

$$= \frac{1}{a} e^u \Bigg|_{u = ax + b} + C = \frac{1}{a} e^{ax+b} + C.$$

Thus

11.19 $$\int e^{ax+b} \, dx = \frac{1}{a} e^{ax+b} + C.$$

Example 1. Find $\int \frac{dx}{e^{4x}}.$

Solution: We have

$$\int \frac{dx}{e^{4x}} = \int e^{-4x}\,dx = -\frac{1}{4}\,e^{-4x} + C.$$

Example 2. Find $\int 10^x\,dx$.

Solution: We have

$$10 = e^{\ln 10},$$

and therefore

$$\int 10^x\,dx = \int e^{x\ln 10}\,dx$$

$$= \frac{1}{\ln 10}\,e^{x\ln 10} + C = (\log_{10} e)10^x + C.$$

Example 3. Find $\int xe^{x^2}\,dx$.

Solution: If we let

$$u = x^2, \qquad du = 2x\,dx,$$

then

$$\int xe^{x^2}\,dx = \frac{1}{2}\int e^u\,du\,\bigg|_{u=x^2} = \frac{1}{2}\,e^{x^2} + C.$$

■ ■ ■ EXERCISES

Find:

1. $\int e^{3x-4}\,dx$.

2. $\int (e^x - x^e)\,dx$.

3. $\int (\sec^2 x)e^{\tan x}\,dx$.

4. $\int \frac{1}{e^{4x+1}}\,dx$.

5. $\int 10^{-2x}\,dx$.

6. $\int e^x \tan e^x \sec^2 e^x\,dx$.

7. $\int (e^x - e^{-x})^2\,dx$.

8. $\int x3^{x^2}\,dx$.

9. $\int \left(\frac{1}{3}\right)^x dx$.

10. $\int \frac{e^{\sqrt{x}}}{\sqrt{x}}\,dx$.

11. $\int \frac{e^{\ln x}}{x}\,dx$.

12. $\int \frac{x}{e^{5x^2}}\,dx$.

13. $\int (e^x)^3\,dx$.

14. $\int \frac{e^{1/x}}{x^2}\,dx$.

15. $\int \frac{e^{2x} - 1}{e^{2x} + 1}\,dx$.

16. $\int e^{(x+e^x)}\,dx$.

17. $\displaystyle\lim_{x\to\infty} \int_0^x e^{-at}\,dt$.

18. $\displaystyle\lim_{t\to\infty} \int_0^t 10^{-x}\,dx$.

7. *Some algebraic integrals*

The inverse trigonometric functions, having algebraic derivatives, will themselves be integrals of certain algebraic functions. We give these in the following form:

11.20
$$\int \frac{1}{\sqrt{a^2 - x^2}} \, dx = \sin^{-1} \frac{x}{a} + C.$$

11.21
$$\int \frac{1}{a^2 + x^2} \, dx = \frac{1}{a} \tan^{-1} \frac{x}{a} + C.$$

11.22
$$\int \frac{1}{x\sqrt{x^2 - a^2}} \, dx = \frac{1}{a} \sec^{-1} \frac{x}{a} + C.$$

In each case, a is assumed to be a positive number.

Proof of 11.20: We have by 10.54

$$D_x \sin^{-1} \frac{x}{a} = \frac{1/a}{\sqrt{1 - (x/a)^2}}$$

$$= \frac{1}{\sqrt{a^2 - x^2}}.$$

The proofs of 11.21 and 11.22, being similar, are omitted.

Certain logarithmic functions are integrals of algebraic functions similar to those in 11.20 and 11.21. They are listed below.

11.23
$$\int \frac{1}{\sqrt{x^2 \pm a^2}} \, dx = \ln |x + \sqrt{x^2 \pm a^2}| + C.$$

11.24
$$\int \frac{1}{x^2 - a^2} \, dx = \frac{1}{2a} \ln \left| \frac{x - a}{x + a} \right| + C.$$

The proof of 11.23 is as follows:

$$D_x \ln |x + \sqrt{x^2 \pm a^2}| = \frac{1}{x + \sqrt{x^2 \pm a^2}} \left(1 + \frac{x}{\sqrt{x^2 \pm a^2}} \right)$$

$$= \frac{1}{x + \sqrt{x^2 \pm a^2}} \cdot \frac{\sqrt{x^2 \pm a^2} + x}{\sqrt{x^2 \pm a^2}} = \frac{1}{\sqrt{x^2 \pm a^2}}.$$

The identity

$$\frac{1}{x^2 - a^2} = \frac{1}{2a} \left(\frac{1}{x - a} - \frac{1}{x + a} \right), \quad a \neq 0,$$

is easily verified. Hence

$$\int \frac{1}{x^2 - a^2} \, dx = \frac{1}{2a} \int \left(\frac{1}{x - a} - \frac{1}{x + a} \right) dx$$

$$= \frac{1}{2a} \left(\ln |x - a| - \ln |x + a| \right) + C$$

$$= \frac{1}{2a} \ln \left| \frac{x - a}{x + a} \right| + C,$$

and we have proved 11.24.

Example 1. Find $\int \dfrac{1}{9+x^2}\, dx.$

Solution: By 11.21, (with $a = 3$)

$$\int \frac{1}{9+x^2}\, dx = \frac{1}{3}\tan^{-1}\frac{x}{3} + C.$$

Example 2. Find $\int \dfrac{1}{\sqrt{1-4x^2}}\, dx.$

Solution: If $u = 2x$, then $du = 2\, dx$ and

$$\int \frac{1}{\sqrt{1-4x^2}}\, dx = \frac{1}{2}\int \frac{1}{\sqrt{1-u^2}}\, du \Bigg|_{u=2x}$$

$$= \frac{1}{2}\sin^{-1} u \Bigg|_{u=2x} + C = \frac{1}{2}\sin^{-1} 2x + C.$$

Example 3. Find $\int \dfrac{e^x}{e^{2x}-25}\, dx.$

Solution: If we let $u = e^x$, then $du = e^x\, dx$ and

$$\int \frac{e^x}{e^{2x}-25}\, dx = \int \frac{1}{u^2-25}\, du \Bigg|_{u=e^x}$$

$$= \frac{1}{10}\ln\left|\frac{u-5}{u+5}\right|\Bigg|_{u=e^x} + C = \frac{1}{10}\ln\left|\frac{e^x-5}{e^x+5}\right| + C.$$

Example 4. Find $\int \dfrac{x}{\sqrt{x^4+2}}\, dx.$

Solution: If we let $u = x^2$, then $du = 2x\, dx$ and

$$\int \frac{x}{\sqrt{x^4+2}}\, dx = \frac{1}{2}\int \frac{1}{\sqrt{u^2+2}}\, du \Bigg|_{u=x^2}.$$

This latter integral is in the form 11.23 with $a^2 = 2$. Thus

$$\int \frac{x}{\sqrt{x^4+2}}\, dx = \frac{1}{2}\ln|u+\sqrt{u^2+2}|\Bigg|_{u=x^2} + C$$

$$= \frac{1}{2}\ln(x^2+\sqrt{x^4+2}) + C.$$

■ ■ ■ EXERCISES

Find:

1. $\displaystyle\int \frac{1}{\sqrt{x^2+4}}\, dx.$

2. $\displaystyle\int \frac{1}{\sqrt{9-w^2}}\, dw.$

3. $\displaystyle\int \frac{x}{\sqrt{x^2+4}}\, dx.$

4. $\displaystyle\int \frac{w}{\sqrt{9-w^2}}\, dw.$

5. $\displaystyle\int \frac{1}{x^2-9}\, dx.$

6. $\displaystyle\int \frac{1}{z^2+5}\, dz.$

7. $\displaystyle\int \frac{x}{x^2-9}\, dx.$

8. $\displaystyle\int \frac{z}{z^2+5}\, dz.$

9. $\displaystyle\int \frac{x^2}{x^2-9}\, dx.$

10. $\displaystyle\int \frac{z^2}{z^2+5}\, dz.$

11. $\displaystyle\int \frac{1}{u\sqrt{u^2-4}}\, du.$

12. $\displaystyle\int \frac{1}{x\sqrt{x^4-3}}\, dx.$

13. $\displaystyle\int \frac{e^x}{\sqrt{9-e^x}}\, dx.$

14. $\displaystyle\int \frac{\cos x}{1+\sin^2 x}\, dx.$

15. $\displaystyle\int \frac{z^2}{z^6+4}\, dz.$

16. $\displaystyle\int \frac{x^5}{x^6+4}\, dx.$

17. $\displaystyle\int \frac{\sec^2 x}{9+\tan^2 x}\, dx.$

18. $\displaystyle\int \frac{1}{x\sqrt{1-\ln^2 x}}\, dx.$

19. $\displaystyle\int \frac{1}{\sqrt{e^{2x}-1}}\, dx.$

20. $\displaystyle\int \frac{1}{(x+1)^2+4}\, dx.$

21. $\displaystyle\int \frac{1}{\sqrt{1-(x+1)^2}}\, dx.$

22. $\displaystyle\int \frac{1}{e^x+e^{-x}}\, dx.$

23. $\displaystyle\int_0^1 \frac{1}{\sqrt{4-x^2}}\, dx.$

24. $\displaystyle\int_{-5}^5 \frac{1}{x^2+25}\, dx.$

25. $\displaystyle\int_{-1}^1 \frac{1}{\sqrt{u^2+3}}\, du.$

26. $\displaystyle\int_{-2}^{-1} \frac{1}{4x^2-1}\, dx.$

27. $\displaystyle\lim_{x\to 1}\int_0^x \frac{1}{\sqrt{1-t^2}}\, dt.$

28. $\displaystyle\lim_{x\to 1^+}\int_x^2 \frac{1}{t\sqrt{t^2-1}}\, dt.$

Use Exercises 14–16 of p. 298 to express each of the following integrals in terms of inverse hyperbolic functions:

29. $\displaystyle\int \frac{1}{\sqrt{x^2+a^2}}\, dx.$

30. $\displaystyle\int \frac{1}{\sqrt{x^2-a^2}}\, dx,\ x>a.$

31. $\displaystyle\int \frac{1}{\sqrt{x^2-a^2}}\, dx,\ x<-a.$

32. $\displaystyle\int \frac{1}{x^2-a^2}\, dx.$

8. Further algebraic integrals

An integrand of the form

$$\frac{1}{x^2 + ax + b}$$

can be put in the form

$$\frac{1}{(x + c)^2 \pm d^2}$$

by a completion of squares. For example,

$$x^2 + 4x + 5 = x^2 + 4x + 4 + 1 = (x + 2)^2 + 1,$$

and therefore

$$\frac{1}{x^2 + 4x + 5} = \frac{1}{(x + 2)^2 + 1}.$$

Having completed squares in the integrand, the evaluation of the given integral proceeds by a change of variable as illustrated below.

Example 1. Find $\displaystyle\int \frac{1}{x^2 + 4x + 5}\, dx.$

Solution: We have

$$\int \frac{1}{x^2 + 4x + 5}\, dx = \int \frac{1}{(x + 2)^2 + 1}\, dx$$

$$= \int \frac{1}{u^2 + 1}\, du \bigg|_{u = x + 2}$$

$$= \tan^{-1} u \bigg|_{u = x + 2} + C = \tan^{-1}(x + 2) + C.$$

Example 2. Find $\displaystyle\int \frac{1}{\sqrt{8 + 2x - x^2}}\, dx.$

Solution: We complete squares as follows:

$$8 + 2x - x^2 = 8 - (x^2 - 2x) = 9 - (x^2 - 2x + 1) = 9 - (x - 1)^2.$$

Therefore

$$\int \frac{1}{\sqrt{8 + 2x - x^2}}\, dx = \int \frac{1}{\sqrt{3^2 - (x - 1)^2}}\, dx$$

$$= \int \frac{1}{\sqrt{3^2 - u^2}}\, du \bigg|_{u = x - 1}$$

$$= \sin^{-1}(u/3) \bigg|_{u = x - 1} + C = \sin^{-1}\frac{x - 1}{3} + C.$$

Example 3. Find $\displaystyle\int \frac{x+4}{\sqrt{x^2+2x-3}}\,dx.$

Solution: We have

$$x^2+2x-3 = (x+1)^2 - 4.$$

Thus, if we let

$$u = x+1, \quad du = dx, \quad x = u-1,$$

then

$$\int \frac{x+4}{\sqrt{x^2+2x-3}}\,dx = \int \frac{x+4}{\sqrt{(x+1)^2-4}}\,dx$$

$$= \int \frac{u+3}{\sqrt{u^2-4}}\,du \Bigg|_{u=x+1}$$

$$= \left\{ \int \frac{u}{\sqrt{u^2-4}}\,du + 3\int \frac{1}{\sqrt{u^2-4}}\,du \right\}\Bigg|_{u=x+1}$$

$$= \left\{ \sqrt{u^2-4} + 3\ln|u+\sqrt{u^2-4}| \right\}\Bigg|_{u=x+1} + C$$

$$= \sqrt{x^2+2x-3} + 3\ln|x+1+\sqrt{x^2+2x-3}| + C.$$

■ ■ ■ EXERCISES

Find:

1. $\displaystyle\int \frac{1}{x^2-4x+13}\,dx.$

2. $\displaystyle\int \frac{x-2}{\sqrt{x^2-4x+13}}\,dx.$

3. $\displaystyle\int \frac{1}{\sqrt{5+4x-x^2}}\,dx.$

4. $\displaystyle\int \frac{x-2}{x^2-4x+13}\,dx.$

5. $\displaystyle\int \frac{1}{x^2-2x+1}\,dx.$

6. $\displaystyle\int \frac{x}{x^2-6x+9}\,dx.$

7. $\displaystyle\int \frac{1}{8x-x^2-25}\,dx.$

8. $\displaystyle\int \frac{1}{\sqrt{5x-x^2}}\,dx.$

9. $\displaystyle\int \frac{x+3}{\sqrt{x^2+2x}}\,dx.$

10. $\displaystyle\int \frac{1}{(x+1)\sqrt{x^2+2x}}\,dx.$

11. $\displaystyle\int \frac{8x-2}{4x^2-4x-3}\,dx.$

12. $\displaystyle\int \frac{x}{9x^2+6x-8}\,dx.$

13. $\displaystyle\int \frac{x}{(x-1)\sqrt{x^2-2x}}\,dx.$

14. $\displaystyle\int \frac{4x+10}{x^2+2x+5}\,dx.$

15. $\displaystyle\int \frac{x^2-2x}{x^2+2x}\,dx.$

16. $\displaystyle\int \frac{x}{\sqrt{x^4+2x^2-3}}\,dx.$

9. Separable differential equations

Given an equation in x and y such as, for example,

$$\sin x + y^3 = C,$$

C a constant, it is evident that every differentiable function f such that $y = f(x)$ satisfies this equation also satisfies the differential equation

$$\cos x + 3y^2 \frac{dy}{dx} = 0.$$

We wish to show in this section that, starting with a differential equation such as the one above, we can find an equation in x and y satisfied by any solution of the differential equation.

The above differential equation is of the type

11.25 $$M(x) + N(y)\frac{dy}{dx} = 0,$$

or, letting $y = f(x)$,

11.26 $$M(x) + N(f(x))f'(x) = 0,$$

where M and N are continuous functions. Such an equation as 11.25 is called a *separable differential equation* (since the variables x and y appear in separate terms). In solving 11.26 we shall seek only solutions f such that the function f' is continuous.

If we let

$$F(x) = M(x) + N(f(x))f'(x),$$

then, by 11.26, $F(x) = 0$ and

$$\int F(x)\,dx = C$$

for some constant C. Since

$$\int F(x)\,dx = \int M(x)\,dx + \int N(f(x))f'(x)\,dx,$$

and, by 11.7,

$$\int N(f(x))f'(x)\,dx = \int N(y)\,dy\,\bigg|_{y\,=\,f(x)},$$

the solution of 11.25 is given by

11.27 $$\int M(x)\,dx + \int N(y)\,dy = C.$$

Thus, for every function f such that $y = f(x)$ satisfies 11.25, there is a choice of the constant C such that $y = f(x)$ satisfies 11.27.

For example, the differential equation

$$\cos x + 3y^2 \frac{dy}{dx} = 0$$

has as its solution the equation

$$\int \cos x \, dx + \int 3y^2 \, dy = C,$$

or
$$\sin x + y^3 = C.$$

Separable differential equations appear in a natural way in many applications of mathematics. As a matter of fact, the differential equation

$$\frac{dy}{dt} = ky, \quad y > 0,$$

studied in Section 8 of Chapter 10 is separable, since it can be written in the form

$$k - \frac{1}{y}\frac{dy}{dt} = 0.$$

Let us solve this equation by our present methods.

Example 1. Solve the differential equation

$$k - \frac{1}{y}\frac{dy}{dt} = 0, \quad y > 0.$$

Solution: By 11.27,

$$\int k \, dt - \int \frac{1}{y} dy = C,$$

or
$$kt - \ln y = C.$$

Thus $\ln y = kt - C$, and

$$y = e^{kt-C} = Ae^{kt}$$

where A is a constant (e^{-C}).

Example 2. Solve the differential equation

$$(x + \sec^2 x) + (y - e^y)\frac{dy}{dx} = 0.$$

Solution: For this equation, the functions M and N are defined by

$$M(x) = x + \sec^2 x, \qquad N(y) = y - e^y.$$

By 11.27, its solution is

$$\int (x + \sec^2 x) \, dx + \int (y - e^y) \, dy = C,$$

or
$$\frac{x^2}{2} + \tan x + \frac{y^2}{2} - e^y = C.$$

Example 3. Solve the differential equation

$$\frac{1}{\sqrt{1 - x^2}} + \frac{1}{y}\frac{dy}{dx} = 0, \quad y > 0.$$

Solution: By 11.27, the solution is

$$\int \frac{1}{\sqrt{1 - x^2}} \, dx + \int \frac{1}{y} dy = C,$$

or
$$\sin^{-1} x + \ln y = C.$$

Thus $\ln y = C - \sin^{-1} x$, and

$$y = Ae^{-\sin^{-1} x},$$

where A is a constant (e^C).

In Examples 1 and 3, the solution is given explicitly in the form $y = f(x)$. The solution is given *implicitly* in Example 2 in that the equation is not solved for y in terms of x. It is desirable to give the explicit solution of a differential equation whenever possible. However, the explicit determination of $f(x)$ can offer great difficulties, as it would in the solution of Example 2.

A physical problem that has as its solution a separable differential equation is as follows. Let y be the temperature at time t of a body immersed in a bath of constant temperature a. We shall assume that $y > a$ and hence that the body is being cooled. It is a physical law that the temperature of the body decreases at a rate proportional to the difference between its temperature and the temperature of the surrounding medium. This law leads to the differential equation

11.28
$$\frac{dy}{dt} = k(y - a), \quad y > a,$$

for some constant k.

Example 4. A body is immersed in water having a constant temperature of 20°C. The body has initial temperature of 40° and a temperature of 35°C two minutes later. What will its temperature be at the end of 10 minutes?

Solution: Employing 11.29 with $a = 20$, we have the separable differential equation

$$\frac{1}{y - 20} \frac{dy}{dt} = k, \quad y - 20 > 0,$$

whose solution is

$$\int \frac{1}{y - 20} dy = \int k \, dt + C,$$

or
$$\ln (y - 20) = kt + C.$$

Thus
$$y - 20 = e^{kt+C} = Ae^{kt},$$

and

(1)
$$y = Ae^{kt} + 20.$$

We determine A and k as follows. Since $y = 40$ at $t = 0$,

$$40 = A + 20,$$

and $A = 20$. Thus (1) becomes

(2)
$$y = 20e^{kt} + 20.$$

Next, it is given that $y = 35$ when $t = 2$, so that

$$35 = 20e^{2k} + 20.$$

Thus

$$e^{2k} = \frac{3}{4},$$

and
$$k = \frac{1}{2}\ln\frac{3}{4}.$$

On substituting k in (2), we get

(3)
$$y = 20e^{(\frac{1}{2}\ln \frac{3}{4})t} + 20$$

as the solution of the given problem.

Solution (3) may be written in a more usable form if we observe that

$$e^{\ln \frac{3}{4}} = \frac{3}{4}$$

Then (3) becomes

(4)
$$y = 20\left(\frac{3}{4}\right)^{t/2} + 20.$$

The temperature y when $t = 10$ is given by

$$y = 20\left(\frac{3}{4}\right)^{5} + 20 = 24.7°C \text{ approx.}$$

■ ■ ■ EXERCISES

Solve the following differential equations:

1. $\dfrac{1}{x} + \dfrac{1}{y}\dfrac{dy}{dx} = 0.$

2. $\dfrac{1-x}{x^3} - \dfrac{1}{y^2}\dfrac{dy}{dx} = 0.$

3. $\dfrac{dy}{dx} = xy^2.$

4. $\dfrac{dy}{dx} = y^2.$

5. $\dfrac{y}{y-1}\dfrac{dy}{dx} - \dfrac{x+1}{x} = 0.$

6. $e^{3x} + 1 + \sin y \dfrac{dy}{dx} = 0.$

7. $e^{x-y}\dfrac{dy}{dx} + 1 = 0.$

8. $\dfrac{dy}{dx} = \dfrac{1-x}{1-y}.$

9. $\sec x + \tan y \dfrac{dy}{dx} = 0.$

10. $\dfrac{dy}{dx} = \cos^2 y.$

11. A thermometer reading 80°F is placed in a room whose temperature is 50°F. After 1 min the reading on the thermometer is 70°F.
    (a) What is the reading on the thermometer after 3 min?
    (b) At what time is the reading on the thermometer 56°F?

12. If water is pouring out of a tank through an opening in the bottom of the tank, it is known by experiment that the time rate of flow of the water is proportional to the square root of the depth. A cylindrical tank 9 ft high and 4 ft in diameter, originally full of water and emptying through a hole in the bottom, takes 1 min to reduce the depth of water to 8 ft. How long does it take to empty the tank?

13. A conical funnel, full of water, takes 3 sec to reduce the depth of water by $\frac{1}{2}$. How long does it take to empty the funnel?

14. At what constant rate must water be poured into the tank of Exercise 12 starting at the instant the tank is half empty to keep the water level constant?

15. A thermometer reading 70°F is placed in a refrigerator whose temperature is 35°F. After 2 min, the reading on the thermometer is 50°F.
(a) What is the reading on the thermometer after 4 min?
(b) At what time is the reading on the thermometer 42°F?

In Exercises 16–18 find that solution which satisfies the given boundary condition.

16. $\dfrac{dy}{dx} = y^2$, $y = 1$ when $x = 0$.

17. $x - 1 + y\dfrac{dy}{dx} = 0$, $y = -2$ when $x = 1$.

18. $e^x + \sin y \dfrac{dy}{dx} = 0$, $y = 0$ when $x = 0$.

12

Advanced formal

integration

■ ■ ■ ■ ■ WE SHALL CALL f an *elementary function* if f is either an algebraic, trigonometric, inverse trigonometric, exponential, or logarithmic function, or a combination of these functions. The derivative f' of each elementary function f has been shown to be an elementary function; and the integrals of some of the elementary functions are again elementary according to the results of the previous chapter. However, it is not true that the integral of every elementary function is elementary. For example, it is possible to show that the integrals

$$\int e^{-x^2}\, dx \quad \text{and} \quad \int \sqrt{1 + \cos^2 x}\, dx,$$

which arise naturally in the solutions of certain mathematical problems, are not elementary functions.

We shall give some more advanced methods in this chapter for finding those integrals of elementary functions that are again elementary.

1. Integration by parts

We have not as yet given the integral analogue of the following product differentiation formula:

$$D_x f(x)g(x) = f(x)g'(x) + g(x)f'(x).$$

This is easily done by integrating each side of the equation above, yielding

$$f(x)g(x) = \int f(x)g'(x)\ dx + \int g(x)f'(x)\ dx,$$

or

12.1 $$\int f(x)g'(x)\ dx = f(x)g(x) - \int g(x)f'(x)\ dx.$$

We shall call 12.1 the formula for *integration by parts*.

If we let

$$u = f(x), \quad v = g(x),$$

and $$du = f'(x)\ dx, \quad dv = g'(x)\ dx,$$

then 12.1 can be written in the condensed form

12.2 $$\int u\ dv = uv - \int v\ du.$$

The formula for integration by parts allows us to change certain integrals into forms that can be evaluated by previously developed methods. The use of this formula is illustrated by the following examples.

Example 1.   Find $\int \ln x\ dx$.

Solution: According to 12.1, we must express the integrand $\ln x$ in the form

$$\ln x = f(x)g'(x)$$

for some functions f and g.   The simplest way of doing this is to let

$$f(x) = \ln x \quad \text{and} \quad g'(x) = 1,$$

so that

$$f'(x) = \frac{1}{x} \quad \text{and} \quad g(x) = x.$$

It would not be sensible to let $f(x) = 1$ and $g'(x) = \ln x$, since the problem of finding g is the problem of finding an antiderivative of the logarithmic function, which is equivalent to that of evaluating the given integral.

Furthermore, we note that the logarithm has an algebraic derivative and hence the choice $f(x) = \ln x$ effects a simplification.   (Other transcendental functions with algebraic derivatives are the inverse trigonometric functions.)

In the u, v notation, we let

$$u = \ln x, \quad dv = dx,$$

so that

$$du = \frac{1}{x}\ dx, \quad v = x.$$

Hence, by 12.2,

$$\int \ln x\ dx = x \ln x - \int x \frac{1}{x}\ dx = x \ln x - x + C.$$

Example 2.   Find $\int_0^\pi x \sin x\ dx$.

Solution: These are two obvious choices for u and v, namely,

(1) $\qquad\qquad\qquad\qquad u = x, \qquad dv = \sin x \, dx,$

(2) $\qquad\qquad\qquad\qquad u = \sin x, \qquad dv = x \, dx.$

In case (1), we have

(3) $\qquad\qquad\qquad\qquad du = dx, \qquad v = -\cos x;$

in case (2),

(4) $\qquad\qquad\qquad\qquad du = \cos x \, dx, \qquad v = \dfrac{x^2}{2}.$

Integrating by parts in case (1), we have

$$\int_0^\pi x \sin x \, dx = -x \cos x \Big|_0^\pi - \int_0^\pi (-\cos x) \, dx$$

$$= -\pi \cos \pi + 0 \cos 0 + \sin \pi - \sin 0 = \pi.$$

Integrating by parts in case (2), we get

$$\int_0^\pi x \sin x \, dx = \frac{x^2}{2} \sin x \Big|_0^\pi - \frac{1}{2} \int_0^\pi x^2 \cos x \, dx.$$

This latter integral certainly is no easier to evaluate than the given one. Clearly case (1) is the better choice of u and v.

Example 3. Find $\displaystyle\int \frac{x^3}{\sqrt{1 + x^2}} \, dx.$

Solution: If we let

$$u = x^3, \qquad dv = \frac{1}{\sqrt{1 + x^2}} \, dx,$$

then the new integral $\int v \, du$ is no easier to evaluate than the given one. However, if we let

$$u = x^2, \qquad dv = \frac{x}{\sqrt{1 + x^2}} \, dx = x(1 + x^2)^{-1/2} \, dx,$$

then $\qquad du = 2x \, dx, \qquad v = \displaystyle\int x(1 + x^2)^{-1/2} \, dx = \sqrt{1 + x^2},$

and

$$\int \frac{x^3}{\sqrt{1 + x^2}} \, dx = x^2 \sqrt{1 + x^2} - \int 2x\sqrt{1 + x^2} \, dx$$

$$= x^2 \sqrt{1 + x^2} - \frac{2}{3}(1 + x^2)^{3/2} + C = \frac{x^2 - 2}{3} \sqrt{1 + x^2} + C.$$

Example 4. Find $\displaystyle\int e^x \cos x \, dx.$

Solution: If we let

$$u = e^x, \qquad dv = \cos x \, dx,$$

then $\qquad\qquad\qquad du = e^x \, dx, \qquad v = \sin x,$

and

(1) $\qquad\qquad \displaystyle\int e^x \cos x \, dx = e^x \sin x - \int e^x \sin x \, dx.$

Clearly the new integral is of the same type as the given one, and cannot be evaluated by known methods.

If we try to integrate by parts

$$\int e^x \sin x \, dx$$

by letting

$$u = e^x, \qquad dv = \sin x \, dx,$$

then

$$du = e^x \, dx, \qquad v = -\cos x,$$

and we get

(2) $$\int e^x \sin x \, dx = -e^x \cos x + \int e^x \cos x \, dx.$$

Substituting (2) in (1), we have

$$\int e^x \cos x \, dx = e^x \sin x - \left(-e^x \cos x + \int e^x \cos x \, dx \right)$$

$$= e^x \sin x + e^x \cos x - \int e^x \cos x \, dx.$$

Transposing the latter integral to the other side of the equation, we get

$$2 \int e^x \cos x \, dx = e^x \sin x + e^x \cos x,$$

and thus

$$\int e^x \cos x \, dx = \frac{e^x}{2} (\sin x + \cos x) + C.$$

Example 5.   Prove that if the integer $n > 1$,

12.3 $$\int \sec^n x \, dx = \frac{1}{n-1} \left[\sec^{n-2} x \tan x + (n-2) \int \sec^{n-2} x \, dx \right].$$

Solution: The easy power of the secant to integrate is $\sec^2 x$; thus let

$$u = \sec^{n-2} x, \qquad dv = \sec^2 x \, dx,$$

so that

$$du = (n-2) \sec^{n-3} x \sec x \tan x \, dx = (n-2) \sec^{n-2} x \tan x \, dx, \qquad v = \tan x.$$

Hence

(1) $$\int \sec^n x \, dx = \sec^{n-2} x \tan x - (n-2) \int \sec^{n-2} x \tan^2 x \, dx.$$

In order to put this equation into the desired form, let us replace $\tan^2 x$ by $\sec^2 x - 1$ in the new integral to yield

$$-(n-2) \int \sec^{n-2} x \tan^2 x \, dx = -(n-2) \int \sec^n x \, dx + (n-2) \int \sec^{n-2} x \, dx.$$

On substituting this in (1) and collecting the integrals involving $\sec^n x$, we get

$$(n-1) \int \sec^n x \, dx = \sec^{n-2} x \tan x + (n-2) \int \sec^{n-2} x \, dx.$$

This easily reduces to 12.3.

Formula 12.3 is known as a *reduction formula* for the reason that the integral of a power of the secant has been expressed in terms of an integral of a reduced power of the secant.   Many reduction formulas are to be found in the table of integrals in the appendix.

With the aid of 12.3, perhaps using it several times, we can integrate any positive integral power of the secant.   For example, letting $n = 3$, we get

$$\int \sec^3 x \, dx = \frac{1}{2} \left(\sec x \tan x + \int \sec x \, dx \right)$$

$$= \frac{1}{2} \left(\sec x \tan x + \ln |\sec x + \tan x| \right) + C;$$

letting $n = 4$, we get

$$\int \sec^4 x \, dx = \frac{1}{3} \left(\sec^2 x \tan x + 2 \int \sec^2 x \, dx \right)$$

$$= \frac{1}{3} \left(\sec^2 x \tan x + 2 \tan x \right) + C;$$

and so on.

■■■ EXERCISES

Find:

1. $\int x \ln x \, dx.$

2. $\int x^2 \ln x \, dx.$

3. $\int_1^2 \sqrt{x} \ln x \, dx.$

4. $\int_0^1 \tan^{-1} x \, dx.$

5. $\int x \tan^{-1} x \, dx.$

6. $\int x^2 \sin x \, dx.$

7. $\int x \cos x \, dx.$

8. $\int_{-1}^1 x e^x \, dx.$

9. $\int_{-1}^0 \sin^{-1} x \, dx.$

10. $\int \sec^5 x \, dx.$

11. $\int x^2 e^x \, dx.$

12. $\int_0^{\sqrt{3}/2} \frac{x^3}{\sqrt{1 - x^2}} \, dx.$

13. $\int \frac{x}{\sqrt{2x + 1}} \, dx.$

14. $\int \frac{x \ln x}{(x^2 - 1)^{3/2}} \, dx.$

15. $\int e^{2x} \sin 3x \, dx.$

16. $\int e^{-x} \cos x \, dx.$

17. $\int_0^1 x^3 \sqrt{1 - x^2} \, dx.$

18. $\int x \sec^2 x \, dx.$

19. $\int \ln (x^2 + 1) \, dx.$

20. $\int \frac{x^3}{e^{x^2}} \, dx.$

21. Find:

(a) $\int x^r \ln x \, dx, r \neq -1.$

(b) $\int x^{-1} \ln x \, dx.$

22. Prove that

$$\int \sec^{-1} x \, dx = x \sec^{-1} x - \ln |x + \sqrt{x^2 - 1}| + C.$$

23. Prove that

$$\int \sin (\ln x) \, dx = \frac{x}{2} [\sin (\ln x) - \cos (\ln x)] + C.$$

Prove each of the following reduction formulas:

24. $\displaystyle\int x^n e^x \, dx = x^n e^x - n \int x^{n-1} e^x \, dx.$

25. $\displaystyle\int x^n \cos x \, dx = x^n \sin x - n \int x^{n-1} \sin x \, dx.$

26. $\displaystyle\int \sin^n x \, dx = -\frac{\sin^{n-1} x \cos x}{n} + \frac{n-1}{n} \int \sin^{n-2} x \, dx, \, n \geq 2.$

27. $\displaystyle\int \cos^n x \, dx = \frac{\cos^{n-1} x \sin x}{n} + \frac{n-1}{n} \int \cos^{n-2} x \, dx, \, n \geq 2.$

28. $\displaystyle\int \tan^n x \, dx = \frac{\tan^{n-1} x}{n-1} - \int \tan^{n-2} x \, dx, \, n \geq 2.$

29. $\displaystyle\int x^n \sin^{-1} x \, dx = \frac{1}{n+1}\left(x^{n+1} \sin^{-1} x - \int \frac{x^{n+1}}{\sqrt{1-x^2}} \, dx\right), n \geq 1.$

Find:

30. $\displaystyle\int \sinh^{-1} x \, dx.$ **31.** $\displaystyle\int \tanh^{-1} x \, dx.$

32. $\displaystyle\int x \tanh^{-1} x \, dx.$ **33.** $\displaystyle\int x \sinh^{-1} x \, dx.$

34. Derive reduction formulas for:

     (a) $\displaystyle\int \sinh^n x \, dx.$ (b) $\displaystyle\int \cosh^n x \, dx.$

2. Another form of the change of variable formula

If in the change of variable formula 11.7 the function g has an inverse g^{-1} in some interval, then the integral of $f(g(x))g'(x)$ becomes the integral of $f(u)$ if we let $x = g^{-1}(u)$, that is,

$$\int f(u) \, du = \int f(g(x))g'(x) \, dx \Big|_{x = g^{-1}(u)}.$$

For convenience, let us interchange x and u in this formula, obtaining

12.4 $$\int f(x) \, dx = \int f(g(u))g'(u) \, du \Big|_{u = g^{-1}(x)}.$$

Written in this form, the change of variable formula has many uses, as illustrated below.

We may remember 12.4 by a substitution of $g(u)$ for x and $g'(u)\,du$ for dx,

$$x = g(u), \qquad dx = g'(u)\,du.$$

After the new integral is evaluated, u is replaced by $g^{-1}(x)$.

Example 1. Find $\displaystyle\int \frac{x+4}{\sqrt{x+2}}\,dx.$

Solution: The given integrand will be simplified if we let $x + 2 = u^2$, that is, if we let

$$x = u^2 - 2, \qquad dx = 2u\,du.$$

Then $u = \sqrt{x+2}$ and

$$\int \frac{x+4}{\sqrt{x+2}}\,dx = \int \frac{(u^2+2)}{u}\,(2u)\,du \,\Big|_{u=\sqrt{x+2}}$$

$$= 2\int (u^2+2)\,du \,\Big|_{u=\sqrt{x+2}}$$

$$= 2\left(\frac{u^3}{3} + 2u\right)\Big|_{u=\sqrt{x+2}} + C$$

$$= \frac{2}{3}\sqrt{x+2}\,(x+8) + C.$$

An integral of an algebraic function involving square roots of the form

$$\sqrt{a^2 - x^2} \quad \text{or} \quad \sqrt{x^2 \pm a^2}, \quad a > 0,$$

can often be evaluated by a trigonometric substitution. We illustrate this technique with the following examples.

Example 2. Find $\displaystyle\int_{-a}^{a} \sqrt{a^2 - x^2}\,dx.$

Solution: We note that this is the integral we must evaluate to find the area of the semicircle bounded by the graph of the equation $y = \sqrt{a^2 - x^2}$ and the x-axis. If we let

$$x = a\sin\theta, \qquad -\frac{\pi}{2} \le \theta \le \frac{\pi}{2},$$

then

$$\sqrt{a^2 - x^2} = \sqrt{a^2(1 - \sin^2\theta)} = a\sqrt{\cos^2\theta} = a\,|\cos\theta| = a\cos\theta.$$

Thus the substitution $x = a\sin\theta$ removes the radical in the integrand. We now use Formula 12.4 with

$$x = a\sin\theta, \quad dx = a\cos\theta\,d\theta, \quad \theta = \sin^{-1}\frac{x}{a}.$$

Thus

$$\int \sqrt{a^2 - x^2}\,dx = \int (a\cos\theta)a\cos\theta\,d\theta \,\Big|_{\theta = \sin^{-1}\frac{x}{a}}$$

$$= a^2 \int \cos^2\theta\,d\theta \,\Big|_{\theta = \sin^{-1}\frac{x}{a}}$$

$$= a^2 \left(\frac{\theta}{2} + \frac{1}{4} \sin 2\theta \right) \Bigg|_{\theta \, = \, \sin^{-1} \frac{x}{a}} + C,$$

the integral of $\cos^2 \theta$ being evaluated by methods of Chapter 11.

From above,

$$\sin \theta = \frac{x}{a}, \quad \cos \theta = \frac{\sqrt{a^2 - x^2}}{a},$$

and therefore

$$\sin 2\theta = 2 \sin \theta \cos \theta = \frac{2x}{a^2} \sqrt{a^2 - x^2}.$$

Hence

$$\int \sqrt{a^2 - x^2} \, dx = \frac{a^2}{2} \sin^{-1} \frac{x}{a} + \frac{x}{2} \sqrt{a^2 - x^2} + C.$$

This gives

$$\int_{-a}^{a} \sqrt{a^2 - x^2} \, dx = \frac{a^2}{2} (\sin^{-1} 1 - \sin^{-1} (-1)) = \frac{\pi a^2}{2}$$

for the area of a semicircle, and therefore πa^2 for the area of a circle of radius a.

The trigonometric identities

$$\sin^2 \theta + \cos^2 \theta = 1, \qquad \sec^2 \theta = \tan^2 \theta + 1,$$

play a basic role in determining the proper substitution for the change of variable. Since we are employing 12.4 with g as a trigonometric function, we must remember to restrict sufficiently the domain of g so that its inverse g^{-1} exists.

If the integrand involves $\sqrt{a^2 - x^2}$, $a > 0$, then for

$$x = a \sin \theta, \quad -\frac{\pi}{2} \le \theta \le \frac{\pi}{2},$$

$\cos \theta \ge 0$ and

$$\sqrt{a^2 - x^2} = \sqrt{a^2 - a^2 \sin^2 \theta} = a \cos \theta$$

as in Example 2. We may solve for θ, getting $g^{-1}(x)$ to be

$$\theta = \sin^{-1} \frac{x}{a}.$$

If the integrand involves $\sqrt{x^2 - a^2}$, $a > 0$, then let

$$x = a \sec \theta, \quad 0 \le \theta < \frac{\pi}{2} \quad \text{or} \quad \pi \le \theta < \frac{3\pi}{2}.$$

In this range of θ, $\tan \theta \ge 0$ and

$$\sqrt{x^2 - a^2} = \sqrt{a^2 \sec^2 \theta - a^2} = a \sqrt{\sec^2 \theta - 1} = a \tan \theta.$$

We may again solve for θ in this range,

$$\theta = \sec^{-1} \frac{x}{a}.$$

The third possible case is illustrated by the following example.

Example 3.   Find $\int \sqrt{x^2 + a^2}\, dx$.

Solution: If we let

$$x = a \tan \theta, \quad -\frac{\pi}{2} < \theta < \frac{\pi}{2},$$

then $dx = a \sec^2 \theta\, d\theta$

and $\sqrt{x^2 + a^2} = \sqrt{a^2 \tan^2 \theta + a^2} = a \sec \theta.$

Since $\theta = \tan^{-1}(x/a)$, we have by 12.4

$$\int \sqrt{x^2 + a^2}\, dx = \int (a \sec \theta)a \sec^2 \theta\, d\theta \,\Big|_{\theta\,=\,\tan^{-1}\frac{x}{a}}$$

$$= a^2 \int \sec^3 \theta\, d\theta \,\Big|_{\theta\,=\,\tan^{-1}\frac{x}{a}}$$

$$= \frac{a^2}{2} (\sec \theta \tan \theta + \ln |\sec \theta + \tan \theta|) \,\Big|_{\theta\,=\,\tan^{-1}\frac{x}{a}} + C'$$

by 12.3.   By our previous remarks,

$$\tan \theta = \frac{x}{a}, \quad \sec \theta = \frac{1}{a} \sqrt{x^2 + a^2},$$

and therefore

$$\int \sqrt{x^2 + a^2}\, dx = \frac{1}{2} x\sqrt{x^2 + a^2} + \frac{a^2}{2} \ln\left[\frac{1}{a}\left(\sqrt{x^2 + a^2} + x\right)\right] + C'$$

$$= \frac{1}{2} x\sqrt{x^2 + a^2} + \frac{a^2}{2} \ln\left(\sqrt{x^2 + a^2} + x\right) + C,$$

where $C = C' - (a^2 \ln a)/2$, a constant.

■ ■ ■ EXERCISES

Find:

1. $\int \dfrac{x}{\sqrt{x+4}}\, dx.$ **2.** $\int \dfrac{\sqrt{x+4}}{x}\, dx.$

3. $\int x\sqrt[3]{x+1}\, dx.$ **4.** $\int \dfrac{x}{\sqrt[3]{2x-1}}\, dx.$

5. $\int \dfrac{1}{1+\sqrt{x}}\, dx.$ **6.** $\int \dfrac{1}{1-\sqrt[3]{x}}\, dx.$

7. $\int \sqrt{25 - x^2}\, dx.$ **8.** $\int \dfrac{\sqrt{25 - x^2}}{x}\, dx.$

9. $\int \dfrac{1}{\sqrt{25 - x^2}}\, dx.$ **10.** $\int \sqrt{x^2 - 4}\, dx.$

11. $\int \sqrt{9x^2 - 4}\, dx.$ **12.** $\int x\sqrt{9x^2 - 4}\, dx.$

13. $\int \dfrac{1}{x\sqrt{x^2 + 9}}\, dx.$

14. $\int \dfrac{1}{(x^2 + 9)^2}\, dx.$

15. $\int \dfrac{1}{(x^2 - 4)^2}\, dx.$

16. $\int \dfrac{x}{(x^2 - 4)^2}\, dx.$

17. $\int \dfrac{\sqrt{x^2 - q^2}}{x}\, dx.$

18. $\int \dfrac{\sqrt{x^2 - a^2}}{x^2}\, dx.$

19. $\int \dfrac{\sqrt{a^2 - x^2}}{x^2}\, dx.$

20. $\int x^2\sqrt{a^2 - x^2}\, dx.$

21. $\int \dfrac{x^2}{\sqrt{a^2 + x^2}}\, dx.$

22. $\int \dfrac{\sqrt{a^2 + x^2}}{x^2}\, dx.$

23. $\int \dfrac{x^2}{\sqrt{x^2 - a^2}}\, dx.$

24. $\int \dfrac{x^2}{\sqrt{a^2 - x^2}}\, dx.$

25. $\int \dfrac{1}{x\sqrt{a^2 - x^2}}\, dx.$

26. $\int \dfrac{1}{x\sqrt{a^2 + x^2}}\, dx.$

27. $\int \dfrac{1}{(x^2 - 4x + 5)^2}\, dx.$

28. $\int (x + 3)^2\sqrt{x^2 + 6x + 8}\, dx.$

29. Solve the differential equation
$$\sqrt{x^2 + 1} - y\sin y\,\frac{dy}{dx} = 0.$$

30. Solve the differential equation
$$\ln^2 x - \frac{1}{(1 + y^2)^{3/2}}\frac{dy}{dx} = 0.$$

31. The hyperbolic functions are related to the hyperbola $x^2 - y^2 = 1$ much as the trigonometric functions are related to the circle $x^2 + y^2 = 1$. That is, if $P(x,y)$ is a point in the first quadrant on the hyperbola $x^2 - y^2 = 1$, if Q is the vertex $(1,0)$, and if O is the origin, then the area t of the region bounded by the hyperbola and the line segments OP and OQ is given by $t = (\sinh^{-1} y)/2$. Hence the point P has coordinates $(\cosh 2t, \sinh 2t)$. Prove the above statements, and state the analogous results for the trigonometric functions relative to the circle $x^2 + y^2 = 1$.

3. Integration of rational functions

Let us consider as an example the problem of evaluating the integral

(1)
$$\int \frac{2x^4 + 3x^3 - x^2 + x - 1}{x^3 - x}\, dx.$$

By long division we can show that

(2)
$$\frac{2x^4 + 3x^3 - x^2 + x - 1}{x^3 - x} = 2x + 3 + \frac{x^2 + 4x - 1}{x^3 - x},$$

and hence

(3) $$\int \frac{2x^4 + 3x^3 - x^2 + x - 1}{x^3 - x} \, dx = x^2 + 3x + \int \frac{x^2 + 4x - 1}{x^3 - x} \, dx.$$

The integrand of (1) is of the form

$$f(x) = \frac{F(x)}{G(x)}$$

where F and G are polynomial functions. Such a function f is called a rational function. Equation (2) illustrates a general theorem which states that

$$\frac{F(x)}{G(x)} = Q(x) + \frac{R(x)}{G(x)}$$

where $Q(x)$ (the quotient) and $R(x)$ (the remainder) are polynomials and $R(x)$ is of degree less than the degree of $G(x)$. If $F(x)$ is of degree less than that of $G(x)$, then $Q(x) = 0$, and $R(x) = F(x)$. Thus the problem of integrating a rational function can always be reduced to one of integrating a quotient of two polynomials where the degree of the numerator is less than the degree of the denominator [as in (3)].

It is easy to verify that

(4) $$\frac{x^2 + 4x - 1}{x^3 - x} = \frac{1}{x} + \frac{2}{x - 1} - \frac{2}{x + 1},$$

and therefore

$$\int \frac{x^2 + 4x - 1}{x^3 - x} \, dx = \int \frac{1}{x} \, dx + 2 \int \frac{1}{x - 1} \, dx - 2 \int \frac{1}{x + 1} \, dx$$

$$= \ln |x| + 2 \ln |x - 1| - 2 \ln |x + 1| + C$$

$$= \ln \left| \frac{x(x - 1)^2}{(x + 1)^2} \right| + C,$$

so that the integral (1) has the value

$$x^2 + 3x + \ln \left| \frac{x(x - 1)^2}{(x + 1)^2} \right| + C.$$

In equation (4) we have reduced the quotient $(x^2 + 4x - 1)/(x^3 - x)$ to a sum of *partial fractions*. Obviously it is this equation which allows us to proceed with the evaluation of (1). It is our purpose in this section to give methods by which these partial fractions may be determined. (Note that this procedure was employed in the proof of 11.24.)

Although we shall not give the proof, it can be proved that every polynomial $G(x)$ with real number coefficients can be expressed as a product of linear and quadratic polynomials. For example,

$$x^3 - x = x(x - 1)(x + 1),$$

$$x^3 + 8 = (x + 2)(x^2 - 2x + 4),$$

$$x^4 + 4x^2 + 4 = (x^2 + 2)^2.$$

Therefore, starting with a quotient

$$\frac{F(x)}{G(x)}$$

of two polynomials, with the degree of $F(x)$ less than that of $G(x)$, we can first of all factor $G(x)$ into linear and quadratic factors. Having done so, we can hope to express the given quotient as a sum of partial fractions having as denominators factors of $G(x)$.

If $(ax + b)^r$, $r \geq 1$, is the highest power of the linear polynomial $ax + b$ that is a factor of $G(x)$, then included in the sum of partial fractions of $F(x)/G(x)$ will be r terms of the form

$$\frac{A_1}{ax + b} + \frac{A_2}{(ax + b)^2} + \cdots + \frac{A_r}{(ax + b)^r},$$

where $A_1, A_2, \cdots, A_r$ are constants. There will be such a sum associated with each different linear factor of $G(x)$.

If $ax^2 + bx + c$ is a quadratic factor of $G(x)$ that cannot be further factored, and if $(ax^2 + bx + c)^s$, $s \geq 1$, is the highest power of it that is a factor of $G(x)$, then in the sum of partial fractions of $F(x)/G(x)$, there will be included s terms of the form

$$\frac{B_1 x + C_1}{ax^2 + bx + c} + \frac{B_2 x + C_2}{(ax^2 + bx + c)^2} + \cdots + \frac{B_s x + C_s}{(ax^2 + bx + c)^s},$$

where the B_i and C_i are constants. Such a sum will be associated with each distinct quadratic factor of $G(x)$.

We shall see in the examples below how the numerators of these partial fractions are determined.

Example 1.   Find $\displaystyle\int \frac{x^2 + x + 1}{(2x + 1)(x^2 + 1)}\, dx.$

Solution: We have that

$$\frac{x^2 + x + 1}{(2x + 1)(x^2 + 1)} = \frac{A}{2x + 1} + \frac{Bx + C}{x^2 + 1}$$

for some constants A, B, and C according to our previous discussion. To determine A, B, and C, we multiply out the right side of the above equation, obtaining

$$\frac{x^2 + x + 1}{(2x + 1)(x^2 + 1)} = \frac{(A + 2B)x^2 + (B + 2C)x + (A + C)}{(2x + 1)(x^2 + 1)}.$$

In order for these fractions to be identically the same, their numerators must be equal:

$$x^2 + x + 1 = (A + 2B)x^2 + (B + 2C)x + (A + C).$$

In turn, these two polynomials are identically the same if the corresponding powers of x have the same coefficients; that is, if

$$A + 2B = 1, \quad B + 2C = 1, \quad A + C = 1.$$

These three equations in the three unknowns A, B, and C may be solved in the usual way to yield

$$A = \frac{3}{5}, \quad B = \frac{1}{5}, \quad C = \frac{2}{5}.$$

Hence
$$\frac{x^2 + x + 1}{(2x + 1)(x^2 + 1)} = \frac{1}{5}\left(\frac{3}{2x + 1} + \frac{x + 2}{x^2 + 1}\right),$$

and

$$\int \frac{x^2 + x + 1}{(2x + 1)(x^2 + 1)}\, dx = \frac{1}{5}\left(\int \frac{3}{2x + 1}\, dx + \int \frac{x}{x^2 + 1}\, dx + \int \frac{2}{x^2 + 1}\, dx\right)$$

$$= \frac{1}{5}\left[\frac{3}{2}\ln |2x + 1| + \frac{1}{2}\ln (x^2 + 1) + 2\tan^{-1} x\right] + C.$$

Example 2. Find $\displaystyle\int \frac{2x^2 - 3x - 2}{x^3 + x^2 - 2x}\, dx.$

Solution: The denominator factors as $x(x + 2)(x - 1)$; hence

$$\frac{2x^2 - 3x - 2}{x^3 + x^2 - 2x} = \frac{A}{x} + \frac{B}{x + 2} + \frac{C}{x - 1}.$$

On multiplying out the right side of this equation and equating numerators, we get

(1) $2x^2 - 3x - 2 = A(x + 2)(x - 1) + Bx(x - 1) + Cx(x + 2).$

We can use the method of Example 1 to determine A, B, and C. However, there is an easier way for this example. Since Equation (1) is an identity, it holds for every number x. In particular, it holds for $x = 0$, 1, -2. (Note that these are the numbers that make the denominator equal zero.) If we let $x = 0$ in (1), we get

$$-2 = A(2)(-1),$$

and therefore $A = 1$. If we let $x = 1$ in (1), we get

$$-3 = C(1)(3),$$

and hence $C = -1$. When $x = -2$, we have

$$12 = B(-2)(-3),$$

and $B = 2$.

Thus

$$\int \frac{2x^2 - 3x - 2}{x^3 + x^2 - 2x}\, dx = \int \frac{1}{x}\, dx + \int \frac{2}{x + 2}\, dx - \int \frac{1}{x - 1}\, dx$$

$$= \ln |x| + 2\ln |x + 2| - \ln |x - 1| + C$$

$$= \ln \left|\frac{x(x + 2)^2}{x - 1}\right| + C.$$

Example 3. Find $\displaystyle\int \frac{x}{(x - 1)^2}\, dx.$

Solution: Here for the first time we have a repeated factor in the denominator. For a repeated linear factor, we have the following sum of partial fractions:

$$\frac{x}{(x - 1)^2} = \frac{A}{x - 1} + \frac{B}{(x - 1)^2}.$$

Equating numerators of each side of this equation, we get

$$x = A(x - 1) + B = Ax + (-A + B).$$

Thus we must have

$$A = 1, \qquad -A + B = 0,$$

or $A = 1$, $B = 1$. Hence

$$\int \frac{x}{(x-1)^2}\, dx = \int \frac{1}{x-1}\, dx + \int \frac{1}{(x-1)^2}\, dx$$

$$= \ln |x - 1| - \frac{1}{x-1} + C.$$

Example 4. Find $\displaystyle \int \frac{x^3 - 3x^2 + 2x - 3}{(x^2 + 1)^2}\, dx$.

Solution: In this example, there is a repeated quadratic polynomial in the denominator. Hence, according to our previous discussion,

$$\frac{x^3 - 3x^2 + 2x - 3}{(x^2 + 1)^2} = \frac{A_1 x + B_1}{x^2 + 1} + \frac{A_2 x + B_2}{(x^2 + 1)^2}$$

for some constants A_1, B_1, A_2, and B_2.

An easy way to determine these constants is as follows. By long division,

$$\frac{x^3 - 3x^2 + 2x - 3}{x^2 + 1} = x - 3 + \frac{x}{x^2 + 1},$$

and therefore

$$\frac{x^3 - 3x^2 + 2x - 3}{(x^2 + 1)^2} = \frac{x - 3}{x^2 + 1} + \frac{x}{(x^2 + 1)^2}.$$

Thus $A_1 = 1$, $B_1 = -3$, $A_2 = 1$, and $B_2 = 0$.

We now have

$$\int \frac{x^3 - 3x^2 + 2x - 3}{(x^2 + 1)^2}\, dx = \int \frac{x}{x^2 + 1}\, dx - \int \frac{3}{x^2 + 1}\, dx + \int \frac{x}{(x^2 + 1)^2}\, dx$$

$$= \frac{1}{2} \ln (x^2 + 1) - 3 \tan^{-1} x - \frac{1}{2(x^2 + 1)} + C.$$

■ ■ ■ EXERCISES

Find:

1. $\displaystyle \int \frac{x + 1}{x^2 - x}\, dx.$

2. $\displaystyle \int \frac{x}{x^2 - 5x + 6}\, dx.$

3. $\displaystyle \int \frac{x^3}{x^2 - 2x - 3}\, dx.$

4. $\displaystyle \int \frac{6x^2 + 1}{2 - x - 6x^2}\, dx.$

5. $\displaystyle \int \frac{3x - 1}{4x^2 - 4x + 1}\, dx.$

6. $\displaystyle \int \frac{1}{4x^2 + 12x + 9}\, dx.$

7. $\displaystyle\int \frac{x^2 + 1}{x^3 + x^2 - 2x}\, dx.$ 8. $\displaystyle\int \frac{4x^2 - 3x}{(x + 2)(x^2 + 1)}\, dx.$

9. $\displaystyle\int \frac{x^2}{x^4 - 16}\, dx.$ 10. $\displaystyle\int \frac{1}{x^3 - x^2}\, dx.$

11. $\displaystyle\int \frac{x^3 + 1}{x^3 - 4x}\, dx.$ 12. $\displaystyle\int \frac{x^3 + 1}{x^3 - 1}\, dx.$

13. $\displaystyle\int \frac{2x^2 + 1}{(x - 2)^3}\, dx.$ 14. $\displaystyle\int \frac{x^2 + x + 1}{(x + 1)^3}\, dx.$

15. $\displaystyle\int \frac{2x^3 + x^2 + 5x + 4}{x^4 + 8x^2 + 16}\, dx.$ 16. $\displaystyle\int \frac{x^4 + x^3 + 18x^2 + 10x + 81}{(x^2 + 9)^3}\, dx.$

17. $\displaystyle\int \frac{3x + 1}{(x^2 - 4)^2}\, dx.$ 18. $\displaystyle\int \frac{x^3 + 1}{(4x^2 - 1)^2}\, dx.$

4. Integral tables

A short table of indefinite integrals is to be found in the appendix.   Each of these may be verified by methods of Chapters 11 and 12, or by differentiation.

Some of these are in the form of reduction formulas.   An interesting one, for example, is number 41: If $a \neq 0$ and $n \neq -1$,

$$12.5 \quad \int \frac{1}{(x^2 + a^2)^n}\, dx = \frac{1}{2a^2(n - 1)}\left\{ \frac{x}{(x^2 + a^2)^{n-1}} \right.$$

$$\left. + (2n - 3) \int \frac{1}{(x^2 + a^2)^{n-1}}\, dx \right\}.$$

This formula allows us to evaluate such integrals as, for example,

$$\int \frac{1}{(x^2 + a^2)^2}\, dx = \frac{1}{2a^2}\left(\frac{x}{x^2 + a^2} + \frac{1}{a}\tan^{-1}\frac{x}{a} \right) + C.$$

The reduction formula above may be proved by differentiating the right side and showing that this is the integrand of the left side.   We leave the details for the reader to verify.

■ ■ ■ EXERCISES

1. Prove 12.5.
2. Use 12.5 and methods of the previous section to find

(a) $\displaystyle\int \frac{x^2}{(x^2 + a^2)^2}\, dx.$ (b) $\displaystyle\int \frac{x^3}{(x^2 + a^2)^2}\, dx.$

13

Further applications
of the calculus

■ ■ ■ ■ ■   APPLICATIONS OF THE CALCULUS to such problems as finding the center of gravity of a body and the force of water
against a dam will be given in this chapter. Before giving these applications, we shall discuss a topic interwoven
in the history of mathematics, the differential. Although
the calculus could be carried through completely without
the use of the differential, this concept still appears often
enough in the physical applications of the calculus so
that the student must be aware of its meaning.

1. Differentials

The integration formula

$$\int f(g(x))g'(x)\, dx = \int f(u)\, du \Big|_{u\,=\,g(x)}$$

is formally justified by the substitutions

$$u = g(x), \quad du = g'(x)\, dx.$$

The symbols du and dx are called *differentials* of u and x,
respectively.

If for the differentiable functions f and g we let

$$y = f(u), \qquad u = g(x),$$

and if we formally define the differentials dy, du, and dx by the equations

$$dy = f'(u)\, du, \qquad du = g'(x)\, dx,$$

then the purely formal equation

$$\frac{dy}{dx} = \frac{dy}{du}\frac{du}{dx}$$

can be interpreted as the chain rule of differentiation. That is, $y = f(g(x))$ and

$$\frac{dy}{dx} = D_x f(g(x)) = f'(\overline{g(x)})g'(x) = \frac{dy}{du}\frac{du}{dx}.$$

While we have interpreted dx and dy above as symbols having certain formal properties, it is possible to interpret them as numbers in the following way.

The delta notation was introduced in Chapter 9 to signify a difference. We shall now call the number Δx an *increment of x*. If f is a differentiable function and if

$$y = f(x),$$

then the *increment of y* with respect to Δx at x is defined to be

$$\Delta y = f(x + \Delta x) - f(x).$$

Clearly Δy is the change in y brought about by a change of Δx in x. By the definition of the derivative of f,

$$\lim_{\Delta x \to 0} \frac{\Delta y}{\Delta x} = f'(x),$$

and therefore

$$\lim_{\Delta x \to 0} \frac{\Delta y - f'(x)\, \Delta x}{\Delta x} = 0.$$

It is evident from this limit that

13.1 $\qquad \Delta y \doteq f'(x)\, \Delta x$

($\doteq$ means "approximately equal to") when Δx is close to zero.

We now let the differential of x, dx, be the number Δx, and define the differential of y (with respect to dx at x) by the equation

13.2 $\qquad dy = f'(x)\, dx.$

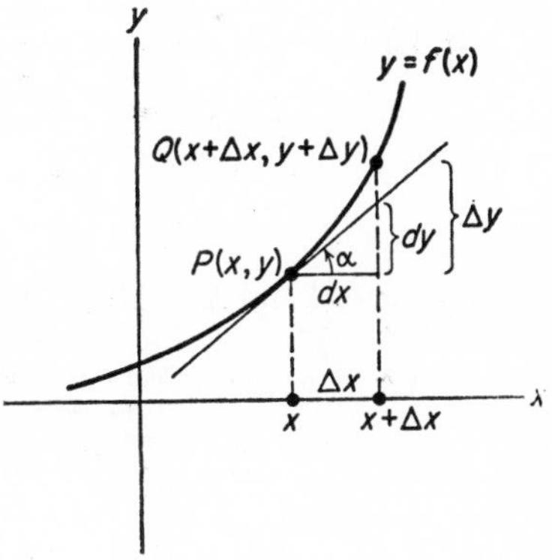

Figure 13.1

By 13.1, the differential of y and the increment of y are approximately equal to each other when dx is close to zero.

The relationship between dy and Δy is indicated geometrically in Figure 13.1. Thus Δy is the actual difference in ordinates between the points

P and Q, whereas dy is the rise (or fall) in the tangent line at P when x changes by $\Delta x = dx$.   This is evident, since

$$\tan \alpha = f'(x) = \frac{dy}{dx}.$$

Example 1.   If $y = x^2 - 5x + 1$, find Δy and dy.

Solution: If we let $f(x) = x^2 - 5x + 1$, then

$$\Delta y = f(x + \Delta x) - f(x) = [(x + \Delta x)^2 - 5(x + \Delta x) + 1] - (x^2 - 5x + 1),$$

which simplifies to

$$\Delta y = (2x - 5) \Delta x + \Delta x^2.$$

On the other hand,

$$dy = f'(x) \, dx = (2x - 5) \, dx.$$

If, for example, $\Delta x = dx = .1$ and $x = 2$, then

$$\Delta y = (4 - 5)(.1) + (.1)^2 = -.09, \qquad dy = (4 - 5)(.1) = -.1.$$

And if $\Delta x = dx = .01$ and $x = 2$, then

$$\Delta y = (4 - 5)(.01) + (.01)^2 = -.0099, \qquad dy = (4 - 5)(.01) = -.01.$$

Clearly $\Delta y \doteq dy$ when Δx is close to 0.

Example 2.   If $y = \sqrt{x}$, find Δy and dy.

Solution: If $g(x) = \sqrt{x}$, then

$$\Delta y = g(x + \Delta x) - g(x) = \sqrt{x + \Delta x} - \sqrt{x}$$

whereas

$$dy = g'(x) \, dx = \frac{dx}{2\sqrt{x}}.$$

If, for example, $x = 4$ and $\Delta x = dx = -.39$, then

$$\Delta y = \sqrt{4 - .39} - \sqrt{4} = \sqrt{3.61} - \sqrt{4} = -.1,$$

$$dy = \frac{-.39}{2\sqrt{4}} = \frac{-.39}{4} = -.098.$$

And if $x = 4$ and $\Delta x = dx = .04$, then

$$\Delta y = \sqrt{4.04} - \sqrt{4} \doteq 2.00998 - 2 \doteq .00998,$$

$$dy = \frac{.04}{2\sqrt{4}} = .01.$$

Since $\Delta y \doteq dy$ when dx is close to zero, dy is an approximation of Δy when dx is small.   Thus, if we change x by a small amount, the corresponding change in $f(x)$ is approximately dy.

Example 3.   A box in the form of a cube has an edge of length $x = 4 \pm .05$ in. Approximate the volume of the box.

Solution: Since the volume $V = x^3$,

$$dV = 3x^2 \, dx.$$

Letting $x = 4$ and $dx = \pm.05$, the differential of volume is given by

$$dV = 3(4)^2(\pm.05) = \pm2.4.$$

Hence

$$V = 4^3 \pm 2.4 = 64 \pm 2.4 \text{ in.}^3.$$

We can interpret this to say that an error of .05 in. in the measurement of the length of an edge of the box gives rise to a possible error of 2.4 in.^{3} in the volume of the box.

▪ ▪ ▪ EXERCISES

In each of the following exercises, find the differential of the defined function:

1. $A = \pi r^2$.

2. $V = \dfrac{4}{3}\pi r^3$.

3. $y = \sin x$.

4. $z = \tan \theta$.

5. $v = \cos t$.

6. $x = t^3 - t^2$.

7. $M = mv$. (m constant)

8. $P = -\dfrac{m}{r}$. (m constant)

9. $F = \dfrac{m}{r^2}$. (m constant)

10. $w = \ln r$.

In each of the following exercises, find dy and Δy under the given conditions:

11. $y = 2x - x^2$, $x = -1$, $dx = \Delta x = .02$.
12. $y = 2x - x^2$, $x = 1$, $dx = \Delta x = -.05$.
13. $y = x^3$, $x = 1$, $dx = \Delta x = 2$.
14. $y = x^3$, $x = 1$, $dx = \Delta x = .2$.
15. $y = \dfrac{1}{x}$, $x = 2$, $dx = \Delta x = .1$.

16. $y = \dfrac{1}{x}$, $x = -1$, $dx = \Delta x = -.02$.

17. Approximate $\sqrt[3]{65}$. (*Hint:* If $y = \sqrt[3]{x}$, find dy for $x = 64$, $dx = 1$.)
18. Approximate $\sin 59°$. (*Hint:* If $y = \sin x$, find dy for $x = \pi/3$, $dx = -\pi/180$ radian.)
19. What is the possible error in the area of a square 30 ft on a side if there is a possible error of ± 1 in. in the measurement of each side?
20. The radius of a sphere is 20 in., with a possible error of $\pm.1$ in. Find the error in the volume and in the surface area of the sphere.

2. *Simpson's rule*

The trapezoidal rule for approximating a definite integral was given in Section 8 of Chapter 9. A rule that is as easy as the trapezoidal rule to apply and is generally more accurate is the following.

13.3 Simpson's rule. If the function f is continuous in the interval $[a,b]$, if n is an even integer, and if $r_n = [x_0, x_1, \cdots, x_n]$ is the regular partition of $[a,b]$ into n subintervals, then

$$\int_a^b f(x)\, dx \doteq \frac{b-a}{3n} \left[f(x_0) + 4f(x_1) + 2f(x_2) + 4f(x_3) \right.$$
$$\left. + 2f(x_4) + \cdots + 2f(x_{n-2}) + 4f(x_{n-1}) + f(x_n) \right].$$

This rule might well be called the *parabolic rule*, since the basic idea behind the rule is the approximating of the graph of f by arcs of parabolas. Before proving 13.3, let us make a few preliminary remarks on parabolas.

There is a unique curve with equation of the form

$$y = ax^2 + bx + c$$

passing through the three points $(-\Delta x, y_0)$, $(0, y_1)$, and $(\Delta x, y_2)$. That is to say, the following three equations:

$$(1) \qquad \begin{aligned} y_0 &= a\,(-\Delta x)^2 + b\,(-\Delta x) + c \\ y_1 &= c \\ y_2 &= a\,(\Delta x)^2 + b\,\Delta x + c \end{aligned}$$

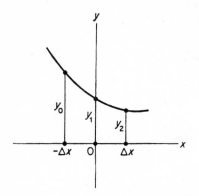

Figure 13.2

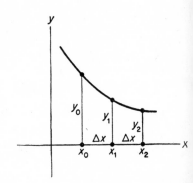

Figure 13.3

have a unique solution for a, b, and c. The area under this curve from $-\Delta x$ to Δx (see Figure 13.2) is given by

$$\int_{-\Delta x}^{\Delta x} (ax^2 + bx + c)\, dx = \frac{ax^3}{3} + \frac{bx^2}{2} + cx \,\Big|_{-\Delta x}^{\Delta x}$$

$$= \frac{\Delta x}{3} \left[2a\,(\Delta x)^2 + 6c \right].$$

From Equations (1), it is easily verified that

$$y_0 + 4y_1 + y_2 = 2a\,(\Delta x)^2 + 6c.$$

Thus

$$\int_{-\Delta x}^{\Delta x} (ax^2 + bx + c)\, dx = \frac{\Delta x}{3}(y_0 + 4y_1 + y_2)$$

gives the area under the parabola of Figure 13.2.

If a congruent parabola is located elsewhere in the plane as in Figure 13.3, say a parabola of the form

$$y = ax^2 + bx + c$$

passing through the three points (x_0, y_0), (x_1, y_1), and (x_2, y_2), where $\Delta x = x_2 - x_1 = x_1 - x_0$, then it is clear that the area under the parabola is the same, that is,

$$\int_{x_0}^{x_2} (ax^2 + bx + c)\, dx = \frac{\Delta x}{3}(y_0 + 4y_1 + y_2).$$

We are now ready to prove Simpson's rule.

Proof of 13.3: Let $\Delta x = (b - a)/n$, the norm of r_n. Since n is even, we may write

$$\int_a^b f(x)\, dx = \int_{x_0}^{x_2} f(x)\, dx + \int_{x_2}^{x_4} f(x)\, dx + \cdots + \int_{x_{n-4}}^{x_{n-2}} f(x)\, dx + \int_{x_{n-2}}^{x_n} f(x)\, dx.$$

Each of the integrals

$$\int_{x_i}^{x_{i+2}} f(x)\, dx$$

may be approximated by the area under a parabola through the three points $(x_i, f(x_i))$, $(x_{i+1}, f(x_{i+1}))$, and $(x_{i+2}, f(x_{i+2}))$. (See Figure 13.4.) Thus,

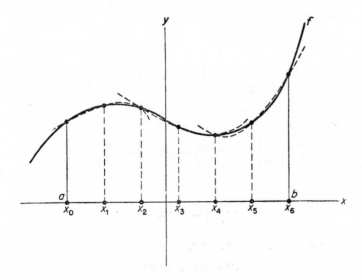

Figure 13.4

by our remarks above we have

$$\int_{x_0}^{x_2} f(x)\, dx \doteq \frac{\Delta x}{3}\, (f(x_0) + 4f(x_1) + f(x_2)),$$

$$\int_{x_2}^{x_4} f(x)\, dx \doteq \frac{\Delta x}{3}\, (f(x_2) + 4f(x_3) + f(x_4)),$$

$$\vdots \qquad \vdots \qquad \vdots$$

$$\int_{x_{n-4}}^{x_{n-2}} f(x)\, dx \doteq \frac{\Delta x}{3}\, (f(x_{n-4}) + 4f(x_{n-3}) + f(x_{n-2})),$$

$$\int_{x_{n-2}}^{x_n} f(x)\, dx \doteq \frac{\Delta x}{3}\, (f(x_{n-2}) + 4f(x_{n-1}) + f(x_n)).$$

On adding these together, we obtain 13.3.

We shall not give the proof, but it may be shown that the error E incurred by the use of Simpson's rule satisfies the inequality

13.4 $$E \leq \frac{(b-a)^5 K}{180 n^4},$$

where the number K is chosen so that $K \geq |f^{[4]}(x)|$, $a \leq x \leq b$.

Example 1.   Approximate $\displaystyle\int_0^1 \frac{1}{1+x^2}\, dx$ by Simpson's rule with $n = 4$.

Solution: We make the following table of values:

x	0	$\frac{1}{4}$	$\frac{1}{2}$	$\frac{3}{4}$	1
$\dfrac{1}{1+x^2}$	1	$\frac{16}{17}$	$\frac{4}{5}$	$\frac{16}{25}$	$\frac{1}{2}$

Then, by 13.3,

$$\int_0^1 \frac{1}{1+x^2}\, dx \doteq \frac{1}{12}\left[1 + 4\left(\frac{16}{17}\right) + 2\left(\frac{4}{5}\right) + 4\left(\frac{16}{25}\right) + \frac{1}{2} \right] \doteq .785392.$$

We know that

$$\int_0^1 \frac{1}{1+x^2}\, dx = \tan^{-1} 1 = \frac{\pi}{4}.$$

Thus we have as an approximation of π,

$$4(.785392) \doteq 3.141568,$$

accurate, as we know, to four decimal places.

■ ■ ■ EXERCISES

Approximate each of the following integrals by Simpson's rule with the given value of n.

1. $\displaystyle\int_1^3 \frac{1}{x}\,dx,\ n = 4.$

2. $\displaystyle\int_0^1 \frac{1}{1 + x^2}\,dx,\ n = 6.$

3. $\displaystyle\int_0^\pi \sqrt{\theta}\sin\theta\,d\theta,\ n = 4.$

4. $\displaystyle\int_0^\pi \sqrt{1 + \sin^2\theta}\,d\theta,\ n = 4.$

5. $\displaystyle\int_0^1 \frac{1}{1 + x + x^3}\,dx,\ n = 4.$

6. $\displaystyle\int_{-1}^1 \sqrt{1 + x^4}\,dx,\ n = 4.$

Approximate each of the following numbers by expressing it as a definite integral of some function and then using Simpson's rule.

7. $\tan^{-1}\dfrac{1}{2}$

8. $\sin^{-1}\dfrac{1}{3}.$

9. $\ln 2.$

10. $\sec^{-1} 3.$

11. $\sinh^{-1} 1.$

12. $\tanh^{-1}\dfrac{1}{2}.$

3. Moments and centers of gravity

The *moment* (of force) of a particle about a line is defined to be the product of the weight of the particle and its distance from the line. We shall find it convenient to consider the particle located on a coordinate plane, and to find the moment of the particle about a coordinate axis (or a line parallel to a coordinate axis). Also, directed distances will be used so that the moment will be positive, negative, or zero depending on whether the point is on the positive or negative side of the axis, or is on the axis.

In Figure 13.5, the particle of weight w is at the point (x,y) in a coordinate plane. Its moments M_x and M_y about the x- and y-axes, respectively, are given by

$$M_x = wy, \qquad M_y = wx.$$

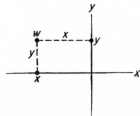

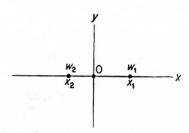

Figure 13.5   Figure 13.6

If the particle is in the second quadrant, as in the figure, then $M_x > ($ and $M_y < 0$.

Moments are used to find the *center of gravity* of a physical object. As an illustration, consider a seesaw with boys of weights w_1 and w_2 on it. For convenience, we think of the seesaw as being on the x-axis with balance point at the origin O (Figure 13.6). The moments of the two boys about the y-axis are

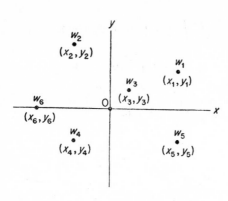

Figure 13.7

$$M_1 = w_1x_1, \qquad M_2 = w_2x_2.$$

The two boys will balance each other provided the sum of their moments is zero, that is,

$$w_1x_1 + w_2x_2 = 0.$$

If they balance each other, the balance point O is called the center of gravity of the physical system made up of two boys.

The moments of a system of n particles located in a coordinate plane are defined similarly. Thus if the particles of weights $w_1, w_2, \cdots, w_n$ are at the respective points $(x_1,y_1), (x_2,y_2), \cdots, (x_n,y_n)$ (Figure 13.7), then the moments M_x and M_y of the system of n particles are defined as follows:

$$M_x = \sum_{i=1}^{n} w_iy_i, \qquad M_y = \sum_{i=1}^{n} w_ix_i.$$

If $M_x = M_y = 0$, the origin is the center of gravity of this system. However, even if $M_x \neq 0$ or $M_y \neq 0$, the given system still has a center of gravity, namely the point O' such that relative to the translated axes with center at O', $M_{x'} = M_{y'} = 0$. The following theorem gives the location of the point O'.

13.5 Theorem. Consider a physical system made up of n particles of weights $w_1, w_2, \cdots, w_n$ located at the respective points $(x_1,y_1), (x_2,y_2),$ $\cdots, (x_n,y_n)$. If M_x and M_y are the moments of the system and $w = \sum_{i=1}^{n} w_i$ is its weight, then the center of gravity of this system is the point $(\bar{x},\bar{y})$ given by

$$\bar{x} = \frac{M_y}{w}, \qquad \bar{y} = \frac{M_x}{w}.$$

Proof: Let us translate the coordinate axes to a new origin $O'(h,k)$. Relative to the new x'- and y'-axes, the given particles have coordinates

$(x_1', y_1'), (x_2', y_2'), \cdots, (x_n', y_n')$, where

$$x_i' = x_i - h, \quad y_i' = y_i - k, \quad i = 1, 2, \cdots, n.$$

Hence

$$M_x' = \sum_{i=1}^{n} w_i y_i' = \sum_{i=1}^{n} w_i(y_i - k) = \sum_{i=1}^{n} w_i y_i - k \sum_{i=1}^{n} w_i,$$

and therefore

$$M_x' = M_x - kw.$$

Similarly,

$$M_y' = M_y - hw.$$

Now the new origin $O'(h,k)$ will be the center of gravity of the given system provided that $M_x' = M_y' = 0$, that is,

$$M_x - kw = 0 \quad \text{and} \quad M_y - hw = 0.$$

On solving these equations for h and k, we get $h = M_y/w$ and $k = M_x/w$ as stated in the theorem.

An interesting conclusion that can be drawn from this theorem is that the given system of n particles has the same moments relative to the x- and y-axes as a system made up of one particle of weight $w = w_1 + w_2 + \cdots + w_n$ and located at the point $(\bar{x}, \bar{y})$. This follows immediately from the equations

$$M_x = w\bar{y}, \qquad M_y = w\bar{x}$$

of the theorem. Thus each moment of the system may be found by assuming that the weight of the system is concentrated at the center of gravity of the system.

The center of gravity of a thin homogeneous sheet of substance, called a *lamina*, may be thought of as the balance point of the lamina. If the lamina has a geometric center, then this point will also be the center of gravity. For example, the center of gravity of a rectangular lamina is the point of intersection of the diagonals of the rectangle.

The moment of a lamina about a line in the plane of the lamina may be defined with the aid of the calculus. We assume that the moment M_L of a lamina of weight w about an axis L is between wd_1 and wd_2,

$$wd_1 \leq M_L \leq wd_2,$$

where d_1 is the minimum (directed) distance of any point of the lamina from L, and d_2 is the maximum (directed) distance of any point of the lamina from L (Figure 13.8). We also assume that if the lamina is cut up into pieces, the moment of the lamina is the sum of the moments of its pieces.

Let us illustrate the use of these two assumptions in finding the moment of a rectangular lamina of density ρ about an axis parallel to a side of the lamina.* We divide the given rectangle into n congruent rectangles as

---

* The weight of a square unit of a lamina is called its density. The weight of a (homogeneous) lamina is ρA where ρ is its density and A is its area.

in Figure 13.9.   The height of each smaller rectangle is $\Delta y = b/n$ and its
weight is $\rho a\,\Delta y$.

The moment about the x-axis of the first rectangle is between $(\rho a\,\Delta y)c$
and $(\rho a\,\Delta y)(c + \Delta y)$; of the second rectangle is between $(\rho a\,\Delta y)(c + \Delta y)$

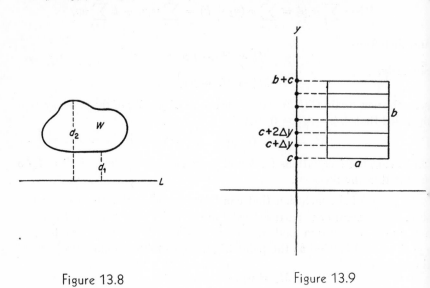

Figure 13.8   Figure 13.9

and $(\rho a\,\Delta y)(c + 2\,\Delta y)$; and so on.   Hence the moment M_x of the given
rectangle satisfies the inequality

$$\sum_{i=1}^{n} (\rho a\,\Delta y)(c + (i - 1)\,\Delta y) \le M_x \le \sum_{i=1}^{n} (\rho a\,\Delta y)(c + i\,\Delta y).$$

Using 9.13, this may be simplified as follows $(n\,\Delta y = b)$:

$$\sum_{i=1}^{n} (\rho a\,\Delta y)c + \sum_{i=1}^{n} (\rho a\,\Delta y^2)(i - 1) \le M_x \le \sum_{i=1}^{n} (\rho a\,\Delta y)c + \sum_{i=1}^{n} (\rho a\,\Delta y^2)$$

$$n(\rho a\,\Delta y)c + \rho a\,\Delta y^2\,\frac{(n - 1)n}{2} \le M_x \le n(\rho a\,\Delta y)c + \rho a\,\Delta y^2\,\frac{n(n + 1)}{2},$$

$$\rho abc + \rho ab\,\frac{b - \Delta y}{2} \le M_x \le \rho abc + \rho ab\,\frac{b + \Delta y}{2}.$$

The limit of each side of this inequality is the same as n approaches ∞
(and Δy approaches 0).   Therefore, this common limit must be M_x,

$$M_x = \rho ab\left(c + \frac{b}{2}\right).$$

Thus the moment of a rectangular lamina about an axis parallel to a side
is the weight ρab of the lamina times the distance $c + b/2$ from the axis

to the center of the lamina.   In other words, the moment of a rectangular
lamina of weight w about an axis parallel to a side is the same as that of
a particle of weight w located at the
center of gravity of the lamina.

Once we have defined the moments
of a lamina of weight w about the
axes, then the center of gravity can
be defined as the point at which a
particle of weight w would be located
so that the moments of the particle
about the axes would equal the moments of the lamina.

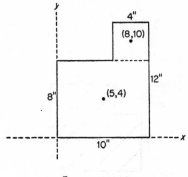

Example. Find the center of gravity of
a lamina of density ρ lb/in.^{2} having
the shape of Figure 13.10.

Figure 13.10

Solution: The lamina is made up of two
rectangles and has a total area of 96
in.^{2}. If we place coordinate axes as
indicated in the figure, then the centers of gravity of the two rectangles are
(5,4) and (8,10). Thus the moments of the lamina about the axes are as follows:

$$M_x = (80\rho)4 + (16\rho)10 = 480\rho.$$

$$M_y = (80\rho)5 + (16\rho)8 = 528\rho.$$

Therefore the center of gravity $(\bar{x}, \bar{y})$ is given by

$$\bar{x} = \frac{M_y}{w} = \frac{528\rho}{96\rho} = \frac{11}{2}, \qquad \bar{y} = \frac{M_x}{w} = \frac{480\rho}{96\rho} = 5,$$

that is, by $(\tfrac{11}{2}, 5)$.

■ ■ ■ EXERCISES

In the following exercises, the notation $w(x,y)$ signifies that a particle of weight
w is located at the point (x,y).   Find the center of gravity of each of the following systems of particles.

1. $3(2,2),\ 4(2,-2),\ 5(-2,2),\ 2(-2,-2)$.
2. $8(4,4),\ 6(4,-4),\ 3(-4,4),\ 5(-4,-4)$.
3. $6(0,0),\ 6(8,0),\ 6(0,8),\ 6(8,8),\ 3(4,4)$.
4. $3(0,0),\ 5(6,0),\ 10(0,6),\ 8(-6,0),\ 4(0,-6)$.
5. $2(1,3),\ 7(4,2),\ 6(3,-3),\ 8(-4,2),\ 5(-3,-4)$.
6. $3(0,0),\ 5(4,0),\ 7(8,0),\ 2(-10,0),\ 8(-5,0)$.

In each of the following exercises, find the center of gravity of the lamina of
density ρ having the shape in the given figure.

7. Figure 13.11.   8. Figure 13.12.

9. Figure 13.13.   10. Figure 13.14.

11. Assume that for a given system of n particles $M_x = 0$ and $M_y = 0$. Prove that $M_L = 0$ for every line L passing through the origin.

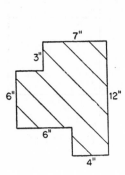

Figure 13.11

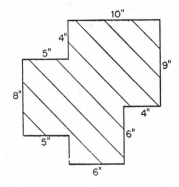

Figure 13.12

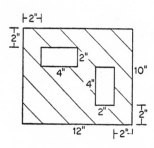

Figure 13.13

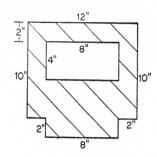

Figure 13.14

4. *Centroid of a plane region*

Let us turn now to the problem of finding the center of gravity of a lamina with a possibly curved boundary.   In order to make the problem solvable mathematically, we assume that the boundary of the lamina is made up of the graphs of continuous functions.

We first assume that a lamina of density ρ has the shape of a region bounded by the lines $x = a$ and $x = b$, where $0 \leq a < b$, the x-axis, and the graph of a continuous nonnegative function f as in Figure 13.15.   Associated with each partition $p = [x_0, x_1, \cdots, x_n]$ of the interval $[a, b]$ are the inscribed and circumscribed rectangular polygons of f, as illustrated in Figure 13.16. A lamina having the shape of the inscribed polygon will have the following moments about the axes:

$$M_{px} = \sum_{i=1}^{n} \frac{1}{2} f(u_i)[\rho f(u_i)\, \Delta x_i],$$

$$M_{py} = \sum_{i=1}^{n} x_i'[\rho f(u_i)\, \Delta x_i].$$

In these sums, $f(u_i)$ is the minimum value of f in the ith subinterval of the partition p, $\frac{1}{2}f(u_i)$ and $x_i'\,(=x_i - \Delta x_i/2)$ are the distances of the center of the ith rectangle from the x- and y-axes, respectively, and $\rho f(u_i)\, \Delta x_i$ is the weight of the ith rectangle.

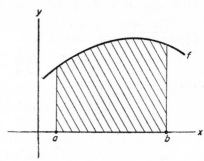

Figure 13.15

The moments M'_{px} and M'_{py} of a lamina having the shape of the circumscribed polygon will be given by

$$M'_{px} = \sum_{i=1}^{n} \frac{1}{2} f(v_i)[\rho f(v_i)\, \Delta x_i], \qquad M'_{py} = \sum_{i=1}^{n} x_i'[\rho f(v_i)\, \Delta x_i],$$

where $f(v_i)$ is the maximum value of f in the ith subinterval of p.

Since the given lamina can be thought of as being cut up into $n+1$ pieces, namely, the inscribed polygonal lamina and n little pieces, one above each rectangle, the moment M_x of the given lamina cannot be less than M_{px}, the moment of one of its pieces. Similarly, the given lamina is contained in the circumscribed polygonal lamina and we must have $M_x \le M'_{xp}$. Analogous remarks can be made for M_y, and we conclude that

$$M_{px} \le M_x \le M'_{px}, \qquad M_{py} \le M_y \le M'_{py}$$

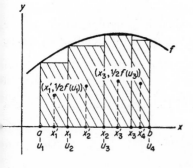
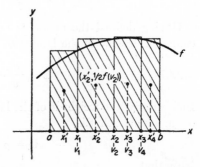

Figure 13.16

for every partition p of $[a,b]$. We now proceed to show that there is a unique choice for each of the numbers M_x and M_y satisfying these inequalities for every partition p.

It is clear that M_{px} and M'_{px} are Riemann sums, not for the function f but for the function $\frac{1}{2}\rho f^2$. Thus, if we select a sequence $p_1, p_2, \cdots, p_n, \cdots$ of partitions of $[a,b]$ for which

$$\operatorname*{limit}_{n\to\infty} |p_n| = 0,$$

then

$$\operatorname*{limit}_{n\to\infty} M_{p_n x} = \operatorname*{limit}_{n\to\infty} M'_{p_n x} = \int_a^b \frac{1}{2}\, \rho f^2(x)\, dx.$$

While M_{py} and M'_{py} are not quite Riemann sums (they would be if $x'_i = u_i = v_i$), still we may use Theorem 9.18 [with $g(x) = \rho_x$] to obtain

$$\operatorname*{limit}_{n\to\infty} M_{p_n y} = \operatorname*{limit}_{n\to\infty} M'_{p_n y} = \int_a^b \rho x f(x)\, dx.$$

Since M_x lies between two converging sequences having a common limit, M_x must be this limit,

$$M_x = \frac{\rho}{2} \int_a^b f^2(x)\, dx,$$

and similarly for M_y,

$$M_y = \rho \int_a^b x f(x)\, dx.$$

The assumption $a \geq 0$ was necessary for the arguments above in that $M_{py} \leq M_y \leq M'_{py}$ does not necessarily hold if $a < 0$. However, it may be argued by translating the y-axis that the formula above for M_y holds even if $a < 0$. We are therefore led to the following definition.

13.6 Definition. The moments of a lamina of density ρ having the shape of the region bounded by the lines $x = a$, $x = b$, and $y = 0$, and by the graph of the equation of a continuous nonnegative function f are given by

$$M_x = \frac{\rho}{2} \int_a^b f^2(x)\, dx, \qquad M_y = \rho \int_a^b x f(x)\, dx.$$

Having defined the moments of a lamina, it is natural to define the center of gravity of the lamina of weight w to be the point $(\bar{x}, \bar{y})$, where

13.7 $$\bar{x} = \frac{M_y}{w}, \qquad \bar{y} = \frac{M_x}{w}.$$

Incidentally, the weight w of the lamina of 13.6 is ρA, where A is the area of the lamina; that is,

$$w = \rho \int_a^b f(x)\, dx.$$

Note that

$$M_x = w\bar{y}, \qquad M_y = w\bar{x}.$$

according to 13.7.   Thus, again, the moments of the lamina may be found
by assuming that the weight of the lamina is concentrated at the center
of gravity of the lamina.

For the lamina of 13.6, we may write the coordinates of the center of
gravity in the form

$$\bar{x} = \frac{\int_a^b xf(x)\,dx}{\int_a^b f(x)\,dx}, \qquad \bar{y} = \frac{\frac{1}{2}\int_a^b f^2(x)\,dx}{\int_a^b f(x)\,dx}.$$

An interesting feature of the equations for $\bar{x}$ and $\bar{y}$ in this form is that the
density factor ρ cancels out, proving that the center of gravity of a homogeneous lamina depends only on the shape of the lamina and not on its
substance.   For this reason, we may speak of the center of gravity of a
plane region in place of the center of gravity of a lamina of that shape.
We shall use the word *centroid* for the center of gravity of a plane region,
reserving the words *center of gravity* for a material object.

By mathematical arguments similar to those above (c.f. Section 9,
Chapter 8) we may find the moments and centroids of many different
plane regions.   If, for example, a region is bounded by the graphs of two
functions, then we can imagine the region as
being the difference between two regions, one
under the graph of each function.   Hence
its moments will be the difference of two
moments, etc.

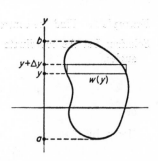

Figure 13.17

A mnemonic device for finding moments
of a region such as in Figure 13.17 is as
follows.   We assume that the region is between the lines $y = a$ and $y = b$, and that
for every y in the interval $[a,b]$ the width
$W(y)$ of the region is known, W being a
continuous function.   We imagine the region
as being approximated by a polygon made
up of n rectangles, a representative one of which, shown in the figure,
has the approximate moment $yW(y)\,\Delta y$ about the x-axis.   By summing up the moments of the n rectangles and taking a limit, we even-
tually obtain

13.8 $$M_x = \int_a^b yW(y)\,dy$$

for the moment of the given region about the x-axis.   If the region has
area A, then $\bar{y} = M_x/A$ is the y-coordinate of its centroid.   A similar
device may be used to find $\bar{x}$.

Example 1.   Find the centroid of the region bounded by the lines $x = -1$ and
$y = 0$, and the graph of the equation $y = 4 - x^2$.

Solution: For this region, sketched in Figure 13.18, we have by 13.6 (with $\rho = 1$)

$$M_x = \frac{1}{2} \int_{-1}^{2} (4 - x^2)^2 \, dx = \frac{153}{10}, \qquad M_y = \int_{-1}^{2} x(4 - x^2) \, dx = \frac{9}{4}.$$

The area $A = 9$, as may be easily verified. Hence

$$\bar{x} = \frac{M_y}{A} = .25, \qquad \bar{y} = \frac{M_x}{A} = 1.7,$$

and the centroid of the given region is the point $(.25, 1.7)$.

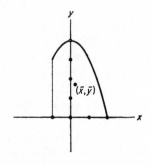

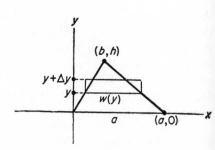

Figure 13.18   Figure 13.19

Example 2.   Find the centroid of a triangle.

Solution: Let the coordinate axes be chosen as in Figure 13.19. By similar triangles,

$$\frac{W(y)}{h - y} = \frac{a}{h},$$

or
$$W(y) = \frac{a}{h} (h - y).$$

Hence, by 13.8,

$$M_x = \frac{a}{h} \int_{0}^{h} y(h - y) \, dy = \frac{ah^2}{6}.$$

Since the triangle has area $A = ah/2$,

$$\bar{y} = \frac{M_x}{A} = \frac{h}{3}.$$

We could have chosen the x-axis on any one of the three sides of the triangle. In each case, we would get that the centroid was one-third the altitude above the base.   Hence the centroid is the unique point one-third the altitude above each base.   By elementary geometry, this is the point of intersection of the medians of the triangle.

■ ■ ■ EXERCISES

Find the centroid of the **region** bounded by the graphs of the following curves. Sketch each region.

1. $y = \sqrt{x}$, $y = 0$, $x = 4$.
2. $y = \dfrac{1}{x+1}$, $x = 0$, $x = 4$, $y = 0$.
3. $y = x^3$, $x = 0$, $x = 2$, $y = 0$.
4. $y = \sin x$, $x = 0$, $x = \pi$, $y = 0$.
5. $y = \cos x$, $x = 0$, $x = \pi/2$, $y = 0$.
6. $y = e^x$, $x = 0$, $x = 2$, $y = 0$.
7. $y = \ln x$, $x = 1$, $x = e$, $y = 0$.
8. $y = \sec^2 x$, $x = -\pi/4$, $x = \pi/4$, $y = 0$.
9. $y = 1/\sqrt{x^2 + 1}$, $x = 0$, $x = 1$, $y = 0$.
10. $x^2 - y^2 = 1$, $x = 3$.
11. Find the centroid of a quarter-circle of radius r.
12. Find the centroid of a semielliptic region bounded by the major axis.
13. Find the centroid of the region bounded by the x-axis, the curve $y = \sinh x$, and the line $x = a$ $(a > 0)$.
14. Find the centroid of the region bounded by the x-axis, the curve $y = \cosh x$, and the lines $x = -a$ and $x = a$.

5. Centroids of solids of revolution

The general problem of finding the center of gravity of a solid object will be considered in a later chapter. However, we can find the center of gravity of a homogeneous object having the shape of a solid of revolution, assuming that the center of gravity is on the axis of revolution.

Let us assume that a homogeneous object of density* ρ has the shape of a solid generated by rotating about the x-axis the region under the graph of a continuous, nonnegative function f between $x = a$ and $x = b$ (Figure 13.20).

We "slice" this object up into discs as in Section 4 of Chapter 9. A representative disc, shown in the figure, has weight $\rho\pi f^2(x)\,\Delta x$ which we imagine as being concentrated at its center. The moment M_y of this disc about the y-axis (in reality, with respect to a plane containing the y-axis and perpendicular to the x-axis) is $x[\rho\pi f^2(x)\,\Delta x]$. Summing up the moments of all the discs and taking a limit, just as in Chapter 9, we finally get

$$M_y = \rho\pi \int_a^b x f^2(x)\,dx.$$

Clearly the object has weight $w = \rho V$ where V is its volume. Hence the center of gravity, $(\bar{x},0)$, of the object is given by

$$\bar{x} = \frac{M_y}{\rho V} = \frac{\int_a^b x f^2(x)\,dx}{\int_a^b f^2(x)\,dx}.$$

* Density now means the weight of a cubic unit of the substance.

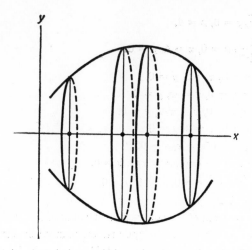

Figure 13.20

We see from the equation above that the center of gravity of the homogeneous object depends only on the shape of the object and not on its substance. Thus we may speak of the center of gravity of this geometrical solid; this point, as in the case of a region, is called the *centroid* of the solid of revolution.

Example. Find the centroid of a hemisphere.

Solution: Let the hemisphere be generated by rotating about the x-axis the quarter-circle of radius r having equation

$$y = \sqrt{r^2 - x^2}, \quad 0 \leq x \leq r.$$

Then

$$M_y = \pi \int_0^r x(\sqrt{r^2 - x^2})^2 \, dx = \frac{\pi r^4}{4},$$

$$\bar{x} = \frac{M_y}{V} = \frac{\pi r^4}{4} \cdot \frac{3}{2\pi r^3} = \frac{3r}{8},$$

and the centroid is the point $(3r/8, 0)$.

■ ■ ■ EXERCISES

In each of the following exercises, the region bounded by the given curves is rotated about the x-axis. Find the centroid of the solid generated.

1. $y = \sqrt{x}, y = 0, x = 4$.

2. $y = \dfrac{1}{x + 1}, x = 0, x = 4, y = 0$.

3. $y = \sin x, x = 0, x = \pi/2, y = 0$.

4. $y = \sec x$, $x = 0$, $x = \pi/6$, $y = 0$.

5. $y = 1/\sqrt{x^2 + 1}$, $x = 0$, $x = 2$, $y = 0$.

6. $x^2 - y^2 = 4$, $x = 4$.

7. Find the centroid of a right circular cone having radius of base r and altitude h.

8. The region in the first quadrant bounded by the ellipse $x^2/a^2 + y^2/b^2 = 1$ is rotated about the x-axis. Find the centroid of the solid generated.

9. The region bounded by a parabola and its latus rectum is rotated about the axis of the parabola. Find the centroid of the solid generated.

10. Prove the following theorem of Pappus: The volume of the solid generated by rotating about the x-axis the region R bounded by the graph of a continuous, nonnegative function f and the lines $x = a$, $x = b$, and $y = 0$ is the product of the area of R and the circumference of the circle described by the center of gravity of R under the rotation.

6. Force on a dam

A liquid in a container exerts a force on the bottom of the container, namely, the weight of the liquid therein. The force per square unit of the bottom is called the *pressure* of the liquid at the bottom. Actually, the pressure exerted by a liquid of density ρ at a point d units below the surface is ρd; and this pressure is the same in all directions.

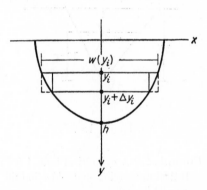

Figure 13.21

In this section we are interested in finding the total force of a liquid of density ρ against a vertical dam. Let us introduce a coordinate system on a blueprint of the dam, placing the x-axis along the line of the surface of the liquid and the positive y-axis downward as illustrated in Figure 13.21. In order to make the problem mathematically solvable, we assume that the width $W(y)$ of the dam at depth y is given by a continuous function W.

Let $p = [y_0, y_1, \cdots, y_n]$ be a partition of the interval $[0, h]$, and let rectangular polygons be inscribed in and circumscribed about the region of the dam. The force against the ith inscribed rectangle exceeds $\rho y_i W(u_i) \Delta y_i$, where $W(u_i)$ is the width of this rectangle; and the force against the ith circumscribed rectangle is exceeded by $\rho y_{i+1} W(v_i) \Delta y_i$, where $W(v_i)$ is the width of this rectangle. Hence the force F against the dam satisfies the inequality

$$\sum_{i=1}^{n} \rho y_i W(u_i) \Delta y_i \leq F \leq \sum_{i=1}^{n} \rho y_{i+1} W(v_i) \Delta y_i.$$

On taking a sequence of partitions of $[0,h]$ with disappearing norms and taking limits of the above sums relative to the sequence of partitions, it is clear that F is given by the integral

13.9 $$F = \rho \int_0^h yW(y)\, dy.$$

Note that this integral is precisely the moment of a lamina of density ρ having the shape of the dam about the x-axis (13.6).

Example 1. Find the force of water against a triangular dam 40 ft wide and 30 ft deep.

Solution: Let the coordinate axes be selected as in Figure 13.22. By similar triangles,

$$\frac{W(y)}{30 - y} = \frac{40}{30}, \quad \text{or} \quad W(y) = \frac{4}{3}(30 - y).$$

The density of water is 62.5 lb/ft³. Hence, by 13.9,

$$F = 62.5 \int_0^{30} y \cdot \frac{4}{3}(30 - y)\, dy = 3.75 \cdot 10^5 \text{ lb}.$$

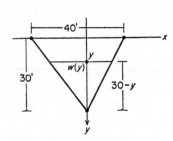

Figure 13.22

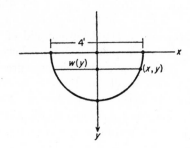

Figure 13.23

Example 2. A cylindrical tank 4 ft in diameter and 6 ft long is half full of oil. If the tank is lying on its side, find the force exerted by the oil on one end (assume $\rho = 60$ lb/ft³).

Solution: If the coordinate axes are chosen on an end of the tank as in Figure 13.23, then the semicircle has equation $y = \sqrt{4 - x^2}$ and

$$W(y) = 2x = 2\sqrt{4 - y^2}$$

for each y. Hence, by 13.9,

$$F = 60 \int_0^2 2y\sqrt{4 - y^2}\, dy$$

$$= -40(4 - y^2)^{3/2}\Big|_0^2 = 320 \text{ lb}.$$

Note that the length of the tank is immaterial.

We need not choose a coordinate axis at the surface of the liquid if it is more convenient to do otherwise. If, for example, we wish to find the force F against the shaded region of Figure 13.24, and if the axes are chosen as in the figure, with the x-axis d units above the water level, then by the same reasoning as above,

$$F = \rho \int_a^{a+h} (y - d)W(y)\, dy.$$

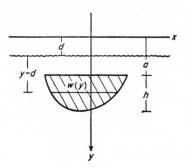

Figure 13.24

■ ■ ■ EXERCISES

1. Find the force of water against an elliptical dam if the major axis of length 50 ft is at the surface of the water and if the semiminor axis has length 20 ft.

2. Find the force of water against a rectangular gate in a dam, if the gate is 6 ft wide and 4 ft high, with the top of the gate parallel to the surface of water and 10 ft below the surface.

3. Find the force of water against the lower half of the gate of the preceding exercise.

4. The gate of Exercise 2 is cut into two triangular gates by a diagonal of the gate. Find the force of water against each triangular gate.

5. A dam has a parabolic shape, with the axis of the parabola vertical. If the dam is 50 ft across at the water level and is 60 ft deep, find the force of water against the dam.

6. A trough has a trapezoidal cross section and is 4 ft wide at the top, 2 ft wide at the bottom, and 2 ft deep. Find the force against an end of the trough if it is full of water.

7. A cylindrical tank 6 ft long and 4 ft in diameter is lying on its side. Find the force against the end of the tank if there is 1 ft of water in the tank.

8. Show that the force against any vertical region of a dam is the product of the density of the liquid, the area of the region, and the depth to the centroid of the region.

14

Basic properties of continuous and differentiable functions

■ ■ ■ ■ ■ THIS CHAPTER MARKS the transition from the more elementary topics of the calculus, such as formal differentiation and integration, to some of the deeper properties of functions. In the first place, proofs are given of the boundedness properties of continuous functions, properties that were used without proof in previous chapters. A generalization of the mean value theorem is proved, thus paving the way for a discussion of approximations of functions by polynomial functions. Integrals of a more general type, called improper integrals, are introduced, along with some general limit theorems.

1. Boundedness of a continuous function

We recall that the function f is continuous at a number c if

$$\lim_{x \to c} f(x) = f(c),$$

that is, if for every number $\epsilon > 0$ there exists some num-

364

ber $\delta > 0$ such that $|f(x) - f(c)| < \epsilon$ for every x (of the domain of f) in the interval $(c - \delta, c + \delta)$.

The following theorem on continuous functions, used without proof in Chapters 8 and 9, is of basic importance in the calculus.

14.1 Theorem. If the function f is continuous in a closed interval $[a,b]$, then for every number $\epsilon > 0$ there exists a partition p of $[a,b]$ such that

$$|f(x') - f(x'')| < \epsilon$$

for every pair of numbers x', x'' in the same subinterval of p.

Proof: If f has the property of the theorem in the intervals $[a,c]$ and $[c,b]$, then f also has this property in $[a,b]$. Thus, if for $\epsilon > 0$ there exist partitions p_1 of $[a,c]$ and p_2 of $[c,b]$ such that $|f(x') - f(x'')| < \epsilon$ for x', x'' in the same subinterval of p_1 or p_2, then let p be the partition of $[a,b]$ made up of the subintervals of p_1 and p_2. Clearly the theorem holds for f relative to p.

We shall prove 14.1 by assuming that the theorem is false, thereby arriving at a contradiction. If the theorem is false, there exists some number $\epsilon > 0$ for which the conclusion of the theorem does not hold. In view of our previous remarks, the conclusion of the theorem is also invalid for the same ϵ over the interval $[a_1, b_1]$, where $[a_1, b_1]$ is one of the halves

$$\left[a, \frac{a + b}{2} \right], \qquad \left[\frac{a + b}{2}, b \right]$$

of $[a,b]$. In turn, the conclusion of the theorem is invalid for the same ϵ over $[a_2, b_2]$, where $[a_2, b_2]$ is one of the halves

$$\left[a_1, \frac{a_1 + b_1}{2} \right], \qquad \left[\frac{a_1 + b_1}{2}, b_1 \right]$$

of $[a_1, b_1]$, and so on. In this way, we obtain a sequence of intervals

$$[a_1, b_1], [a_2, b_2], \cdots, [a_n, b_n], \cdots,$$

each contained in the preceding one and of half its length, for which the theorem is invalid for the chosen ϵ. By the very nature of our selection, $a_1 \leq a_2 \leq \cdots \leq a_n \leq \cdots < b$ and

$$\Delta_n = b_n - a_n = \frac{b - a}{2^n}.$$

Let A be the set made up of the numbers $a_1, a_2, \cdots, a_n, \cdots$. The set A has an upper bound, namely b, and therefore A has a least upper bound c. Since $a \leq c \leq b$, the function f is continuous at c. Therefore, corresponding to the positive number $\epsilon/2$ is some number $\delta > 0$ such that

$$|f(x) - f(c)| < \frac{\epsilon}{2} \text{ for every } x \text{ in the interval } (c - \delta, c + \delta).$$

Since c is the least upper bound of the set A, some a_k is necessarily in the interval $(c - \delta, c + \delta)$; and a_n also will be in $(c - \delta, c + \delta)$ for every $n > k$.

Since

$$\lim_{n\to\infty} \Delta_n = 0,$$

we may select an integer $n \geq k$ so that $\Delta_n < \delta$. For such a choice of n,

$$b_n = a_n + \Delta_n < c + \delta,$$

and therefore (since $n \geq k$) the whole interval $[a_n, b_n]$ is contained in the interval $(c - \delta, c + \delta)$. Hence, if x' and x'' are numbers in $[a_n, b_n]$,

$$|f(x') - f(x'')| = |[f(x') - f(c)] - [f(x'') - f(c)]|$$

$$\leq |f(x') - f(c)| + |f(x'') - f(c)| < \frac{\epsilon}{2} + \frac{\epsilon}{2} = \epsilon.$$

However, this gives us the conclusion of the theorem for the simplest partition p of $[a_n, b_n]$, namely, $p = [a_n, b_n]$, in contradiction to the way $[a_n, b_n]$ was chosen. This contradiction proves the theorem.

If

$$N \leq f(x) \leq M$$

for every x in a given interval, then the function f is said to be *bounded* in that interval, with the number M an upper bound and the number N a lower bound of f. For example,

$$0 \leq \sin x \leq 1 \quad \text{if} \quad 0 < x < \frac{\pi}{2},$$

and thus the sine function is bounded in the interval $(0, \pi/2)$. On the other hand, the tangent function has a lower bound but no upper bound in this interval.

A function f bounded in an interval is also bounded in any subinterval of the interval. Furthermore, if f is bounded in an open interval (a, b) and if $f(a)$ and $f(b)$ exist, then f is bounded in the closed interval $[a, b]$. Thus, if M is an upper bound of f in (a, b), the largest of the three numbers $M, f(a)$, and $f(b)$ is an upper bound of f in $[a, b]$, and similarly for the lower bound.

It is also clear that if f is bounded in each of the overlapping intervals $[a, b]$ and $[c, d]$, then f is bounded in the composite interval of $[a, b]$ and $[c, d]$. If for example, $a \leq c \leq b \leq d$, then the composite interval of $[a, b]$ and $[c, d]$ is $[a, d]$; and if M_1 and M_2 are upper bounds of f in $[a, b]$ and $[c, d]$, respectively, then the larger of M_1 and M_2 is an upper bound of f in $[a, d]$. Similar remarks may be made for lower bounds.

One of the most useful criteria for the boundedness of a function is contained in the following theorem.

14.2 Theorem. Every function f continuous in a closed interval $[a, b]$ is bounded in this interval.

Proof: By 14.1, with $\epsilon = 1$, there exists a partition p of $[a, b]$ such that $|f(x') - f(x'')| < 1$ for every pair of numbers x', x'' in the same subinterval of p. Thus, if $p = [x_0, x_1, \cdots , x_n]$,

$$f(x_i) - 1 < f(x) < f(x_i) + 1$$

for every x in $[x_{i-1}, x_i]$ and evidently f is bounded in $[x_{i-1}, x_i]$. Consequently, f is bounded over the composite of all subintervals of p, that is, in $[a,b]$.

We call the set of values $f(x)$ of a function in an interval $[a,b]$ the *range of f over* $[a,b]$. If the function f is bounded in $[a,b]$, then the range of f over $[a,b]$ has a least upper bound V and a greatest lower bound U. Such is the case, for example, if f is continuous in $[a,b]$. If the numbers U and V are in the range of f over $[a,b]$, so that $V = f(v)$ and $U = f(u)$ for some v and u in $[a,b]$, then $f(v)$ is the maximum and $f(u)$ is the minimum value of f in $[a,b]$.

14.3 Theorem. If the function f is continuous in the closed interval $[a,b]$, then there exist numbers u and v in $[a,b]$ such that $f(u)$ is the minimum and $f(v)$ is the maximum value of f in $[a,b]$.

Proof: Let V be the least upper bound of the range of f over $[a,b]$. If $f(v) = V$ for some number v in $[a,b]$, then $f(v)$ is the maximum value of f in $[a,b]$ and the desired conclusion follows.

On the other hand, if $f(x) \neq V$ for every number x in $[a,b]$, then $f(x) < V$ and $V - f(x) > 0$ for every x in $[a,b]$. If we define the function g by the equation

$$g(x) = \frac{1}{V - f(x)}, \quad x \text{ in } [a,b],$$

then clearly g is defined and is continuous in $[a,b]$. By 14.2, g has an upper bound W in $[a,b]$, so that

$$0 < \frac{1}{V - f(x)} \leq W \quad \text{for every } x \text{ in } [a,b].$$

Solving this inequality for $f(x)$, we have

$$f(x) \leq V - \frac{1}{W} \quad \text{for every } x \text{ in } [a,b].$$

Thus $V - 1/W$ is an upper bound of the range of f over $[a,b]$ less than the least upper bound V. This contradiction shows that $f(x)$ cannot be different from V for every x in $[a,b]$. Hence f assumes a maximum value in $[a,b]$.

The existence of the minimum value of f in $[a,b]$ is established in an analogous way.

Example. The function f defined by

$$f(x) = x^3 - 2x^2 - 4$$

is continuous everywhere and, in particular, in the interval $[-5,2]$. Describe a partition p of $[-5,2]$ corresponding to a given $\epsilon > 0$ for which the conclusion of 14.1 holds. Also find the maximum and minimum values of f in the interval $[-5,2]$ as described in 14.3.

Solution: If w and z are to be two numbers in the same subinterval of p, then we must have
$$|f(w) - f(z)| < \epsilon.$$
Now
$$f(w) - f(z) = (w^3 - 2w^2 - 4) - (z^3 - 2z^2 - 4)$$
$$= (w^3 - z^3) - 2(w^2 - z^2)$$
$$= (w - z)(w^2 + wz + z^2 - 2w - 2z),$$
and
(1) $$|f(w) - f(z)| = |w - z|\,|w^2 + wz + z^2 - 2w - 2z|.$$
Evidently
$$|w^2 + wz + z^2 - 2w - 2z| \le |w|^2 + |w||z| + |z|^2 + 2|w| + 2|z|$$
by repeated use of 1.11 and 1.14. Since w and z are in $[-5,2]$, we must have $|w| \le 5$ and $|z| \le 5$. Hence
(2) $$|w|^2 + |w|\,|z| + |z|^2 + 2|w| + 2|z| \le 95.$$
On combining (1) and (2), we have
$$|f(w) - f(z)| \le 95\,|w - z|.$$
If we choose w and z so that
$$95|w - z| < \epsilon,$$
then in turn we will have
$$|f(w) - f(z)| < \epsilon.$$
Hence,
$$|f(w) - f(z)| < \epsilon \quad \text{if} \quad |w - z| < \epsilon/95.$$
Thus, we may choose for p any partition of $[-5,2]$ for which the norm of p is less than $\epsilon/95$,
$$|p| < \epsilon/95.$$
For such a partition, $|w - z| < \epsilon/95$ if w and z are numbers in the same subinterval of p.

For example, if $\epsilon = .1$, we select $|p| < .1/95$, say, $|p| = .001$. Then if we take p to be a regular partition of $[-5,2]$, it will have 7,000 subintervals. We must realize that this is not necessarily the most economical way of finding p. There surely are partitions with a smaller number of subintervals. However, we are only seeking one partition p satisfying 14.1, and any one will do.

The function f has derivative
$$f'(x) = 3x^2 - 4x = x(3x - 4).$$
Therefore the critical numbers of f are 0 and $4/3$. The function f is increasing in the interval $[-5,0]$, decreasing in the interval $[0,4/3]$, and increasing in the interval $[4/3,2]$, as we see from the accompanying table.

x	-5	0	$\frac{4}{3}$	2
$f(x)$	-179	-4	$-\frac{140}{27}$	-4

Thus $f(0) = f(2) = -4$ is the maximum value and $f(-5) = -179$ is the mini-mum value of f in $[-5,2]$. Hence, using the notation of 14.3, $u = -5$ and $v = 0$ or $v = 2$.

■ ■ ■ EXERCISES

In each of the following exercises, describe a partition p of the given interval such that the conclusion of 14.1 holds for the given function and the given ϵ. Also find the numbers at which the function assumes its maximum and mini-mum values for the given interval.

1. $f(x) = x^3 - 2x^2 - 4$, $[-5,2]$, $\epsilon = .01$.
2. $g(x) = \sqrt{2} - x$, $[-2,3]$, $\epsilon > 0$.
3. $f(x) = x^2 + x + 1$, $[-1,2]$, $\epsilon = .1$.
4. $f(x) = 3x^4 + 8x^3 - 6x^2 - 24x + 12$, $[-2,2]$, $\epsilon > 0$.
5. $g(x) = \sqrt{x} + 2$, $[1,4]$, $\epsilon > 0$.
6. $f(x) = \dfrac{1}{x}$, $[-5,-2]$, $\epsilon = .1$.

7. $g(x) = \ln x$, $[1,e]$, $\epsilon > 0$.
8. $f(x) = \cos x$, $[0,\pi/2]$, $\epsilon > 0$.
(Hint: $|\cos x - \cos y| = 2 \left| \sin \dfrac{x+y}{2} \sin \dfrac{x-y}{2} \right| \le 2 \sin \dfrac{|x-y|}{2} \le |x - y|$.)

In each of the following exercises, the function is continuous in the given interval. Find numbers in the interval at which the function assumes its maximum and minimum values in that interval. Sketch the graph of the function in the given interval.

9. $f(x) = x^2 + 9$, $[-3,3]$.   10. $g(x) = -x^2 + x + 2$, $[-2,2]$.
11. $g(x) = 2x^3 - 3x^2 - 12x$, $[-2,3]$.   12. $f(x) = \sin x$, $[0,\pi]$.

13. $F(x) = \sin x + \cos x$, $[0,2\pi]$.   14. $G(x) = \ln x$, $\left[\dfrac{1}{e}, e^2 \right]$.

15. $f(x) = e^x$, $[-1,2]$.   16. $f(x) = \sin^{-1} x$, $\left[\dfrac{1}{2}, 1 \right]$.

17. $F(x) = |x|$, $[-2,3]$.   18. $g(x) = |x^2 - 1|$, $[-2,1]$.

19. Find the maximum and minimum values, whenever they exist, for the function f defined by $f(x) = \tan x$ in each of the following intervals, and discuss the continuity of f in that interval.

(a) $\left(-\dfrac{\pi}{2}, \dfrac{\pi}{2} \right)$.   (b) $\left[0, \dfrac{\pi}{2} \right]$.   (c) $\left[-\dfrac{\pi}{4}, \dfrac{\pi}{4} \right]$.   (d) $[0,\pi]$.

20. Let the function f be defined as follows:

$f(x) = x$ for every x in the open interval $(0,1)$, $f(0) = f(1) = \dfrac{1}{2}$.

(a) Is f continuous in the closed interval $[0,1]$?

(b) Is f bounded in $[0,1]$? If so, what are least upper and greatest lower bounds for f in this interval?

(c) Does f attain either a maximum or a minimum value in $[0,1]$?

21. Give an example of a function which is not continuous in the closed interval $[0,1]$ but is bounded and attains its maximum and minimum values in $[0,1]$.

22. Write out the proof that the function f of 14.3 attains its minimum value in $[a,b]$.

23. Let the function f be continuous and increasing in the closed interval $[a,b]$. For a given number $\epsilon > 0$, how would you go about finding a partition p satisfying 14.1?

24. Prove that the partition p in 14.1 can always be chosen as a regular partition.

2. Cauchy's formula

We recall that Rolle's theorem and the theorem of the mean, proved in Chapter 6, had to do with a function f continuous in a closed interval $[a,b]$.

Rolle's theorem stated that if $f(a) = f(b)$ then f has a critical number z in (a,b). Hence, if $f'(z)$ exists, necessarily $f'(z) = 0$.

The theorem of the mean stated that if f' exists in (a,b), then even if $f(a) \neq f(b)$, there exists a number z in (a,b) such that

$$f(b) - f(a) = (b - a)f'(z).$$

A useful generalization of these theorems is the following result.

14.4 Cauchy's formula.* If f and g are functions defined in the closed interval $[a,b]$ such that

(1) f and g are continuous in $[a,b]$,

(2) f' and g' exist in (a,b),

(3) $g'(x) \neq 0$ for every x in (a,b),

then there exists a number z in (a,b) such that

$$\frac{f(b) - f(a)}{g(b) - g(a)} = \frac{f'(z)}{g'(z)}.$$

Proof: Clearly $g(b) \neq g(a)$, for otherwise $g'(z) = 0$ for some z in (a,b) by Rolle's theorem, contrary to Property (3).

Let the function F be defined as follows:

$$F(x) = [f(b) - f(a)]g(x) - [g(b) - g(a)]f(x).$$

Then $F'(x)$ exists for every x in (a,b) and is given by

$$F'(x) = [f(b) - f(a)]g'(x) - [g(b) - g(a)]f'(x).$$

Also, the function F is continuous at both a and b since the functions f

*Augustin Louis Cauchy (1789–1857) was a French mathematician who had much to do with the modern rigorous development of the calculus.

and g appearing in the definition of F are continuous at a and b.   Finally, we may easily show that

$$F(a) = F(b) = f(b)g(a) - f(a)g(b).$$

The function F satisfies all the conditions of Rolle's theorem, and therefore there exists a number z in (a,b) such that $F'(z) = 0$.   Thus

$$[f(b) - f(a)]g'(z) - [g(b) - g(a)]f'(z) = 0,$$

and, since both $g(b) - g(a)$ and $g'(z)$ are unequal to zero,

$$\frac{f(b) - f(a)}{g(b) - g(a)} = \frac{f'(z)}{g'(z)}.$$

This proves Cauchy's formula.

We note that Cauchy's formula is just the mean value theorem in case

$$g(x) = x,$$

for then $g'(x) = 1$ and Cauchy's formula becomes

$$\frac{f(b) - f(a)}{b - a} = f'(z).$$

Example.   Prove that for every $x > 0$, $\dfrac{x}{x^2 + 1} < \tan^{-1} x < x$.

Proof: By Cauchy's formula (or the theorem of the mean),

$$\frac{\tan^{-1} x - 0}{x - 0} = \frac{\dfrac{1}{1 + z^2}}{1}$$

for some number z, $0 < z < x$.   Thus,

$$\tan^{-1} x = \frac{x}{1 + z^2}$$

for some z, $0 < z < x$.   Since $z > 0$, $1 + z^2 > 1$ and $x/(1 + z^2) < x$. On the other hand, $z < x$ and $z^2 < x^2$.   Hence $x/(1 + z^2) > x/(1 + x^2)$. Thus

$$\frac{x}{1 + x^2} < \tan^{-1} x < x$$

as desired.

For example, if $x = .1$, this inequality states that

$$.099 < \tan^{-1} .1 < .1.$$

■ ■ ■ EXERCISES

Use Cauchy's formula to show that there exists a number z satisfying the following conditions:

1. (a) $\dfrac{\sin x}{x} = \cos z,\ 0 < z < x.$

(b) $\dfrac{\sin x}{x} = \cos z,\ x < z < 0.$

2. (a) $\dfrac{\tan x}{x} = \sec^2 z,\ 0 < z < x < \dfrac{\pi}{2}.$

(b) $\dfrac{\tan x}{x} = \sec^2 z,\ -\dfrac{\pi}{2} < x < z < 0.$

3. (a) $\dfrac{\tan^{-1} x}{x} = \dfrac{1}{1+z^2},\ 0 < z < x.$

(b) $\dfrac{\tan^{-1} x}{x} = \dfrac{1}{1+z^2},\ x < z < 0.$

4. (a) $\dfrac{\sin b - \sin a}{b - a} = \cos z,\ 0 < a < z < b.$

(b) Use Part (a) to prove that $\sin b - \sin a < b - a$ if $0 < a < b < \dfrac{\pi}{2}.$

5. $\dfrac{\sin x - x}{x^3} = -\dfrac{1}{6}\cos z,\ 0 < z < x.$ (*Hint:* Cauchy's formula will have to

be used several times.)

6. Show that $e^x > 1 + x$ for every $x \neq 0$.

7. Show that if $x > 0$, $\dfrac{x}{x+1} < \ln(x+1) < x$. (*Hint:* Prove that

$\dfrac{\ln(x+1)}{x} = \dfrac{1}{z+1}$ for some z, $0 < z < x$.)

3. *Indeterminate forms*

If we define the function H by

$$H(x) = \dfrac{\ln(x+1)}{x},\quad x \geq -1,\quad x \neq 0,$$

then

$$H(x) = \dfrac{f(x)}{g(x)},\quad \text{where } f(x) = \ln(x+1),\quad g(x) = x.$$

We cannot evaluate

$$\lim_{x \to 0} H(x)$$

by use of the quotient limit theorem

$$\lim_{x \to 0} H(x) = \dfrac{\lim_{x \to 0} f(x)}{\lim_{x \to 0} g(x)},$$

since

$$\lim_{x \to 0} g(x) = 0.$$

However, also

$$\lim_{x \to 0} f(x) = 0,$$

and therefore

$$\underset{x \to 0}{\text{limit }} H(x)$$

still might exist. (If $\underset{x \to 0}{\text{limit }} g(x) = 0$ and $\underset{x \to 0}{\text{limit }} f(x) \neq 0$, $\underset{x \to 0}{\text{limit }} H(x)$ cannot possibly exist.) Let us show how Cauchy's formula can be used to evaluate this limit.

Since $f(0) = 0$ and $g(0) = 0$,

$$H(x) = \frac{f(x) - f(0)}{g(x) - g(0)}.$$

Therefore, by Cauchy's formula,

$$H(x) = \frac{f'(z)}{g'(z)}$$

for some number z between 0 and x. Since

$$f'(x) = \frac{1}{x + 1} \quad \text{and} \quad g'(x) = 1,$$

$$H(x) = \frac{1}{z + 1}.$$

Also, since z is between 0 and x,

$$\underset{x \to 0}{\text{limit }} z = 0.$$

It follows that

$$\underset{x \to 0}{\text{limit }} H(x) = 1,$$

that is, that

$$\underset{x \to 0}{\text{limit }} \frac{\ln (x + 1)}{x} = 1.$$

The fraction $[\ln (x + 1)]/x$ is said to have the *indeterminate form* $0/0$ at $x = 0$. The following rule allows us to investigate limits of functions possessing indeterminate forms.

14.5 L'Hospital's rule.* Let the functions f and g be differentiable at every number other than c in some interval, with $g'(x) \neq 0$ if $x \neq c$. If $\underset{x \to c}{\text{limit }} f(x) = \underset{x \to c}{\text{limit }} g(x) = 0$, or $\underset{x \to c}{\text{limit }} f(x) = \pm\infty$ and $\underset{x \to c}{\text{limit }} g(x) = \pm\infty$

then

$$\underset{x \to c}{\text{limit }} \frac{f(x)}{g(x)} = \underset{x \to c}{\text{limit }} \frac{f'(x)}{g'(x)},$$

provided this latter limit exists or is infinite.

Proof: (0/0). Assume that

$$\underset{x \to c}{\text{limit }} f(x) = \underset{x \to c}{\text{limit }} g(x) = 0.$$

* Guillaume François Marquis de l'Hospital (1661–1704) was a French mathematician who made several important contributions to the calculus in its early formative stage. He wrote the first textbook on the calculus.

if we define the functions F and G as follows,

$$F(x) = f(x) \quad \text{if} \quad x \neq c; \quad F(c) = \mathbf{0},$$

$$G(x) = g(x) \quad \text{if} \quad x \neq c; \quad G(c) = \mathbf{0},$$

then the functions F and G are continuous at c as well as being differentiable elsewhere in the given interval. Hence, by Cauchy's formula, for every $x \neq c$ in the given interval there exists a number z between x and c such that

$$\frac{F(x) - F(c)}{G(x) - G(c)} = \frac{F'(z)}{G'(z)}.$$

Since $F(c) = G(c) = 0$ and $F(x) = f(x)$, $G(x) = g(x)$, $F'(x) = f'(x)$, $G'(x) = g'(x)$ if $x \neq c$, we have shown that

$$\frac{f(x)}{g(x)} = \frac{f'(z)}{g'(z)}$$

for some number z between c and x. If

$$\lim_{x \to c} \frac{f'(x)}{g'(x)} = L,$$

then also

$$\lim_{x \to c} \frac{f'(z)}{g'(z)} = L,$$

since for each x the corresponding number z is between c and x. Thus

$$\lim_{x \to c} \frac{f(x)}{g(x)} = \lim_{x \to c} \frac{f'(z)}{g'(z)} = L,$$

and l'Hospital's rule is proved.

If

$$\lim_{x \to c} \frac{f'(x)}{g'(x)} = \infty \quad (\text{or} -\infty),$$

then, by the same reasoning as above,

$$\lim_{x \to c} \frac{f(x)}{g(x)} = \infty \quad (\text{or} -\infty).$$

This shows that l'Hospital's rule holds for infinite limits also.

We will not offer a proof here of the more difficult case (∞/∞) when

$$\lim_{x \to c} f(x) = \pm\infty \quad \text{and} \quad \lim_{x \to c} g(x) = \pm\infty.$$

This may be found in many books on advanced calculus.*

Example 1. Find $\lim\limits_{x \to \pi} \dfrac{\sin x}{x - \pi}$.

Solution: Since

$$\lim_{x \to \pi} \sin x = \lim_{x \to \pi} (x - \pi) = 0,$$

* For example, see P. Franklin, *A Treatise on Advanced Calculus*, Wiley, 1940, p. 132.

we apply l'Hospital's rule to obtain

$$\operatorname*{limit}_{x\to\pi} \frac{\sin x}{x - \pi} = \operatorname*{limit}_{x\to\pi} \frac{\cos x}{1} = -1.$$

Example 2. Find $\operatorname*{limit}_{x\to 0^+} \frac{\ln x}{1/x}$.

Solution: Since

$$\operatorname*{limit}_{x\to 0^+} \ln x = -\infty \quad \text{and} \quad \operatorname*{limit}_{x\to 0^+} \frac{1}{x} = \infty,$$

we may apply l'Hospital's rule **to get**

$$\operatorname*{limit}_{x\to 0^+} \frac{\ln x}{1/x} = \operatorname*{limit}_{x\to 0^+} \frac{1/x}{-1/x^2} = \operatorname*{limit}_{x\to 0^+} (-x) = 0.$$

The fraction $(1/x)/-(1/x^2)$ also is an indeterminate form (∞/∞), but we have chosen to reduce the fraction algebraically rather than to employ l'Hospital's rule, which, as is easily seen, would lead us to no conclusion.

In the following example, we see that l'Hospital's rule may profitably be applied more than once in certain instances.

Example 3. Find $\operatorname*{limit}_{x\to 0} \frac{\sin x - x}{x^3}$.

Solution: We may use l'Hospital's rule, since

$$\operatorname*{limit}_{x\to 0} (\sin x - x) = \operatorname*{limit}_{x\to 0} x^3 = 0.$$

Hence

$$\operatorname*{limit}_{x\to 0} \frac{\sin x - x}{x^3} = \operatorname*{limit}_{x\to 0} \frac{\cos x - 1}{3x^2},$$

if the latter limit exists.
  Since

$$\operatorname*{limit}_{x\to 0} (\cos x - 1) = \operatorname*{limit}_{x\to 0} 3x^2 = 0,$$

we may again use l'Hospital's rule to obtain

$$\operatorname*{limit}_{x\to 0} \frac{\cos x - 1}{3x^2} = \operatorname*{limit}_{x\to 0} \frac{-\sin x}{6x}.$$

The fraction $-\sin x/6x$ still is indeterminate $(0/0)$, so we reapply the rule to get finally

$$\operatorname*{limit}_{x\to 0} \frac{-\sin x}{6x} = \operatorname*{limit}_{x\to 0} \frac{-\cos x}{6} = -\frac{1}{6}.$$

We might equally well have recalled in the final step that $\operatorname*{limit}_{x\to 0} \sin x/x = 1$ by 10.32. Thus

$$\operatorname*{limit}_{x\to 0} \frac{\sin x - x}{x^3} = -\frac{1}{6}.$$

As indicated in Example 2, l'Hospital's rule applies equally well to the evaluation of one-sided limits such as

$$\operatorname*{limit}_{x\to c^+} \frac{f(x)}{g(x)} \quad \text{and} \quad \operatorname*{limit}_{x\to c^-} \frac{f(x)}{g(x)}.$$

Example 4. Find $\displaystyle\lim_{\theta\to\pi/2^-}\frac{\sec\theta}{\tan\theta}$.

Solution: This is an ∞/∞ form to which we apply l'Hospital's rule as follows.

$$\lim_{\theta\to\pi/2^-}\frac{\sec\theta}{\tan\theta}=\lim_{\theta\to\pi/2^-}\frac{\sec\theta\tan\theta}{\sec^2\theta}=\lim_{\theta\to\pi/2^-}\frac{\tan\theta}{\sec\theta}.$$

Reapplying the rule, we get

$$\lim_{\theta\to\pi/2^-}\frac{\tan\theta}{\sec\theta}=\lim_{\theta\to\pi/2^-}\frac{\sec\theta}{\tan\theta}.$$

Clearly l'Hospital's rule gives us no information in this example. However, since $\sec\theta/\tan\theta=1/\sin\theta$,

$$\lim_{\theta\to\pi/2^-}\frac{\sec\theta}{\tan\theta}=\lim_{\theta\to\pi/2^-}\frac{1}{\sin\theta}=1.$$

■ ■ ■ EXERCISES

Evaluate, if possible, each of the following limits:

1. $\displaystyle\lim_{x\to0}\frac{\tan x}{x}$.

2. $\displaystyle\lim_{x\to2}\frac{x^2-4}{x-2}$.

3. $\displaystyle\lim_{x\to0}\frac{e^x-1}{x}$.

4. $\displaystyle\lim_{y\to0}\frac{\tan^{-1}y}{y}$.

5. $\displaystyle\lim_{t\to0}\frac{\sqrt{1+t}-\sqrt{1-t}}{t}$.

6. $\displaystyle\lim_{z\to\pi}\frac{\ln\cos 2z}{(\pi-z)^2}$.

7. $\displaystyle\lim_{\theta\to\pi/2}\frac{\ln\left|\theta-\frac{\pi}{2}\right|}{\tan\theta}$.

8. $\displaystyle\lim_{x\to0}\frac{\tan x-x}{x-\sin x}$.

9. $\displaystyle\lim_{x\to0}\frac{e^x-2\cos x+e^{-x}}{x\sin x}$.

10. $\displaystyle\lim_{x\to0}\frac{1-\cos x}{x^2}$.

11. $\displaystyle\lim_{x\to-1}\frac{\ln|x|}{x+1}$.

12. $\displaystyle\lim_{t\to0}\frac{t\sin t}{1-\cos t}$.

13. $\displaystyle\lim_{\theta\to\pi/2}\frac{\ln|\sin\theta|}{\cot\theta}$.

14. $\displaystyle\lim_{y\to0}\frac{\tan^{-1}y-y}{y^3}$.

15. $\displaystyle\lim_{y\to0}\frac{\sin^{-1}y-y}{y^3}$.

16. $\displaystyle\lim_{x\to0}\frac{\sin^{-1}x}{\sin^{-1}3x}$.

17. $\displaystyle\lim_{\theta\to\pi/2}\frac{\sec^2 3x}{\sec^2 x}$.

18. $\displaystyle\lim_{x\to0}\frac{e^x-2+e^{-x}}{1-\cos 2x}$.

19. $\displaystyle\lim_{x\to0}\frac{\cot 3x}{\cot 2x}$.

20. $\displaystyle\lim_{u\to0}\frac{\tan 2u}{u\sec u}$.

21. $\displaystyle\lim_{x\to0}\frac{10^x-e^x}{x}$.

22. $\displaystyle\lim_{x\to0}\frac{x-\tan^{-1}x}{\sin^{-1}x-x}$.

4. Further indeterminate forms

L'Hospital's rule may be used in the evaluation of limits of the form

$$\lim_{x \to \infty} \frac{f(x)}{g(x)},$$

as we shall now prove.

14.6 L'Hospital's second rule. Let the functions f and g be differentiable at every x greater than some number a, with $g'(x) \neq 0$. If $\lim_{x \to \infty} f(x) = \lim_{x \to \infty} g(x) = 0$, or $\lim_{x \to \infty} f(x) = \pm \infty$ and $\lim_{x \to \infty} g(x) = \pm \infty$,

then

$$\lim_{x \to \infty} \frac{f(x)}{g(x)} = \lim_{x \to \infty} \frac{f'(x)}{g'(x)},$$

provided this latter limit exists or is infinite.

Proof: We shall prove the (0/0) case and omit the proof of the other one. So let us assume that

$$\lim_{x \to \infty} f(x) = \lim_{x \to \infty} g(x) = 0.$$

If we let $x = 1/y$, then

$$\lim_{x \to \infty} \frac{f(x)}{g(x)} = \lim_{y \to 0^+} \frac{f(1/y)}{g(1/y)}.$$

Since

$$D_y f\left(\frac{1}{y}\right) = f'\left(\frac{1}{y}\right) D_y \left(\frac{1}{y}\right) = -\frac{f'(1/y)}{y^2}$$

and similarly for $D_y g\left(\frac{1}{y}\right)$, we may apply the first l'Hospital rule to obtain

$$\lim_{y \to 0^+} \frac{f(1/y)}{g(1/y)} = \lim_{y \to 0^+} \frac{\dfrac{f'(1/y)}{y^2}}{\dfrac{g'(1/y)}{y^2}} = \lim_{y \to 0^+} \frac{f'(1/y)}{g'(1/y)} = \lim_{x \to \infty} \frac{f'(x)}{g'(x)}.$$

This proves 14.6.

Rule 14.6 also applies to the evaluation of

$$\lim_{x \to -\infty} \frac{f(x)}{g(x)}.$$

Example 1. Find $\lim_{x \to \infty} \dfrac{\ln x}{x}$.

Solution: This limit is indeterminate of the form ∞ / ∞. Thus we may use 14.6 to obtain

$$\lim_{x \to \infty} \frac{\ln x}{x} = \lim_{x \to \infty} \frac{1/x}{1} = 0.$$

If

$$\lim_{x \to a} f(x) = 0 \quad \text{and} \quad \lim_{x \to a} g(x) = \pm \infty,$$

then $f(x)g(x)$ is indeterminate of the form $0 \cdot \infty$. We change it to either the form $(0/0)$ or (∞/∞) as follows:

$$\operatorname*{limit}_{x \to a} f(x)g(x) = \operatorname*{limit}_{x \to a} \frac{f(x)}{1/g(x)} = \operatorname*{limit}_{x \to a} \frac{g(x)}{1/f(x)}.$$

L'Hospital's rule is applicable to these latter two limits. For example,

$$\operatorname*{limit}_{x \to 0^+} x \ln x = \operatorname*{limit}_{x \to 0^+} \frac{\ln x}{1/x} = 0$$

by Example 2 of the previous section.

Other indeterminate forms are encountered in evaluating limits of the form

$$\operatorname*{limit} [f(x)]^{g(x)}.$$

If $\operatorname*{limit} f(x) = \operatorname*{limit} g(x) = 0$, we have the 0^0 form; other forms are 1^∞ and ∞^0. Each of these types is attacked by writing

$$[f(x)]^{g(x)} = e^{g(x) \ln f(x)}.$$

By the continuity of the exponential function (and 4.20), we have that

$$\operatorname*{limit}_{x \to a} e^{g(x) \ln f(x)} = e^{\operatorname*{limit}_{x \to a} g(x) \ln f(x)}$$

Thus we have only to evaluate

$$\operatorname*{limit}_{x \to a} g(x) \ln f(x)$$

in order to find the desired limit.

Example 2. Find $\operatorname*{limit}_{x \to 0^+} x^x$.

Solution: This 0^0 indeterminate form is evaluated as follows:

$$\operatorname*{limit}_{x \to 0^+} x^x = \operatorname*{limit}_{x \to 0^+} e^{x \ln x}$$

$$= e^{\operatorname*{limit}_{x \to 0^+} x \ln x} = e^0 = 1.$$

Example 3. Find $\operatorname*{limit}_{h \to 0^+} (1 + ah)^{1/h}$.

Solution: Since $1 + ah$ has limit 1 and $1/h$ has limit ∞ as h approaches 0^+, we have the indeterminate form 1^∞. We evaluate this limit as follows:

$$\operatorname*{limit}_{h \to 0^+} (1 + ah)^{1/h} = \operatorname*{limit}_{h \to 0^+} e^{(1/h) \ln (1+ah)} = e^{\operatorname*{limit}_{h \to 0^+} [\ln (1+ah)]/h}$$

By l'Hospital's rule,

$$\operatorname*{limit}_{h \to 0^+} \frac{\ln (1 + ah)}{h} = \operatorname*{limit}_{h \to 0^+} [a/(1 + ah)]/1 = a.$$

Hence $$\operatorname*{limit}_{h \to 0^+} (1 + ah)^{1/h} = e^a.$$

Example 4. Sketch the graph of the function f defined by

$$f(x) = x \ln x.$$

Solution: The domain of f is the set of positive real numbers. Since
$$\lim_{x \to 0^+} x \ln x = 0,$$
the graph approaches the origin when x approaches zero. Now
$$f'(x) = 1 + \ln x,$$
and $f'(x) = 0$ if and only if $\ln x = -1$. Thus $e^{-1} = 1/e$ is the only critical number of f. Since $f''(x) = 1/x$, $f''(1/e) > 0$, and the point $(1/e, -1/e)$ is a minimum point on the graph. Clearly $f(1) = 0$. The graph is sketched in Figure 14.1.

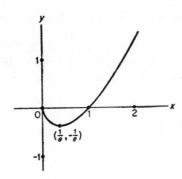

Figure 14.1

■ ■ ■ EXERCISES

Evaluate, if possible, each of the following limits:

1. $\displaystyle \lim_{x \to \infty} x e^{-x}$.

2. $\displaystyle \lim_{x \to \infty} \frac{\ln x}{\sqrt{x}}$.

3. $\displaystyle \lim_{x \to \infty} \frac{x^n}{e^x}$, n a positive integer.

4. $\displaystyle \lim_{x \to -\infty} x^2 e^x$.

5. $\displaystyle \lim_{x \to \infty} \frac{\ln x}{x^a}$, $a > 0$.

6. $\displaystyle \lim_{x \to 0^+} \left(1 + \frac{1}{x} \right)^x$.

7. $\displaystyle \lim_{x \to 0} (1 - x)^{1/x}$.

8. $\displaystyle \lim_{x \to \infty} x^{1/x}$.

9. $\displaystyle \lim_{x \to 0^+} \left(\frac{1}{\sin x} - \frac{1}{x} \right)$.

10. $\displaystyle \lim_{x \to \pi/2} (\sec x - \tan x)$.

11. $\displaystyle \lim_{x \to \pi/2} (\sin x)^{\tan x}$.

12. $\displaystyle \lim_{x \to 0} (1 + 2 \sin x)^{\cot x}$.

13. $\displaystyle \lim_{x \to 0} (x + e^{2x})^{1/x}$.

14. $\displaystyle \lim_{x \to 0^+} (\sin x)^x$.

15. $\displaystyle \lim_{x \to 0^+} x^{\sin x}$.

16. $\displaystyle \lim_{x \to 0} \left(\frac{1}{x} - \frac{1}{\tan x} \right)$.

17. $\displaystyle \lim_{x \to 0^+} x^{a/\ln x}$.

18. $\displaystyle \lim_{x \to 1} x^{1/(1-x)}$.

19. If $a > 0$, prove that there exists a number N_a such that $\ln x < x^a$ for every $x > N_a$.

20. If $a > 1$ and n is a positive integer, prove that there exists a number N such that $x^n < a^x$ for every $x > N$.

5. Improper integrals

If

$$f(x) = xe^{-x},$$

then

$$\text{limit}_{x \to \infty} f(x) = \text{limit}_{x \to \infty} \frac{x}{e^x} = \text{limit}_{x \to \infty} \frac{1}{e^x} = 0.$$

The part of the graph of f in the first quadrant is sketched in Figure 14.2.

The region R between the graph of f and the positive x-axis is a region of infinite extent. Let us show how we can assign a finite area to this region.

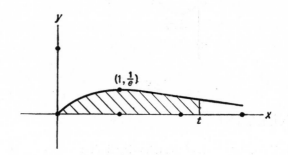

Figure 14.2

Consider the area $A(t)$ of the shaded region under the graph of f between 0 and t; clearly

$$A(t) = \int_0^t xe^{-x}\, dx = (-xe^{-x} - e^{-x})\Big|_0^t$$

$$= -te^{-t} - e^{-t} + 1.$$

Now

$$\text{limit}_{t \to \infty} A(t) = \text{limit}_{t \to \infty}\left(-\frac{t}{e^t} - \frac{1}{e^t} + 1\right) = 1.$$

Hence we assign to the region R the area 1.

It is convenient to introduce the following definitions.

14.7 $$\int_a^\infty f(x)\, dx = \text{limit}_{t \to \infty} \int_a^t f(x)\, dx \quad \text{if this limit exists.}$$

14.8 $$\int_{-\infty}^a f(x)\, dx = \text{limit}_{t \to -\infty} \int_t^a f(x)\, dx \quad \text{if this limit exists.}$$

Thus the area of the region R above is given by

$$\int_0^\infty xe^{-x}\,dx = \lim_{t\to\infty}\int_0^t xe^{-x}\,dx.$$

The integrals defined in 14.7 and 14.8 are called *improper integrals*. They differ from ordinary definite integrals in that they have infinite limits of integration.

Example 1. The graph of the function f defined by

$$f(x) = \frac{1}{x}$$

is sketched in the first quadrant in Figure 14.3. Can an area be assigned to

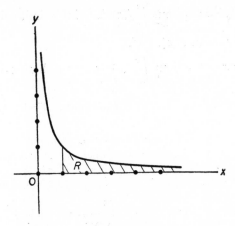

Figure 14.3

the shaded region R? If the region R is rotated about the x-axis, can a volume be assigned to the solid so formed?

Solution: If R is to have an area consistent with the area of a finite region, it must be given by

$$\int_1^\infty \frac{1}{x}\,dx.$$

However,

$$\int_1^\infty \frac{1}{x}\,dx = \lim_{t\to\infty}\int_1^t \frac{1}{x}\,dx = \lim_{t\to\infty}\ln t = \infty.$$

Thus R does not have a finite area.

The volume of the solid obtained by rotating R about the x-axis must be given by

$$\pi \int_1^\infty \frac{1}{x^2}\,dx.$$

Since

$$\int_1^\infty \frac{1}{x^2}\,dx = \underset{t\to\infty}{\text{limit}}\int_1^t \frac{1}{x^2}\,dx$$

$$= \underset{t\to\infty}{\text{limit}}\left(-\frac{1}{t}+1\right) = 1,$$

the volume assigned to this solid is π.

If the function f is continuous at every number x such that $a \le x < b$ but f is discontinuous at b, the definition of the definite integral of f from a to b given in Chapter 8 does not apply. This leads to the second type of an *improper integral*, as defined below.

14.9 Definition. (1) If the function f is continuous in the half-open interval $[a,b)$, then

$$\int_a^b f(x)\,dx = \underset{t\to b^-}{\text{limit}}\int_a^t f(x)\,dx \quad \text{if this limit exists.}$$

(2) If f is continuous in $(a,b]$, then

$$\int_a^b f(x)\,dx = \underset{t\to a^+}{\text{limit}}\int_t^b f(x)\,dx \quad \text{if this limit exists.}$$

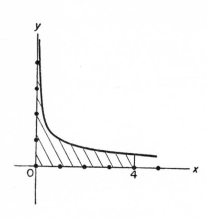

Figure 14.4

Example 2. Find $\displaystyle\int_0^4 \frac{1}{\sqrt{x}}\,dx$.

Solution: Since $1/\sqrt{0}$ does not exist, whereas the integrand is continuous if $x \ne 0$, this is an improper integral of type 14.9, (2). Hence

$$\int_0^4 \frac{1}{\sqrt{x}}\,dx = \underset{t\to 0^+}{\text{limit}}\int_t^4 x^{-1/2}\,dx$$

$$= \underset{t\to 0^+}{\text{limit}}\ 2x^{1/2}\Big|_t^4 = \underset{t\to 0^+}{\text{limit}}\ (4 - 2\sqrt{t}) = 4.$$

Geometrically, we have shown that the shaded region of Figure 14.4, a region of infinite extent, has a finite area of 4 square units.

Example 3. Find $\displaystyle\int_1^0 x\ln x\,dx$. (This is the area of the region bounded by the graph of $y = x\ln x$ and the x-axis sketched in Figure 14.1.)

Solution: The integrand has a discontinuity at 0 since $\ln 0$ does not exist. Hence

$$\int_1^0 x\ln x\,dx = \underset{t\to 0^+}{\text{limit}}\int_1^t x\ln x\,dx$$

$$= \underset{t\to 0^+}{\text{limit}}\ \frac{1}{4}\,(2x^2\ln x - x^2)\Big|_1^t$$

$$= \underset{t\to 0^+}{\text{limit}}\ \frac{1}{4}\,(2t^2\ln t - t^2 + 1).$$

By l'Hospital's rule,

$$\underset{t \to 0^+}{\text{limit}}\; t^2 \ln t = \underset{t \to 0^+}{\text{limit}}\; \frac{\ln t}{1/t^2}$$

$$= \underset{t \to 0^+}{\text{limit}}\; \frac{1/t}{-2/t^3} = \underset{t \to 0^+}{\text{limit}}\left(-\frac{t^2}{2}\right) = 0.$$

Thus

$$\underset{t \to 0^+}{\text{limit}}\; \frac{1}{4}\,(2t^2 \ln t - t^2 + 1) = \frac{1}{4},$$

and

$$\int_1^0 x \ln x\, dx = \frac{1}{4}.$$

■ ■ ■ EXERCISES

Find the value of each of the following improper integrals, if it exists:

1. $\displaystyle\int_1^\infty \frac{1}{x\sqrt{x}}\, dx.$

2. $\displaystyle\int_{-\infty}^4 \frac{1}{(5-x)^2}\, dx.$

3. $\displaystyle\int_{-\infty}^3 \frac{1}{\sqrt{7-x}}\, dx.$

4. $\displaystyle\int_0^\infty \frac{x}{1+x^2}\, dx.$

5. $\displaystyle\int_3^4 \frac{1}{\sqrt{x-3}}\, dx.$

6. $\displaystyle\int_{-2}^0 \frac{1}{\sqrt{4-x^2}}\, dx.$

7. $\displaystyle\int_0^\infty \frac{1}{\sqrt{e^x}}\, dx.$

8. $\displaystyle\int_0^\infty e^{-ax}\, dx,\; a > 0.$

9. $\displaystyle\int_0^1 \frac{1}{\sqrt[3]{x}}\, dx.$

10. $\displaystyle\int_0^4 \frac{1}{x\sqrt{x}}\, dx.$

11. $\displaystyle\int_1^\infty \frac{1}{1+x^2}\, dx.$

12. $\displaystyle\int_3^\infty \frac{1}{x^2 - 2x}\, dx.$

13. $\displaystyle\int_{\pi/4}^{\pi/2} \sec x\, dx.$

14. $\displaystyle\int_0^{\pi/2} \frac{1}{1 - \sin x}\, dx.$

15. $\displaystyle\int_{-1}^\infty \frac{x}{e^{x^2}}\, dx.$

16. $\displaystyle\int_2^\infty \frac{1}{x^2 - 1}\, dx.$

17. If f is continuous at each real number x, define

(1) $$\int_{-\infty}^\infty f(x)\, dx = \int_{-\infty}^0 f(x)\, dx + \int_0^\infty f(x)\, dx$$

provided each integral on the right side of (1) exists.

(a) Show that if the integral (1) exists, then

$$\int_{-\infty}^\infty f(x)\, dx = \int_{-\infty}^a f(x)\, dx + \int_a^\infty f(x)\, dx$$

for every real number a.

(b) Show by example that $\lim\limits_{t\to\infty} \int_{-t}^{t} f(x)\,dx$ can exist even though $\int_{-\infty}^{\infty} f(x)\,dx$ does not exist.

Find:

18. $\displaystyle\int_{-\infty}^{\infty} \frac{1}{1+x^2}\,dx.$ 19. $\displaystyle\int_{-\infty}^{\infty} \frac{1}{e^x + e^{-x}}\,dx.$

20. If f is continuous at each number in the closed interval $[a,b]$ except c, $a < c < b$, then define

(1) $\qquad \displaystyle\int_a^b f(x)\,dx = \int_a^c f(x)\,dx + \int_c^b f(x)\,dx$

provided each integral on the right side of (1) exists.

(a) Does

$$\int_a^b f(x)\,dx = \lim_{\epsilon\to 0^+}\left[\int_a^{c-\epsilon} f(x)\,dx + \int_{c+\epsilon}^b f(x)\,dx\right]?$$

(b) What is wrong with the reasoning,

$$\int_{-1}^{1}\frac{1}{x}\,dx = \ln|x|\,\Big|_{-1}^{1} = \ln 1 - \ln 1 = 0?$$

Find:

21. $\displaystyle\int_{-2}^{1}\frac{1}{\sqrt[3]{x^2}}\,dx.$ 22. $\displaystyle\int_0^4 \frac{1}{(x-2)^2}\,dx.$

23. Show that $\displaystyle\int_0^1 \frac{1}{\sqrt[3]{x^2}}\,dx$ exists but that $\displaystyle\int_0^1 \frac{1}{\sqrt[3]{x^4}}\,dx$ does not, and interpret the results geometrically.

24. Show that

$$\int_0^4 \frac{1}{(x+4)\sqrt{x}}\,dx = \frac{\pi}{4}, \qquad \int_4^\infty \frac{1}{(x+4)\sqrt{x}}\,dx = \frac{\pi}{4}.$$

Hence find $\displaystyle\int_0^\infty \frac{1}{(x+4)\sqrt{x}}\,dx.$

Find:

25. $\displaystyle\int_1^\infty \frac{\ln x}{x^2}\,dx.$ 26. $\displaystyle\int_0^{\pi/2}\left(\frac{1}{x^2} - \csc x \cot x\right)dx.$

27. $\displaystyle\int_0^{\pi/2}(\sec x \tan x - \sec^2 x)\,dx.$ 28. $\displaystyle\int_0^e x^2 \ln x\,dx.$

6. Taylor's formula

Let f be a function for which the nth derivative $f^{[n]}$ exists at some number c. The polynomial*

* $n!$, read "n factorial," equals $n(n-1)(n-2)\cdots 1$.

14.10 $P_n(x) = f(c) + f'(c)(x - c) + \dfrac{f''(c)}{2!}(x - c)^2 + \cdots$

$$+ \dfrac{f^{[n]}(c)}{n!}(x - c)^n,$$

of degree n in x, is called the nth degree *Taylor's** *polynomial* of f at c.
Using the Σ notation, with $0! = 1$ and $f^{[0]} = f$,

$$P_n(x) = \sum_{k=0}^{n} \dfrac{f^{[k]}(c)}{k!}(x - c)^k.$$

Since

$$D_x \dfrac{f^{[k]}(c)}{k!}(x - c)^k = \dfrac{kf^{[k]}(c)}{k!}(x - c)^{k-1} = \dfrac{f^{[k]}(c)}{(k-1)!}(x - c)^{k-1},$$

evidently

$$P'_n(x) = \sum_{k=1}^{n} \dfrac{f^{[k]}(c)}{(k-1)!}(x - c)^{k-1},$$

and, in general,

14.11 $P_n{}^{[j]}(x) = \displaystyle\sum_{k=j}^{n} \dfrac{f^{[k]}(c)}{(k-j)!}(x - c)^{k-j}, \quad 0 \le j \le n.$

Since $P_n(x)$ is a polynomial of degree n [or less if $f^{[n]}(c) = 0$], clearly

$$P_n{}^{[j]}(x) = 0, \quad j > n.$$

If we replace x by c in 14.10, each term becomes zero with the exception
of the first one; thus

$$P_n(c) = f(c).$$

Similarly, each term of the right side of 14.11 after the first one becomes
zero if we replace x by c; that is,

14.12 $P_n{}^{[j]}(c) = f^{[j]}(c), \quad 0 \le j \le n.$

Thus, not only does the Taylor's polynomial $P_n(x)$ have the same value
as f at c, but also each derivative of P_n through the nth has the same value
as the corresponding derivative of f at c.

Example 1.   Find the fourth-degree Taylor's polynomial of the sine function
at $\pi/2$.

Solution: If $f(x) = \sin x$, then by 14.10,

$$P_4(x) = f\left(\dfrac{\pi}{2}\right) + f'\left(\dfrac{\pi}{2}\right)\left(x - \dfrac{\pi}{2}\right) + \dfrac{f''(\pi/2)}{2}\left(x - \dfrac{\pi}{2}\right)^2$$

$$+ \dfrac{f'''(\pi/2)}{3!}\left(x - \dfrac{\pi}{2}\right)^3 + \dfrac{f^{[4]}(\pi/2)}{4!}\left(x - \dfrac{\pi}{2}\right)^4.$$

---

* Brook Taylor (1685–1731) gave methods of expanding a function in a series in his
book *Methodus Incrementorum Directa et Inversa*, published in 1715.   His methods were
made mathematically rigorous a century later, notably by Gauss and Cauchy.

Since

$$f(x) = \sin x, f\left(\frac{\pi}{2}\right) = 1,$$

$$f'(x) = \cos x, f'\left(\frac{\pi}{2}\right) = 0,$$

$$f''(x) = -\sin x, f''\left(\frac{\pi}{2}\right) = -1,$$

$$f'''(x) = -\cos x, f'''\left(\frac{\pi}{2}\right) = 0,$$

$$f^{[4]}(x) = \sin x, f^{[4]}\left(\frac{\pi}{2}\right) = 1,$$

we obtain

$$P_4(x) = 1 - \frac{1}{2}\left(x - \frac{\pi}{2}\right)^2 + \frac{1}{24}\left(x - \frac{\pi}{2}\right)^4.$$

We come now to the fundamental Taylor's formula, relating a function to its Taylor's polynomials.

14.13 Taylor's formula. Let f be a function and n be an integer such that $f^{[n+1]}(x)$ exists for every number x in a closed interval $[a,b]$ containing the number c. Then if $P_n(x)$ is the nth degree Taylor's polynomial of f at c, there exists some number z (depending on x) between x and c such that

$$f(x) = P_n(x) + \frac{f^{[n+1]}(z)}{(n+1)!}(x - c)^{n+1}, \quad a \le x \le b.$$

Proof: We shall consider x a constant, distinct from c, in our arguments to follow. Define the functions F and G by

$$F(t) = f(x) - \sum_{k=0}^{n} \frac{f^{[k]}(t)}{k!}(x - t)^k, \quad a \le t \le b,$$

$$G(t) = (x - t)^{n+1}.$$

It is evident that

(1) $F(c) = f(x) - P_n(x),$ $F(x) = f(x) - f(x) = 0.$

While $F(t)$ is a sum of $n + 2$ terms, the derivative of F is very simply given by

(2) $F'(t) = -\frac{f^{[n+1]}(t)}{n!}(x - t)^n.$

To prove (2), we note that each term of the summation in F involves a product of two functions. Thus [since $D_t f(x) = 0$]

$$F'(t) = -\sum_{k=0}^{n} \frac{f^{[k+1]}(t)}{k!}(x - t)^k - \sum_{k=0}^{n} \frac{f^{[k]}(t)}{k!}k(x - t)^{k-1}(-1).$$

The limits of summation can always be changed as follows:

$$\sum_{k=0}^{n} a_k = \sum_{k=1}^{n+1} a_{k-1}.$$

Making such a change in the first summation of $F'(t)$, we have

$$(3) \qquad F'(t) = -\sum_{k=1}^{n+1} \frac{f^{[k]}(t)}{(k-1)!} (x-t)^{k-1} + \sum_{k=1}^{n} \frac{f^{[k]}(t)}{(k-1)!} (x-t)^{k-1}.$$

The lower limit of the second summation was made 1, since the term for $k = 0$ is zero. The two summations in (3) are identical except that the first summation has one more term for $k = n + 1$. Thus, all the terms cancel except for the last term of the first summation. This proves (2).

Let us now use Cauchy's formula with the functions F and G. Thus

$$\frac{F(c) - F(x)}{G(c) - G(x)} = \frac{F'(z)}{G'(z)}$$

for some number z between c and x according to Cauchy's formula. Since $G'(t) = -(n+1)(x-t)^n$ and $G(x) = 0$, we have by (1) and (2) that

$$\frac{f(x) - P_n(x)}{(x-c)^{n+1}} = \frac{\frac{f^{[n+1]}(z)}{n!}(x-z)^n}{-(n+1)(x-z)^n} = \frac{f^{[n+1]}(z)}{(n+1)!},$$

and

$$f(x) = P_n(x) + \frac{f^{[n+1]}(z)}{(n+1)!}(x-c)^{n+1}.$$

This proves Taylor's formula.

The term

14.14 $$R_n(x) = \frac{f^{[n+1]}(z)}{(n+1)!}(x-c)^{n+1}$$

appearing in Taylor's formula is called the nth *remainder term* of f at c. Using 14.14, Taylor's formula may be written in the form

$$f(x) = P_n(x) + R_n(x).$$

We shall soon show that under certain conditions the remainder term is very small, and hence

$$f(x) \doteq P_n(x).$$

Example 2. Write Taylor's formula for the sine function of Example 1.

Solution: Since $f^{[5]}(x) = \cos x$, we have

$$R_4(x) = \frac{f^{[5]}(z)}{5!}\left(x - \frac{\pi}{2}\right)^5 = \frac{\cos z}{120}\left(x - \frac{\pi}{2}\right)^5.$$

Hence, using P_4 from Example 1,

$$\sin x = 1 - \frac{1}{2}\left(x - \frac{\pi}{2}\right)^2 + \frac{1}{24}\left(x - \frac{\pi}{2}\right)^4 + \frac{\cos z}{120}\left(x - \frac{\pi}{2}\right)^5,$$

for some number z between x and $\pi/2$.

If $c = 0$, Taylor's formula becomes

14.15 $f(x) = f(0) + f'(0)x + \dfrac{f''(0)}{2!} x^2 + \cdots + \dfrac{f^{[n]}(0)}{n!} x^n$

$$+ \dfrac{f^{[n+1]}(z)}{(n+1)!} x^{n+1},$$

with z a number between 0 and x.   This special case of Taylor's formula is called *Maclaurin's formula.**

Example 3.   Write Maclaurin's formula for the exponential function.

Solution: If $f(x) = e^x$, then $f^{[k]}(x) = e^x$ for each k and therefore $f^{[k]}(0) = e^0 = 1$. Thus Maclaurin's formula becomes

$$e^x = 1 + x + \frac{x^2}{2!} + \frac{x^3}{3!} + \cdots + \frac{x^n}{n!} + \frac{e^z}{(n+1)!} x^{n+1},$$

with z a number between 0 and x.

■ ■ ■ EXERCISES

In each of the following exercises, find $P_n(x)$, $R_n(x)$, and write the Taylor's formula for the given function, value of n, and value of c.

1. $f(x) = \cos x,\ n = 5,\ c = \dfrac{\pi}{2}.$

2. $g(x) = \ln x,\ n = 5,\ c = 1.$

3. $F(x) = \tan^{-1} x,\ n = 3,\ c = 1.$

4. $G(x) = e^x,\ n = 4,\ c = -1.$

5. $f(x) = \sec x,\ n = 3,\ c = \dfrac{\pi}{4}.$

6. $h(x) = \dfrac{1}{x+1},\ n = 6,\ c = -2.$

In each of the following exercises, write the Maclaurin's formula for the given function and value of n.

7. $f(x) = \sin x,\ n = 6.$ **8.** $f(x) = \cos x,\ n = 5.$

9. $g(x) = \ln (x + 1),\ n = 5.$ **10.** $F(x) = \tan^{-1} x,\ n = 4.$

11. $F(x) = \sin^{-1} x,\ n = 3.$ **12.** $g(x) = \sqrt{1 + x},\ n = 5.$

13. $f(x) = \dfrac{1}{\sqrt{1 - x}},\ n = 4.$ **14.** $f(x) = e^{-x},\ n = 5.$

15. $g(x) = \tan x,\ n = 4.$ **16.** $g(x) = \dfrac{1}{(1 - x)^2},\ n = 4.$

17. $F(x) = \dfrac{1}{1 + e^x},\ n = 3.$ **18.** $g(x) = x^5,\ n = 6.$

---

* Colin Maclaurin (1698–1746), a Scotch mathematician and contemporary of Taylor's, gave this formula in his *Treatise of Fluxions* in 1742.   However, this formula had appeared 25 years earlier in a publication by Stirling.

19. Show that if $f(x)$ is a polynomial in x of degree n, then $f(x) = P_n(x)$, the Taylor's polynomial of f at a number c.

20. Write down the general Maclaurin's formula for $\ln (1 - x)$ and for $\ln (1 + x)$.

21. The nth derivative test for extrema of a function may be stated as follows. Let c be a critical number of the function f such that

$$f'(c) = 0, \quad f''(c) = 0, \quad \ldots, \quad f^{[n-1]}(c) = 0, \quad f^{[n]}(c) \neq 0.$$

Assume that $f^{[n]}$ exists in some interval containing c and that $f^{[n]}$ is continuous at c. Then

(a) $f(c)$ is a maximum value of f if n is even and $f^{[n]}(c) < 0$;

(b) $f(c)$ is a minimum value of f if n is even and $f^{[n]}(c) > 0$;

(c) $f(c)$ is not an extrema of f if n is odd.

Prove this test. (*Hint:* $f(x) - P_{n-1}(x) = f(x) - f(c) = R_{n-1}(x)$. Since $f^{[n]}$ is continuous at c, we can choose an interval containing c such that $f^{[n]}$ has the same sign throughout this interval. Hence $f(x) - f(c)$ has the same sign as $f^{[n]}(c)$ if n is even for every x in this interval, etc.)

22. Let $f(x) = e^{-1/x^2}$ if $x \neq 0$ and $f(0) = 0$. Since $1/x^2$ gets large as x gets close to zero, it is clear that

$$\operatorname*{limit}_{x \to 0} \frac{1}{e^{1/x^2}} = 0,$$

and also that

$$\operatorname*{limit}_{x \to 0} \frac{1}{x^n e^{1/x^2}} = 0$$

for every positive integer n. Hence infer that f has derivatives of all order, and that $f^{[n]}(0) = 0$ for each n. What does Maclaurin's formula look like for this function?

7. *Approximations by Taylor's polynomials*

One of the easiest functions for which to compute values is the polynomial function. Thus, it is an easy matter to find values of

$$f(x) = x - \frac{x^3}{6}$$

corresponding to various choices of x. For example,

$$f(.2) = .2 - \frac{.008}{6} \doteq .19867.$$

The theory of the previous section allows us to approximate many functions by polynomial functions. Thus, if $P_n(x)$ and $R_n(x)$ are the Taylor's polynomial and the remainder term for a function f at c,

$$f(x) = P_n(x) + R_n(x),$$

and

$$|f(x) - P_n(x)| = |R_n(x)|.$$

If we can find a number d such that

$$|R_n(x)| \leq d,$$

then we will have

$$|f(x) - P_n(x)| \leq d,$$

or

$$P_n(x) - d \leq f(x) \leq P_n(x) + d.$$

We shall write

$$f(x) = P_n(x) \pm d$$

in this case, with the understanding that this equation means $f(x) \doteq P_n(x)$, with an error of not more than d units.

Example 1. Approximate sin x by a fourth-degree polynomial in x, if $0 \leq x \leq .2$.

Solution: If $f(x) = \sin x$, then

$$f(0) = 0, \quad f'(0) = 1, \quad f''(0) = 0, \quad f'''(0) = -1, \quad f^{[4]}(0) = 0, \quad f^{[5]}(x) = \cos x.$$

Hence the fourth-degree Taylor's polynomial of f at 0 is given by

$$P_4(x) = x - \frac{x^3}{3!}.$$

Note that this polynomial is actually of the third degree, since the coefficient $f^{[4]}(0)$ of the term of fourth degree is zero. Also,

$$R_4(x) = \frac{\cos z}{5!} x^5,$$

where $0 < z < .2$.

Since $\cos z \leq 1$,

$$0 < R_4(x) \leq \frac{(.2)^5}{5!} < .000003$$

in the given range $0 \leq x \leq .2$. Thus

$$\sin x = x - \frac{x^3}{6} \pm .000003, \quad 0 \leq x \leq .2.$$

For example,

$$\sin .2 \doteq .19867,$$

accurate to 5 decimal places.

If we increased the range of x in the above example to $0 \leq x \leq .5$, then it is easily shown that $R_4(x) < .0003$. Hence

$$\sin x = x - \frac{x^3}{6} \pm .0003, \quad 0 \leq x \leq .5.$$

We still have 3 decimal place accuracy, allowing x to range up to .5 radian (about 28°). Thus,

$$\sin .5 \doteq .479,$$

accurate to 3 decimal places. The accuracy could be increased by choosing a higher degree Taylor's polynomial.

Example 2. Approximate ln x by a fifth-degree polynomial in x, if $1 \leq x \leq 1.2$.

Solution: Let us find $P_5(x)$ and $R_5(x)$ for $f(x) = \ln x$ at $c = 1$. Since

$$f'(x) = \frac{1}{x}, \quad f''(x) = -\frac{1}{x^2}, \quad f'''(x) = \frac{2}{x^3}, \quad f^{[4]}(x) = -\frac{6}{x^4}, \quad f^{[5]}(x) = \frac{24}{x^5},$$

we have

$$f(1) = 0, \quad f'(1) = 1, \quad f''(1) = -1, \quad f'''(1) = 2, \quad f^{[4]}(1) = -6, \quad f^{[5]}(1) = 24.$$

Thus

$$P_5(x) = (x - 1) - \frac{1}{2!}(x - 1)^2 + \frac{2}{3!}(x - 1)^3 - \frac{6}{4!}(x - 1)^4 + \frac{24}{5!}(x - 1)^5,$$

or

$$P_5(x) = (x - 1) - \frac{1}{2}(x - 1)^2 + \frac{1}{3}(x - 1)^3 - \frac{1}{4}(x - 1)^4 + \frac{1}{5}(x - 1)^5.$$

The remainder term is given by

$$R_5(x) = \frac{f^{[6]}(z)}{6!}(x - 1)^6 = -\frac{(x - 1)^6}{6z^6}$$

for some number z, $1 < z < 1.2$. Since $1/z < 1$,

$$|R_5(x)| < \frac{(.2)^6}{6} < .000011.$$

Thus

$$\ln x = (x - 1) - \frac{1}{2}(x - 1)^2 + \frac{1}{3}(x - 1)^3 - \frac{1}{4}(x - 1)^4 + \frac{1}{5}(x - 1)^5$$

$$\pm .000011,$$

if $1 \leq x \leq 1.2$.

For example,

$$\ln 1.2 = .2 - \frac{(.2)^2}{2} + \frac{(.2)^3}{3} - \frac{(.2)^4}{4} + \frac{(.2)^5}{5} \pm .000011,$$

and $\ln 1.2 \doteq .18233,$

with a possible error of 1 in the fifth decimal place.

Example 3. Find $\sqrt[3]{e}$ to 5 decimal place accuracy.

Solution: By Example 3 of the previous section,

$$e^x = 1 + x + \frac{x^2}{2!} + \frac{x^3}{3!} + \ldots + \frac{x^n}{n!} + R_n(x),$$

where $R_n(x) = \frac{e^z}{(n + 1)!} x^{n+1}, \quad 0 < z < x \quad \text{if} \quad x > 0.$

We wish to choose n so that $\left|R_n\left(\frac{1}{3}\right)\right| < 10^{-5}$. Clearly $e^{1/3} < 2$; therefore

$$\left|R_n\left(\frac{1}{3}\right)\right| < \frac{2}{3^{n+1}(n + 1)!}.$$

If $n = 5$,

$$\left|R_5\left(\frac{1}{3}\right)\right| < \frac{2}{3^6 \, 6!} = \frac{1}{729 \times 360} < 10^{-5}.$$

Thus

$$\sqrt[3]{e} \doteq 1 + \frac{1}{3} + \frac{1}{2}\left(\frac{1}{3}\right)^2 + \frac{1}{6}\left(\frac{1}{3}\right)^3 + \frac{1}{24}\left(\frac{1}{3}\right)^4 + \frac{1}{120}\left(\frac{1}{3}\right)^5,$$

or $\sqrt[3]{e} \doteq 1.39563.$

■ ■ ■ EXERCISES

In each of the following exercises, approximate the given function by a polynomial of given degree n in the given interval. State the error of approximation and compute the value of the function at the given number d as accurately as possible with the polynomial at hand.

1. $f(x) = \sin x$, $0 \leq x \leq .5$, $n = 6$, $d = .5$.
2. $g(x) = \cos x$, $0 \leq x \leq .2$, $n = 3$, $d = .2$.
3. $F(x) = e^x$, $0 \leq x \leq 1$, $n = 5$, $d = 1$.
4. $G(x) = e^{-x}$, $0 \leq x \leq 1$, $n = 6$, $d = 1$.
5. $f(x) = \ln(1 + x)$, $0 \leq x \leq \frac{1}{2}$, $n = 6$, $d = \frac{1}{2}$.
6. $g(x) = \sqrt{x}$, $1 \leq x \leq 1.2$, $n = 5$, $d = 1.2$.

7. $F(x) = \sinh x = \dfrac{e^x - e^{-x}}{2}$, $0 \leq x \leq 1$, $n = 6$, $d = 1$.

8. $G(x) = \cosh x = \dfrac{e^x + e^{-x}}{2}$, $0 \leq x \leq \frac{1}{2}$, $n = 4$, $d = \frac{1}{2}$.

9. $g(x) = \tan^{-1} x$, $0 \leq x \leq .2$, $n = 3$, $d = .2$.
10. $f(x) = \sin^{-1} x$, $0 \leq x \leq \frac{1}{2}$, $n = 4$, $d = \frac{1}{2}$.

Approximate each of the following to n decimal places, using Taylor polynomials:

11. $\sqrt{e}$, $n = 4$.   12. $\sin .3$, $n = 5$.

13. $\cos .05$, $n = 8$.   14. $\ln 1.1$, $n = 5$.

15. $\sqrt[3]{1.2}$, $n = 4$.   16. $\sqrt[5]{1.08}$, $n = 6$.

17. $\sinh .5$, $n = 5$.   18. $\cosh .2$, $n = 6$.

19. $\sqrt[5]{28}$, $n = 3$.   (*Hint:* Let $f(x) = \sqrt[5]{x}$, $c = 32$ in 14.10.)

20. Given $\ln 2 \doteq .6931$, find $\ln 3$ to the same degree of accuracy. (*Hint:* Let $f(x) = \ln x$, $c = 2$ in 14.10.)

15

Parametric equations, polar coordinates, and applications

■ ■ ■ ■ ■ HERETOFORE, A CURVE has been understood to be the graph of a function in a rectangular coordinate system. Two new ways of representing a curve analytically will be studied in the present chapter, one as the graph of parametric equations in the usual rectangular coordinate system and the other as the graph of a function in a polar coordinate system. Applications of these new analytic tools will be made to the study of the motion of a point in a plane, the length of an arc of a curve, and the area of a surface of revolution.

1. Parametric equations

Let θ be the radian measure of an angle in standard position relative to a rectangular coordinate system in a plane, and let P be the point of intersection of the terminal side of the angle and the circle $x^2 + y^2 = 1$ (Figure 15.1). Then P has coordinates $(\cos \theta, \sin \theta)$. Conversely, for each point (x,y) on this circle, there is at least one num-

393

ber θ [namely, the radian measure of an angle in standard position whose terminal side intersects the circle in the point (x,y)] such that

$$x = \cos \theta, \qquad y = \sin \theta.$$

The equations above are called *parametric equations* of the circle having its center at the origin and radius equal to 1, and θ is called the *parameter* of the equations.

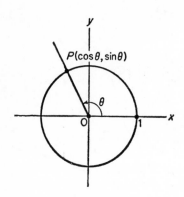

Figure 15.1

More generally, if F and G are functions having a common domain D, then

15.1 $x = F(t), \qquad y = G(t)$

are *parametric equations* with *parameter* t. The graph of 15.1 is defined to be the set of all points (x,y) satisfying 15.1. That is, the graph is the set of all points $(F(t),G(t))$ obtained by giving t values from D.

For example, the graph of the parametric equations $x = \cos \theta, y = \sin \theta$ is the circle $x^2 + y^2 = 1$, since for each number θ the point $(\cos \theta, \sin \theta)$ lies on the circle, and conversely, for each point P on the circle there is a number θ such that P is the point $(\cos \theta, \sin \theta)$.

Example 1.   Describe the graph of the parametric equations

(1) $x = \sin t, \qquad y = \cos^2 t.$

Solution: Since $\sin^2 t + \cos^2 t = 1$, it is evident that each point (x,y) on the graph of (1) satisfies the equation

(2) $x^2 + y = 1.$

Thus each point on the graph of (1) lies on the parabola (2). (Incidentally, the derivation of Equation (2) is called the *elimination of the parameter from* (1).)

While the graph of (1) is a part of the graph of (2), it is not true that the graph of (1) is the complete parabola (2). Thus, since $x = \sin t$ and $y = \cos^2 t$ in (1), necessarily $-1 \leq x \leq 1$ and $0 \leq y \leq 1$ for every point (x,y) on the graph of (1). Hence the graph of (1) consists of at most the part of the parabola (2) for which $-1 \leq x \leq 1$ and $0 \leq y \leq 1$. That the graph of (1) is precisely this part of

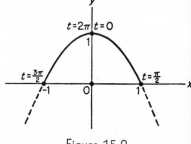

Figure 15.2

the parabola (2) is easily seen, since for each point (x,y) of the parabola such that

$-1 \leq x \leq 1$ and $0 \leq y \leq 1$ there exists a number $t = \sin^{-1} x$ for which $x = \sin t$ and $y = 1 - x^2 = \cos^2 t$. The graph of (1) is sketched in Figure 15.2.

The graph of a pair of parametric equations such as 15.1 may be sketched by making a table of values of x and y corresponding to values of t and then plotting the points (x,y) of the table. For example, we might make the accompanying table of values for the parametric equations of Example 1. From this table, we obtain

t	0	$\dfrac{\pi}{6}$	$\dfrac{\pi}{4}$	$\dfrac{\pi}{2}$	$\dfrac{3\pi}{4}$	$\dfrac{5\pi}{6}$	π	$\dfrac{7\pi}{6}$	$\dfrac{5\pi}{4}$	$\dfrac{3\pi}{2}$	$\dfrac{7\pi}{4}$	$\dfrac{11\pi}{6}$	2π
$x = \sin t$	0	$\frac{1}{2}$	$\dfrac{\sqrt{2}}{2}$	1	$\dfrac{\sqrt{2}}{2}$	$\frac{1}{2}$	0	$-\frac{1}{2}$	$-\dfrac{\sqrt{2}}{2}$	-1	$-\dfrac{\sqrt{2}}{2}$	$-\frac{1}{2}$	0
$y = \cos^2 t$	1	$\frac{3}{4}$	$\frac{1}{2}$	0	$\frac{1}{2}$	$\frac{3}{4}$	1	$\frac{3}{4}$	$\frac{1}{2}$	0	$\frac{1}{2}$	$\frac{3}{4}$	1

the points $(0,1)$, $(\pm\frac{1}{2},\frac{3}{4})$, $(\pm\sqrt{2}/2,\frac{1}{2})$, and $(\pm 1,0)$ on the graph.

In many applications of parametric equations, the parameter t is interpreted as time. For example, 15.1 might be interpreted as giving the position $P(F(t),G(t))$ at time t of a point P moving in a coordinate plane. If we so interpret the parametric equations of Example 1, then the above table of values gives the position $P(x,y)$ of a moving point at time t. Thus P has the position $(0,1)$ when $t = 0$, moves to $(1,0)$ as t increases to $\pi/2$, returns to $(0,1)$, and proceeds on to $(-1,0)$ as t increases from $\pi/2$ to $3\pi/2$, and returns to the original position $(0,1)$ when $t = 2\pi$. This motion is periodic; and the point P will retrace its path during every interval of time of length 2π.

Example 2. Determine the graph of the equations

$$(1) \qquad x = 1 + 4t, \qquad y = 3 - 2t.$$

Solution: We may eliminate the parameter from (1) by solving the first equation for t:

$$(2) \qquad t = \frac{1}{4}(x - 1),$$

and substituting this value of t in the second equation, getting

$$(3) \qquad y - 3 = -\frac{1}{2}(x - 1).$$

Hence the graph of (1) is on the line L with slope $-\frac{1}{2}$, passing through the point $(1,3)$. Since each point (x,y) on L may be obtained from (1) by giving t the value of (2), it is clear that the graph of (1) is the whole line L with equation (3).

It is interesting to note that the point $P(x,y)$ given by (1) is the point $(1,3)$ if $t = 0$, that P lies to the right of and below $(1,3)$ if $t > 0$, and that P lies to the left of and above $(1,3)$ if $t < 0$. Thus, as t increases, the point $P(x,y)$ will move in the direction indicated in Figure 15.3. As can be

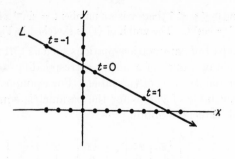

Figure 15.3

seen from this and the previous example, parametric equations offer a convenient method of assigning a direction to a curve in a plane.

If the functions F and G are continuous at the number a, then for each number $\epsilon > 0$, there exists a number $\delta > 0$ such that

$$|F(t) - F(a)| < \frac{\epsilon}{\sqrt{2}}, \qquad |G(t) - G(a)| < \frac{\epsilon}{\sqrt{2}}$$

provided that $|t - a| < \delta$. That is to say, if $A(F(a),G(a))$ and $P(F(t),G(t))$, then

$$|PA| = \sqrt{[F(t) - F(a)]^2 + [G(t) - G(a)]^2} < \sqrt{\frac{\epsilon^2}{2} + \frac{\epsilon^2}{2}},$$

and $|PA| < \epsilon$ if $|t - a| < \delta$. Hence each point $P(F(t),G(t))$ on the graph of 15.1 lies within the circle with center $A(F(a),G(a))$ and radius ϵ if $|t - a| < \delta$ (Figure 15.4). Thus the graph of 15.1 is continuous at a in the sense that each point $P(F(t),G(t))$ is close to $A(F(a),G(a))$ if t is close to a.

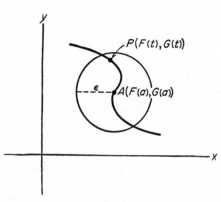

Example 3. If a circle rolls along a straight line, the path described by a fixed point P on the circle is called a *cycloid*. Find parametric equations for the cycloid.

Solution: We shall assume that the circle has radius r, that it rolls along the x-axis and above it, and that the origin is so chosen on the x-axis that the point P

Figure 15.4

makes contact with the x-axis at the origin. Let us choose as parameter the angle ϑ (in radians) of rotation of the circle from the position when P is at the origin (Figure 15.5).

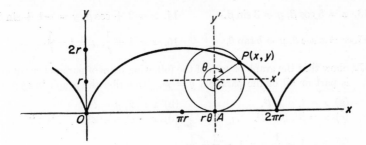

Figure 15.5

When the circle has revolved through an angle of θ radians, it will have rolled a distance $OA = r\theta$ from the origin. Hence the center of the circle will be the point $C(r\theta, r)$. If we translate axes to the new origin C, then the coordinates of P relative to the new axes will be

(1) $\quad x' = x - r\theta, \qquad y' = y - r.$

A close-up view of the new coordinate axes, given in Figure 15.6, shows us that

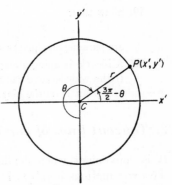

$$x' = r\cos\left(\frac{3\pi}{2} - \theta\right) = -r\sin\theta$$

(2)

$$y' = r\sin\left(\frac{3\pi}{2} - \theta\right) = -r\cos\theta.$$

Finally, on combining (1) and (2) we get

$$x = r(\theta - \sin\theta), \qquad y = r(1 - \cos\theta)$$

as parametric equations of the cycloid.

Figure 15.6

■ ■ ■ EXERCISES

In each of the following exercises, make a table of values and sketch the graph of the given parametric equations. Check your graph by eliminating the parameter, thus deriving an equation in x and y. Is every point on the graph of the equation in x and y on the graph of the given parametric equations?

1. $x = 3t, y = 2 - t.$

2. $x = t^2, y = t + 1.$

3. $x = 1 - t^2, y = 1 + t.$

4. $x = 1 - t^2, y = 1 + t^2.$

5. $x = |\sin t|, y = \cos^2 t.$

6. $x = e^t, y = e^{-t}.$

7. $x = \sin 2\alpha, y = 2\sin^2\alpha.$

8. $x = \sin\alpha, y = 2\cos\alpha.$

In each of the following exercises, describe the graph of the given parametric equations and sketch:

9. $x = t^3, y = t^2.$

10. $x = \tan\alpha, y = \sec\alpha.$

11. $x = \tan^2\theta, y = \sec\theta.$

12. $x = 3e^t, y = 1 - e^t.$

13. $x = 5 \cos \beta$, $y = 3 \sin \beta$.   **14.** $x = 2 + \cos \beta$, $y = -1 + \sin \beta$.

15. $x = a \sec \theta$, $y = b \tan \theta$.   **16.** $x = 1 + \frac{1}{t}$, $y = t - \frac{1}{t}$.

17. Show that the graph of each of the following pairs of parametric equations is part or all of the parabola $y = x^2$. Describe the graph in each case.

    (a) $x = t$, $y = t^2$.   (b) $x = t^2$, $y = t^4$.

    (c) $x = |t|$, $y = t^2$.   (d) $x = e^t$, $y = e^{2t}$.

    (e) $x = 1 - \frac{1}{t^2}$, $y = 1 - \frac{2}{t^2} + \frac{1}{t^4}$.

    (f) $x = \sec t$, $y = 1 + \tan^2 t$.

18. Show that

$$x = x_1 + (x_2 - x_1)t, \quad y = y_1 + (y_2 - y_1)t$$

are parametric equations of the line on the distinct points (x_1, y_1) and (x_2, y_2).

19. Show that

$$x = h + a \cos \theta, \quad y = k + b \sin \theta$$

are parametric equations of an ellipse. Describe the ellipse.

20. A bicycle is going along a straight road at the constant rate of v ft/sec. If the wheels have radius r ft, find parametric equations of the motion of a point P on the bicycle tire in terms of time t.

2. Tangent lines of curves in parametric form

It is convenient when dealing with parametric equations to designate the two functions involved by x and y, and to give the parametric equations of a curve C in the form

15.2 $x = x(t), \quad y = y(t)$.

This practice will be followed henceforth.

A secant line L on two points $P(x(t), y(t))$ and $Q(x(t + h), y(t + h))$ of C has slope given by

$$\tan \alpha(h) = \frac{y(t + h) - y(t)}{x(t + h) - x(t)},$$

where $\alpha(h)$ is the inclination of L (Figure 15.7). If

$$\lim_{h \to 0} \tan \alpha(h) = m,$$

then the line on P with slope m is defined to be the tangent line to C at the point $P(x(t), y(t))$.

If $x'(t)$ and $y'(t)$ exist, and if $x'(t) \neq 0$, then

$$\lim_{h \to 0} \tan \alpha(h) = \lim_{h \to 0} \frac{[y(t + h) - y(t)]/h}{[x(t + h) - x(t)]/h},$$

and

15.3 $m = \frac{y'(t)}{x'(t)}$.

Thus the slope m of the tangent line to the curve C with parametric equations 15.2 at a point $P(x,y)$ such that $x'(t) \neq 0$ is given by 15.3.

To determine vertical tangent lines, we must consider (c.f. Chapter 6, Section 1)

$$\cot \alpha(h) = \frac{x(t+h) - x(t)}{y(t+h) - y(t)}.$$

The curve C has a vertical tangent line at $P(x(t),y(t))$ if

$$\lim_{h \to 0} \cot \alpha(h) = 0.$$

Using our previous arguments, we can assert that C has a vertical tangent line at $P(x,y)$ if $x'(t) = 0$ and $y'(t) \neq 0$.

Combining the above results, we may assert that *if $x'(t)$ and $y'(t)$ exist and are not both zero, then the curve C with parametric equations 15.2 has a tangent line at the point $(x(t),y(t))$.*

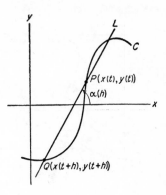

Figure 15.7

Even if $x'(t)$ and $y'(t)$ are both zero, however, the curve C might still have a tangent line at the point $(x(t),y(t))$. The following example illustrates this fact.

Example 1. Let the curve C have parametric equations

$$x = 1 - \cos t, \qquad y = t^2.$$

Find the tangent line to C at the origin.

Solution: Since

$$x'(t) = \sin t, \qquad y'(t) = 2t,$$

evidently $x'(0) = 0$ and $y'(0) = 0$. Thus we cannot use the above results to get the tangent line at the origin.

Let us go back to the definition of the tangent line as the line on the point $(0,0)$ with slope m given by

$$m = \lim_{h \to 0} \tan \alpha(h) = \lim_{h \to 0} \frac{y(h) - y(0)}{x(h) - x(0)} = \lim_{h \to 0} \frac{h^2}{1 - \cos h}.$$

Employing l'Hospital's rule twice, we obtain

$$m = \lim_{h \to 0} \frac{2h}{\sin h} = \lim_{h \to 0} \frac{2}{\cos h} = 2.$$

Hence the tangent line to C at the origin has slope 2 and equation

$$y = 2x.$$

According to Cauchy's formula (14.4), if the functions x and y are continuous in a closed interval $[a,b]$ and if $x'(t)$ and $y'(t)$ exist in the open interval (a,b) with $x'(t) \neq 0$ in (a,b), then

$$\frac{y(b) - y(a)}{x(b) - x(a)} = \frac{y'(z)}{x'(z)}.$$

for some number z, $a < z < b$.   The left side of this equation is the slope of the secant line on $A(x(a),y(a))$ and $B(x(b),y(b))$, but the right side is the slope of the tangent line on $P(x(z),y(z))$. Thus we see Cauchy's formula has an analogous geometrical interpretation to the mean value theorem, namely, that there is a tangent line at some point P on the arc between A and B that is parallel to the secant line on A and B (Figure 15.8).

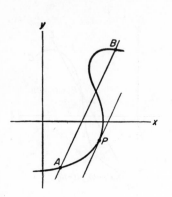

Figure 15.8

If the graph of the parametric equations

$$x = x(t), \qquad y = y(t)$$

is also the graph of the equation

$$y = f(x),$$

then

$$y(t) = f(x(t))$$

for every t in the common domains of the functions x and y.   Hence, by the chain rule,

$$y'(t) = f'(x(t))x'(t),$$

and

15.4
$$f'(x) = \frac{y'(t)}{x'(t)}, \quad x'(t) \neq 0.$$

This equation is often written in the form

$$\frac{dy}{dx} = \frac{dy/dt}{dx/dt}, \qquad \frac{dx}{dt} \neq 0.$$

Example 2.   Find the slope of the tangent line at each point (x,y) on the cycloid

$$x = r(\theta - \sin\theta), \qquad y = r(1 - \cos\theta).$$

Solution: Clearly

$$\frac{dx}{d\theta} = r(1 - \cos\theta), \qquad \frac{dy}{d\theta} = r\sin\theta.$$

Thus the slope of the tangent line at (x,y) is given by

$$\frac{dy/d\theta}{dx/d\theta} = \frac{\sin\theta}{1 - \cos\theta}, \qquad \theta \neq 2n\pi, \quad n \text{ an integer.}$$

If $\theta = 2n\pi$, n an integer, then it may be shown by l'Hospital's rule that the tangent line exists and is vertical.   These are the points at which the cycloid touches the x-axis in Figure 15.5.

■ ■ ■ EXERCISES

Find an equation of the tangent line to each of the following curves at the specified value of the parameter:

1. $x = t^2$, $y = t^3$; $t = 2$.   **2.** $x = e^t$, $y = e^{-t}$; $t = 1$.

3. $x = \dfrac{1}{t}$, $y = t$; $t = -1$.   **4.** $x = \tan t$, $y = \cot t$; $t = 3\pi/4$.

5. $x = a \cos t$, $y = a \sin t$; $t = \tan^{-1}(\tfrac{3}{4})$.

6. $x = 3 \cos t$, $y = 2 \sin t$; $t = \pi/3$.

7. $x = \ln t$, $y = \sin^{-1} t$; $t = \tfrac{1}{2}$.

8. $x = \tan^{-1}(t^2 + 1)$, $y = \cos 2t$; $t = \pi/3$.

9. $x = 1 - \cos t$, $y = t^2$; $t = 0$.

10. $x = e^t - 2 \cos t + e^{-t}$, $y = t \sin t$; $t = 0$.

Sketch each of the following curves and find each point on the curve at which the tangent line is horizontal or vertical:

11. $x = 5 \sin 2\alpha$, $y = 5 \cos 2\alpha$.   **12.** $x = \cos 2t$, $y = \cos t$.

13. $x = 2\theta - \sin \theta$, $y = 2 - \cos \theta$.   **14.** $x = \theta - 2 \sin \theta$, $y = 1 - 2 \cos \theta$.

15. $x = 2 - 3 \cos \beta$, $y = -1 + 2 \sin \beta$.

16. $x = a \cos^3 \theta$, $y = a \sin^3 \theta$, $a > 0$.

17. If the curve with parametric equations

$$x = x(t), \quad y = y(t)$$

also has equation $y = f(x)$, then show that

$$\frac{d^2 y}{dx^2} = \frac{D_t\,(dy/dx)}{dx/dt} = \frac{x'(t)y''(t) - y'(t)x''(t)}{(x'(t))^3}.$$

$\left(\textit{Hint: } \text{The derivative } f' \text{ is given parametrically by}\right.$

$$x = x(t), \quad \frac{dy}{dx} = \frac{y'(t)}{x'(t)}. \Bigg)$$

Assume that each curve given parametrically below also is the graph of an equation $y = f(x)$. Then use Exercise 17 above to find dy/dx and d^2y/dx^2 for each curve:

18. $x = 3t$, $y = 2t^3$.   **19.** $x = e^t$, $y = te^{-t}$.

20. $x = r(\theta - \sin \theta)$, $y = r(1 - \cos \theta)$.

21. $x = a \cos^3 \theta$, $y = a \sin^3 \theta$.   **22.** $x = \ln t$, $y = t^3$.

23. Show that the parametric equations

$$x = a \cos^4 t, \quad y = a \sin^4 t, \quad a > 0,$$

have the same graph as the equation

$$\sqrt{x} + \sqrt{y} = \sqrt{a},$$

and sketch this graph. Show that for this curve, the sum of the intercepts of every tangent line is the constant a.

24. Prove that if $x'(a)$ and $y'(a)$ are not both zero, then

$$x = x(a) + x'(a)t, \quad y = y(a) + y'(a)t$$

are parametric equations of the tangent line to the graph of

$$x = x(t), \quad y = y(t)$$

at the point $(x(a), y(a))$.

3. *Two-dimensional vector algebra*

By a two-dimensional *vector*, we shall mean an ordered pair (x,y) of numbers.   Lower-case boldfaced letters such as a, b, and x will be used to
designate vectors.   For example,

$$a = (-3,2), \quad b = (1,\pi), \quad x = (0,5)$$

are (two-dimensional) vectors.   A vector will always be a two-dimensional
vector in this chapter.

Operations of addition, subtraction, and multiplication can be defined
for vectors much as they can for numbers.

The sum of two vectors is another vector defined as follows:

$$(a_1,a_2) + (b_1,b_2) = (a_1 + b_1, a_2 + b_2).$$

For example,

$$(1,2) + (3,-5) = (4,-3).$$

The usual rules for addition of numbers hold for the addition of vectors.
Thus, for any vectors a, b, and c,

$$a + b = b + a \qquad \text{(Commutative law)},$$
$$a + (b + c) = (a + b) + c \qquad \text{(Associative law)},$$
$$a + 0 = a \qquad \text{(Zero element)},$$
$$a + (-a) = 0 \qquad \text{(Negative element)},$$

where

$$0 = (0,0),$$

and if

$$a = (a_1,a_2), \quad \text{then} \quad -a = (-a_1,-a_2).$$

Subtraction of vectors is defined in the obvious way:

$$(a_1,a_2) - (b_1,b_2) = (a_1 - b_1, a_2 - b_2).$$

That is, $a - b = a + (-b)$.   The rules for subtraction of vectors are
similar to those for numbers.

The rules stated above for addition of vectors may be proved from corresponding rules for addition of numbers.   For example, the proof of the
associative law is as follows:

If $a = (a_1,a_2)$, $b = (b_1,b_2)$, and $c = (c_1,c_2)$, then $a + (b + c) = (a_1,a_2)$
$+ (b_1 + c_1, b_2 + c_2) = (a_1 + (b_1 + c_1), a_2 + (b_2 + c_2))$.
On the other hand,

$$(a + b) + c = (a_1 + b_1, a_2 + b_2) + (c_1,c_2)$$
$$= ((a_1 + b_1) + c_1, \quad (a_2 + b_2) + c_2).$$

Since

$$a_1 + (b_1 + c_1) = (a_1 + b_1) + c_1, \quad a_2 + (b_2 + c_2) = (a_2 + b_2) + c_2,$$

we have proved the associative law

$$a + (b + c) = (a + b) + c.$$

There are two useful multiplication operations involving vectors: the scalar multiple and the dot product.

Given a vector $\boldsymbol{a} = (a_1, a_2)$ and a number c (called a scalar), the *scalar multiple* of $\boldsymbol{a}$ by c is the vector $c\,\boldsymbol{a}$ defined as follows:

$$c(a_1, a_2) = (ca_1, ca_2).$$

For example,

$$3(2, -1) = (6, -3), \qquad (-2)(5, -4) = (-10, 8).$$

The following rules hold for scalar multiples. For any vectors $\boldsymbol{a}$ and $\boldsymbol{b}$, and any scalars c and d,

$$c(\boldsymbol{a} + \boldsymbol{b}) = c\boldsymbol{a} + c\boldsymbol{b}, \qquad (c + d)\boldsymbol{a} = c\boldsymbol{a} + d\boldsymbol{a},$$

$$(cd)\boldsymbol{a} = c(d\boldsymbol{a}), \qquad (-c)\boldsymbol{a} = -(c\boldsymbol{a}),$$

$$1\boldsymbol{a} = \boldsymbol{a} \qquad 0\boldsymbol{a} = \boldsymbol{0}, \qquad c\boldsymbol{0} = \boldsymbol{0}.$$

Proof that $c(\boldsymbol{a} + \boldsymbol{b}) = c\boldsymbol{a} + c\boldsymbol{b}$: We have

$$\begin{aligned}
c[(a_1, a_2) + (b_1, b_2)] &= c(a_1 + b_1, a_2 + b_2) \\
&= (ca_1 + cb_1, ca_2 + cb_2) \\
&= (ca_1, ca_2) + (cb_1, cb_2) \\
&= c(a_1, a_2) + c(b_1, b_2).
\end{aligned}$$

The proofs of the other laws are left to the reader.

An important use of the scalar multiple is to express each vector (a_1, a_2) in terms of the simple vectors $(1, 0)$ and $(0, 1)$:

$$(a_1, a_2) = a_1(1, 0) + a_2(0, 1).$$

For example,

$$(-2, -1) = -2(1, 0) - (0, 1),$$

$$(3, \sqrt{2}) = 3(1, 0) + \sqrt{2}(0, 1),$$

$$(4, 0) = 4(1, 0).$$

The *dot product* of two vectors $\boldsymbol{a}$ and $\boldsymbol{b}$ is a number designated by $\boldsymbol{a} \cdot \boldsymbol{b}$ and defined as follows:

$$(a_1, a_2) \cdot (b_1, b_2) = a_1 b_1 + a_2 b_2.$$

We emphasize that the dot product of two vectors is a *number* and not a vector.

For example,

$$(2, -2) \cdot (4, 3) = 2 \cdot 4 + (-2) \cdot 3 = 2,$$

$$(\sqrt{2}, \pi) \cdot (2\sqrt{2}, -1) = (\sqrt{2}) \cdot (2\sqrt{2}) + \pi \cdot (-1) = 4 - \pi,$$

$$(3, -7) \cdot (7, 3) = 3 \cdot 7 + (-7) \cdot 3 = 0.$$

Some of the useful properties of the dot product are listed below. For any vectors $\boldsymbol{a}$, $\boldsymbol{b}$, and $\boldsymbol{c}$ and any scalar k,

$$a \cdot b = b \cdot a, \qquad (a + b) \cdot c = a \cdot c + b \cdot c,$$
$$(ka) \cdot b = a \cdot (kb) = k(a \cdot b),$$
$$0 \cdot a = 0, \qquad a \cdot a > 0 \quad \text{if} \quad a \neq 0.$$

Proof that $(a + b) \cdot c = a \cdot c + b \cdot c$: We have

$$
\begin{aligned}
[(a_1,a_2) + (b_1,b_2)] \cdot (c_1,c_2) &= (a_1 + b_1, a_2 + b_2) \cdot (c_1,c_2) \\
&= (a_1 + b_1)c_1 + (a_2 + b_2)c_2 \\
&= (a_1 c_1 + a_2 c_2) + (b_1 c_1 + b_2 c_2) \\
&= (a_1,a_2) \cdot (c_1,c_2) + (b_1,b_2) \cdot (c_1,c_2).
\end{aligned}
$$

Proof that $a \cdot a > 0$ if $a \neq 0$: If $(a_1,a_2) \neq (0,0)$, then either $a_1 \neq 0$ or $a_2 \neq 0$ and

$$(a_1,a_2) \cdot (a_1,a_2) = a_1^2 + a_2^2 > 0.$$

The proofs of the other properties of the dot product are similar and are omitted.

The *length* of any vector a is designated by $|a|$ and defined by

$$|a| = \sqrt{a \cdot a}.$$

Thus,

$$|(a_1,a_2)| = \sqrt{a_1^2 + a_2^2}.$$

The length of a vector is a nonnegative number, and $|a| = 0$ if and only if $a = 0$. A vector of length 1 is called a *unit vector*. Clearly $(1,0)$ and $(0,1)$ are unit vectors. Since

$$\left| \left(\frac{3}{5}, \frac{4}{5} \right) \right| = \sqrt{ \left(\frac{3}{5} \right)^2 + \left(\frac{4}{5} \right)^2 } = 1,$$

$(3/5, 4/5)$ also is a unit vector.

Given a nonzero vector a of length c, the vector $(1/c)a$ is a unit vector, since

$$\left| \frac{1}{c} a \right| = \frac{1}{c} |a| = 1.$$

Thus, some scalar multiple of a nonzero vector is a unit vector.

For example, if $a = (2, -\sqrt{2})$, then $|a| = \sqrt{6}$ and the vector

$$\frac{1}{\sqrt{6}} (2, -\sqrt{2}) = \left(\frac{\sqrt{6}}{3}, -\frac{\sqrt{3}}{3} \right)$$

is a unit vector that is a scalar multiple of a.

■ ■ ■ EXERCISES

1. Prove that $|ca| = |c||a|$.
2. Prove the stated, but unproved, properties of vector addition.
3. Prove the stated, but unproved, properties of scalar multiples.

4. Prove the stated, but unproved, properties of the dot product operation.

5. Prove that

$$|a + b|^2 = |a|^2 + |b|^2 + 2a \cdot b$$

$$|a - b|^2 = |a|^2 + |b|^2 - 2a \cdot b.$$

6. Prove that

$$(a \cdot b)^2 \leq |a|^2 \cdot |b|^2.$$

When does the equality sign hold?

4. Vectors as directed segments

A vector $a = (a_1, a_2)$ may be represented in a coordinate plane by a directed line segment $\overrightarrow{PQ}$ having any point $P(x,y)$ as its initial point and $Q(x + a_1, y + a_2)$ as its endpoint (Figure 15.9). If the initial point of a is taken as

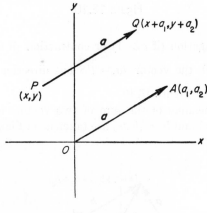

Figure 15.9

the origin 0, then the endpoint of a is $A(a_1, a_2)$. We shall call a a *position vector* if it is represented by directed line segment $\overrightarrow{OA}$ having its initial point at the origin. If $\overrightarrow{PQ}$ and $\overrightarrow{RS}$ are two representations of a vector a by directed line segments, then $\overrightarrow{PQ}$ and $\overrightarrow{RS}$ are parallel and have the same length and direction; that is, $PQSR$ is a parallelogram. In this section, we shall consider a vector a to be any directed line segment in the plane representing a.

If $a = \overrightarrow{PQ}$, as in Figure 15.9, then the length of a as defined in the preceding section is the actual length of the segment PQ,

$$|a| = |PQ| = \sqrt{a_1^2 + a_2^2}.$$

The ratio a_2/a_1, $a_1 \neq 0$, is the slope of the line on P and Q.

If $a = \overrightarrow{PQ}$ and $c > 0$, then ca is the vector $\overrightarrow{PR}$ having the same direction as $\overrightarrow{PQ}$ and having length c times that of $\overrightarrow{PQ}$, $|PR| = c|PQ|$ (Figure 15.10).

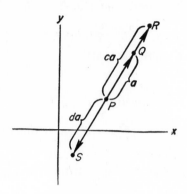

Figure 15.10

Thus, ca is an elongation (if $c > 1$) or contraction (if $0 < c < 1$) of the vector a. If $d < 0$, the vector $da = \overrightarrow{PS}$ has direction opposite to that of $\overrightarrow{PR}$ as indicated in Figure 15.10.

The geometric meaning of the sum of two vectors is seen as follows. If vectors $a = (a_1,a_2)$ and $b = (b_1,b_2)$ are taken as in Figure 15.11, with the

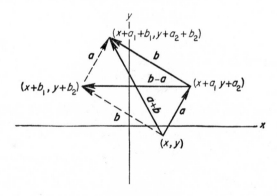

Figure 15.11

endpoint of a the initial point of b, then $a + b$ is the vector with initial point that of a and endpoint that of b. If we interchange the roles of a and b (as indicated by the dotted lines in Figure 15.11), then we get the same vector for $b + a$, i.e.,

$$a + b = b + a,$$

as expected.   This gives us the usual *parallelogram law* for the sum of two vectors: $a + b$ is the diagonal of a parallelogram having a and b as adjacent sides.   The other diagonal of this parallelogram is $b - a$, since $a + (b - a) = b$.

We shall use the notation

$$(a,b)$$

to designate the angle of least nonnegative measure between the nonzero vectors a and b which are assumed to have the same initial point (Figure 15.12).   Necessarily

$$0 \le (a,b) \le \pi,$$

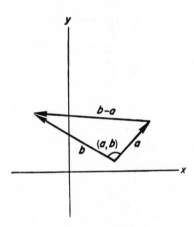

Figure 15.12

with $(a,b) = 0$ if and only if vectors a and b have the same direction and $(a,b) = \pi$ if and only if they have opposite direction.

Referring to Figure 15.12, we have

$$|b - a|^2 = |a|^2 + |b|^2 - 2|a||b| \cos (a,b)$$

by the law of cosines.   On the other hand,

$$|b - a|^2 = |a|^2 + |b|^2 - 2\, a \cdot b$$

by Exercise 5 of the preceding section.   On comparing these two equations, we see that

$$a \cdot b = |a||b| \cos (a,b).$$

This gives the geometric significance of the dot product of two vectors.

The nonzero vectors a and b are perpendicular if and only if $\cos (a,b) = 0$.   In view of the equation above, we have that *the nonzero vectors a and b are perpendicular if and only if their dot product is zero.*   We note that if a and b are unit vectors, then

$$a \cdot b = \cos (a,b).$$

Each vector $a = (a_1, a_2)$ may be given as the sum

$$a = a_1 i + a_2 j, \quad i = (1,0), \quad j = (0,1).$$

Geometrically, we have resolved a as a sum of its *horizontal component* $a_1 i$ and *vertical component* $a_2 j$ (Figure 15.13).

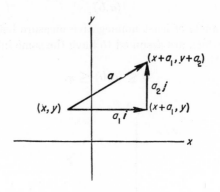

Figure 15.13

For example, if $a = (4,3)$, then $a = 4i + 3j$ where $4i$ is the horizontal component and $3j$ the vertical component of a.

■ ■ ■ EXERCISES

1. Give a geometric interpretation to the inequality $|a + b| \leq |a| + |b|$. (Assume that a and b have the same initial point.)

2. Let a and b have the origin as a common initial point. Let a and b have the points $A(2,-1)$ and $B(1,3)$ respectively as terminal points.
   (a) Sketch a, b, $a + b$, $a - b$, and $b - a$.
   (b) Sketch $2a$, $3b$, $2a + 3b$, and $2a - 3b$.
   (c) Sketch $-a$, $-2b$, $-a - 2b$, and $-a + 2b$.

3. Let a, b, c be vectors with a common initial point such that $a + b + c = 0$. Show that $\sin(b,c)/|a| = \sin(c,a)/|b| = \sin(a,b)/|c|$.

5. *Motion in a plane*

If x and y are functions with a common domain, then to each number t in this domain corresponds a vector

15.5 $r(t) = (x(t), y(t)).$

We shall call r a *vector* function. Letting C be the curve in the plane with parametric equations

$$x = x(t), \quad y = y(t),$$

then $r(t)$ is the position vector whose endpoint generates C (**Figure 15.14**).

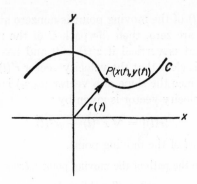

Figure 15.14

The limit of a **vector function** r is defined in a coordinatewise manner. Thus, if

$$\text{limit}_{t \to c} x(t) = a_1, \qquad \text{limit}_{t \to c} y(t) = a_2,$$

then we define

$$\text{limit}_{t \to c} r(t) = (a_1, a_2).$$

The *limit of a vector function is a vector.* If

$$\text{limit}_{t \to c} r(t) = (x(c), y(c))$$

then the vector function r is said to be *continuous at c.*

Having defined the limit of a vector function, the derivative of a vector function can be defined in the usual way. If $r(t) = (x(t), y(t))$, then

$$r'(t) = \text{limit}_{h \to 0} \frac{r(t+h) - r(t)}{h}$$

$$= (x'(t), y'(t))$$

if the functions x and y have derivative at t. Similarly, the second derivative of r is given by

$$r''(t) = (x''(t), y''(t)).$$

Let us now assume that a point is moving in a coordinate plane, and that at time t it is the endpoint of the position vector

$$r(t) = (x(t), y(t)).$$

The path of the moving point is the curve C generated by r. The vector

$$\frac{r(t+h) - r(t)}{h}$$

is called the *average velocity vector* from time t to time $t + h$. Its limit as h approaches 0, which is $r'(t)$ by our previous discussion, is called the (instantaneous) *velocity vector* of the moving point at time t. In turn, $r''(t)$ is called the *acceleration vector* of the moving point at time t.

If the velocity $r'(t)$ of the moving point is nonzero at time t, so that not both $x'(t)$ and $y'(t)$ are zero, then the path C of the moving point has a tangent line at t that is vertical if $x'(t) = 0$ and has slope $y'(t)/x'(t)$ if $x'(t) \neq 0$. Thus it is clear that the velocity vector $r'(t)$ lies along the tangent line at time t, since the slope of a vector (a_1, a_2) is known to be a_2/a_1. The length of the velocity vector is given by

$$|r(t)| = \sqrt{x'^2(t) + y'^2(t)}$$

and is called the *speed* of the moving point.

Example 1. Describe the path of the moving point having position vector

$$r(t) = (2 - t, t^2 - 1).$$

Sketch in the velocity and acceleration vectors at $t = 0$ and $t = 1$.

Solution: If we eliminate t from the equations

$$x = 2 - t, \qquad y = t^2 - 1,$$

we see that the path is the parabola

$$y + 1 = (x - 2)^2$$

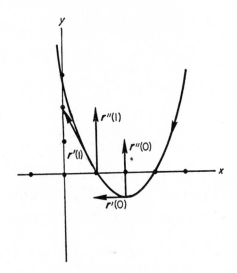

Figure 15.15

sketched in Figure 15.15. The velocity and acceleration vectors are given by

$$r'(t) = (-1, 2t), \qquad r''(t) = (0, 2)$$

at time t. Hence

$$r'(0) = (-1, 0), \qquad r''(0) = (0, 2)$$

and

$$r'(1) = (-1, 2), \qquad r''(1) = (0, 2)$$

are the velocity and acceleration vectors at $t = 0$ and $t = 1$ respectively. These

are sketched in Figure 15.15.   Note that the acceleration vector is constant.
As t increases the point is moving from right to left on the curve.

The *vector of force* F acting on a moving particle with position vector $r(t)$
is defined to be

$$F(t) = mr''(t),$$

where m is the mass of the particle.

Example 2.   Show that if a particle P moves uniformly in a circular path, the
force (centripetal force) acting on P is directed toward the center of the circle.

Solution: If P has a constant angular velocity of w revolutions per unit of time,
then the position vector $r(t)$ sweeps out an angle of

$$\theta = 2\pi wt$$

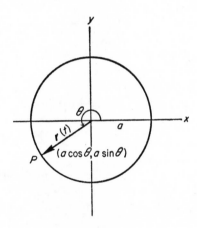

Figure 15.16

radians in time t (Figure 15.16).   Hence the position vector $r(t)$ is given by

$$r(t) = (a \cos 2\pi wt, \ a \sin 2\pi wt)$$

if we assume that

$$r(0) = (a,0).$$

We easily compute,

$$r'(t) = (-2\pi wa \sin 2\pi wt, \ 2\pi wa \cos 2\pi wt),$$

$$r''(t) = (-4\pi^2 w^2 a \cos 2\pi wt, \ -4\pi^2 w^2 a \sin 2\pi wt).$$

Evidently

$$r''(t) = -kr(t), \qquad k = 4\pi^2 w^2,$$

and

$$F(t) = -mkr(t)$$

where m is the mass of P.   Since $-mk$ is a negative number, F is always directed
opposite to $r(t)$; i.e., F is directed toward the center of the circle.

■ ■ ■ EXERCISES

In each of the following exercises $r(t)$ is the position vector of a moving point P. Sketch the path of P and find the velocity and acceleration vectors. Sketch the velocity and acceleration vectors and find the speed at the given time t.

1. $r(t) = (t^2, 2t); t = 2.$ 2. $r(t) = (2t, t^4); t = 2.$

3. $r(t) = (2 \sin t, 2 \cos t); t = \pi/4.$ 4. $r(t) = (\tan t, \cot t); t = 3\pi/4.$

5. $r(t) = (\cos t, \cos 2t); t = \pi/2.$ 6. $r(t) = (2t, e^{-t}); t = 0.$

7. $r(t) = (e^t, e^{-t}); t = 0.$ 8. $r(t) = (\sin t, \cos^2 t); t = \pi/2.$

9. $r(t) = (2 \sin t, 2(1 - \cos t)); t = \pi/6.$

10. $r(t) = (\sqrt{t}, \sqrt{2 - t}); t = 1.$

11. $r(t) = (a \cos wt, a \sin wt), a > 0, w > 0;$ at time t.

12. $r(t) = ((v_o \cos \alpha)t, (v_o \sin \alpha)t - 16t^2), v_o > 0, 0 < \alpha < \pi/2;$ at time t.

13. Describe the motion of P during the time interval $-2 \le t \le 2$ if $r(t) = (t^2/2, t^4/4)$. Find $r'(t)$ and $r''(t)$ when $t = -2, -1, 0, 1, 2$, and sketch the velocity vector at each of the corresponding points.

14. What is the significance of the fact that $r(t) \cdot r'(t) = 0$ in Example 2 above?

15. Show that if $r(t) = (e^t \cos t, e^t \sin t)$, then the acceleration vector is perpendicular to the position vector at each time t.

6. Polar coordinate systems

Another convenient way of introducing coordinates in a plane is by the so-called polar coordinate system described below.

We start off with a fixed point O, called the *pole*, and the positive half of a coordinate line, called the *polar axis*, emanating from O. The presence of the polar axis allows us to assign a length to each line segment in the plane.

Each point P in the plane may now be assigned coordinates (r, θ), where r is the length of the vector $\overrightarrow{OP}$ and θ is the measure of an angle with initial side along the polar axis and terminal side along $\overrightarrow{OP}$ (Figure 15.17). We shall also allow the coordinates $(-r, \theta)$ for the point P if $|OP| = r$ and θ is the measure of an angle with initial side along the polar axis and terminal

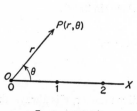

Figure 15.17

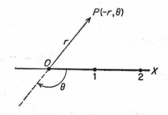

Figure 15.18

side along the extension of OP through the pole (Figure 15.18). The pole O is assigned coordinates $(0,\theta)$, where θ is any real number.

There certainly is nothing unique about the polar coordinates of a point. The point P of Figure 15.19, for example, has as possible polar coordinates

$$(3,120°), \ (-3,-60°), \ (3,480°), \ (3,-240°), \ (-3,300°),$$

and so on. In general, if P has polar coordinates (r,θ), then P also has polar coordinates $(r,\theta \pm 2n\pi)$ and $(-r,\theta \pm (2n - 1)\pi)$ for every interger n. However, if P is not the pole, P does have a unique set of coordinates (r,θ) where $r > 0$ and $0° \leq \theta < 360°$. The only coordinates of P in Figure 15.19 satisfying these restrictions are $(3,120°)$.

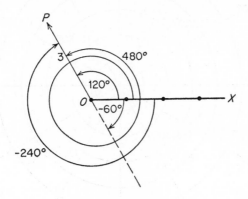

Figure 15.19

Every pair of numbers (r,θ) determines a unique point P such that $|OP| = |r|$ and θ is the (radian) measure of an angle having initial side along the polar axis and terminal side along $\overrightarrow{OP}$ if $r > 0$ and along $\overrightarrow{OP}$ extended through the origin if $r < 0$. This association of pairs of numbers with points is called a *polar coordinate system* in the plane.

Just as an equation in x and y has a graph in a rectangular coordinate plane, so does an equation in r and θ have a graph in a polar coordinate plane. Thus, the graph of an equation in r and θ consists of those and only those points P having some pair of coordinates satisfying the given equation.

The graph of the equation

$$r = c,$$

c a constant, is a circle of radius $|c|$ having its center at the pole, since each point P on this circle has a pair of coordinates of the form (c,θ) for some θ whereas each point $P(r,\theta)$ off this circle has $|r| \neq |c|$. The graph of $r = -c$ is the same circle.

The graph of the equation

$$\theta = c,$$

c a constant, is a straight line passing through the pole and making an angle of measure c with the polar axis. The graph of $\theta = c \pm n\pi$, n any integer, is the same line.

It is natural to make coordinate paper for a polar coordinate system as indicated in Figure 15.20, with each circle having a constant value of r

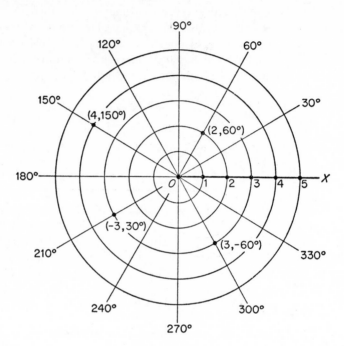

Figure 15.20

and each line a constant value of θ. Some points are plotted in the figure to indicate how the paper is used.

Example 1. Sketch the graph of the equation

$$r = 4 \sin \theta.$$

Solution: We need only graph this equation for $0 \le \theta \le 2\pi$, since the sine function has period 2π. Using the accompanying table of values, the graph is sketched in Figure 15.21. The graph is traced out twice, once as θ ranges from 0 to π

θ	0	$\dfrac{\pi}{6}$	$\dfrac{\pi}{4}$	$\dfrac{\pi}{3}$	$\dfrac{\pi}{2}$	$\dfrac{2\pi}{3}$	$\dfrac{3\pi}{4}$	$\dfrac{5\pi}{6}$	
r	0	2	$2\sqrt{2}$	$2\sqrt{3}$	4	$2\sqrt{3}$	$2\sqrt{2}$	2	
π	$\dfrac{7\pi}{6}$	$\dfrac{5\pi}{4}$	$\dfrac{4\pi}{3}$	$\dfrac{3\pi}{2}$	$\dfrac{5\pi}{3}$	$\dfrac{7\pi}{4}$	$\dfrac{11\pi}{6}$	2π
0	-2	$-2\sqrt{2}$	$-2\sqrt{3}$	-4	$-2\sqrt{3}$	$-2\sqrt{2}$	-2	0

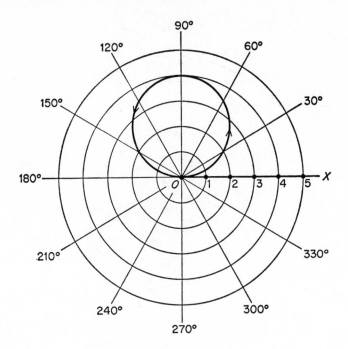

Figure 15.21

and again as θ ranges from π to 2π. Starting from the pole, the graph is traced out as indicated by the arrowhead. The graph is a circle, as we shall presently show.

Example 2. Sketch the graph of the equation

$$r = 2(1 - 2\sin\theta).$$

Solution: We may again limit the range of θ to $0 \le \theta \le 2\pi$. The graph is sketched in Figure 15.22 from the accompanying table of values, with r approximated

θ	0	$\frac{\pi}{6}$	$\frac{\pi}{4}$	$\frac{\pi}{3}$	$\frac{\pi}{2}$	$\frac{2\pi}{3}$	$\frac{3\pi}{4}$	$\frac{5\pi}{6}$	π	$\frac{7\pi}{6}$	$\frac{5\pi}{4}$	$\frac{4\pi}{3}$	$\frac{3\pi}{2}$	$\frac{5\pi}{3}$	$\frac{7\pi}{4}$	$\frac{11\pi}{6}$	2π
r	2	0	$-.8$	-1.5	-2	-1.5	$-.8$	0	2	4	4.8	5.5	6	5.5	4.8	4	2

to one decimal place. This curve is called a limaçon.

If a rectangular and polar coordinate system are placed in the same plane, with the positive x-axis of the first the polar axis of the second (Figure 15.23), then each point P in the plane has both rectangular coordinates (x,y) and polar coordinates (r,θ). If $r > 0$, then according to the definition of the trigonometric functions,

$$\sin\theta = \frac{y}{r}, \qquad \cos\theta = \frac{x}{r},$$

or

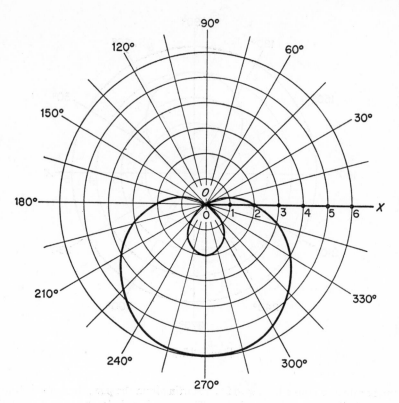

Figure 15.22

15.6 $$x = r \cos \theta, \qquad y = r \sin \theta.$$

It may be verified that even if $r \leq 0$, Equations 15.6 still hold.   Thus the rectangular and polar coordinates of each point in the plane are related by 15.6.   It is clear from 15.6 that x, y, and r are related by the equation

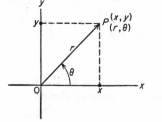

15.7 $$x^2 + y^2 = r^2.$$

In view of 15.6, the graph of the equation

$$r = f(\theta)$$

in polar coordinates is the same as the graph of the parametric equations (with parameter θ)

Figure 15.23 $$x = f(\theta) \cos \theta, \qquad y = f(\theta) \sin \theta$$

in rectangular coordinates.   Conversely, the graph of a given equation in x and y is the same as the graph of the equation in r and θ obtained by replacing x by $r \cos \theta$ and y by $r \sin \theta$.

Example 3. Find an equation in polar coordinates of the hyperbola

$$x^2 - y^2 = 1.$$

Solution: Using 15.6, we get

$$r^2 \cos^2 \theta - r^2 \sin^2 \theta = 1,$$

or, since $\cos^2 \theta - \sin^2 \theta = \cos 2\theta$,

$$r^2 = \sec 2\theta.$$

Example 4. Show that the graph of either $r = a \sin \theta$ or $r = a \cos \theta$, $a > 0$, is a circle of diameter a.

Solution: The equation $r = a \sin \theta$ has the same graph as the equation

$$r^2 = ar \sin \theta,$$

since, if $r \neq 0$, we may cancel out an r in the equation above to obtain $r = a \sin \theta$, while the pole is on both graphs. Hence, by 15.6 and 15.7,

$$x^2 + y^2 = ay$$

is a rectangular-coordinate equation of this graph. This latter equation may be put in the form

$$x^2 + \left(y - \frac{a}{2} \right)^2 = \left(\frac{a}{2} \right)^2,$$

which we recognize as the equation of a circle of radius $a/2$ and with center $(0,a/2)$. Thus the graph of $r = a \sin \theta$ is a circle of diameter a and with center $(a/2,\pi/2)$. By similar arguments, the graph of $r = a \cos \theta$ is a circle of diameter a and with center $(a/2,0)$.

■ ■ ■ EXERCISES

Sketch the graph of each of the following equations:

1. $r = 3$.   2. $\theta = 2\pi/3$.   3. $\theta = -\pi/4$.   4. $r = -4$.

5. $r = 6 \cos \theta$.   6. $r = -2 \sin \theta$.   7. $r = \theta$.   8. $r = 1/\theta$.

9. $r = 2(1 - \cos \theta)$ (cardioid).   10. $r = 2 - \sin \theta$ (limaçon).

11. $r = 4 \sin 3\theta$ (three-leaved rose).   12. $r = 2 \cos 2\theta$ (four-leaved rose).

13. $r = 1 + \sin \theta$ (cardioid).   14. $r^2 = a^2 \cos 2\theta$ (lemniscate).

15. $r = 2 \tan \theta$.   16. $r \cos \theta = 3$.

17. $r = 2 \sec \theta + 1$ (conchoid).   18. $r = a(1 + \sin^2 \theta)$.

19. $r = a \csc \theta$.   20. $r = \sin 4\theta$.

Find an equation in polar coordinates of the graph of each of the following rectangular equations:

21. $x^2 + y^2 = 9$.   22. $x = 4$.   23. $xy = 1$.

24. $y^2 = 8x$.   25. $x^2 + y^2 + 4x = 0$.   26. $x^2 + 4y^2 = 4$.

Find an equation in rectangular coordinates of the graph of each of the following equations:

27. $r = 2 \sin \theta$.   28. $r = 4$.   29. $r = 1 - \sin \theta$.

30. $r = \sec \theta$.   **31.** $r = 2 \csc \theta$.   **32.** $r = 3 \tan \theta$.

33. Use the law of cosines to prove that the distance between the points $P(r_1,\theta_1)$ and $Q(r_2,\theta_2)$ is given by

$$|PQ|^2 = r_1^2 + r_2^2 - 2r_1r_2 \cos (\theta_2 - \theta_1).$$

34. Find an equation of the line on the two points $(a,0)$ and $(b,\pi/2)$, $a \neq 0$ and $b \neq 0$.

35. Find an equation of the line on the point $(a,0)$ and perpendicular to the polar axis.

36. Show that the graph of $r = a \sin \theta + b \cos \theta$ is a circle. Find its center and radius.

7. The conic sections

We recall that the parabola was defined to be the locus of all points equidistant from a fixed point (the focus) and a fixed line (the directrix). In like manner, every conic section (other than the circle) may be defined to be the locus of all points P such that the ratio of the distance between P and a fixed point F (the focus) to the distance between P and a fixed line L (the directrix) is a positive constant e, called the *eccentricity* of the conic section.

In order to find an equation in polar coordinates of a conic section defined as above, let us place the focus F at the pole and the directrix L perpendicular to the polar axis as in Figure 15.24. We let $2p$, $p > 0$,

be the distance between the directrix and the focus as we did for the parabola in 7.8. We limit our discussion to the case

$$e \leq 1,$$

leaving the case $e > 1$ for the reader.

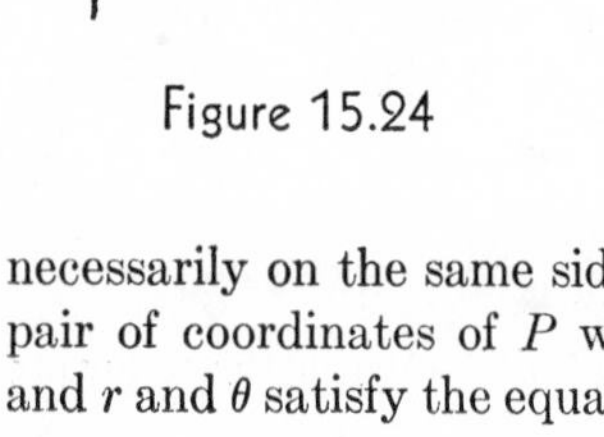

By definition, the point P is on the conic section if and only if (Figure 15.24)

$$\frac{|FP|}{|PQ|} = e.$$

Figure 15.24

Since $e \leq 1$ by assumption, the point P is necessarily on the same side of the directrix as the focus. If (r,θ) is any pair of coordinates of P with $r > 0$, then $|FP| = r$, $|PQ| = 2p + r \cos \theta$, and r and θ satisfy the equation

$$\frac{r}{2p + r \cos \theta} = e.$$

On solving this equation for r, we get

15.8 $$r = \frac{2ep}{1 - e \cos \theta}$$

as the equation satisfied by every point $P(r,\theta)$, $r > 0$, on the conic section.

Conversely, for each point $P(r,\theta)$ satisfying 15.8, necessarily $r > 0$ (since $1 - e \cos \theta \geq 0$) and a reversal of the argument above proves that P is on the conic section. Thus 15.8 is an equation in polar coordinates of the conic section as defined above. Even if $e > 1$, it may be proved that 15.8 is an equation of the conic section, although in this case $r < 0$ for the points $P(r,\theta)$ on the opposite side of the directrix from the focus.

Let us prove that 15.8 actually is an equation of a conic section by finding an equation in rectangular coordinates of the graph of 15.8. We shall still assume that $e \leq 1$.

We may write 15.8 in the form

$$r = e(r \cos \theta + 2p),$$

and since $r > 0$, we have by 15.6 and 15.7 that the graph of this equation has equation

$$\sqrt{x^2 + y^2} = e(x + 2p)$$

in rectangular coordinates. In turn, the graph of this equation is the same as the graph of

(1) $$x^2 + y^2 = e^2(x^2 + 4px + 4p^2).$$

If $e = 1$, (1) becomes

$$y^2 = 4p(x + p),$$

the equation of a parabola with focus at the origin and directrix $x = -2p$.

If $e < 1$, we may complete squares and put (1) in the form

(2) $$\left(x - \frac{2e^2 p}{1 - e^2} \right)^2 + \frac{y^2}{1 - e^2} = \frac{4e^2 p^2}{(1 - e^2)^2}.$$

We recognize (2) as the equation of an ellipse with foci on the x-axis and with

$$a^2 = \frac{4e^2 p^2}{(1 - e^2)^2}, \quad b^2 = \frac{4e^2 p^2}{1 - e^2}, \quad c^2 = \frac{4e^4 p^2}{(1 - e^2)^2}.$$

Since $c = 2e^2 p/(1 - e^2)$, the origin is at a focus. The given directrix has equation $x = -2p$. We note incidentally that $e = c/a$.

If $e > 1$, 15.8 may be shown to be an equation of a hyperbola with a focus at the pole.

By keeping the focus at the origin but varying the directrix to either side of the focus or parallel to the polar axis, either above it or below, the conic section may have an equation of the form

$$r = \frac{2ep}{1 \pm e \cos \theta}, \quad r = \frac{2ep}{1 \pm e \sin \theta}.$$

The conic section is an ellipse if $0 < e < 1$, a parabola if $e = 1$, and a hyperbola if $e > 1$.

Example 1. Find an equation of the ellipse with focus at the pole, eccentricity $e = \frac{1}{2}$, and directrix perpendicular to the polar axis at the point $(-4,0)$.

Solution: We let $e = \frac{1}{2}$ and $p = 2$ in 15.8, obtaining

$$r = \frac{4}{2 - \cos \theta}$$

as the desired equation.

Example 2. Find an equation of the parabola with focus at the pole, and directrix perpendicular to the polar axis at the point $(-3,0)$.

Solution: We let $e = 1$ and $p = \frac{3}{2}$ in 15.8, getting

$$r = \frac{3}{1 - \cos \theta}$$

as an equation of the parabola.

Example 3. Describe and sketch the graph of the equation

$$r = \frac{16}{5 + 3 \sin \theta}.$$

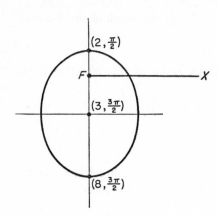

Figure 15.25

Solution: We may put this equation in the form

$$r = \frac{\frac{16}{5}}{1 + \frac{3}{5} \sin \theta},$$

which is an equation of an ellipse with focus at the pole and major axis perpendicular to the polar axis. By giving θ the values $\pi/2$ and $3\pi/2$, we find the ends of the major axis to be $(2, \pi/2)$ and $(8, 3\pi/2)$. Thus the length of the major axis is 10, and $a = 5$. The center of the ellipse is the point $(3, 3\pi/2)$, and $c = 3$. Hence $b^2 = a^2 - c^2 = 16$, and $b = 4$. The ellipse is sketched in Figure 15.25.

■ ■ ■ EXERCISES

Describe and sketch the graph of each of the following equations:

1. $r = \dfrac{2}{1 - \cos \theta}.$ **2.** $r = \dfrac{4}{1 - \sin \theta}.$

3. $r = \dfrac{12}{3 + \cos \theta}.$ **4.** $r = \dfrac{12}{1 - 3 \cos \theta}.$

5. $r = \dfrac{9}{4 + 5 \sin \theta}.$ **6.** $r = \dfrac{9}{5 + 4 \cos \theta}.$

7. $r = \dfrac{1}{\sqrt{2} - \cos \theta}.$ **8.** $r = \dfrac{1}{1 + \sqrt{2} \sin \theta}.$

9. Prove that 15.7 is the equation of a hyperbola if $e > 1$.

10. Prove that if the focus of a conic section of eccentricity e is at the pole and the directrix is parallel to the polar axis and $2p$ units above it, then the conic has equation

$$r = \frac{2ep}{1 + e \sin \theta}.$$

8. Tangent lines of curves in polar coordinates

The graph of

$$r = f(\theta)$$

in polar coordinates is the same as the graph of the parametric equations

15.9 $$x = f(\theta) \cos \theta, \qquad y = f(\theta) \sin \theta$$

in the associated rectangular coordinate system. Thus we may study tangent lines to the graph of $r = f(\theta)$ in polar coordinates by looking at the tangent lines to 15.9 in rectangular coordinates.

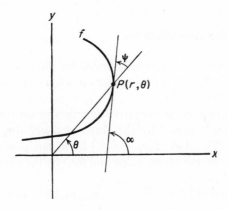

Figure 15.26

If α is the inclination of the tangent line to the graph of $r = f(\theta)$ at the point $P(r,\theta)$ (Figure 15.26) and if $dx/d\theta \neq 0$, then

$$\tan \alpha = \frac{dy}{dx} = \frac{dy/d\theta}{dx/d\theta} = \frac{f(\theta) \cos \theta + f'(\theta) \sin \theta}{-f(\theta) \sin \theta + f'(\theta) \cos \theta},$$

or, if $\cos \theta \neq 0$,

$$\tan \alpha = \frac{f(\theta) + f'(\theta) \tan \theta}{-f(\theta) \tan \theta + f'(\theta)}.$$

On solving this equation for $f'(\theta)$, we get (if $\tan \alpha \neq \tan \theta$)

$$f'(\theta) = \frac{1 + \tan \alpha \tan \theta}{\tan \alpha - \tan \theta} f(\theta),$$

which may be put in the form

15.10 $f'(\theta) = f(\theta) \cot (\alpha - \theta).$

Under certain conditions as indicated in Figure 15.26, $\alpha - \theta = \psi$, an
angle between the position vector and tangent line at P. Hence ψ may be
computed from the equation

$$\cot \psi = \frac{f'(\theta)}{f(\theta)}.$$

Example. Find the angle ψ for the limaçon

$$r = 2(1 - 2 \sin \theta)$$

sketched in Figure 15.22 at the point $(2,0)$.

Solution: We have $r = f(\theta)$, and

$$\cot (\alpha - \theta) = -\frac{4 \cos \theta}{2(1 - 2 \sin \theta)}$$

by 15.10. If $\theta = 0$, $\cot (\alpha - \theta) = \cot \alpha = -2$. In this case, $\alpha = \psi = \tan^{-1}$
$(-\frac{1}{2}) \doteq 153°26'$.

9. *Areas in polar coordinates*

We may find the area of a region bounded by the graph of a function in
polar coordinates and two radius vectors much as we found areas in rectangular coordinates.

Let f be a continuous, nonnegative function in an interval $[a,b]$, and
let R be the region bounded by the graph of f and the lines $\theta = a$ and
$\theta = b$ (Figure 15.27). Let $[\theta_0, \theta_1, \cdots, \theta_n]$ be a partition of $[a,b]$, and, as
usual, let $f(u_i)$ be the minimum value and $f(v_i)$ be the maximum value of f
in the subinterval $[\theta_{i-1}, \theta_i]$.

The region bounded by the lines $\theta = \theta_{i-1}$ and $\theta = \theta_i$ and the graph of f

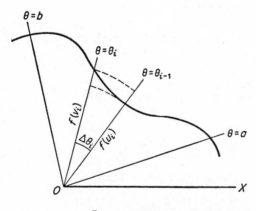

Figure 15.27

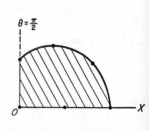

Figure 15.28

contains the sector of a circle with radius $f(u_i)$ and central angle $\Delta\theta_i = \theta_i - \theta_{i-1}$, and in turn is contained in the sector with radius $f(v_i)$ and central angle $\Delta\theta_i$ (Figure 15.27); thus

$$\frac{1}{2} f^2(u_i)\, \Delta\theta_i \leq \Delta A_i \leq \frac{1}{2} f^2(v_i)\, \Delta\theta_i,$$

where ΔA_i designates the area of this region. Since the sum of the ΔA_i, $i = 1, 2, \cdots, n$, is just A, the area of R, we have

$$\sum_{i=1}^{n} \frac{1}{2} f^2(u_i)\, \Delta\theta_i \leq A \leq \sum_{i=1}^{n} \frac{1}{2} f^2(v_i)\, \Delta\theta_i.$$

If now we take a sequence of partitions with norms having limit zero, then each of the above sums approaches the same definite integral, and A must equal this integral: thus the area A of the region R bounded by the graph of f and the lines $\theta = a$ and $\theta = b$ is given by

15.11
$$A = \frac{1}{2} \int_a^b f^2(\theta)\, d\theta.$$

Example 1. Find the area A of the region bounded by the graph of $r = 1 + \cos\theta$ and the lines $\theta = 0$ and $\pi/2$ (Figure 15.28).

Solution: By 15.11,

$$A = \frac{1}{2} \int_0^{\pi/2} (1 + \cos\theta)^2\, d\theta = \frac{1}{2} \int_0^{\pi/2} (1 + 2\cos\theta + \cos^2\theta)\, d\theta$$

$$= \frac{1}{2}\left(\theta + 2\sin\theta + \frac{\theta}{2} + \frac{\sin 2\theta}{4} \right)\Big|_0^{\pi/2} = 1 + \frac{3\pi}{8}.$$

Example 2. Find the area of one loop of the curve $r = 2\sin 3\theta$.

Solution: The least positive angle θ for which $r = 0$ is $\pi/3$. Thus there is a loop of the curve between $\theta = 0$ and $\theta = \pi/3$ whose area A is given by

$$A = \frac{1}{2} \int_0^{\pi/3} (2\sin 3\theta)^2\, d\theta = 2 \int_0^{\pi/3} \sin^2 3\theta\, d\theta$$

$$= \frac{2}{3}\left(\frac{3\theta}{2} - \frac{\sin 6\theta}{4} \right)\Big|_0^{\pi/3} = \frac{\pi}{3}.$$

■ ■ ■ EXERCISES

Find the area of the region bounded by each of the following curves and the given radius vectors; sketch each region:

1. $r = \theta$; $\theta = 0$, $\theta = \dfrac{\pi}{2}$.   **2.** $r = \tan\theta$; $\theta = \dfrac{\pi}{6}$, $\theta = \dfrac{\pi}{4}$.

3. $r = \dfrac{1}{\cos\theta}$; $\theta = -\dfrac{\pi}{4}$, $\theta = \dfrac{\pi}{4}$.   **4.** $r = a\sec^2\dfrac{\theta}{2}$; $\theta = 0$, $\theta = \dfrac{\pi}{2}$.

5. $r = e^{\theta}; \theta = 0, \theta = \pi.$ **6.** $r = \sqrt{\sin \theta}; \theta = \dfrac{\pi}{6}, \theta = \dfrac{\pi}{2}.$

7. $r = \sqrt{1 - \cos \theta}; \theta = \dfrac{\pi}{2}, \theta = \pi.$ **8.** $r = \sin \theta + \cos \theta; \theta = -\dfrac{\pi}{4}, \theta = 0.$

Find the area of the region bounded by each of the following curves (find the area of just one loop if there is more than one loop); sketch each region:

9. $r = 10 \cos \theta.$ **10.** $r = 3 \sin \theta.$

11. $r = 1 - \cos \theta.$ **12.** $r = 2(1 + \sin \theta).$

13. $r = 2 \sin 2\theta.$ **14.** $r = \cos 4\theta.$

15. $r^2 = \cos 2\theta.$ **16.** $r^2 = \sin \theta.$

17. $r = a \sin n\theta,$ n a positive integer, $a > 0.$

18. $r^2 = a \cos n\theta,$ n a positive integer, $a > 0.$

In each of the following exercises, find the area of the region in common to the two given regions:

19. $r = \cos \theta, r = \sin \theta.$ **20.** $r = 3 \cos \theta, r = 1 + \cos \theta.$

21. $r = 4(1 + \cos \theta), r = -4 \sin \theta.$

22. Find the area of the region between the two loops of the limaçon $r = 2 + 4 \cos \theta.$

23. Find $\cot \psi$ at that point on the graph of $r = \sin 3\theta$ where $\theta = \pi/6.$

24. Find $\cot \psi$ at the point (r,θ) on the graph of $r = 1/(1 + \cos \theta).$

25. Justify the use of the term "equiangular spiral" in reference to the graph of $r = e^{\theta}.$

10. Length of arc of a curve

It is intuitively clear that an arc of a parabola or of a sine curve has length. That is, such an arc can be assigned a number that describes the linear extent of the arc. We shall now show that by proceeding according to our intuition, a length can be assigned to such an arc.

Let a given curve C have parametric equations

$$x = x(t), \qquad y = y(t).$$

We shall assume that the functions x' and y' exist and are continuous in each interval under discussion. For convenience the point $(x(t),y(t))$ on C will be designated by $P(t)$. As usual, $P(a)P(b)$ designates the line segment joining $P(a)$ and $P(b)$.

If $[a,b]$ is a closed interval such that $P(t_1) \neq P(t_2)$ if t_1 and t_2 are distinct numbers of the interval (a,b), then the set of all points $P(t)$ as t ranges over $[a,b]$ is called an *arc* of the curve C. We shall designate this arc by the symbol $\overparen{P(a)P(b)}$.

The obvious way to approximate the length of arc $\overparen{P(a)P(b)}$ is to inscribe a broken line in the arc and measure its length. Thus, if $p =$

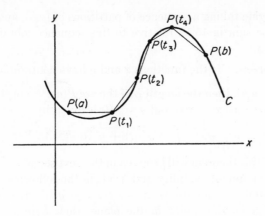

Figure 15.29

$[t_0, t_1, \cdots, t_n]$ is a partition of $[a,b]$, form the broken line $P(t_0)P(t_1) \cdots P(t_n)$ as indicated in Figure 15.29. Such a broken line will be called an *inscrip-ture* of arc $\overset{\frown}{P(a)P(b)}$ and will be designated by I_p. Its length, $|I_p|$, is just the sum of the lengths of its segments:

$$|I_p| = \sum_{i=1}^{n} |P(t_{i-1})P(t_i)|.$$

Using the distance formula, this may be written in the form

(1) $$|I_p| = \sum_{i=1}^{n} \sqrt{[x(t_i) - x(t_{i-1})]^2 + [y(t_i) - y(t_{i-1})]^2}.$$

By the mean value theorem, there exist numbers w_i and z_i in each subin-terval $[t_{i-1}, t_i]$ of p such that

$$x(t_i) - x(t_{i-1}) = x'(w_i)\, \Delta t_i$$

$$y(t_i) - y(t_{i-1}) = y'(z_i)\, \Delta t_i,$$

where $\Delta t_i = t_i - t_{i-1}$ as usual. With the aid of these equations, (1) may be put in the form

15.12 $$|I_p| = \sum_{i=1}^{n} \sqrt{x'^2(w_i) + y'^2(z_i)}\, \Delta t_i.$$

It is clear that $|I_p|$ should be less than or equal to the number we wish to assign as the length of arc $\overset{\frown}{P(a)P(b)}$. Furthermore, we expect $|I_p|$ to be close to the length of this arc if the norm of partition p is small. Such considerations lead us to make the following definition.

15.13 Definition. The length of arc $\overset{\frown}{P(a)P(b)}$ of the curve C is the least upper bound of the set of all lengths of inscriptures of the arc.

We can imagine taking a sequence of partitions of $[a,b]$, and then taking the limit of the sum in 15.12 relative to this sequence, obtaining the following theorem.

15.14 Theorem. If the functions x and y have continuous derivatives in the interval $[a,b]$, then the length L of the arc $\overparen{P(a)P(b)}$ of the curve with parametric equations $x = x(t)$ and $y = y(t)$ is given by

$$L = \int_a^b \sqrt{x'^2(t) + y'^2(t)}\ dt.$$

The proof of this theorem will be given in the next section. In the meantime, we shall assume its validity and use it in the following examples.

If the parametric equations $x = x(t)$, $y = y(t)$ give the position $P(x(t),y(t))$ of a moving point in the plane, then L in 15.14 gives the distance the point travels between times $t = a$ and $t = b$.

If $r(t) = (x(t),y(t))$ is the position vector of a moving point in the plane, then L in 15.14 is the integral of the speed of the point,

$$L = \int_a^b |r'(t)|\ dt,$$

and L is the distance traveled by the point between times $t = a$ and $t = b$.

Example 1. Find the length of one arch of the cycloid with parametric equations

$$x = a(1 - \cos t), \quad y = a(t - \sin t), \quad a > 0.$$

Solution: One arch of the cycloid is traced out as t varies from 0 to 2π (see Figure 15.5). Since

$$x' = a \sin t, \qquad y' = a(1 - \cos t),$$

we have

$$L = \int_0^{2\pi} \sqrt{a^2 \sin^2 t + a^2(1 - \cos t)^2}\ dt$$

$$= a \int_0^{2\pi} \sqrt{2(1 - \cos t)}\ dt.$$

Using the identity $1 - \cos t = 2 \sin^2 (t/2)$, we have

$$L = 2a \int_0^{2\pi} \sin \frac{t}{2}\ dt = -4a \cos \frac{t}{2} \Big|_0^{2\pi} = 8a.$$

Example 2. The position vector of a moving point is

$$r(t) = (t, 2t\sqrt{t}\,).$$

Find the distance traveled by the point between $t = 0$ and $t = 4$.

Solution: Since

$$r'(t) = (1, 3\sqrt{t}\,),$$

the speed is given by

$$|r'(t)| = \sqrt{1 + 9t}.$$

Hence

$$L = \int_0^4 \sqrt{1 + 9t}\ dt = \frac{2}{27}(1 + 9t)^{3/2}\Big|_0^4 = \frac{2}{27}(37\sqrt{37} - 1) \doteq 16.6.$$

If the function f has a continuous derivative in the interval $[a,b]$, then the length of the arc of the graph of

$$y = f(x)$$

between $x = a$ and $x = b$ may be found by expressing the graph in parametric form

$$x = t, \qquad y = f(t)$$

and using 15.14. Thus $x' = 1$, $y' = f'(t)$ and 15.14 becomes (replacing t by x)

15.15 $$L = \int_a^b \sqrt{1 + f'^2(x)}\, dx.$$

A similar device for polar coordinates yields

15.16 $$L = \int_a^b \sqrt{f^2(\theta) + f'^2(\theta)}\, d\theta$$

for the length of arc of the polar curve $r = f(\theta)$ between $\theta = a$ and $\theta = b$.

■ ■ ■ EXERCISES

In each of the following exercises find the distance traveled by a moving point in the plane with position vector r during the given time interval:

1. $r(t) = (3 \cos 2t, 3 \sin 2t)$; $0 \le t \le 2$.
2. $r(t) = (2t + 1, t^2)$; $0 \le t \le 2$.
3. $r(t) = (\cos t, \cos^2 t)$; $0 \le t \le \pi$.
4. $r(t) = (3t^2, 2t^3)$; $0 \le t \le 3$.
5. $r(t) = (e^t \cos t, e^t \sin t)$; $0 \le t \le 2$.
6. $r(t) = (3t, t^3)$; $0 \le t \le 2$. (Approximate by Simpson's rule.)

Find the length of the specified arc for each of the following curves:

7. $y = x^{3/2}$ from $(0,0)$ to $(4,8)$.
8. $y = \ln x$ from $(1,0)$ to $(e^2,2)$.
9. $y = \ln \cos x$ from $(0,0)$ to $(\pi/3, -\ln 2)$.
10. $y = 1/x$ from $(1,1)$ to $(5,1/5)$. (Approximate by Simpson's rule.)
11. $y = 4 - x^2$ from $(-2,0)$ to $(2,0)$.
12. $y = \ln (x^2 - 1)$ from $(-3, \ln 8)$ to $(-2, \ln 3)$.
13. Prove Formula 15.16. (*Hint:* Use 15.9.)
14. If the function g has a continuous derivative in the interval $[c,d]$, derive the following formula for the length of the arc of the graph of $x = g(y)$ from $y = c$ to $y = d$:

$$L = \int_c^d \sqrt{1 + g'^2(y)}\, dy.$$

Find the length of the specified arc for each of the following curves:

15. $r = e^\theta$; $\theta = 0$ to $\theta = \ln 4$.

16. $r = a(1 - \cos \theta)$; complete curve.

17. $r = \sin^2 (\theta/2)$; $\theta = 0$ to $\theta = \pi$.

18. $r = \cos^3 (\theta/3)$; complete curve.

19. Find the length of the hypocycloid $x = a \cos^3 \theta$, $y = a \sin^3 \theta$.

20. Set up the integral for the circumference of an ellipse.

21. Prove that the length of arc of the curve $y = \cosh x$ between the points $(0,1)$ and $(x,\cosh x)$, $x > 0$, is $\sinh x$.

11. Proof of the arc-length formula

As in the previous section, x and y are assumed to be functions with continuous derivatives in the interval $[a,b]$, and the curve C is the graph of the parametric equations

$$x = x(t), \qquad y = y(t).$$

The proof of Theorem 15.14 will be given after a few preliminary results are established.

Since the functions x' and y' are continuous in $[a,b]$, so are the functions x'^2 and y'^2 and each of these functions assumes a maximum value in $[a,b]$. Let $x'^2(u)$ and $y'^2(v)$ be the maximum values of x'^2 and y'^2, respectively, in $[a,b]$.

We recall that corresponding to the partition p of $[a,b]$ is the inscripture I_p of $\overparen{P(a)P(b)}$ with length given by 15.12. Since

$$\sqrt{x'^2(w_i) + y'^2(z_i)} \leq \sqrt{x'^2(u) + y'^2(v)}$$

for each number w_i and z_i appearing in 15.12, evidently

$$|I_p| \leq \sqrt{x'^2(u) + y'^2(v)} \sum_{i=1}^{n} \Delta t_i.$$

The sum of the Δt_i is just $b - a$, and therefore

15.17 $$|I_p| \leq (b - a)\sqrt{x'^2(u) + y'^2(v)}.$$

Inequality 15.17 holds for every partition p of $[a,b]$. Thus the right side of 15.17 is an upper bound of the set S of all lengths of inscriptures of arc $\overparen{P(a)P(b)}$. This proves, incidentally, that arc length is well defined by 15.13, since every set S of numbers with an upper bound has a least upper bound by 8.3.

For convenience of notation, the symbol

$$L_a^b$$

will be used to designate the length of arc $\overparen{P(a)P(b)}$. From 15.17 and the very definition of L_a^b, we have that

$$|I_r| \le L_a^b \le (b - a)\sqrt{x'^2(u) + y'^2(v)},$$

for every partition p of $[a,b]$.

A desirable property of arc length is that of *additivity*. That is, if an arc is cut into two pieces, then the length of the whole arc is the sum of the lengths of the two pieces:

15.18 If $a < c < b$, then $L_a^b = L_a^c + L_c^b$.

Proof of 15.18: If p is a partition of $[a,c]$ and q of $[c,b]$, then p and q together form a partition r of $[a,b]$. Clearly

$$|I_p| + |I_q| = |I_r|.$$

Since $|I_r| \le L_a^b$, we have

$$|I_p| \le L_a^b - |I_q|$$

for every partition p of $[a,c]$. Thus $L_a^b - |I_q|$ is an upper bound of the set of all lengths of inscriptures of arc $\widehat{P(a)P(c)}$, and since L_a^c is the least upper bound of this set, we must have

$$L_a^c \le L_a^b - |I_q|.$$

This inequality may be put in the form

$$|I_q| \le L_a^b - L_a^c,$$

from which we deduce that

$$L_c^b \le L_a^b - L_a^c$$

by the same argument as before. Hence we have proved that

$$L_a^c + L_c^b \le L_a^b.$$

On the other hand, if r is a partition of $[a,b]$, let us form the partition r' by dividing the subinterval $[t_{i-1},t_i]$ of r containing c into two subintervals $[t_{i-1},c]$ and $[c,t_i]$. Thus r' has one more subinterval than r, or the same number if $c = t_i$ for some i. In either case, it is clear that

$$|I_r| \le |I_{r'}|$$

as indicated in Figure 15.30. The partition r' of $[a,b]$ is made up of a partition p of $[a,c]$ and a partition q of $[c,b]$, so that

$$|I_r| \le |I_p| + |I_q| \le L_a^c + L_c^b.$$

Hence $$L_a^b \le L_a^c + L_c^b,$$

and this inequality together with the one of the previous paragraph proves 15.18.

We may define an *arc-length function* s for the curve C in the following way:

$$s(t) = L_a^t \quad \text{if } t > a,$$

$$s(a) = 0.$$

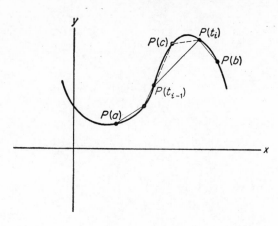

Figure 15.30

Thus $s(t)$ is the length of the arc $\overparen{P(a)P(t)}$. Let us prove now that the function s has a derivative given by

15.19 $s'(t) = \sqrt{x'^2(t) + y'^2(t)}.$

Proof: If $h > 0$, then

$$s(t + h) - s(t) = L_t^{t+h}$$

by the additivity of arc length. Hence, by 15.17 (with $a = t$, $b = t + h$),

(1) $s(t + h) - s(t) \leq h\sqrt{x'^2(u) + y'^2(v)}$

for some numbers u and v in the interval $[t, t + h]$. If we let $p = [t, t + h]$, the partition of $[t, t + h]$ into one subinterval, we have by 15.12

$$|I_p| = h\sqrt{x'^2(w) + y'^2(z)}$$

for some numbers w and z in the interval $[t, t + h]$. Since $|I_p| \leq L_t^{t+h}$, we must have

(2) $h\sqrt{x'^2(w) + y'^2(z)} \leq s(t + h) - s(t).$

We may combine (1) and (2) into one inequality

$$h\sqrt{x'^2(w) + y'^2(z)} \leq s(t + h) - s(t) \leq h\sqrt{x'^2(u) + x'^2(v)}.$$

On dividing throughout this inequality by the positive number h, we get

(3) $\sqrt{x'^2(w) + y'^2(z)} \leq \dfrac{s(t + h) - s(t)}{h} \leq \sqrt{x'^2(u) + x'^2(v)}.$

It may be verified that (3) holds even if $h < 0$.

Since the numbers u, v, w, and z are between t and $t + h$,

$$\lim_{h \to 0} x'^2(w) = \lim_{h \to 0} x'^2(u) = x'^2(t),$$

$$\lim_{h \to 0} y'^2(z) = \lim_{h \to 0} y'^2(v) = y'^2(t),$$

and the two extremes of (3) have the same limit as h approaches 0.   Thus

$$s'(t) = \lim_{h \to 0} \frac{s(t+h) - s(t)}{h} = \sqrt{x'^2(t) + y'^2(t)},$$

and 15.19 is established.

Theorem 15.14 follows readily from this last result by integration.   Thus

$$\int_a^b \sqrt{x'^2(t) + y'^2(t)}\ dt = \int_a^b s'(t)\ dt = s(b) - s(a) = s(b),$$

and $s(b) = L$, the length of arc $\overgroup{P(a)P(b)}$.

If $x = x(t)$ and $y = y(t)$ are parametric equations of a moving point P, then $\sqrt{x'^2(t) + y'^2(t)}$ is the speed of the point P at time t.   Thus we can conclude from 15.19 that the speed of P is the derivative of the arc length function s, as our intuition tells us must be the case.

■ ■ ■ EXERCISES

1. Prove that the limit as h approaches 0 of the ratio of the length of the chord $P(t)P(t+h)$ to the length of the arc $\overgroup{P(t)P(t+h)}$ equals 1 for the curve C of this section.

2. Let $s(t)$ be the length of arc of the curve C from a fixed point A to the point $P(x(t),y(t))$, and let $\theta(s)$ be the inclination of the tangent line at P (Figure 15.31).   The instantaneous rate of change of θ with respect to s is called the *curvature* of the curve C at P; thus $D_s\theta$ is the curvature at P. Show that

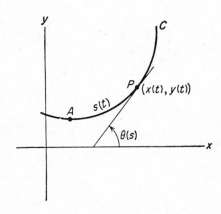

$$D_s\theta = \frac{x'(t)y''(t) - y'(t)x''(t)}{[x'^2(t) + y'^2(t)]^{3/2}}.$$

(*Hint:* $\theta = \tan^{-1}[(y'(t)/x'(t)]$, and $D_t\theta = D_s\theta \cdot D_t s$.)

Figure 15.31

3. Show that the curvature of a circle is the reciprocal of its radius.

4. Show that if the curve C of Exercise 2 is the graph of the equation $y = f(x)$, then the curvature is given by

$$\frac{f''(x)}{[1 + f'^2(x)]^{3/2}}.$$

12. *Areas of surfaces of revolution*

If an arc of a curve is rotated about an axis, it sweeps out a surface of revolution. The theory of the previous sections may be used to assign an area to such a surface.

As in the previous sections, let a curve C be the graph of the parametric equations

$$x = x(t), \qquad y = y(t),$$

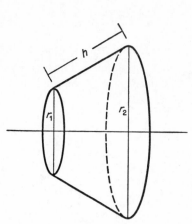

and let $[a,b]$ be an interval for which both x' and y' exist and are continuous. We shall also assume that the arc $\overparen{P(a)P(b)}$ of curve C is above the x-axis; that is, that $y(t) \geq 0$ for every t in $[a,b]$. Let us find the area of the surface swept out by rotating arc $\overparen{P(a)P(b)}$ of C about the x-axis.

If $p = [t_0, t_1, \cdots, t_n]$ is a partition of $[a,b]$, the inscripture I_p was used to approximate the length of arc $\overparen{P(a)P(b)}$. Hence, it seems reasonable that if I_p is rotated about the x-axis, I_p will sweep out a surface

Figure 15.32

with area approximating that of the given surface. The surface generated by I_p is made up of n frustums of cones. A frustum of a cone of slant height h and radii of bases r_1 and r_2 (Figure 15.32) has lateral surface area

$$\pi(r_1 + r_2)h$$

according to a formula of geometry. Hence the ith segment $P(t_{i-1})P(t_i)$ of I_p (Figure 15.33) sweeps out a frustum of a cone of lateral area

$$\pi[y(t_{i-1}) + y(t_i)]|P(t_{i-1})P(t_i)|.$$

Using the value of $|P(t_{i-1})P(t_i)|$ given in 15.12, the total area S_p of the surface swept out by I_p is given by

$$S_p = \pi \sum_{i=1}^{n} [y(t_{i-1}) + y(t_i)]\sqrt{x'^2(w_i) + y'^2(z_i)}\,\Delta t_i,$$

where w_i and z_i are numbers in the interval $[t_{i-1}, t_i]$.

In the limit as the norm of p approaches zero, we can imagine that the above formula yields

15.20 $$S = 2\pi \int_a^b y(t)\sqrt{x'^2(t) + y'^2(t)}\,dt$$

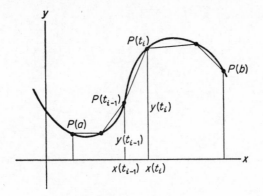

Figure 15.33

as the area of the surface swept out by rotating arc $\overparen{P(a)P(b)}$ about the x-axis.   We shall not give a formal proof of 15.20, but nevertheless accept its validity.

If the arc $\overparen{P(a)P(b)}$ is rotated about the y-axis, we get the same formula with the factor $y(t)$ replaced by $x(t)$ in the integrand.

If the curve C is the graph of the equation

$$y = f(x),$$

then 15.20 becomes [letting $x = t$, $y = f(t)$]

15.21 $S = 2\pi \int_a^b f(x)\sqrt{1 + f'^2(x)}\ dx.$

Example 1.   Find the area of the surface generated by rotating the arc of the curve

$$x = t^2, \quad y = 2t, \quad 0 \le t \le 4,$$

about the x-axis.

Solution: By 15.20,

$$S = 2\pi \int_0^4 2t\sqrt{(2t)^2 + (2)^2}\ dt$$

$$= \frac{8\pi}{3}\ (t^2 + 1)^{3/2}\bigg|_0^4 = \frac{8\pi}{3}\ (17\sqrt{17} - 1).$$

Example 2.   Find the area of the surface generated by rotating one arch of the sine curve about its axis.

Solution: If we rotate the arc of the curve $y = \sin x$ between $x = 0$ and $x = \pi$ about the x-axis, we obtain a surface with area (using 15.21)

$$S = 2\pi \int_0^\pi \sin x\sqrt{1 + \cos^2 x}\ dx.$$

This may be integrated by letting $u = \cos x$, thus obtaining

$$S = -2\pi \int_1^{-1} \sqrt{1 + u^2}\, du$$

$$= -2\pi \left[\frac{u}{2} \sqrt{1 + u^2} + \frac{1}{2} \ln \left(u + \sqrt{1 + u^2} \right) \right]\Big|_1^{-1}$$

$$= 2\pi [\sqrt{2} + \ln (\sqrt{2} + 1)].$$

■ ■ ■ EXERCISES

Find the area of the surface obtained by rotating each of the following arcs about the x-axis:

1. $x = t^2/2,\ y = t;\ 1 \le t \le 3$.
2. $x = 2t^3,\ y = 3t^2;\ 0 \le t \le 2$.
3. $x = \cos^2 \theta,\ y = \sin \theta \cos \theta;\ 0 \le \theta \le \pi/2$.
4. $x = 2 \ln t,\ y = t^2;\ 1 \le t \le 3$.
5. $y = x^3;\ 0 \le x \le 2$.
6. $y = \cosh x;\ -1 \le x \le 1$.
7. $y = e^x;\ -2 \le x \le 2$.
8. $y = 2\sqrt{x};\ 1 \le x \le 4$.
9. Find the surface area of a sphere. (*Hint:* Use parametric equations for a circle.)
10. The part of a sphere between two parallel planes is called a zone. Show that the area of a zone of a sphere is $2\pi a h$, where a is the radius of the sphere and h is the height of the zone, i.e., the distance between the parallel planes.
11. Find the area of the surface of an ellipsoid of revolution formed by rotating an ellipse about its major axis; its minor axis.
12. A loop of the cycloid of Figure 15.5 is rotated about the x-axis. Find the area of the surface generated.
13. The cardioid $r = a(1 + \cos \theta)$ is rotated about the polar axis, sweeping out a surface. Find the area of this surface. (*Hint:* Change to parametric form.)
14. One loop of the lemniscate $r^2 = a^2 \cos 2\theta$ is rotated about the polar axis. Find the area of the surface generated.

$$\underline{}\ \LARGE 16$$

Infinite series

■ ■ ■ ■ ■ SEQUENCES AND THEIR LIMITS were discussed in the first
section of Chapter 9.   Given a sequence

$$a_1, a_2, \cdots, a_n, \cdots,$$

it is the purpose of the present chapter to discuss the
infinite series

$$a_1 + a_2 + \cdots + a_n + \cdots$$

associated with the sequence.

1. Convergence and divergence

Associated with an infinite series

$$a_1 + a_2 + \cdots + a_n + \cdots$$

are its *partial sums*

$$S_1 = a_1,$$
$$S_2 = a_1 + a_2,$$
$$S_3 = a_1 + a_2 + a_3,$$

. . . .

. . . .

$$S_n = a_1 + a_2 + \cdots + a_n,$$

. . . .

. . . .

If the sigma notation is used, we write

$$\sum_{k=1}^{\infty} a_k$$

for the given infinite series (or just Σa_k without limits at times) and

$$S_n = \sum_{k=1}^{n} a_k$$

for the nth partial sum.

An infinite series need not have a sum. As a matter of fact we must define what we mean by a sum of an infinite sequence of numbers, since the usual operation of addition applies only to a finite set of numbers. Thus, whereas the sum of an infinite sequence of numbers is as yet undefined, each partial sum of the infinite series is a sum of a finite set of numbers and hence is itself a well-defined number. It is natural to define the sum of an infinite series as the number approached by the partial sum S_n as n gets large.

16.1 Definition. An infinite series

$$a_1 + a_2 + \cdots + a_n + \cdots$$

with partial sums $S_1, S_2, \cdots, S_n, \cdots$ is said to be *convergent* if and only if

$$\underset{n \to \infty}{\text{limit}} \, S_n$$

exists. If this limit does not exist, the infinite series is said to be *divergent*. The number

$$S = \underset{n \to \infty}{\text{limit}} \, S_n$$

is called the *sum* of a convergent infinite series. A divergent infinite series does not have a sum.

If a convergent infinite series Σa_k has sum S, then we shall write

$$S = \sum_{k=1}^{\infty} a_k.$$

An infinite series of the form

$$\sum_{k=1}^{\infty} ar^{k-1} = a + ar + ar^2 + \cdots + ar^{n-1} + \cdots$$

is called a *geometric series*. From the identity

$$1 - r^n = (1 - r)(1 + r + r^2 + \cdots + r^{n-1}),$$

we easily deduce that the nth partial sum S_n of the geometric series is given by

$$S_n = a \sum_{k=1}^{n} r^{k-1} = \frac{a(1 - r^n)}{1 - r},$$

or
$$S_n = \frac{a}{1-r} - \frac{ar^n}{1-r}, \quad r \neq -1.$$

Since
$$\lim_{n\to\infty} r^n = 0 \quad \text{if } |r| < 1,$$

evidently
$$\lim_{n\to\infty} S_n = \frac{a}{1-r} - \frac{a}{1-r} \lim_{n\to\infty} r^n = \frac{a}{1-r}$$

if $|r| < 1$. This proves that the geometric series converges and has sum $a/(1-r)$ if $|r| < 1$; that is,

16.2
$$\sum_{k=1}^{\infty} ar^{k-1} = \frac{a}{1-r}, \quad |r| < 1.$$

(It is a corollary of the next theorem that the geometric series diverges if $|r| \geq 1$.)

For example,
$$1 + \frac{1}{2} + \frac{1}{4} + \cdots + \frac{1}{2^{n-1}} + \cdots = \frac{1}{1 - 1/2} = 2,$$

$$.3 + .03 + .003 + \cdots + \frac{3}{10^n} + \cdots = \frac{.3}{1 - 10^{-1}} = \frac{1}{3}.$$

We recognize this latter series to be $.3333\cdots$, the infinite decimal representation of $\frac{1}{3}$.

Every sequence of numbers
$$S_1, S_2, \cdots, S_n, \cdots$$

is the sequence of partial sums of some infinite series, namely, the series
$$S_1 + (S_2 - S_1) + (S_3 - S_2) + \cdots + (S_n - S_{n-1}) + \cdots.$$

For example,
$$\frac{1}{2}, \frac{2}{3}, \cdots, \frac{n}{n+1}, \cdots$$

is the sequence of partial sums of the infinite series
$$\frac{1}{2} + \left(\frac{2}{3} - \frac{1}{2}\right) + \cdots + \left(\frac{n}{n+1} - \frac{n-1}{n}\right) + \cdots,$$

or

(1)
$$\frac{1}{1\cdot 2} + \frac{1}{2\cdot 3} + \cdots + \frac{1}{n(n+1)} + \cdots.$$

Since
$$\lim_{n\to\infty} S_n = \lim_{n\to\infty} \frac{n}{n+1} = \lim_{n\to\infty} \frac{1}{1 + 1/n} = 1,$$

series (1) is convergent with sum equal to 1,
$$\sum_{k=1}^{\infty} \frac{1}{k(k+1)} = 1.$$

It is an immediate consequence of the definition of the limit of a sequence that if the sequence

$$S_1, S_2, \cdots, S_n, \cdots$$

has a limit, then so does the sequence

$$S_m, S_{m+1}, \cdots, S_{m+n}, \cdots$$

obtained by deleting the first $m - 1$ elements of the first sequence. Furthermore, the two sequences have the same limit,

$$\lim_{n\to\infty} S_n = \lim_{n\to\infty} S_{m+n}.$$

In particular, if S_n is the nth partial sum of the convergent infinite series Σa_k, then

$$a_n = S_n - S_{n-1}$$

and (9.5),

$$\lim_{n\to\infty} a_n = \lim_{n\to\infty} S_n - \lim_{n\to\infty} S_{n-1} = 0.$$

Thus we have the following result.

16.3 Theorem. If the infinite series Σa_k converges, then

$$\lim_{n\to\infty} a_n = 0.$$

An immediate corollary of this theorem is as follows.

16.4 Theorem. If $\lim_{n\to\infty} a_n \neq 0$, then the infinite series Σa_k diverges.

We may use this theorem to prove that the geometric series Σar^{k-1}, $a \neq 0$, diverges if $|r| \geq 1$. Thus,

$$\lim_{n\to\infty} r^n \neq 0 \quad \text{if } |r| \geq 1,$$

and the divergence of the geometric series if $|r| \geq 1$ follows from 16.4.

If the infinite series Σa_k with nth partial sum S_n converges and has sum S, then for every number $\epsilon > 0$, there exists a number N such that

$$|S - S_n| < \epsilon \quad \text{for every } n > N.$$

Consequently

$$|S_n - S_m| \leq |S_n - S| + |S - S_m| < 2\epsilon \quad \text{if } m, n > N.$$

In words, the difference between any two partial sums S_m and S_n is small if $m > N$ and $n > N$. This fact may be used at times to prove the divergence of an infinite series, as is shown below.

The series

$$\sum_{k=1}^{\infty} \frac{1}{k} = 1 + \frac{1}{2} + \cdots + \frac{1}{n} + \cdots$$

is called the *harmonic series*. For this series,

$$S_{2n} - S_n = \frac{1}{n+1} + \frac{1}{n+2} + \cdots + \frac{1}{2n} > \frac{1}{2n} + \frac{1}{2n} + \cdots + \frac{1}{2n} = \frac{1}{2},$$

that is,
$$S_{2n} - S_n > \frac{1}{2}$$

for every integer n. Since $S_{2n} - S_n < \frac{1}{2}$ for n large enough if a series is convergent, we conclude that the harmonic series $\Sigma 1/k$ is divergent.

■ ■ ■ EXERCISES

Find the sum of each of the following convergent series:

1. $5 + \dfrac{5}{7} + \cdots + \dfrac{5}{7^{n-1}} + \cdots$.

2. $5 - \dfrac{5}{7} + \cdots + \dfrac{(-1)^{n-1}\,5}{7^{n-1}} + \cdots$.

3. $\pi + \dfrac{\pi}{\sqrt{2}} + \cdots + \dfrac{\pi}{\sqrt{2^{n-1}}} + \cdots$.

4. $.232323\cdots$.

5. $.612612612\cdots$.

6. $1 - \dfrac{1}{4} + \dfrac{1}{16} - \dfrac{1}{64} + \cdots$.

Each of the following is the nth partial sum of an infinite series. Find the infinite series, tell whether it is convergent or divergent, and if convergent, find its sum:

7. $S_n = \dfrac{n}{2n + 1}$.

8. $S_n = \dfrac{3n}{4n + 1}$.

9. $S_n = \dfrac{n^2}{n + 1}$.

10. $S_n = \ln(n + 1)$.

11. $S_n = \dfrac{1}{2^n}$.

12. $S_n = 2^n$.

13. $S_n = \dfrac{n^2}{n^2 + 1}$.

14. $S_n = \dfrac{n^3 - 1}{n^3}$.

Show that each of the following infinite series diverges:

15. $\dfrac{1}{2} + \dfrac{2}{3} + \cdots + \dfrac{n}{n + 1} + \cdots$.

16. $-1 + 1 + \cdots + (-1)^n + \cdots$.

17. $1 + \dfrac{1}{\sqrt{2}} + \cdots + \dfrac{1}{\sqrt{n}} + \cdots$.

18. $1 + \dfrac{1}{2} + \dfrac{1}{2} + \dfrac{1}{4} + \dfrac{1}{4} + \dfrac{1}{4} + \dfrac{1}{4} + \dfrac{1}{8} + \cdots$.

19. $\dfrac{3}{2} + \dfrac{9}{4} + \dfrac{27}{8} + \dfrac{81}{16} + \cdots$.

20. $\dfrac{1}{\ln 2} + \dfrac{1}{\ln 3} + \dfrac{1}{\ln 4} + \cdots .$

21. If Σa_k is a convergent infinite series and

$$R_n = a_{n+1} + a_{n+2} + \cdots ,$$

the *remainder* of the series after n terms, then prove that

$$\lim_{n \to \infty} R_n = 0.$$

22. Let $b_1, b_2, \cdots, b_n, \cdots$ be a sequence of nonzero numbers such that $\lim\limits_{n \to \infty} b_n = \pm\infty$. Prove that the infinite series $\Sigma(b_{k+1} - b_k)$ diverges whereas the series $\Sigma(1/b_k - 1/b_{k+1})$ converges.

23. Using the preceding exercise, show that the infinite series

$$\sum_{k=1}^{\infty} \ln\left(1 + \frac{1}{k}\right)$$

diverges.

2. Positive term series

The convergence or divergence of an infinite series Σa_k is not changed by modifying a finite number of its terms. Thus, if the two series

$$\sum_{k=1}^{\infty} a_k, \qquad \sum_{k=1}^{\infty} b_k,$$

with nth partial sums S_n and T_n, respectively, differ only in their first m terms (i.e., $a_k = b_k$ if $k > m$), then

$$S_n - T_n = S_m - T_m$$

for every integer $n \geq m$. Hence

$$\lim_{n \to \infty} S_n = (S_m - T_m) + \lim_{n \to \infty} T_n,$$

and either both limits exist or both limits do not exist; that is, the series Σa_k and Σb_k either both converge or both diverge. If the series converge, their sums differ by $S_m - T_m$.

Another useful fact is that if either of the infinite series Σa_k and $\Sigma c a_k$, $c \neq 0$, converges, then so does the other and

16.5 $$\sum_{k=1}^{\infty} c a_k = c \sum_{k=1}^{\infty} a_k, \quad c \neq 0.$$

We prove 16.5 by noting that if S_n is the nth partial sum of Σa_k then $c S_n$ is the nth partial sum of $\Sigma c a_k$, and

$$\lim_{n \to \infty} c S_n = c \lim_{n \to \infty} S_n,$$

where either both limits exist or both do not exist.

Using similar arguments, it can easily be proved that if Σa_k and Σb_k are convergent infinite series then so are the series $\Sigma(a_k + b_k)$ and $\Sigma(a_k - b_k)$, and

16.6
$$\sum_{k=1}^{\infty} (a_k \pm b_k) = \sum_{k=1}^{\infty} a_k \pm \sum_{k=1}^{\infty} b_k.$$

The following theorem on sequences may be used to establish the convergence of certain infinite series.

16.7 Theorem. If $S_1, S_2, \cdots, S_n, \cdots$ is a sequence for which $S_1 \leq S_2 \leq \cdots \leq S_n \leq \cdots$, and if there exists a number K such that every $S_n \leq K$, then the given sequence has a limit, and

$$\lim_{n \to \infty} S_n \leq K.$$

Proof: By assumption, the set of all S_n has an upper bound K. Hence this set has a least upper bound S by 8.3. For every number $\epsilon > 0$, $S - \epsilon$ is not an upper bound of the set of all S_n, and therefore $S_N > S - \epsilon$ for some integer N (depending on ϵ). By assumption, $S_n \geq S_N > S - \epsilon$ for every $n > N$, so that

$$0 \leq S - S_n < \epsilon \quad \text{for every } n > N.$$

This proves that

$$\lim_{n \to \infty} S_n = S,$$

where S is a number less than or equal to K.

A series Σa_k with each $a_k > 0$ is called a *positive-term series*. For such a series, evidently

$$S_1 < S_2 < \cdots < S_n < \cdots.$$

Hence, if each $S_n < K$ for some number K, the given series converges by the previous theorem. If no such number K exists, then

$$\lim_{n \to \infty} S_n = \infty$$

and the series Σa_k diverges. Clearly, if the series Σa_k converges and has the sum S, then $S_n < S$ for every n.

From a given positive-term series Σa_k, we may form other series by grouping the terms in some order. For example, we might form the series

$$a_1 + (a_2 + a_3) + (a_4 + a_5 + a_6) + (a_7 + a_8 + a_9 + a_{10}) + \cdots.$$

Designating this series by Σb_k, we have

$$b_1 = a_1, \quad b_2 = a_2 + a_3, \quad b_3 = a_4 + a_5 + a_6, \quad \cdots.$$

It is evident that each partial sum of the series Σb_k is also a partial sum of the series Σa_k. Thus, if the series Σa_k converges, so does the series Σb_k and their sums are equal. Similar remarks hold for any grouping of the terms of Σa_k.

We may also form a new series from a series Σa_k by rearranging the terms.   For example, we might form the sum

$$a_3 + a_1 + a_5 + a_2 + a_7 + a_4 + \cdots .$$

If the series Σa_k is convergent with sum S and if T_n is the nth partial sum of a series Σb_k formed by rearranging the terms of Σa_k, then $T_n < S$ since T_n is a sum of terms of the series Σa_k.   Hence Σb_k converges and has a sum $T \leq S$ by 16.7.   Since the series Σa_k may be obtained by rearranging the terms of Σb_k, we have $S \leq T$ by the same reasoning.   Thus $S = T$, and we have proved that each rearrangement of a positive-term convergent series is a convergent series having the same sum.

Let us establish the following test for convergence.

16.8 Comparison test.   Let Σa_k and Σb_k be positive-term series. (1) If Σa_k converges and if $b_k \leq a_k$ for every integer k, then the series Σb_k converges. (2) If Σa_k diverges and if $b_k \geq a_k$ for every integer k, then the series Σb_k diverges.

Proof: Designate the nth partial sums of Σa_k and Σb_k by S_n and T_n, respectively.   If Σa_k converges and every $b_k \leq a_k$, then

$$T_n \leq S_n < \sum_{k=1}^{\infty} a_k$$

for every integer n.   Hence the series Σb_k converges by 16.7.   We omit the proof of (2) because of its similarity to that of (1).

If $0 < b_k \leq a_k$ for every integer k, then the series Σa_k is said to *dominate* the series Σb_k.   According to the theorem above, every infinite series dominated by a convergent series also is convergent.

In view of the fact that a finite number of terms of a series may be changed without affecting the convergence or divergence of the series, it is clear that the comparison test need only hold from the mth term on, where m is any positive integer.

Example 1.   Prove that the series

$$\frac{1}{2} + \frac{1}{3} + \frac{1}{5} + \cdots + \frac{1}{2^{n-1} + 1} + \cdots$$

converges.

Solution: We compare the given series with the convergent geometric series $\sum \dfrac{1}{2^{k-1}}$. Thus

$$\frac{1}{2^{k-1} + 1} < \frac{1}{2^{k-1}}$$

for every integer k, and the given series must converge.

Example 2.   Prove that the so-called *p series*

$$1 + \frac{1}{2^p} + \frac{1}{3^p} + \cdots + \frac{1}{n^p} + \cdots$$

diverges if $p \leq 1$.

Solution: The given series is the divergent harmonic series $\Sigma 1/k$ if $p = 1$.   If $p < 1$, then $k^p \leq k$ and

$$\frac{1}{k^p} \geq \frac{1}{k}$$

for every integer k.   Hence the series $\Sigma 1/k^p$ diverges by 16.8, (2).

For example, if $p = \frac{1}{2}$, we have that the series

$$1 + \frac{1}{\sqrt{2}} + \frac{1}{\sqrt{3}} + \cdots + \frac{1}{\sqrt{n}} + \cdots$$

is divergent.

The following test is essentially a corollary of the comparison test.

16.9 Theorem.   If $c_1, c_2, \cdots, c_n, \cdots$ is a sequence of positive numbers such that

$$\lim_{n \to \infty} c_n = c, \quad c > 0,$$

then the two positive-term series

$$\sum_{k=1}^{\infty} a_k, \quad \sum_{k=1}^{\infty} c_k a_k$$

either both converge or both diverge.

Proof: Since $\lim_{n \to \infty} c_n = c > 0$, there exists an integer N such that

$$\frac{c}{2} < c_k < \frac{3c}{2} \quad \text{for every integer } k \geq N.$$

Hence $\frac{c}{2} a_k < c_k a_k < \frac{3c}{2} a_k \quad \text{if } k \geq N,$

and if the series Σa_k converges, then so does the series $\Sigma c_k a_k$ since it is dominated by a convergent series $\Sigma (3c/2) a_k$.   Conversely, if the series $\Sigma c_k a_k$ is convergent, then so is the series $\Sigma (c/2) a_k$ and in turn $\Sigma a_k = (2/c)\Sigma(c/2)a_k$.   This proves part of the theorem.   The rest of the proof is left to the reader.

Example 3.   Show that the series

$$\sum_{k=1}^{\infty} \frac{k+1}{k(2k-1)}$$

diverges.

Solution: We may put the given series in the form

$$\sum_{k=1}^{\infty} \left(\frac{1 + 1/k}{2 - 1/k} \right) \frac{1}{k}.$$

Since

$$\lim_{n \to \infty} \frac{1 + 1/n}{2 - 1/n} = \frac{1}{2}$$

and the harmonic series $\Sigma 1/k$ diverges, the given series diverges by the theorem above.

The theory of improper integrals may be used to give the following test for convergence of an infinite series.

16.10 Integral test.   If f is a positive-valued, continuous, and decreasing function, then the infinite series

$$f(1) + f(2) + \cdots + f(n) + \cdots$$

converges or diverges according as the improper integral

$$\int_1^\infty f(x)\, dx$$

exists or is infinite.

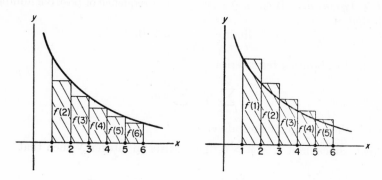

Figure 16.1

Proof: It is clear from Figure 16.1 that

$$f(2) + f(3) + \cdots + f(n)$$

is a lower sum and

$$f(1) + f(2) + \cdots + f(n-1)$$

is an upper sum of f over the interval $[1,n]$.   Hence

(1) $$\sum_{k=2}^{n} f(k) \leq \int_1^n f(x)\, dx \leq \sum_{k=1}^{n-1} f(k).$$

If the given improper integral exists, then

$$\sum_{k=2}^{n} f(k) \leq \int_1^n f(x)\, dx < \int_1^\infty f(x)\, dx$$

and the infinite series $\Sigma f(k)$ converges by 16.7.   If the given improper integral is infinite, then clearly $\Sigma f(k) = \infty$ also by (1) above.   This proves the integral test.

If we let

$$f(x) = \frac{1}{x^p},$$

then the series $\Sigma f(k)$ is just the p *series*

$$1 + \frac{1}{2^p} + \frac{1}{3^p} + \cdots + \frac{1}{n^p} + \cdots .$$

We easily verify that

$$\int_1^\infty \frac{1}{x^p}\, dx = \text{limit}_{t \to \infty} \int_1^t x^{-p}\, dx$$

$$= -\frac{1}{p-1} \, \text{limit}_{t \to \infty} \left(\frac{1}{t^{p-1}} - 1\right)$$

$$= \frac{1}{p-1} \text{ if } p > 1, \quad \text{or} \quad \infty \text{ if } p < 1.$$

Hence the p series converges by the integral test if $p > 1$ and diverges if $p < 1$.

Example 4. Show that the series

$$\sum_{k=1}^\infty \frac{k+3}{k^3 - k + 1}$$

converges.

Solution: We may write the given series in the form

$$\sum_{k=1}^\infty \left(\frac{1 + 3/k}{1 - 1/k^2 + 1/k^3}\right) \frac{1}{k^2}.$$

Since

$$\text{limit}_{n \to \infty} \frac{1 + 3/n}{1 - 1/n^2 + 1/n^3} = 1,$$

and the p series $\Sigma 1/k^2$ converges, the given series converges by 16.9.

■ ■ ■ EXERCISES

Determine whether each of the following series is convergent or divergent:

1. $1 + \frac{1}{2^3} + \frac{1}{3^3} + \cdots + \frac{1}{n^3} + \cdots .$

2. $1 + \frac{1}{2\sqrt{2}} + \frac{1}{3\sqrt{3}} + \cdots + \frac{1}{n\sqrt{n}} + \cdots .$

3. $\frac{1}{2} + \frac{1}{5} + \frac{1}{11} + \cdots + \frac{1}{3^{n-1} + 2} + \cdots .$

4. $\frac{1}{4} + \frac{1}{7} + \frac{1}{10} + \cdots + \frac{1}{3n+1} + \cdots .$

5. $\displaystyle\sum_{k=1}^\infty \frac{k}{k^2 + 1}.$ **6.** $\displaystyle\sum_{k=1}^\infty \frac{\ln k}{k}.$

7. $\displaystyle\sum_{k=3}^{\infty} \frac{1}{\sqrt[k]{2}}.$

8. $\displaystyle\sum_{k=4}^{\infty} \frac{\sqrt{k}}{k^2 - 4}.$

9. $\displaystyle\sum_{k=1}^{\infty} \frac{k+1}{\ln (k+2)}.$

10. $\displaystyle\sum_{k=1}^{\infty} \frac{k}{e^k}.$

11. $\displaystyle\sum_{k=0}^{\infty} \frac{1}{(k+1)(k+3)}.$

12. $\displaystyle\sum_{k=2}^{\infty} \frac{1}{k \ln k}.$

13. $\displaystyle\sum_{k=1}^{\infty} \frac{1}{(3k)^p}, \ p > 1.$

14. $\displaystyle\sum_{k=1}^{\infty} \frac{1}{(3k)^p}, \ p < 1.$

15. $\displaystyle\sum_{k=2}^{\infty} \frac{k^2}{e^k}.$

16. $\displaystyle\sum_{k=1}^{\infty} \frac{\tan^{-1} k}{k^2 + 1}.$

17. $\displaystyle\sum_{k=3}^{\infty} \frac{\ln k}{k^2}.$

18. $\displaystyle\sum_{k=0}^{\infty} \frac{1}{\sqrt{k^3 + 1}}.$

19. $\displaystyle\sum_{k=0}^{\infty} \frac{k+1}{(k+2)2^k}.$

20. $\displaystyle\sum_{k=1}^{\infty} \frac{2 + \sin k}{k^2}.$

21. Use the methods of the proof of the integral test to show that

$$\frac{1}{(p-1)(n+1)^{p-1}} < \sum_{k=1}^{\infty} \frac{1}{k^p} - \sum_{k=1}^{n} \frac{1}{k^p} < \frac{1}{(p-1)n^{p-1}}$$

if $p > 1$.

(a) How good an approximation of the infinite series $\Sigma 1/k^2$ is its nth partial sum in case $n = 10$? $n = 20$?

(b) How good an approximation of the infinite series $\Sigma 1/k^3$ is its nth partial sum in case $n = 10$? $n = 20$?

22. Prove 16.6.

23. Each infinite decimal

$$.a_1 a_2 a_3 \cdots a_n \cdots, \quad a_n \text{ an integer}, \quad 0 \le a_n \le 9,$$

may be defined to be the sum of the infinite series

$$\frac{a_1}{10} + \frac{a_2}{10^2} + \cdots + \frac{a_n}{10^n} + \cdots.$$

Prove that this series is convergent.

(a) Show that a repeating decimal is a sum of a geometric series, and is a rational number.

(b) Prove that every real number r, $0 < r < 1$, may be expressed as an infinite decimal $r = .a_1 a_2 a_3 \cdots a_n \cdots$. (*Hint:* Select the integer a_1 so that

$$\frac{a_1}{10} \le r < \frac{a_1}{10} + \frac{1}{10}, \quad 0 \le a_1 \le 9:$$

and the integer a_2 so that

$$\frac{a_1}{10} + \frac{a_2}{100} \le r < \frac{a_1}{10} + \frac{a_2}{100} + \frac{1}{100}, \quad 0 \le a_2 \le 9:$$

and so on. Thus, if $S_n = .a_1 a_2 \cdots a_n$, then $S_n \leq r < S_n + 10^{-n}$. Prove that $r = \lim\limits_{n\to\infty} S_n$.)

24. Complete the proof of 16.9.

3. Alternating series

An infinite series of the form
$$a_1 - a_2 + a_3 - a_4 + \cdots + (-1)^{n-1} a_n + \cdots,$$
each $a_n > 0$, having alternating positive and negative terms is called an *alternating series*. A classical example of an alternating series is the alternating harmonic series
$$1 - \frac{1}{2} + \frac{1}{3} - \frac{1}{4} + \cdots + \frac{(-1)^{n-1}}{n} + \cdots$$
which we shall show presently to be convergent with sum $\ln 2$. A simple test for the convergence of an alternating series is as follows.

16.11 Alternating series test. If (1) $a_{n+1} \leq a_n$ for each n, and (2) $\lim\limits_{n\to\infty} a_n = 0$, then the alternating series $\Sigma(-1)^{k-1} a_k$ is convergent.

Proof: The partial sums of $\Sigma(-1)^{k-1} a_k$ having an even number of terms may be written as follows: $S_2 = (a_1 - a_2)$, $S_4 = (a_1 - a_2) + (a_3 - a_4)$, and, in general,
$$S_{2n} = (a_1 - a_2) + (a_3 - a_4) + \cdots + (a_{2n-1} - a_{2n}).$$
By assumption, $a_1 - a_2 \geq 0$, $a_3 - a_4 \geq 0$, and, in general, $a_{2n-1} - a_{2n} \geq 0$. Thus it is clear that
$$0 \leq S_2 \leq S_4 \leq \cdots \leq S_{2n} \leq \cdots.$$
On the other hand, S_{2n} may also be written in the form
$$S_{2n} = a_1 - (a_2 - a_3) - (a_4 - a_5) - \cdots - (a_{2n-2} - a_{2n-1}) - a_{2n},$$
from which it is clear that for every integer n,
$$S_{2n} \leq a_1.$$
That
$$\lim_{n\to\infty} S_{2n}$$
exists and is less than or equal to a_1 now follows from 16.7.
Since $S_{2n+1} = S_{2n} + a_{2n+1}$,
$$\lim_{n\to\infty} S_{2n+1} = \lim_{n\to\infty} S_{2n} + \lim_{n\to\infty} a_{2n+1} = \lim_{n\to\infty} S_{2n}.$$
Thus
$$\lim_{n\to\infty} S_n = \lim_{n\to\infty} S_{2n} = \lim_{n\to\infty} S_{2n+1} = S,$$
and $S \leq a_1$. This proves 16.11.
If $\Sigma(-1)^{k-1} a_k$ is an alternating series with the properties of 16.11, then

the remainder R_n of this series after n terms,

$$R_n = (-1)^n(a_{n+1} - a_{n+2} + a_{n+3} - \cdots),$$

is again an alternating series with these same properties. Clearly

$$|R_n| = a_{n+1} - a_{n+2} + a_{n+3} - \cdots,$$

and therefore

$$|R_n| \leq a_{n+1}$$

as shown in the proof of 16.11. If S is the sum of $\Sigma(-1)^{k-1}a_k$, then $S = S_n + R_n$ and

$$|S - S_n| = |R_n| \leq a_{n+1}.$$

This proves the following result.

16.12 Theorem. If $\Sigma(-1)^{k-1}a_k$ is an alternating series having the properties stated in 16.11, and if S_n and S are, respectively, the nth partial sum and the sum of this series, then $S \doteq S_n$ with an error of no more than a_{n+1}.

Example 1. Show that the alternating series

$$1 - \frac{1}{1!} + \frac{1}{2!} - \frac{1}{3!} + \cdots + \frac{(-1)^n}{n!} + \cdots$$

is convergent. Approximate its sum S to 3 decimal places.

Solution: Since

$$\frac{1}{n!} > \frac{1}{(n+1)!} \quad \text{and} \quad \lim_{n\to\infty} \frac{1}{n!} = 0,$$

the series converges by 16.11. We easily verify that

$$\frac{1}{7!} < .0002.$$

Hence

$$S \doteq 1 - 1 + \frac{1}{2} - \frac{1}{6} + \frac{1}{24} - \frac{1}{120} + \frac{1}{720} \doteq .368$$

accurate to 3 decimal places. We shall show presently that this alternating series has sum $1/e$, so $1/e \doteq .368$.

Example 2. Test the alternating series

$$1 - \frac{2}{3} + \frac{3}{5} - \cdots + \frac{(-1)^{n-1}n}{2n-1} + \cdots$$

for convergence.

Solution: Since

$$\frac{n}{2n-1} > \frac{n+1}{2n+1}$$

for each n, 16.11 (1) is satisfied. However,

$$\lim_{n\to\infty} \frac{n}{2n-1} = \lim_{n\to\infty} \frac{1}{2 - 1/n} = \frac{1}{2},$$

and 16.11 (2) is not satisfied. Since the nth term of the given series is not approaching 0, the series diverges by 16.4.

■ ■ ■ EXERCISES

Test each of the following alternating series for convergence:

1. $1 - \dfrac{1}{2} + \dfrac{1}{3} - \cdots + \dfrac{(-1)^{n-1}}{n} + \cdots$.

2. $\dfrac{2}{\ln 2} - \dfrac{2}{\ln 3} + \cdots + \dfrac{2(-1)^{n-1}}{\ln (n + 1)} + \cdots$.

3. $\dfrac{2}{3} - \dfrac{1}{2} + \dfrac{4}{9} - \cdots + \dfrac{(n + 1)(-1)^{n-1}}{3n} + \cdots$.

4. $-\dfrac{1}{2} + \dfrac{2}{5} - \dfrac{3}{10} + \cdots + \dfrac{n(-1)^n}{n^2 + 1} + \cdots$.

5. $\displaystyle\sum_{k=1}^{\infty} \dfrac{(-1)^k}{2k - 1}$.

6. $\displaystyle\sum_{k=1}^{\infty} \dfrac{k(-1)^{k-1}}{2^k}$.

7. $\displaystyle\sum_{k=2}^{\infty} \dfrac{k(-1)^{k-1}}{\ln k}$.

8. $\displaystyle\sum_{k=1}^{\infty} \dfrac{(2k - 1)(-1)^k}{5k + 1}$.

9. $\displaystyle\sum_{k=1}^{\infty} \dfrac{\sqrt{k}(-1)^{k-1}}{2k + 1}$.

10. $\displaystyle\sum_{k=1}^{\infty} \dfrac{(-1)^{k-1} \ln k}{k}$.

Approximate the sum of each of the following series to 3 decimal places:

11. $1 - \dfrac{1}{2^2} + \dfrac{1}{2^4} - \cdots + \dfrac{(-1)^{n-1}}{2^{2(n-1)}} + \cdots$.

12. $1 - \dfrac{1}{2!} + \dfrac{1}{4!} - \dfrac{1}{6!} + \cdots$.

13. $1 - \dfrac{1}{3^3} + \dfrac{1}{5^3} - \dfrac{1}{7^3} + \cdots$.

14. $\dfrac{1}{3} - \dfrac{1}{2 \cdot 3^2} + \dfrac{1}{3 \cdot 3^3} - \dfrac{1}{4 \cdot 3^4} + \cdots$.

4. Absolute convergence

We shall consider in this section series having negative as well as positive terms. Associated with each infinite series Σa_k is its series of absolute values

$$\sum_{k=1}^{\infty} |a_k| = |a_1| + |a_2| + \cdots + |a_n| + \cdots.$$

A series Σa_k is called *absolutely convergent* if its series of absolute values $\Sigma |a_k|$ converges. Let us prove the following theorem on absolutely convergent series.

16.13 Theorem. Every absolutely convergent series Σa_k is convergent, and

$$\left| \sum_{k=1}^{\infty} a_k \right| \leq \sum_{k=1}^{\infty} |a_k|.$$

Proof: Consider the three infinite series Σa_k, $\Sigma|a_k|$, and $\Sigma(a_k + |a_k|)$ having respective nth partial sums S_n, T_n, and U_n. Clearly

$$S_n + T_n = U_n.$$

Since $0 \leq a_k + |a_k| \leq 2|a_k|$,

$$0 \leq U_n \leq 2T_n \leq 2T$$

for every integer n, where T is the sum of $\Sigma|a_k|$. Since $U_1 \leq U_2 \leq \cdots \leq U_n \leq \cdots \leq 2T$, we have by 16.7 that

$$\lim_{n\to\infty} U_n = U \leq 2T.$$

Thus
$$\lim_{n\to\infty} S_n = \lim_{n\to\infty} U_n - \lim_{n\to\infty} T_n = U - T,$$

and the series Σa_k is convergent with sum $S = U - T \leq T$.

The series $\Sigma(-a_k)$ has sum $-S$, and, since $T = \Sigma|-a_k|$, we have $-S \leq T$ by the same argument as above with the series Σa_k replaced by $\Sigma(-a_k)$. Since both S and $-S$ are less than or equal to T, then $|S| \leq T$ and the theorem is proved.

Not every convergent series is absolutely convergent. Thus, by the alternating series test, the alternating harmonic series

$$1 - \frac{1}{2} + \frac{1}{3} - \frac{1}{4} + \frac{1}{5} - \cdots$$

is convergent, whereas its series of absolute values is the divergent harmonic series. A series such as the alternating harmonic series that is convergent without being absolutely convergent is called *conditionally convergent*.

We may easily prove the following results on absolutely convergent series. (Compare these results with 16.5 and 16.6.)

16.14 Theorem. If the series Σa_k and Σb_k are absolutely convergent, then so are the series $\Sigma(a_k \pm b_k)$ and $\Sigma c a_k$ for any constant c.

Proof: These follow readily from the inequalities

$$\sum_{k=1}^{n} |a_k \pm b_k| \leq \sum_{k=1}^{n} |a_k| + \sum_{k=1}^{n} |b_k| \leq \sum_{k=1}^{\infty} |a_k| + \sum_{k=1}^{\infty} |b_k|,$$

$$\sum_{k=1}^{\infty} |c a_k| = |c| \sum_{k=1}^{\infty} |a_k|,$$

and theorem 16.7.

A very useful test for absolute convergence of a series is the ratio test that follows.

16.15 Ratio test. The series Σa_k is:

(1) absolutely convergent if $\displaystyle\lim_{n\to\infty} \left|\frac{a_{n+1}}{a_n}\right| = L < 1$;

(2) divergent if either $\displaystyle\lim_{n\to\infty} \left|\frac{a_{n+1}}{a_n}\right| = \begin{cases} L > 1. \\ \infty \end{cases}$

Proof: To prove (1), let r be any number such that
$$L < r < 1.$$
Since the limit of $|a_{n+1}/a_n|$ as n approaches ∞ is L, there exists a positive integer N such that
$$\left|\frac{a_{n+1}}{a_n}\right| < r \quad \text{for every integer } n \geq N.$$
Thus
$$|a_{N+1}| < r|a_N|,$$
$$|a_{N+2}| < r|a_{N+1}| < r^2|a_N|,$$
$$|a_{N+3}| < r|a_{N+2}| < r^2|a_{N+1}| < r^3|a_N|,$$
and, in general,
$$|a_{N+k}| < r^k|a_N| \quad \text{for every integer } k > 0.$$
Hence the series
$$|a_{N+1}| + |a_{N+2}| + \cdots + |a_{N+n}| + \cdots$$
is convergent, since it is dominated by the convergent geometric series
$$|a_N|r + |a_N|r^2 + \cdots + |a_N|r^n + \cdots.$$
Therefore the series
$$\sum_{k=1}^{\infty} |a_k| = \sum_{k=1}^{N} |a_k| + \sum_{k=1}^{\infty} |a_{N+k}|$$
is convergent, and the given series Σa_k is absolutely convergent.

To prove (2), if $L > 1$ then there exists a number N such that
$$\left|\frac{a_{n+1}}{a_n}\right| > 1 \quad \text{for every integer } n > N.$$
Thus $|a_{n+1}| > |a_n|$ for every $n > N$, and
$$\lim_{n\to\infty} |a_n|$$
cannot equal zero. Hence, by 9.9,
$$\lim_{n\to\infty} a_n \neq 0,$$
and therefore the series Σa_k is divergent by 16.4. An analogous argument proves the other part of (2).

If

$$\lim_{n\to\infty} \left|\frac{a_{n+1}}{a_n}\right| = 1,$$

nothing can be said directly about the convergence of the series Σa_k. For example,

$$\lim_{n\to\infty} \frac{1/(n+1)^p}{1/n^p} = \lim_{n\to\infty} \left(\frac{n}{n+1}\right)^p = 1$$

for every p series $\Sigma 1/k^p$. We have already shown that the p series converges if $p > 1$ and diverges if $p \leq 1$. The ratio test is of no help in testing series similar to the p series for convergence.

Example 1. Test the convergence of the series

$$1 + \frac{1}{2!} + \frac{1}{3!} + \cdots + \frac{1}{n!} + \cdots.$$

Solution: Since

$$\lim_{n\to\infty} \frac{1/(n+1)!}{1/n!} = \lim_{n\to\infty} \frac{1}{n+1} = 0,$$

the series converges by the ratio test.

Example 2. Test the convergence of the series

$$\frac{1}{5} - \frac{2}{5^2} + \frac{3}{5^3} - \cdots + \frac{n(-1)^{n-1}}{5^n} + \cdots.$$

Solution: We have

$$\lim_{n\to\infty} \left|\frac{(n+1)(-1)^n/5^{n+1}}{n(-1)^{n-1}/5^n}\right| = \lim_{n\to\infty} \frac{n+1}{5n} = \frac{1}{5},$$

and therefore the series converges absolute by the ratio test.

Example 3. Test the convergence of the series

$$1 + \frac{2^2}{2!} + \frac{3^3}{3!} + \cdots + \frac{n^n}{n!} + \cdots.$$

Solution: The ratio a_{n+1}/a_n for this series is given by

$$\frac{a_{n+1}}{a_n} = \frac{(n+1)^{n+1}}{(n+1)!} \cdot \frac{n!}{n^n} = \frac{(n+1)^n \cdot (n+1) \cdot n!}{(n+1)! \cdot n^n} = \left(\frac{n+1}{n}\right)^n,$$

or

$$\frac{a_{n+1}}{a_n} = \left(1 + \frac{1}{n}\right)^n.$$

Since

$$\lim_{n\to\infty} \left(1 + \frac{1}{n}\right)^n = e$$

and $e > 1$, the series diverges by the ratio test.

■ ■ ■ EXERCISES

Test the following series for convergence and absolute convergence:

1. $1 - \frac{1}{3!} + \frac{1}{5!} - \frac{1}{7!} + \cdots.$

2. $2 - \dfrac{2^2}{2!} + \dfrac{2^3}{3!} - \dfrac{2^4}{4!} + \cdots$.

3. $\dfrac{1}{2} + \dfrac{3}{5} + \dfrac{9}{10} + \cdots + \dfrac{3^{n-1}}{n^2 + 1} + \cdots$.

4. $\dfrac{1}{9} - \dfrac{2}{81} + \dfrac{6}{729} - \cdots + \dfrac{n!(-1)^{n-1}}{9^n} + \cdots$.

5. $\displaystyle\sum_{k=1}^{\infty} \dfrac{k!}{1 \cdot 3 \cdot 5 \cdots (2k-1)}$.

6. $\displaystyle\sum_{k=1}^{\infty} \dfrac{7^k}{2 \cdot 4 \cdot 6 \cdots (2k)}$.

7. $\displaystyle\sum_{k=1}^{\infty} \dfrac{k!(-1)^k}{10^{k+1}}$.

8. $\displaystyle\sum_{k=1}^{\infty} \dfrac{7^{k+1} \cdot k^2 \cdot (-1)^{k+1}}{8^k}$.

9. $\displaystyle\sum_{k=1}^{\infty} \dfrac{k+3}{k^3}$.

10. $\displaystyle\sum_{k=1}^{\infty} \dfrac{3^k(-1)^{k+1}}{k^2 \cdot 2^{k+1}}$.

11. $\displaystyle\sum_{k=1}^{\infty} \dfrac{(1+4k)(-1)^k}{7k^2 - 1}$.

12. $\displaystyle\sum_{k=1}^{\infty} \dfrac{1 \cdot 3 \cdot 5 \cdots (2k+1)}{3 \cdot 6 \cdot 9 \cdots (3k)}$.

13. Prove that the series Σa_k diverges if there exists a number N such that $|a_{n+1}/a_n| > 1$ for every $n > N$.

14. The positive-term series Σa_k has the property that

$$\operatorname*{limit}_{n \to \infty} \frac{a_{n+1}}{a_n} = L < 1.$$

Prove that for every number r, $L < r < 1$, there exists an integer n such that

$$\sum_{k=1}^{\infty} a_k - \sum_{k=1}^{n} a_k < a_n \left(\frac{r}{1-r} \right).$$

15. Prove that if Σa_k is absolutely convergent and if $|b_k| \leq |a_k|$ for every integer k, then Σb_k is absolutely convergent.

16. Form the series

$$\frac{a}{1} - \frac{b}{2} + \frac{a}{3} - \frac{b}{4} + \frac{a}{5} - \frac{b}{6} + \cdots$$

where a and b are given positive numbers. Express this infinite series in the Σ notation. For what choices of a and b is this series absolutely convergent? Conditionally convergent?

5. *Power series*

An infinite series of the form

$$\sum_{k=0}^{\infty} a_k x^k = a_0 + a_1 x + a_2 x^2 + \cdots + a_n x^n + \cdots$$

is called a *power series* in x. A power series in x is the infinite series analogue of a polynomial in x.

If the power series $\Sigma a_k x^k$ is absolutely convergent, so that the series $\Sigma |a_k||x|^k$ converges, then it is evident by the comparison test that the power series $\Sigma a_k z^k$ is absolutely convergent for every number z such that $|z| \le |x|$. Similarly, if the series $\Sigma |a_k||x|^k$ is divergent, then so is the series $\Sigma |a_k||z|^k$ whenever $|z| \ge |x|$.

16.16 Definition. The *radius of convergence* r of a power series $\Sigma a_k x^k$ is the least upper bound of the set of all numbers x such that the series is absolutely convergent. If the series is absolutely convergent for every number x, let $r = \infty$.

If the power series $\Sigma |a_k||z|^k$ is divergent, then the number $|z|$ is an upper bound of the set S of all numbers x such that the given power series $\Sigma a_k x^k$ is absolutely convergent. Incidentally, the set S has at least one number in it, namely 0. Thus it is clear that the radius of convergence r is well defined by the above definition, and that either $r = 0$, r is a positive number, or $r = \infty$.

If r is the radius of convergence of the power series $\Sigma a_k x^k$ and if the series $\Sigma |a_k||z|^k$ diverges, then necessarily $|z| \ge r$ in view of our remarks above. Therefore we conclude that the series $\Sigma a_k x^k$ converges absolutely if $|x| < r$, and we have proved part of the following theorem.

16.17 Theorem. If r is the radius of convergence of the power series $\Sigma a_k x^k$, then the series converges absolutely if $|x| < r$ and diverges if $|x| > r$.

Proof: The only part of the theorem not proved is that if $|x| > r$ then the series $\Sigma a_k x^k$ diverges. This will be proved by showing that if the series $\Sigma a_k x^k$ converges, then $|x| \le r$. In order to prove that $r \ge |x|$, we will show that for every number z such that $|z| < |x|$ the series $\Sigma a_k z^k$ converges absolutely. Hence the least upper bound r of the set of all numbers z such that the series $\Sigma a_k z^k$ is absolutely convergent exceeds or is equal to $|x|$.

If $\Sigma a_k x^k$ converges, $x \ne 0$, then

$$\lim_{n \to \infty} |a_n x^n| = 0$$

and there exists a number M such that

$$|a_k x^k| \le M \quad \text{for every integer } k.$$

Since $|z| < |x|$, the number

$$s = |z|/|x|$$

is less than 1. Evidently

$$|a_k z^k| = |a_k x^k s^k| \le M s^k$$

for every k, and therefore the series $\Sigma |a_k||z|^k$ is dominated by the convergent geometric series $\Sigma M s^k$. Thus $\Sigma a_k z^k$ is absolutely convergent, and the proof is completed.

A useful corollary of 16.17 is as follows.

16.18 Theorem. Let r be the radius of convergence of the power series $\Sigma a_k x^k$ and let s be any number such that $0 < s < r$. If $c_1, c_2, \cdots,$ $c_n, \cdots$ is a sequence of numbers such that $|c_k| \leq s$ for every integer k, then the series

$$a_0 + a_1 c_1 + a_2 (c_2)^2 + \cdots + a_n (c_n)^n + \cdots$$

is absolutely convergent.

Proof: Evidently $\Sigma |a_k||c_k|^k$ is dominated by the convergent series $\Sigma |a_k| s^k$.

If the power series $\Sigma a_k x^k$ has radius of convergence $r > 0$, then the series converges absolutely for every number x in the open interval $(-r,r)$ by 16.17. The only other numbers for which the series might converge are $x = -r$ and $x = r$. Thus the set of all numbers at which the power series $\Sigma a_k x^k$ converges is either an open interval $(-r,r)$, a half-closed interval $[-r,r)$ or $(-r,r]$, or a closed interval $[-r,r]$. Of course, there are also the two other possibilities that $r = 0$ or $r = \infty$. The interval in which a power series converges is called the *interval of convergence* of the series.

Knowing the interval of convergence of the power series $\Sigma a_k x^k$, we can easily find the interval of convergence of the power series

$$\sum_{k=0}^{\infty} a_k (x - c)^k = a_0 + a_1 (x - c) + a_2 (x - c)^2 + \cdots + a_n (x - c)^n + \cdots .$$

If, for example, $\Sigma a_k x^k$ has interval of convergence $[-r,r)$, then the series $\Sigma a_k (x - c)^k$ converges for $-r \leq x - c < r$; that is, for every x in the interval $[c - r, c + r)$. This interval is called the interval of convergence of the series $\Sigma a_k (x - c)^k$.

The ratio test may often be used to find the interval of convergence of a power series, as the following example shows.

Example. Find the interval of convergence of each of the following power series:

(a) $\qquad 1 + x + \dfrac{x^2}{2!} + \cdots + \dfrac{x^n}{n!} + \cdots .$

(b) $\qquad 1 - x + \dfrac{x^2}{2} - \cdots + \dfrac{(-1)^{n-1} x^n}{n} + \cdots .$

(c) $\qquad 1 + x + 2x^2 + \cdots + nx^n + \cdots .$

(d) $\qquad \dfrac{1}{3} + \dfrac{(x - 2)}{36} + \dfrac{(x - 2)^2}{243} + \cdots + \dfrac{(x - 2)^n}{3^n n^2} + \cdots .$

Solution: (a) Since

$$\lim_{n \to \infty} \left| \frac{x^{n+1}/(n + 1)!}{x^n/n!} \right| = \lim_{n \to \infty} \frac{|x|}{n + 1} = 0$$

for every number x, this series converges for every number x by the ratio test. Its interval of convergence is $(-\infty, \infty)$.

(b) We have

$$\lim_{n \to \infty} \left| \frac{(-1)^n x^{n+1}/(n + 1)}{(-1)^{n-1} x^n/n} \right| = \lim_{n \to \infty} \frac{n}{n + 1} |x| = |x|,$$

and therefore the series converges if $|x| < 1$ and diverges if $|x| > 1$ by the ratio test. Hence $r = 1$ for this series. Clearly the series converges if $x = 1$ and diverges if $x = -1$. Hence $(-1,1]$ is its interval of convergence.

(c) Since

$$\underset{n \to \infty}{\text{limit}} \left| \frac{(n+1)x^{n+1}}{nx^n} \right| = \underset{n \to \infty}{\text{limit}} \frac{n+1}{n} |x| = |x|,$$

again $r = 1$ by the ratio test. This series evidently diverges if $x = \pm 1$. Hence its interval of convergence is the open interval $(-1,1)$.

(d) We have

$$\underset{n \to \infty}{\text{limit}} \left| \frac{(x-2)^{n+1}}{3^{n+1}(n+1)^2} \cdot \frac{3^n n^2}{(x-2)^n} \right| = \underset{n \to \infty}{\text{limit}} \frac{n^2}{3(n+1)^2} |x-2| = \frac{|x-2|}{3}.$$

Hence the series converges if $|x-2|/3 < 1$, or, if

$$|x - 2| < 3.$$

If $|x - 2| = 3$, the series is just the p series (or alternating p series) for $p = 2$. Since these series also converge, the interval of convergence of the given series is the set of all x such that $|x - 2| \leq 3$, that is, the closed interval $[-1,5]$.

The multiplication of a series termwise by a nonzero number does not alter the convergence or divergence of a series (16.5). Thus, for example, the power series

$$a_0 x + a_1 x^2 + \cdots + a_n x^{n+1} + \cdots$$

has the same interval of convergence as $\Sigma a_k x^k$, since it is obtained by multiplying $\Sigma a_k x^k$ termwise by x. If we multiply $\Sigma a_k x^k$ termwise by $1/x$ and omit the first term of the resulting series, we obtain the series

$$a_1 + a_2 x + \cdots + a_n x^{n-1} + \cdots .$$

which again has the same interval of convergence as $\Sigma a_k x^k$. The coefficients of a power series may also be altered in certain ways without affecting the radius of convergence of the series, as the following theorem shows.

16.19 Theorem. If $c_0, c_1, \cdots, c_n, \cdots$ is a sequence of positive numbers for which

$$\underset{n \to \infty}{\text{limit}} \sqrt[n]{c_n} = 1,$$

then the two power series $\Sigma a_k x^k$ and $\Sigma c_k a_k x^k$ have the same radius of convergence.

Proof: Let r be the radius of convergence of the series $\Sigma a_k x^k$ and r' that of $\Sigma c_k a_k x^k$. We shall first of all assume that r is a positive number and that x is chosen so that

$$0 < |x| < r.$$

Then $(r - |x|)/|x| > 0$, and we can select a number $\epsilon > 0$ so that $\epsilon < (r - |x|)/|x|$, that is, so that

$$(1 + \epsilon)|x| < r.$$

Since $\lim_{n \to \infty} \sqrt[n]{c_n} = 1$, we can find an integer N such that

$$1 - \epsilon < \sqrt[n]{c_n} < 1 + \epsilon \quad \text{for every } n \geq N.$$

Hence

$$|c_n x^n| = (\sqrt[n]{c_n} \, |x|)^n < [(1 + \epsilon)|x|]^n \quad \text{for every } n \geq N,$$

and the series

$$\sum_{k=N}^{\infty} |c_k a_k x^k|$$

is dominated by the series

$$\sum_{k=N}^{\infty} |a_k| [(1 + \epsilon)|x|]^k.$$

This latter series converges since $(1 + \epsilon)|x| < r$, and therefore the former series converges also. By adding on N terms to this series, we can conclude that the series $\Sigma c_k a_k x^k$ is absolutely convergent if $|x| < r$. Therefore the series $\Sigma c_k a_k x^k$ has a radius of convergence $r' \geq r$.

Since

$$\sum_{k=0}^{\infty} a_k x^k = \sum_{k=0}^{\infty} \frac{1}{c_k} (c_k a_k x^k),$$

and

$$\lim_{n \to \infty} \sqrt[n]{\frac{1}{c_n}} = 1,$$

we may start with the series $\Sigma c_k a_k x^k$, use our arguments above, and end up with the radius of convergence r of the series $\Sigma a_k x^k$ satisfying the inequality $r \geq r'$. This together with the inequality $r' \geq r$ proves that $r = r'$ as desired.

If $r = \infty$, then we can prove that $r' = \infty$ by a slight modification of our previous proof. If either r or r' is a positive number, then $r = r'$ by our arguments above. Hence, if either r or r' is 0, then both must equal zero. Thus $r = r'$ always, and 16.19 is proved.

16.20 Corollary. The series $\Sigma a_k x^k$ and $\Sigma k a_k x^{k-1}$ have the same radius of convergence.

Proof: Since

$$\lim_{n \to \infty} \sqrt[n]{n} = \lim_{n \to \infty} e^{(\ln n)/n} = e^0 = 1,$$

we may use 16.19 with $c_k = k$ to conclude that $\Sigma k a_k x^k$, and hence also $\Sigma k a_k x^{k-1}$, has the same radius of convergence as $\Sigma a_k x^k$.

Note that the series

$$a_1 + 2a_2 x + 3a_3 x^2 + \cdots + n a_n x^{n-1} + \cdots$$

of 16.20 is in a formal sense the "derivative" of the power series

$$a_0 + a_1 x + a_2 x^2 + a_3 x^3 + \cdots + a_n x^n + \cdots.$$

That it actually is the derivative will be shown in the next section.

■ ■ ■ EXERCISES

Find the interval of convergence of each of the following power series:

1. $x - \dfrac{x^3}{3!} + \dfrac{x^5}{5!} - \dfrac{x^7}{7!} + \cdots$.

2. $1 - x + x^2 - x^3 + x^4 - \cdots$.

3. $1 + x + \dfrac{x^2}{\sqrt{2}} + \dfrac{x^3}{\sqrt{3}} + \cdots + \dfrac{x^n}{\sqrt{n}} + \cdots$.

4. $1 + \dfrac{x}{2} + \dfrac{2x^2}{2^2} + \dfrac{3x^3}{2^3} + \cdots + \dfrac{nx^n}{2^n} + \cdots$.

5. $\displaystyle\sum_{k=0}^{\infty} \dfrac{x^{2k}}{k!}$.

6. $\displaystyle\sum_{k=0}^{\infty} \dfrac{(-1)^k x^k}{(k+1)^2}$.

7. $\displaystyle\sum_{k=0}^{\infty} \dfrac{(3x)^k}{2^{k+1}}$.

8. $\displaystyle\sum_{k=0}^{\infty} \dfrac{k! x^k}{10^k}$.

9. $\displaystyle\sum_{k=1}^{\infty} (-1)^k k^2 x^k$.

10. $\displaystyle\sum_{k=1}^{\infty} \dfrac{(-1)^{k-1} x^{2k-1}}{k+1}$.

11. $\displaystyle\sum_{k=1}^{\infty} \dfrac{k(x-1)^{k-1}}{3^k}$.

12. $\displaystyle\sum_{k=0}^{\infty} \dfrac{(x+2)^k}{(k+1)2^k}$.

13. $\displaystyle\sum_{k=0}^{\infty} \dfrac{(-1)^{k+1}(x+1)^{2k}}{(k+1)^2 5^k}$.

14. $\displaystyle\sum_{k=1}^{\infty} \dfrac{(-1)^k(2x-1)^k}{k!}$.

15. $\displaystyle\sum_{k=1}^{\infty} \dfrac{k^k}{k!} x^k$.

16. $\displaystyle\sum_{k=1}^{\infty} \dfrac{x^k}{\ln(k+1)}$.

17. $\displaystyle\sum_{k=2}^{\infty} \dfrac{(-1)^k x^k}{k(\ln k)^2}$.

18. $\displaystyle\sum_{k=0}^{\infty} \dfrac{(2x+1)^k}{3^k}$.

19. $\displaystyle\sum_{k=0}^{\infty} \dfrac{(x-2)^k}{2^k \sqrt{k+1}}$.

20. $\displaystyle\sum_{k=0}^{\infty} \dfrac{k x^k}{(k+1)(k+2)2^k}$.

21. Let r be the radius of convergence of the power series $\Sigma a_k x^k$. Show that if there exists a constant M such that $|a_k| \le M$ for every integer k, then $r \ge 1$. Also show that if there exists a constant N such that $0 \le N \le |a_k| \le M$ for every integer k, then $r = 1$.

22. Prove that if $\lim\limits_{n\to\infty} \sqrt[n]{|a_n|} = r > 0$, then the power series $\Sigma a_k x^k$ has radius of convergence $1/r$.

23. Complete the proof of 16.19 by showing that if $\Sigma a_k x^k$ has infinite radius of convergence, then so does $\Sigma c_k a_k x^k$.

24. If $a_k = 2^{-k}$, k an even integer, and $a_k = 2^{-k+1}$, k an odd integer, show that the power series $\Sigma a_k x^k$ has the open interval $(-2,2)$ as its interval of convergence.

6. *Derivative and integral of a power series*

Each power series $\Sigma a_k x^k$ defines a function f,

$$f(x) = \sum_{k=0}^{\infty} a_k x^k.$$

The domain of f is the interval of convergence of the series. Let us show that f is a differentiable function, having as its derivative the formal derivative discussed in the preceding section.

16.21 Theorem. If $\Sigma a_k x^k$ is a power series with nonzero radius of convergence r, then the function f defined by

$$f(x) = \sum_{k=0}^{\infty} a_k x^k$$

has a derivative given by

$$f'(x) = \sum_{k=1}^{\infty} k a_k x^{k-1}$$

at every number x in the open interval $(-r,r)$.

Proof: Let x and c be distinct numbers in the open interval $(-r,r)$. By Taylor's formula 14.13, with $n = 1$,

$$(1) \qquad x^k = c^k + kc^{k-1}(x - c) + \frac{k(k - 1)}{2}(z_k)^{k-2}(x - c)^2$$

for every integer k, where z_k is always a number between x and c. Now

$$\frac{f(x) - f(c)}{x - c} = \frac{1}{x - c}\left(\sum_{k=0}^{\infty} a_k x^k - \sum_{k=0}^{\infty} a_k c^k\right)$$

$$= \frac{1}{x - c}\sum_{k=1}^{\infty} a_k(x^k - c^k)$$

$$= \frac{1}{x - c}\sum_{k=1}^{\infty} a_k\left[kc^{k-1}(x - c) + \frac{k(k - 1)}{2}(z_k)^{k-2}(x - c)^2\right]$$

by (1). Hence

$$(2) \qquad \frac{f(x) - f(c)}{x - c} = \sum_{k=1}^{\infty} k a_k c^{k-1} + \frac{(x - c)}{2}\sum_{k=2}^{\infty} k(k - 1)a_k(z_k)^{k-2},$$

where each of the above series may be shown to be absolutely convergent using results of the previous sections.

From (2) we easily derive that

$$(3) \qquad \left|\frac{f(x) - f(c)}{x - c} - \sum_{k=1}^{\infty} k a_k c^{k-1}\right| < \frac{|x - c|}{2}\sum_{k=2}^{\infty} k(k - 1)|a_k|d^{k-2},$$

where d is any positive constant such that $|c| < d < r$ and $|x| < d < r$.

On taking limits in (3) as x approaches c, the right side has limit 0, and therefore

$$f'(c) = \underset{x \to c}{\text{limit}} \frac{f(x) - f(c)}{x - c} = \sum_{k=1}^{\infty} k a_k c^{k-1}.$$

This proves the theorem.

If

$$f(x) = \sum_{k=0}^{\infty} a_k x^k, \qquad g(x) = \sum_{k=0}^{\infty} \frac{a_k}{k+1} x^{k+1},$$

then $f(x)$ and $g(x)$ have the same radius of convergence by 16.20, and $g'(x) = f(x)$ by the theorem above. Since $g(0) = 0$,

$$\int_0^x f(x) \, dx = g(x),$$

and we have proved the following result.

16.22 Theorem. If the power series $\Sigma c_k x^k$ has radius of convergence $r \neq 0$, then

$$\int_0^x \sum_{k=0}^{\infty} a_k x^k \, dx = \sum_{k=0}^{\infty} \frac{a_k}{k+1} x^{k+1}, \quad |x| < r.$$

Example 1. Show that

$$\tan^{-1} x = x - \frac{x^3}{3} + \frac{x^5}{5} - \frac{x^7}{7} + \cdots, \quad |x| < 1.$$

Solution: The geometric series

$$\frac{1}{1 + x^2} = 1 - x^2 + x^4 - x^6 + \cdots$$

has radius of convergence $r = 1$. Hence we may integrate the series termwise by 16.22 to obtain

$$\int_0^x \frac{1}{1 + x^2} \, dx = \tan^{-1} x = x - \frac{x^3}{3} + \frac{x^5}{5} - \frac{x^7}{7} + \cdots, \quad |x| < 1.$$

Example 2. Approximate $\tan^{-1}\frac{1}{2}$ to 3 decimal places.

Solution: By the previous example,

$$\tan^{-1}\frac{1}{2} \doteq \frac{1}{2} - \frac{1}{3}\left(\frac{1}{2}\right)^3 + \frac{1}{5}\left(\frac{1}{2}\right)^5 - \frac{1}{7}\left(\frac{1}{2}\right)^7 \doteq .463.$$

By 16.12, the error does not exceed

$$\frac{1}{9}\left(\frac{1}{2}\right)^9 < 3 \times 10^{-4}.$$

If

$$f(x) = \sum_{k=0}^{\infty} a_k (x - c)^k, \quad g(x) = \sum_{k=0}^{\infty} a_k x^k,$$

then $f(x) = g(x - c)$, and by the chain rule

$$f'(x) = g'(x - c) \, D_x(x - c) = g'(x - c).$$

Hence
$$f'(x) = \sum_{k=1}^{\infty} k a_k (x - c)^{k-1},$$

and the power series $\Sigma a_k(x - c)^k$ is differentiated just as the power series $\Sigma a_k x^k$. The integral of $f(x)$ also is found by integrating the series termwise.

■■■ EXERCISES

1. Show that
$$\ln (1 + x) = x - \frac{x^2}{2} + \frac{x^3}{3} - \frac{x^4}{4} + \cdots, \quad |x| < 1.$$
   Approximate $\ln (1.2)$ to 3 decimal places.

2. Show that
$$\ln (1 - x) = -x - \frac{x^2}{2} - \frac{x^3}{3} - \frac{x^4}{4} - \cdots, \quad |x| < 1.$$
   Approximate $\ln \frac{3}{4}$ to 3 decimal places.

3. By combining the series in Exercises 1 and 2, show that
$$\ln \left(\frac{1 + x}{1 - x} \right) = 2 \left(x + \frac{x^3}{3} + \frac{x^5}{5} + \cdots \right), \quad |x| < 1.$$
   Approximate $\ln 3$ to 3 decimal places.

4. Approximate $\displaystyle\int_0^{1/2} \frac{x}{1 + x^3} \, dx$ to 4 decimal places.

5. Find an infinite series for the improper integral
$$\int_0^x \frac{\ln (1 + x)}{x} \, dx.$$

6. Find an infinite series for the improper integral
$$\int_0^x \frac{\tan^{-1} x}{x} \, dx.$$

7. Prove that if the two series $\Sigma a_k x^k$ and $\Sigma b_k x^k$ have the same radius of convergence $r \neq 0$, and if
$$\sum_{k=0}^{\infty} a_k x^k = \sum_{k=0}^{\infty} b_k x^k$$
   for every x such that $|x| < r$, then the two series are identical, i.e., $a_k = b_k$ for every k.

7. Binomial series

According to the binomial theorem,
$$(a + b)^m = a^m + m a^{m-1} b + \frac{m(m - 1)}{2!} a^{m-2} b^2 + \cdots$$
$$+ \frac{m(m - 1) \cdots (m - k + 1)}{k!} a^{m-k} b^k + \cdots + b^m,$$

where m is a positive integer. If we let $a = 1$ and $b = x$, this series has the form

$$(1 + x)^m = 1 + mx + \frac{m(m - 1)}{2!} x^2 + \cdots$$
$$+ \frac{m(m - 1) \cdots (m - k + 1)}{k!} x^k + \cdots + x^m.$$

If m is not a positive integer, we may still formally write down the above series, although the series will not terminate as the one above does. The resulting series is called a *binomial series* and has the form (replacing m by a)

$$\textbf{16.23} \quad \sum_{k=0}^{\infty} c_k x^k = 1 + ax + \frac{a(a - 1)}{2!} x^2 + \cdots$$
$$+ \frac{a(a - 1) \cdots (a - n + 1)}{n!} x^n + \cdots,$$

where $c_k = \dfrac{a(a - 1)(a - 2) \cdots (a - k + 1)}{k!}, \quad k = 1, 2, \cdots.$

The binomial series is finite if and only if a is a nonnegative integer.

We can find the radius of convergence of 16.23 by the ratio test. Thus

$$\lim_{n \to \infty} \left| \frac{c_{n+1} x^{n+1}}{c_n x^n} \right| = \lim_{n \to \infty} \left| \frac{a - n}{n + 1} \right| |x| = |x|,$$

and the series is convergent if $|x| < 1$ and divergent if $|x| > 1$. Hence its radius of convergence is 1.

The binomial series 16.23 defines a function f,

$$f(x) = \sum_{k=0}^{\infty} c_k x^k, \quad |x| < 1,$$

for each real number a. If a is a nonnegative integer, the function f is just the power function

$$f(x) = (1 + x)^a$$

by the binomial theorem. Let us prove that f is this power function for each real number a, regardless of whether or not a is a nonnegative integer. We shall prove that $f(x) = (1 + x)^a$ by showing that

$$D_x[f(x)(1 + x)^{-a}] = f'(x)(1 + x)^{-a} - af(x)(1 + x)^{-a-1} = 0.$$

On multiplying this differential equation throughout by $(1 + x)^{1+a}$, we obtain the differential equation

(1) $f'(x)(1 + x) - af(x) = 0.$

Let us now prove that (1) holds for the function f defined by the binomial series.

By 16.21, if $|x| < 1$,

$$f'(x) = \sum_{k=1}^{\infty} k c_k x^{k-1} = \sum_{k=0}^{\infty} (k + 1) c_{k+1} x^k,$$

$$xf'(x) = \sum_{k=1}^{\infty} kc_k x^k = \sum_{k=0}^{\infty} kc_k x^k.$$

Hence

$$f'(x)(1+x) = \sum_{k=0}^{\infty} [(k+1)c_{k+1} + kc_k]x^k.$$

Now

$$(k+1)c_{k+1} + kc_k$$
$$= \frac{(k+1)a(a-1)(a-2)\cdots(a-k)}{(k+1)!} + \frac{ka(a-1)(a-2)\cdots(a-k+1)}{k!}$$
$$= \frac{a(a-1)(a-2)\cdots(a-k+1)}{k!}(a-k+k) = ac_k,$$

and therefore

$$f'(x)(1+x) = \sum_{k=0}^{\infty} ac_k x^k = af(x).$$

This proves that

$$D_x[f(x)(1+x)^{-a}] = 0,$$

and hence that

$$f(x)(1+x)^{-a} = K,$$

for some constant K. Since $f(0) = 1$, it is clear that $K = 1$, and hence that

$$f(x) = (1+x)^a.$$

Thus we have proved the generalized binomial theorem

16.24 $(1+x)^a = 1 + ax + \dfrac{a(a-1)}{2!}x^2 + \cdots$
$$+ \frac{a(a-1)\cdots(a-n+1)}{n!}x^n + \cdots,$$

which holds for every real number a and every x such that $|x| < 1$.

Example. Find the series expansion of $\sqrt{1+x}$.

Solution: By 16.24 with $a = \frac{1}{2}$, we have

$$\sqrt{1+x} = 1 + \frac{1}{2}x + \frac{\frac{1}{2}(\frac{1}{2}-1)}{2!}x^2 + \cdots + \frac{\frac{1}{2}(\frac{1}{2}-1)\cdots(\frac{1}{2}-n+1)}{n!}x^n + \cdots$$

$$= 1 + \frac{1}{2}x - \frac{1}{2^2 2!}x^2 + \cdots + \frac{(-1)^{n+1}1\cdot3\cdots(2n-3)}{2^n n!}x^n + \cdots,$$

if $|x| < 1$.

■ ■ ■ EXERCISES

Find an infinite series for each of the following functions:

1. $\sqrt{1-x}$.   2. $\sqrt[3]{1+z^2}$.

3. $\dfrac{1}{(1+x)^2}.$

4. $\dfrac{z}{\sqrt{1-z^3}}.$

5. $\dfrac{1}{\sqrt{1-x^2}}.$

6. $(1+2x)^{-3}.$

7. $x(4-x)^{3/2}.$ (*Hint:* Factor out the number 4.)

8. $\sqrt{2+z}.$ (*Hint:* Find a power series for $\sqrt{1+x}.$)

9. By integration, find a power series for $\sin^{-1} x.$

10. By integration, find a power series for $\ln(x+\sqrt{1+x^2}).$

11. By integration, find a power series for $\sec^{-1} x.$

12. We observe that if $a=-1$, $c_k=(-1)^k$ in 16.23. Thus the binomial series diverges if $|x|=1$ and $a=-1$. Prove that the binomial series diverges if $|x|=1$ and $a<-1$.

8. Taylor's series

A function defined by a power series in x possesses derivatives of all orders, obtainable by differentiating the power series termwise according to 16.21. We might well ask whether, conversely, if a function has derivatives of all orders, then may it be represented by a power series? While this is not true in general, it is true for most of the elementary functions studied in this book.

If

$$f(x) = \sum_{k=0}^{\infty} a_k(x-c)^k$$

has an open interval containing c as its domain, then

$$f'(x) = \sum_{k=1}^{\infty} ka_k(x-c)^{k-1}, \qquad f''(x) = \sum_{k=2}^{\infty} k(k-1)a_k(x-c)^{k-2},$$

and, in general,

$$f^{[n]}(x) = \sum_{k=n}^{\infty} k(k-1)\cdots(k-n+1)a_k(x-c)^{k-n}.$$

The function f and its derivatives have the same radius of convergence according to 16.21. Evaluating the function f and its derivatives at the number c, we get

$$f(c) = a_0, \quad f'(c) = a_1, \quad f''(c) = 2a_2,$$

and, in general,

$$f^{[n]}(c) = n!a_n.$$

Thus

$$a_n = \frac{f^{[n]}(c)}{n!}$$

for each integer n, and the power series for f is given by

16.25 $f(x) = f(c) + f'(c)(x - c) + \dfrac{f''(c)}{2!}(x - c)^2 + \cdots$

$$+ \dfrac{f^{[n]}(c)}{n!}(x - c)^n + \cdots.$$

Series 16.25 is called the *Taylor's series* of f at c.

The nth partial sum of 16.25 is a Taylor's polynomial $P_n(x)$ as defined in 14.10. The nth degree remainder term $R_n(x)$ is given by (14.14)

$$R_n(x) = \dfrac{f^{[n+1]}(z)}{(n + 1)!}(x - c)^{n+1},$$

where z is a number between x and c, and

$$f(x) = P_n(x) + R_n(x).$$

The fundamental theorem on representing a function by a power series may be stated as follows.

16.26 Theorem. If the function f has derivatives of all orders in an interval containing the number c and if

$$\lim_{n \to \infty} R_n(x) = 0$$

for every x in the interval, then f is given by 16.25 in this interval.

Proof: Since $P_n(x) = f(x) - R_n(x)$, we have

$$\lim_{n \to \infty} P_n(x) = f(x) - \lim_{n \to \infty} R_n(x) = f(x),$$

and the theorem is proved.

If $c = 0$ and the requirements of 16.26 are met, then we get the following *Maclaurin's series* (14.15) for $f(x)$.

16.27 $f(x) = f(0) + f'(0)x + \dfrac{f''(0)}{2!}x^2 + \cdots + \dfrac{f^{[n]}(0)}{n!}x^n + \cdots.$

The power series $\Sigma z^k/k!$ converges for every number z. Hence the limit of its nth term must be 0,

16.28 $$\lim_{n \to \infty} \dfrac{z^n}{n!} = 0.$$

This fact will be used in some of the following examples.

Example 1. Find the Maclaurin's series for e^x.

Solution: If $f(x) = e^x$, then $f^{[n]}(x) = e^x$ for every n. Thus $f^{[n]}(0) = 1$ and the Maclaurin's series for e^x is as follows.

16.29 $e^x = 1 + x + \dfrac{x^2}{2!} + \dfrac{x^3}{3!} + \cdots + \dfrac{x^n}{n!} + \cdots.$

Let us prove that 16.29 is valid for every number x. Evidently

$$R_n(x) = \dfrac{e^{z_n}x^{n+1}}{(n + 1)!},$$

where each z_n is between 0 and x. If $x > 0$, $e^{z_n} < e^x$ for every integer n, and therefore

$$0 < R_n(x) < \frac{e^x x^{n+1}}{(n+1)!}.$$

Since

$$\underset{n \to \infty}{\text{limit}}\, e^x \frac{x^{n+1}}{(n+1)!} = 0$$

by 16.28, also

$$\underset{n \to \infty}{\text{limit}}\, R_n(x) = 0.$$

If $x < 0$, each $e^{z_n} < 1$ and the same conclusion holds. Thus 16.29 is valid for every real number x.

If $x = 1$, 16.29 yields the following expression for e:

$$e = 1 + 1 + \frac{1}{2} + \frac{1}{6} + \cdots + \frac{1}{n!} + \cdots .$$

Let us use this infinite series to show that e is an irrational number. Assume, on the contrary, that e is a rational number. We know that $2 < e < 3$, so that e is not an integer. If $e = k/m$, k and m integers with $m \geq 2$, then

$$e = 1 + 1 + \frac{1}{2} + \cdots + \frac{1}{m!} + \frac{e^z}{(m+1)!}, \quad 0 < z < 1.$$

Hence

$$e \cdot m! = p + \frac{e^z}{m+1},$$

where p is an integer. Since $e \cdot m!$ also is an integer, $e^z/(m+1)$ must be an integer. However, this is impossible, since $m + 1 \geq 3$, whereas $e^z < e < 3$. Thus the assumption that e is rational leads to a contradiction, and e is an irrational number.

Example 2. Find the Maclaurin's series for $\sin x$.

Solution: If $f(x) = \sin x$, then $f(0) = 0$ and

$$f'(x) = \cos x, \quad f'(0) = 1,$$

$$f''(x) = -\sin x, \quad f''(0) = 0,$$

$$f'''(x) = -\cos x, \quad f'''(0) = -1,$$

$$f^{[4]}(x) = \sin x, \quad f^{[4]}(0) = 0,$$

and so on. Thus

$$\sin x = x - \frac{x^3}{3!} + \frac{x^5}{5!} - \frac{x^7}{7!} + \cdots .$$

Since $|f^{[n]}(x)|$ is either $|\sin x|$ or $|\cos x|$, evidently $|f^{[n]}(x)| \leq 1$ and

$$\underset{n \to \infty}{\text{limit}} |R_n(x)| = \underset{n \to \infty}{\text{limit}} |f^{[n+1]}(z_n)| \left| \frac{x^{n+1}}{(n+1)!} \right| = 0.$$

Hence the sine series is valid for every number x.

Example 3. Find the Taylor's series for $\ln x$ in powers of $x - 1$.

Solution: If $f(x) = \ln x$, then $f(1) = 0$ and

$$f'(x) = \frac{1}{x}, \quad f'(1) = 1,$$

$$f''(x) = -\frac{1}{x^2}, \quad f'(1) = -1,$$

$$f'''(x) = \frac{2}{x^3}, \quad f'''(1) = 2,$$

and, in general,

$$f^{[n+1]}(x) = \frac{(-1)^n n!}{x^{n+1}}, \qquad f^{[n+1]}(1) = (-1)^n n!.$$

The Taylor's series for $\ln x$ thus has the form

$$\ln x = (x - 1) - \frac{(x-1)^2}{2} + \frac{(x-1)^3}{3} - \cdots + \frac{(-1)^{n-1}(x-1)^n}{n} + \cdots .$$

This series converges for each x in the interval $(0,2]$ and diverges elsewhere. Evidently

$$R_n(x) = \frac{(-1)^n n!}{(z_n)^{n+1}} \frac{(x-1)^{n+1}}{(n+1)!} = \frac{(-1)^n}{n+1} \left(\frac{x-1}{z_n} \right)^{n+1},$$

where z_n is between 1 and x. If $x > 1$, then $1 < z_n < x \leq 2$ and $0 < x - 1 \leq 1 < z_n$. Hence $(x-1)/z_n < 1$ and

$$\lim_{n \to \infty} |R_n(x)| = \lim_{n \to \infty} \frac{1}{n+1} = 0.$$

Thus this Taylor's series for $\ln x$ has $\ln x$ as its sum if $1 < x \leq 2$. We omit the details, but it may be shown that $\ln x$ is given by this series also if $0 < x \leq 1$.

We remark in passing that it is not true in general that the sum of the Taylor's series of f at c (16.25) necessarily equals $f(x)$ for every x in the interval of convergence of this series. An exercise at the end of this section illustrates this point (Exercise 18).

The infinite series expansion of a function may be used to approximate values of the function, as we have illustrated previously in this chapter. Some more examples of this are given below.

Example 4. Approximate $\int_0^1 e^{-x^2} dx$ to 3 decimal places.

Solution: On replacing x by $-x^2$ in 16.29, we get

$$e^{-x^2} = 1 - x^2 + \frac{x^4}{2!} - \frac{x^6}{3!} + \cdots + \frac{(-1)^n x^{2n}}{n!} + \cdots .$$

We may integrate this series termwise according to 16.22, getting

$$\int_0^1 e^{-x^2} dx = 1 - \frac{1}{3} + \frac{1}{10} - \frac{1}{42} + \cdots + \frac{(-1)^n}{(2n+1)n!} + \cdots .$$

Using five terms, we get

$$\int_0^1 e^{-x^2} dx \doteq .747,$$

with an error less than the next term, $1/1320$, by 16.12.

Example 5. Approximate $\int_0^{1/2} \cos \sqrt{x} \, dx$ to 4 significant digits.

Solution: We may easily verify that

$$\cos x = 1 - \frac{x^2}{2!} + \frac{x^4}{4!} - \frac{x^6}{6!} + \cdots$$

for every number x. Hence

$$\cos \sqrt{x} = 1 - \frac{x}{2!} + \frac{x^2}{4!} - \frac{x^3}{6!} + \cdots$$

for every nonnegative number x, and

$$\int_0^{1/2} \cos \sqrt{x} \, dx = \frac{1}{2} - \frac{1}{2 \cdot 2!}\left(\frac{1}{2}\right)^2 + \frac{1}{3 \cdot 4!}\left(\frac{1}{2}\right)^3 - \frac{1}{4 \cdot 6!}\left(\frac{1}{2}\right)^4 + \cdots \doteq .4392$$

with an error less than the fifth term $1/(2^6 \times 6!)$ by 16.12.

■ ■ ■ EXERCISES

Find an infinite series expansion for each of the following functions. State its radius of convergence.

1. $\cos x$ in powers of $(x - \pi/4)$.

2. xe^x in powers of x.

3. $\ln |x|$ in powers of $(x + 1)$.

4. $\dfrac{\sin x}{x}$ in powers of x.

5. $\sinh x = \dfrac{e^x - e^{-x}}{2}$ in powers of x.

6. $\cosh x = \dfrac{e^x + e^{-x}}{2}$ in powers of x.

7. $\dfrac{1 - \cos x}{x}$ in powers of x.

8. $\sin x$ in powers of $(x + \pi/3)$.

9. $\sin^2 x = \dfrac{1 - \cos 2x}{2}$ in powers of x.

10. $\cos^2 x$ in powers of x.

Approximate each of the following to the stated degree of accuracy.

11. $\sqrt[3]{e}$, 5 decimal places.

12. $\sin 10°$, 4 decimal places. (*Hint:* $1° = .017453$ radian.)

13. $\cos 5°$, 4 decimal places.

14. $\sinh \frac{1}{2}$, 5 decimal places.

15. $\int_0^{.4} \sin x^2 \, dx$, 6 decimal places.

16. $\int_0^{1/2} \frac{\sin x}{x}\, dx$, 5 decimal places.   (*Hint:* This is an improper integral.)

17. Show that e^r is an irrational number for every rational number r.

18. Define the function f as follows: $f(x) = e^{-1/x^2}$ if $x \neq 0$, $f(0) = 0$. Show that $f^{[n]}(0)$ exists and equals 0 for every integer n. Prove that the Maclaurin's series for f is not equal to f over any interval. (See Exercise 22, Section 6, Chapter 14.)

19. Prove that the closest integer to $n!/e$ is divisible by $n - 1$. (*Hint:* Use the series for $1/e$.)

17

Solid analytic geometry

■ ■ ■ ■ ■   COORDINATE SYSTEMS may be introduced into three-dimensional space much as they are in the plane to allow the discussion of space curves and surfaces analytically. We shall indicate how this is done in the present chapter.

1. Rectangular coordinate systems

Two perpendicular coordinate lines in a plane allowed us to introduce coordinates in the plane. In an analogous way, three mutually perpendicular coordinate lines in space will allow us to introduce coordinates in space. The three coordinate lines, called the x-axis, y-axis, and z-axis, are assumed to have the same scale and meet at their origins. If the axes are oriented as in Figure 17.1, the coordinate system is called left-handed. If the x- and y-axes were interchanged, it would be called right-handed. We shall use a left-handed coordinate system for the most part. Three coordinate planes are determined by the axes, namely, the xy-plane containing the x- and y-axes, the xz-plane, and the yz-plane.

Each point P in space may be projected onto the coordinate axes. If the projections of P on the x-, y-, and

470

z-axes, respectively, have coordinates x, y, and z, then P itself is said to have coordinates (x,y,z). The three planes through P parallel to the coordinate planes form a parallelopiped with the coordinate planes. The coordinates of the vertices of this parallelopiped are shown in Figure 17.2.

Just as each point in space has a unique triple of coordinates, so each triple of numbers determines a unique point in space having the triple of numbers as coordinates. This association of triples of numbers with points in space is called a *rectangular coordinate system* in space.

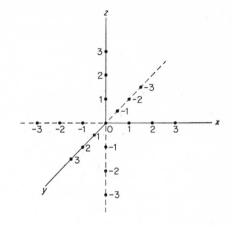

Figure 17.1

The three coordinate planes separate space into eight parts, called *octants*. We shall only need to refer explicitly to the *first octant*, consisting of all points $P(x,y,z)$ such that $x > 0$, $y > 0$, and $z > 0$.

Distances may be found between points in space by the following analogue of the formula for the plane.

17.1 Distance formula. The distance between the points $P(x_1,y_1,z_1)$ and $Q(x_2,y_2,z_2)$ is given by

$$|PQ| = \sqrt{(x_2 - x_1)^2 + (y_2 - y_1)^2 + (z_2 - z_1)^2}.$$

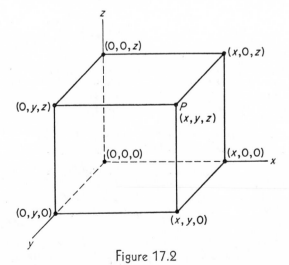

Figure 17.2

Proof: Construct a parallelopiped having its faces parallel to the co-ordinate planes and having P and Q as opposite vertices. If $A(x_2,y_1,z_1)$ and $B(x_2,y_2,z_1)$ are chosen as in Figure 17.3, then

$$|PA| = |x_2 - x_1|, \quad |AB| = |y_2 - y_1|, \quad |BQ| = |z_2 - z_1|.$$

Triangle PAB has a right angle at A, and triangle PBQ has a right angle at B. Hence $|PA|^2 + |AB|^2 = |PB|^2$, $|PB|^2 + |BQ|^2 = |PQ|^2$, and therefore

$$|PQ|^2 = |PA|^2 + |AB|^2 + |BQ|^2 = (x_2 - x_1)^2 + (y_2 - y_1)^2 + (z_2 - z_1)^2.$$

This establishes the distance formula.

The parallelopiped of Figure 17.3 reduces to a rectangle (or a line segment) if P and Q lie in a plane parallel to a coordinate plane. In this case, either $|PA|$, $|AB|$, or $|BQ|$ is zero. However, the distance formula may easily be shown to still hold.

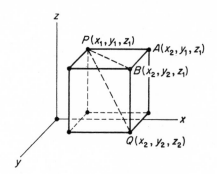

Figure 17.3

As a particular case of 17.1, the distance from the origin O to the point $P(x,y,z)$ is given by

$$|OP| = \sqrt{x^2 + y^2 + z^2}.$$

Thus the point $P(x,y,z)$ is on the sphere having radius r and center at the origin O if and only if

$$x^2 + y^2 + z^2 = r^2.$$

Therefore this is an equation of the sphere. A more general consequence of the distance formula is stated below without proof.

17.2 Theorem. The sphere of radius r having its center at the point (x_0,y_0,z_0) has equation

$$(x - x_0)^2 + (y - y_0)^2 + (z - z_0)^2 = r^2.$$

Since every equation of the form

$$x^2 + y^2 + z^2 + ax + by + cz + d = 0$$

can be put in the form of the equation of 17.2 by completing squares, its graph, if it exists, is a sphere.

Example 1. Discuss the graph of the equation

$$x^2 + y^2 + z^2 - 6x + 2y - z - \frac{23}{4} = 0.$$

Solution: We first complete squares as follows:

$$(x^2 - 6x + 9) + (y^2 + 2y + 1) + \left(z^2 - z + \frac{1}{4}\right) = \frac{23}{4} + 9 + 1 + \frac{1}{4},$$

$$(x - 3)^2 + (y + 1)^2 + \left(z - \frac{1}{2}\right)^2 = 16.$$

Hence the graph is a sphere of radius 4 with center at $(3, -1, \frac{1}{2})$.

If in Figure 17.3 we imagine a plane parallel to the yz-plane cutting the parallelopiped into two equal parts, then this plane will bisect the line segments PA, PB, and PQ. Since the mid-point of PA has x-coordinate $(x_1 + x_2)/2$ by 1.17, the mid-point of PQ will also have this x-coordinate. A continuation of this argument yields the following result.

17.3 Mid-point formula. The segment with end points (x_1, y_1, z_1) and (x_2, y_2, z_2) has mid-point

$$\left(\frac{x_1 + x_2}{2}, \frac{y_1 + y_2}{2}, \frac{z_1 + z_2}{2}\right).$$

Example 2. Show that $A(2, -1, 1)$, $B(5, 2, 1)$, and $C(1, 6, 5)$ are the vertices of a right triangle with hypotenuse AC. Find an equation of the sphere having AC as a diameter and passing through the point B.

Solution: We have

$$|AB|^2 = (5 - 2)^2 + (2 + 1)^2 = 18,$$

$$|AC|^2 = (1 - 2)^2 + (6 + 1)^2 + (5 - 1)^2 = 66,$$

$$|BC|^2 = (1 - 5)^2 + (6 - 2)^2 + (5 - 1)^2 = 48.$$

Since $|AB|^2 + |BC|^2 = |AC|^2$, then ABC is a right triangle with hypotenuse AC. The point M with coordinates

$$\left(\frac{2 + 1}{2}, \frac{-1 + 6}{2}, \frac{1 + 5}{2}\right),$$

or $(\frac{3}{2}, \frac{5}{2}, 3)$, is the mid-point of AC. Thus

$$\left(x - \frac{3}{2}\right)^2 + \left(y - \frac{5}{2}\right)^2 + (z - 3)^2 = \frac{33}{2},$$

or

$$x^2 + y^2 + z^2 - 3x - 5y - 6z + 1 = 0,$$

is an equation of the sphere with center M and radius $|MB| = \frac{1}{2}|AC| = \sqrt{66}/2$.

∎ ∎ ∎ EXERCISES

In each of the following exercises, A and B are the opposite vertices of a parallelopiped having its faces parallel to the coordinate planes. Sketch the parallelopiped, and find the coordinates of its other vertices.

1. $A(0,0,0)$, $B(7,2,3)$.   2. $A(1,1,1)$, $B(3,4,2)$.
3. $A(-1,1,2)$, $B(2,3,5)$.   4. $A(0,-2,2)$, $B(2,0,-2)$.
5. $A(0,-2,-1)$, $B(3,1,0)$.   6. $A(2,-1,-3)$, $B(4,0,-1)$.

Show that the three given points are the vertices of a right triangle, and find the equation of the sphere passing through the three points and having its center on the hypotenuse:

7. $(4,4,1)$, $(1,1,1)$, $(0,8,5)$.   8. $(2,1,3)$, $(0,1,2)$, $(1,3,0)$.
9. $(-3,6,0)$, $(-2,-5,-1)$, $(1,4,2)$.
10. $(2,5,-2)$, $(1,3,0)$, $(4,5,-1)$.

Discuss the graph of each of the following equations.

11. $x^2 + y^2 + z^2 - 2x - 24 = 0$.
12. $x^2 + y^2 + z^2 + 6x - 2y + 4z + 13 = 0$.
13. $4x^2 + 4y^2 + 4z^2 + 12y - 4z + 1 = 0$.
14. $x^2 + y^2 + z^2 - 2x + 4y - 8z + 21 = 0$.
15. $x^2 + y^2 + z^2 - 6x + 2y + 11 = 0$.
16. $x^2 + y^2 + z^2 - 3x + 4y - z = 0$.

17. Show that $(2,4,2)$, $(2,1,5)$, $(5,1,2)$ and $(1,0,1)$ are the vertices of a regular tetrahedron, and sketch.

18. Find an equation of the locus of all points equidistant from the points $(3,1,2)$ and $(7,5,6)$. What is the locus?

19. Find an equation of the locus of all points equidistant from the points $(-1,2,1)$ and $(1,-2,-1)$. What is the locus?

20. Let A, B, C, and D be four points in space, with no three of the points collinear, and let P, Q, R, and S be the mid-points of AB, BC, CD, and DA, respectively. Prove that $PQRS$ is a parallelogram.

2. Direction numbers of a line

The concept of slope proved to be useful in describing lines in a plane. While this concept does not directly extend to space, we can use the closely related concept of direction numbers to describe lines in space, as is shown in this section.

A point P on a line L divides L into two half-lines, each with end point P. For example, the origin divides the x-axis into two half-lines, the positive x-axis and the negative x-axis. If two half-lines have a common end point, there is a plane containing them, and the angle of measure θ, where $0° \le \theta \le 180°$, having the given half-lines as sides is called the *angle between the half-lines*.

A half-line may be considered to be directed from its end point to any other point on the half-line. Through a point P in space, one and only one half-line can be drawn parallel to and with the same direction as a given half-line. With this in mind, the direction angles of a given half-

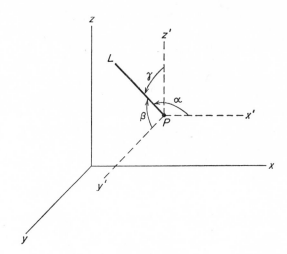

Figure 17.4

line L with end point P are defined as follows. Construct half-lines emanating from P parallel to and with the same direction as the positive halves of the coordinate axes as indicated in Figure 17.4. The angles α, β, and γ between L and the positive x'-, y'-, and z'-axes, respectively (Figure 17.4), are called the *direction angles* of L. Also, the numbers $\cos \alpha$, $\cos \beta$, and $\cos \gamma$ are called the *direction cosines* of L. With these definitions, parallel half-lines with the same direction have the same direction angles and direction cosines.

If L and L' are two halves of a line, and if α, β, γ and α', β', γ' are their respective direction angles, then it is clear from Figure 17.5 that α and α' are supplementary. Similarly, β and β', and γ and γ' are supplementary angles. Since the cosines of supplementary angles are negatives of each other, evidently $\cos \alpha$, $\cos \beta$,

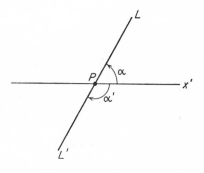

Figure 17.5

$\cos \gamma$ and $-\cos \alpha$, $-\cos \beta$, $-\cos \gamma$ are the respective direction cosines of L and L'.

Conversely, two half-lines L and L' with direction cosines l, m, n, and l', m', n', respectively, are parallel if either

$$l' = l, \quad m' = m, \quad n' = n$$

or $\qquad\qquad l' = -l, \quad m' = -m, \quad n' = -n.$

In the first case, L and L' have the same direction, in the second case, the opposite direction.

Let L be a half-line emanating from the origin O and let $P(a,b,c)$ be any

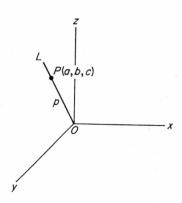

Figure 17.6

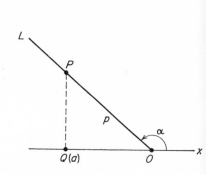

Figure 17.7

point on L distinct from O (Figure 17.6).   The distance p of P from the origin is given by

$$p = \sqrt{a^2 + b^2 + c^2}.$$

If α, β, and γ are the direction angles of L, then the direction cosines of L are given by

17.4 $\qquad\qquad \cos \alpha = \dfrac{a}{p}, \quad \cos \beta = \dfrac{b}{p}, \quad \cos \gamma = \dfrac{c}{p}.$

To prove 17.4, let us look at a plane containing L and the x-axis (Figure 17.7).   Then the projection Q of P on the x-axis has coordinate a, and $\cos \alpha = a/p$ by the definition of the cosine function.   Evidently the rest of 17.4 follows in a similar way.

On solving the equations of 17.4 for a, b, and c, we have that the coordinates of P are $(p \cos \alpha, p \cos \beta, p \cos \gamma)$.   In particular, if P is one unit from the origin, so that $p = 1$, then P has coordinates $(\cos \alpha, \cos \beta, \cos \gamma)$.   Since $|OP|^2 = 1$,

$$\cos^2 \alpha + \cos^2 \beta + \cos^2 \gamma = 1,$$

and we have proved the following result.

17.5 Theorem.   If l, m, and n are direction cosines of a half-line, then

$$l^2 + m^2 + n^2 = 1.$$

If conversely, l, m, and n are three numbers such that $l^2 + m^2 + n^2 = 1$, then there exists a half-line having l, m, and n as its direction cosines. Thus the half-line emanating from the origin and passing through the point $P(l,m,n)$ has l, m, and n as its direction cosines in view of 17.4.

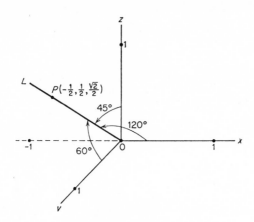

Figure 17.8

For example, the half-line L of Figure 17.8 has direction cosines $-\frac{1}{2}$, $\frac{1}{2}$, and $\sqrt{2}/2$, since

$$\left(-\frac{1}{2}\right)^2 + \left(\frac{1}{2}\right)^2 + \left(\frac{\sqrt{2}}{2}\right)^2 = 1.$$

The direction angles of L are $120°$, $60°$, and $45°$.

It is convenient to give direction numbers to a line as well as to a half-line according to the following definition.

17.6 Definition. Three numbers l, m, and n, not all zero, are *direction numbers* of a line L if there exists a number p such that

$$l = pl', \quad m = pm', \quad n = pn',$$

where l', m', and n' are direction cosines of a half-line on L.

In words, direction numbers of a line L are any three numbers proportional to the direction cosines of a half-line on L. The number p is the constant of proportionality.

If l, m, and n are direction numbers of a line L, then so are kl, km, and kn for any nonzero number k. Thus it is clear that direction numbers of a line are not unique. If l, m, n and a, b, c are two sets of direction numbers of a line L, then

$$l = pl', \quad m = pm', \quad n = pn',$$

and

$$a = ql', \quad b = qm', \quad c = qn'$$

for some nonzero numbers p and q, where l', m', and n' are direction cosines of a half-line on L. Since

$$a = \frac{q}{p}l, \quad b = \frac{q}{p}m, \quad c = \frac{q}{p}n,$$

we conclude that any two sets of direction numbers of a line L are proportional. Clearly, then, parallel lines also have proportional direction numbers.

Given two points on a line, direction numbers of the line may be found by the following theorem.

17.7 Theorem. If $P(x_1,y_1,z_1)$ and $Q(x_2,y_2,z_2)$ are two distinct points on a line L, then

$$x_2 - x_1, \quad y_2 - y_1, \quad z_2 - z_1$$

are direction numbers of L.

Proof: Consider new coordinate axes drawn parallel to the given ones and with origin at P (Figure 17.9). The coordinates of Q relative to the

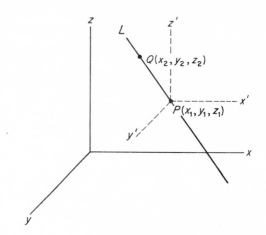

Figure 17.9

new axes are $(x_2 - x_1, y_2 - y_1, z_2 - z_1)$ according to the space analogue of the equations for a translation of axes in the plane (7.19). If $p = |PQ|$, then

$$x_2 - x_1 = p \cos \alpha, \quad y_2 - y_1 = p \cos \beta, \quad z_2 - z_1 = p \cos \gamma$$

according to 17.4, where $\cos \alpha$, $\cos \beta$, and $\cos \gamma$ are direction cosines of the half-line from P through Q. Hence $x_2 - x_1$, $y_2 - y_1$, and $z_2 - z_1$, being proportional to direction cosines of a half-line on L, are direction numbers of L.

If the numbers a, b, and c are not all zero, there is a line L with direction numbers a, b, and c by 17.4. We may choose L as the line on the origin and $P(a,b,c)$.

■ ■ ■ EXERCISES

Find direction cosines and direction angles of the half-line emanating from the origin and passing through each of the following points.

1. $(1,1,\sqrt{2})$.   **2.** $(1,-\sqrt{2},-1)$.   **3.** $(1,2,2)$.

4. $(4,-1,8)$.   **5.** $(2,2,2)$.   **6.** $(-3\sqrt{2},-3,-3)$.

Find direction numbers of the line and direction cosines of any half-line on the line passing through each of the following pairs of points.

7. $(5,1,2)$, $(7,2,4)$.   **8.** $(-3,2,-4)$, $(7,-1,4)$.

9. $(-2,2,-1)$, $(1,5,2)$.   **10.** $(1,-1,-2)$, $(3,-1,4)$.

11. $(4,5,-3)$, $(4,5,1)$.   **12.** $(2,-2,-2)$, $(0,0,1)$.

13. Find the direction cosines and direction angles of the positive coordinate axes; of the negative coordinate axes.

14. Under what conditions are l, m, and n direction numbers of a line parallel to a coordinate plane?

15. If $\pi/3$ and $3\pi/4$ are two of the direction angles of a half-line, find the third direction angle.

16. Prove that only one of the direction angles of a half-line can be less than $45°$.

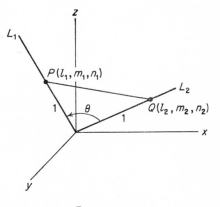

Figure 17.10

3. Angle between two lines

Let l_1, m_1, n_1 and l_2, m_2, n_2 be the direction cosines of two half-lines L_1 and L_2 emanating from the origin. Then the points $P(l_1,m_1,n_1)$ and $Q(l_2,m_2,n_2)$ are on the lines L_1 and L_2, respectively, at a distance of one unit from the origin (Figure 17.10). The angle θ between the half-lines L_1 and L_2 is an angle of the triangle OPQ, and

$$|PQ|^2 = 1^2 + 1^2 - 2\cdot1\cdot1\cdot\cos\theta,$$

or

$$\cos\theta = 1 - \frac{1}{2}|PQ|^2,$$

by the law of cosines.

We find $\cos\theta$ by use of the distance formula to be

$$\cos\theta = 1 - \frac{1}{2}\left[(l_2 - l_1)^2 + (m_2 - m_1)^2 + (n_2 - n_1)^2\right]$$

$$= 1 - \frac{1}{2} [(l_1^2 + m_1^2 + n_1^2) + (l_2^2 + m_2^2 + n_2^2) - 2(l_1 l_2 + m_1 m_2 + n_1 n_2)]$$

$$= 1 - \frac{1}{2} [1 + 1 - 2(l_1 l_2 + m_1 m_2 + n_1 n_2)],$$

or

17.8 $$\cos \theta = l_1 l_2 + m_1 m_2 + n_1 n_2.$$

Let us define an *angle between two lines in space* as an angle between two half-lines emanating from the origin and parallel to the given lines, regardless of whether or not the two lines meet. It is clear that there are two possible angles between two lines, and that these two angles are supplementary. If l_1, m_1, n_1 and l_2, m_2, n_2 are direction numbers of half-lines on the given lines, then the angle θ of measure between $0°$ and $180°$ determined by 17.8 is an angle between the two given lines.

For an angle θ of measure between $0°$ and $180°$, $\cos \theta = 0$ if and only if θ is a right angle. Thus we have the following corollary of 17.8.

17.9 Theorem. Two lines with direction numbers a_1, b_1, c_1 and a_2, b_2, c_2 are perpendicular if and only if

$$a_1 a_2 + b_1 b_2 + c_1 c_2 = 0.$$

Proof: If l_1, m_1, n_1 and l_2, m_2, n_2 are direction cosines of half-lines on the given lines, then there exist nonzero constants p_1 and p_2 such that

$$a_1 = p_1 l_1, \quad b_1 = p_1 m_1, \quad c_1 = p_1 n_1,$$

$$a_2 = p_2 l_2, \quad b_2 = p_2 m_2, \quad c_2 = p_2 n_2.$$

Since $p_1 p_2 \neq 0$ and

$$a_1 a_2 + b_1 b_2 + c_1 c_2 = p_1 p_2 (l_1 l_2 + m_1 m_2 + n_1 n_2),$$

evidently $a_1 a_2 + b_1 b_2 + c_1 c_2 = 0$ if and only if $l_1 l_2 + m_1 m_2 + n_1 n_2 = 0$, that is, if and only if the lines are perpendicular.

4. Equations of planes

A line perpendicular to a plane is called a *normal line* of the plane. We shall use the fact that there is a unique plane on a given point and with a given normal line to find an equation of the plane.

Let the line L with direction numbers a, b, and c be normal to the plane p, and let L and p intersect at the point $Q(x_1, y_1, z_1)$ as shown in Figure 17.11. A point $P(x, y, z)$ distinct from Q is on plane p if and only if the line K on P and Q is perpendicular to L. Since the line K has direction numbers $x - x_1$, $y - y_1$, $z - z_1$, P is on plane p if and only if

(1) $$a(x - x_1) + b(y - y_1) + c(z - z_1) = 0$$

by 17.9. Clearly

$$a(x_1 - x_1) + b(y_1 - y_1) + c(z_1 - z_1) = 0,$$

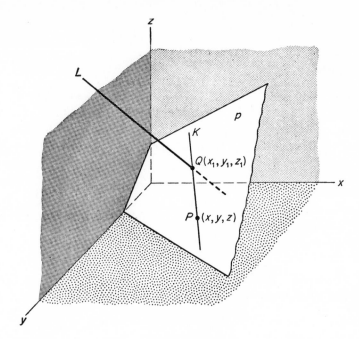

Figure 17.11

and we have that the coordinates of a point $P(x,y,z)$ satisfy (1) if and only if P is on the plane p. Hence (1) is an equation of p. We note that (1) has the form

$$ax + by + cz + d = 0,$$

where d is the constant $-(ax_1 + by_1 + cz_1)$; that is, (1) is a first-degree equation in x, y, and z. Thus we have proved part of the following theorem.

17.10 Theorem.   If a, b, and c are direction numbers of a normal line of a plane, then

$$ax + by + cz + d = 0$$

is an equation of the plane for some choice of the constant d. Conversely, the graph of each first-degree equation in x, y, and z is a plane.

To prove the last statement of the theorem, we need only note that the equation

$$ax + by + cz + d = 0$$

is an equation of the plane p having a normal line L with direction numbers a, b, and c and passing through a point $P(x_1,y_1,z_1)$ satisfying the given equation.

Example 1.   The point $(-2,1,3)$ is on a plane p, and the numbers 3, 1, and 5 are direction numbers of a normal line of p. Find an equation of p.

Solution: By 17.10, p has an equation of the form

$$3x + y + 5z + d = 0.$$

Since $(-2,1,3)$ is a point on p, we must have

$$3(-2) + 1 + 5(3) + d = 0.$$

Hence $d = -10$, and

$$3x + y + 5z - 10 = 0$$

is an equation of p.

Example 2. Describe the plane with equation

$$3x + y + z - 6 = 0.$$

Solution: Points on the plane p may be found by giving arbitrary values to two of the variables in the equation and solving for the third variable. If we let $y = 0$ and $z = 0$, we get $x = 2$; thus the point $(2,0,0)$ is on the plane. The

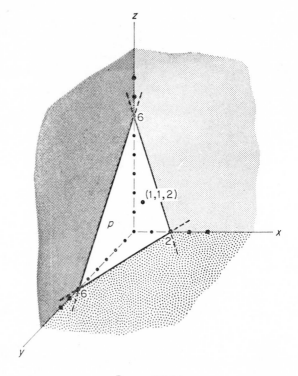

Figure 17.12

other intercepts are found to be $(0,6,0)$ and $(0,0,6)$. These three intercepts completely determine p as sketched in Figure 17.12. Other points on p are $(1,1,2)$, $(0,3,3)$, and $(2,1,-1)$.

The points $(2,0,0)$ and $(0,6,0)$ determine a line in the xy-plane called the *trace* of the plane p in the xy-plane. Thus the trace of p in the xy-plane consists of those points on p for which $z = 0$. On substituting $z = 0$ into the equation of p, we get

$$3x + y - 6 = 0$$

as the equation of the trace of p in the xy-plane. Similarly, the equation of the trace of p in the yz-plane is

$$y + z - 6 = 0,$$

found by substituting $x = 0$ in the equation of p; and the equation of the trace of p in the xz-plane is

$$3x + z - 6 = 0,$$

found by letting $y = 0$ in the equation of p.

The xy-plane has equation $z = 0$, since the point $P(x,y,z)$ is on the xy-plane if and only if $z = 0$. Each plane parallel to the xy-plane has an equation of the form $z = k$. Similarly, the xz- and yz-planes have equations $y = 0$ and $x = 0$, respectively, and planes parallel to the xz- and yz-planes have equations of the form $y = k$ and $x = k$.

Two planes with equations

$$a_1x + b_1y + c_1z + d_1 = 0$$

and

$$a_2x + b_2y + c_2z + d_2 = 0$$

are parallel if and only if their normal lines are parallel, that is, if and only if the sets of numbers a_1, b_1, c_1 and a_2, b_2, c_2 are proportional. In turn, the planes are perpendicular if and only if their normal lines are perpendicular, that is, if and only if

$$a_1a_2 + b_1b_2 + c_1c_2 = 0.$$

For example, the plane with equation

$$ax + by + d = 0$$

is perpendicular to the xy-plane with equation

$$0x - 0y + z = 0,$$

since $0 \cdot a + 0 \cdot b + 1 \cdot 0 = 0$. In other words, the plane having an equation with no z-term is parallel to the z-axis. Analogously, the planes having equations of the form

$$ax + cz + d = 0$$

and

$$by + cz + d = 0$$

are parallel to the y-axis and x-axis, respectively.

■ ■ ■ EXERCISES

Find an equation of the plane passing through the point P and having the given direction numbers for its normal line in each of the following.

1. $P(3,1,3)$; 1, 1, -1.   2. $P(0,2,-2)$; -1, 2, -3.
3. $P(1,-1,3)$; 4, 7, -2.   4. $P(2,-5,4)$; 0, 3, -8.

5. $P(0,0,0)$; 3, 1, -4. **6.** $P(1,1,1)$; 1, 0, 1.

Find the traces in the coordinate planes of each of the following planes and sketch.

7. $2x + y + z = 4$. **8.** $3x + 4y + 6z = 12$.
9. $x - 3y + z = 3$. **10.** $5x + y - z = 10$.
11. $4x + y = 6$. **12.** $2y - 3z = 4$.
13. $2x - 3z = 12$. **14.** $-2x + y - 4z = 8$.

Find an equation of the plane passing through the three given points in each of the following.

15. $(0,0,0)$, $(1,1,1)$, $(-1,1,0)$. **16.** $(2,1,3)$, $(5,2,-1)$, $(3,0,1)$.
17. $(1,2,-1)$, $(3,1,0)$, $(7,-6,2)$. **18.** $(1,2,1)$, $(3,-3,2)$, $(-3,12,-3)$.
19. $(2,1,-1)$, $(-1,3,1)$, $(4,0,1)$. **20.** $(a,0,0)$, $(0,b,0)$, $(0,0,c)$.

21. Find an equation for the plane that passes through the points $(1,0,-1)$ and $(2,1,3)$, and is perpendicular to the plane $x + y - z + 2 = 0$.

22. Find an equation for the plane that passes through the points $(2,-1,1)$ and $(0,0,1)$, and is perpendicular to the plane $2x + z - 1 = 0$.

23. Find an equation for the plane that passes through the point $(1,-1,4)$ and is perpendicular to each of the planes $2x + y - z + 2 = 0$ and $x - y + 3z - 1 = 0$.

24. Find an equation for the plane that passes through the point $(2,1,0)$ and is perpendicular to each of the planes $3x - z + 1 = 0$ and $x + y - z + 4 = 0$.

5. Equations of lines

A line in space may be considered as the line of intersection of two planes, in which case the line may be given analytically as the set of all points (x,y,z) satisfying simultaneously two first-degree equations of the form

$$a_1x + b_1y + c_1z + d_1 = 0, \qquad a_2x + b_2y + c_2z + d_2 = 0.$$

Another way of describing a line analytically is given in the following theorem.

17.11 Theorem. A line L with direction numbers a, b, and c has parametric equations

$$x = x_0 + at, \quad y = y_0 + bt, \quad z = z_0 + ct,$$

where $P(x_0,y_0,z_0)$ is any point on L.

Proof: The coordinates of P satisfy the given parametric equations for $t = 0$. A point $Q(x,y,z)$ other than P is on L if and only if the direction numbers $x - x_0$, $y - y_0$, and $z - z_0$ of the line on P and Q are proportional to a, b, and c; that is, if and only if

$$x - x_0 = at, \quad y - y_0 = bt, \quad z - z_0 = ct$$

for some number t. This proves the theorem.

If a, b, and c are different from 0, we may eliminate t from the parametric equations of L in 17.11 as follows:

$$t = \frac{x - x_0}{a}, \quad t = \frac{y - y_0}{b}, \quad t = \frac{z - z_0}{c},$$

and therefore

17.12 $$\frac{x - x_0}{a} = \frac{y - y_0}{b} = \frac{z - z_0}{c}.$$

This so-called *symmetric form* of the equation of a line is in reality three equations:

$$\frac{x - x_0}{a} = \frac{y - y_0}{b}, \quad \frac{x - x_0}{a} = \frac{z - z_0}{c}, \quad \frac{y - y_0}{b} = \frac{z - z_0}{c}.$$

Thus a point $P(x,y,z)$ is on the line L having 17.12 as its equation if and only if P is on each of the three planes with the equations above; that is, if and only if L is the line of intersection of these three planes.

If $a = 0$, $b \neq 0$, and $c \neq 0$, we get

$$x - x_0 = 0, \quad \frac{y - y_0}{b} = \frac{z - z_0}{c}$$

upon eliminating t from the parametric equations (17.11) of L. A similar argument may be made if other direction numbers are zero.

Example 1. Let L be the line of intersection of the two planes

$$2x - y + z = 4, \quad x + 3y - z = 2.$$

Find parametric equations of L and also a symmetric form of the equation of L.

Solution: Clearly the two given planes are not parallel and therefore have a line of intersection L. We can find parametric equations for L if we can find two distinct points on L. In this example, it is convenient to work with the traces of the given planes in two of the coordinate planes.

Letting $y = 0$, we obtain

$$2x + z = 4, \quad x - z = 2$$

as equations of the traces of the two given planes in the xz-plane. We easily find $x = 2$ and $z = 0$ as the simultaneous solution of these equations. Thus the point $(2,0,0)$ lies on both of the given planes and hence on L.

If $x = 0$, we have

$$-y + z = 4, \quad 3y - z = 2$$

as equations of the traces of the given planes in the yz-plane. These two lines in the yz-plane may easily be shown to intersect in the point $(0,3,7)$, which therefore must be a point on L.

Since $(2,0,0)$ and $(0,3,7)$ are points on L, then 2, -3, and -7 are direction numbers of L and

$$x = 2 + 2t, \quad y = -3t, \quad z = -7t$$

are parametric equations of L.   Eliminating t, we find

$$\frac{x-2}{2} = \frac{y}{-3} = \frac{z}{-7}$$

as a symmetric form of the equation of L.

We emphasize that there is nothing unique about the symmetric form of the equation of a line L or the parametric equations of L.   For example, if in Example 1 above we use the point $(0,3,7)$ instead of the point $(2,0,0)$ in finding equations of L, we get

$$x = 2t, \quad y = 3 - 3t, \quad z = 7 - 7t$$

as parametric equations of L and

$$\frac{x}{2} = \frac{y-3}{-3} = \frac{z-7}{-7}$$

as a symmetric form of the equation of L.

The point of intersection of two lines in space, if indeed they intersect, may be found as in the following example.

Example 2.   Find the point of intersection of the lines with parametric equations

$$x = 4 - 2t, \quad y = -2 + t, \quad z = -6 + 5t$$

and

$$x = 4 + s, \quad y = -\frac{7}{2} - s, \quad z = -\frac{9}{2} - 2s.$$

Solution: If $P(x,y,z)$ is a point on both the given lines, then we must have

$$4 - 2t = 4 + s, \quad -2 + t = -\frac{7}{2} - s, \quad -6 + 5t = -\frac{9}{2} - 2s$$

for some choice of the parameters s and t.   Since $s = -2t$ from the first equation, we have

$$-2 + t = -\frac{7}{2} + 2t,$$

or $t = \frac{3}{2}$, from the second equation.   Thus, $s = -3$ and $t = \frac{3}{2}$ at the point P of intersection of the two lines, if the lines intersect.   Letting $t = \frac{3}{2}$ in the equations of the first line, we obtain $P(1, -\frac{1}{2}, \frac{3}{2})$; letting $s = -3$ in the equations of the second line, we get the same point P.   We conclude that $P(1, -\frac{1}{2}, \frac{3}{2})$ is the point of intersection of the given lines.

■ ■ ■ EXERCISES

Find parametric equations of the line on each of the following pairs of points.

1. $(0,0,0)$, $(2,1,3)$.   2. $(-3,3,2)$, $(2,0,4)$.
3. $(2,1,-1)$, $(-5,1,4)$.   4. $(-7,2,3)$, $(4,2,3)$.
5. $(4,-4,-3)$, $(3,2,-4)$.   6. $(1,0,1)$, $(3,2,1)$.

Find parametric equations of the line on each of the following points which intersects and is perpendicular to the line with given parametric equations.

7. $(0,0,0); x = 2 - t, y = 1 + t, z = 2t.$

8. $(1,-1,1); x = 3t, y = -t, z = 2t.$

9. $(2,0,1); x = -1 - s, y = s, z = 1 + 3s.$

10. $(4,3,-1); x = s, y = 3 + 2s, z = 1.$

Find parametric equations and also a symmetric form of the equation of the line of intersection of each of the following pairs of planes.

11. $x + 2y - z = 7, x - 2y + z = 3.$

12. $3x - y + 2z = 5, 2x + y - z = 0.$

13. $4x + y - 3z = 7, x - 2y + 2z = 4.$

14. $x + z = 5, y - z = 2.$

Find the point of intersection of each of the following pairs of lines.

15. $x = 2 - t, y = -1 + 3t, z = t; x = -1 + 7s, y = 8 - 3s, z = 3 + s.$

16. $x = -3 + 3t, y = -2t, z = 7 + 6t; x = -6 + s, y = -5 - 3s,$
$z = 1 + 2s.$

17. Find an equation of the plane containing the two lines of Exercise 15.

18. Find an equation of the plane containing the two lines of Exercise 16.

19. If lines L_1 and L_2 have respective sets of direction numbers 3, 1, 2 and $-1, 2, 1$, find parametric equations of the line on the origin that is perpendicular to both L_1 and L_2.

20. If lines L_1 and L_2 have respective sets of direction numbers 1, 0, 1 and $-1, 1, 2$, find parametric equations of the line on the point $(2, 3, 0)$ that is perpendicular to both L_1 and L_2.

21. Given the lines L_1 and L_2 with respective parametric equations

$$x = 1 + 2t, \quad y = 3 + t, \quad z = -2 + t,$$

$$x = 1 + s, \quad y = -2 - 4s, \quad z = 9 + 2s,$$

find equations of the unique line L intersecting both L_1 and L_2 at right angles.

22. Prove analytically that there is a unique line intersecting each of two non-parallel lines in a right angle. (*Hint:* Select the coordinate axes so that one of the lines is a coordinate axis, say the x-axis. Then the lines have parametric equations $x = t, y = 0, z = 0$ and $x = x_0 + as, y = y_0 + bs,$ $z = z_0 + cs$, where not both b and c are zero.)

23. Prove that the distance d between the point $P(x_0,y_0,z_0)$ and the plane $ax + by + cz + d = 0$ is given by

$$d = \frac{|ax_0 + by_0 + cz_0 + d|}{\sqrt{a^2 + b^2 + c^2}}.$$

(*Hint:* Find parametric equations of the normal line L to the plane that passes through the point P, and then find the coordinates of the point of intersection Q of L with the plane. Then $d = |PQ|$.)

6. Surfaces

The graph in space of an equation in x, y, and z is called a *surface*. Two examples of surfaces have been studied so far in this chapter, namely, the sphere (17.2) and the plane (17.10).

While it is easy to visualize a plane or a sphere, and even easy to sketch these surfaces on a plane, the general problem of visualizing and sketching a surface is much more difficult than the corresponding problem of sketching a curve in the plane. Of course, this is due to the fact that a surface in space can only be sketched on a piece of paper. Three-dimensional models of the common surfaces are available, and are of great help in visualizing these surfaces.

One of the easiest surfaces to visualize is a cylinder. A *cylinder* is a surface that may be thought of as being generated by a line (called the *generator*) moving along a given curve in such a way as always to remain parallel to its original position. The curve along which the generating line moves is called a *directrix** of the cylinder. Each of the lines on the cylinder parallel to the generator is called a *ruling* of the cylinder.

If the directrix is a straight line, the cylinder is just a plane. Other

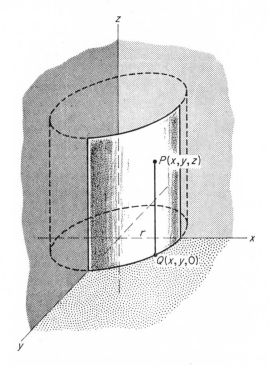

Figure 17.13

---

* A directrix of a cylinder is in no way related to the directrix of a parabola.

than a plane, the most common cylinder is the right circular cylinder, generated by a line moving along a circle so as to always be perpendicular to the plane of the circle.

The right circular cylinder sketched in Figure 17.13 has as its directrix a circle of radius r in the xy-plane with its center at the origin. A point $P(x,y,z)$ is on this cylinder if and only if the projection $Q(x,y,0)$ of P on the xy-plane is on the directrix of the cylinder. Thus $P(x,y,z)$ is a point on the cylinder if and only if

$$x^2 + y^2 = r^2,$$

and we conclude that this equation of the cylinder is just the equation of its directrix in the xy-plane.

It is clear from the preceding example that an equation in x and y has as its graph in space a cylinder with generator parallel to the z-axis. Similarly, an equation in x and z has as its graph in space a cylinder with generator parallel to the y-axis, and so on. In each case, the directrix is the graph in a coordinate plane of the given equation in two variables.

Example 1. Discuss and sketch the graph of the equation

$$z = 4 - x^2.$$

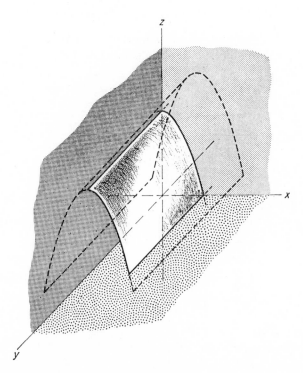

Figure 17.14

Solution: The graph of this equation in the xz-plane is a parabola symmetric to the z-axis with vertex at $(0,0,4)$. The graph in space is a parabolic cylinder with directrix the parabola in the xz-plane and generator parallel to the y-axis. It is sketched in Figure 17.14.

Example 2. Discuss and sketch the graph of the equation

$$z = |y|.$$

Solution: The graph of this equation in the yz-plane consists of two half-lines emanating from the origin. Thus its graph in space is a cylinder with generator parallel to the x-axis and directrix the two half-lines. It looks like a trough made up of two half-planes meeting on the x-axis at an angle of $90°$, as sketched in Figure 17.15.

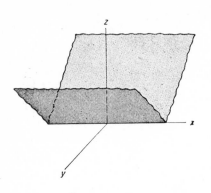

Example 3. Discuss and sketch the graph of the equation

$$y = e^x.$$

Solution: The cylinder has as its directrix the exponential curve $y = e^x$ in the xy-plane and as its generator a line parallel to the z-axis, as sketched in Figure 17.16.

Figure 17.15

A fact that makes the sketching of a cylinder comparatively easy is that the trace of the cylinder in each plane parallel to the plane of the directrix

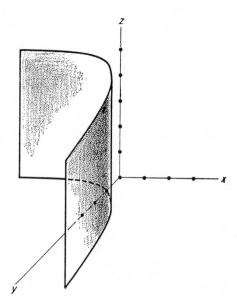

Figure 17.16

is the same as the directrix.   By the *trace* of a surface in a plane, we mean
the set of all points of the surface that are on the given plane.   For example,
the trace of a right circular cylinder in each plane parallel to the plane
of the directrix is a circle.

Another surface that is easy to visualize is the surface of revolution
discussed in previous chapters.   We recall that a surface of revolution is
generated by rotating a plane curve about some fixed axis in its plane.   If
a surface of revolution is generated by rotating a curve in a coordinate
plane about a coordinate axis, then an equation of the surface may be found
quite easily as we shall now show.

Let the surface of revolution be formed by rotating the graph of an
equation

$$f(x,y) = 0$$

about the x-axis.   We shall assume that $y \geq 0$ for each point (x,y) on the
generating curve.   A point $P(x,y,z)$ will be on this surface if and only if
$Q(x,y_0,0)$ is on the generating curve, where

$$y_0 = |PA| = \sqrt{y^2 + z^2}$$

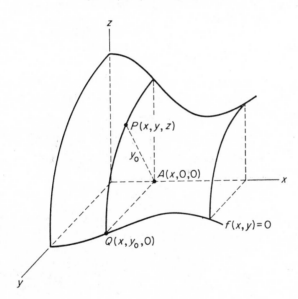

Figure 17.17

as indicated in Figure 17.17.   Since $Q(x,y_0,0)$ is on the generating curve
if and only if $f(x,y_0) = 0$, the point $P(x,y,z)$ is on the surface of revolution
if and only if

$$f(x, \sqrt{y^2 + z^2}) = 0.$$

Hence this equation in x, y, and z is an equation of the surface of revolution.

It is clear that similar remarks can be made if the generating curve is in any one of the coordinate planes and the axis of revolution is a coordinate axis in that plane. If, for example, the surface is generated by rotating a curve in the yz-plane about the y-axis, then the equation of the surface is obtained by replacing each z by $\sqrt{x^2 + z^2}$ in an equation of the generating curve.

We might summarize our remarks above by saying that the graph of an equation in x, y, and z is a surface of revolution if and only if two of the variables occur together in the form $x^2 + y^2$, $x^2 + z^2$, or $y^2 + z^2$.

Example 4. Find an equation of the surface generated by rotating the curve

$$x^2 + 4y^2 = 4$$

in the xy-plane about the x-axis.

Solution: We replace each y by $\sqrt{y^2 + z^2}$ in the equation of the generating curve to obtain

$$x^2 + 4(y^2 + z^2) = 4$$

as an equation of the surface of revolution. This surface, formed by rotating an ellipse about an axis, is called an ellipsoid of revolution.

In the example above, the generating curve should be taken to be the semi-ellipse with equation

$$2y = \sqrt{4 - x^2}$$

in order to meet the assumption that $y \geq 0$ for each point (x,y) on the generating curve. When we replace y by $\sqrt{y^2 + z^2}$ in this equation, we get

$$2\sqrt{y^2 + z^2} = \sqrt{4 - x^2}$$

as an equation of the surface. It is evident that the graph of this equation is the same as that of the equation obtained in Example 4.

Example 5. Find an equation of the surface generated by rotating the curve

$$x^2 = 4z$$

in the xz-plane about the z-axis.

Solution: We replace each x^2 by $x^2 + y^2$ to obtain

$$x^2 + y^2 = 4z$$

as an equation of this surface. Since the surface is formed by rotating a parabola about its axis, it is called a paraboloid of revolution.

Example 6. Describe the graph of the equation

$$x^2 - 9y^2 + z^2 = 36.$$

Solution: Since this equation has the form

$$(x^2 + z^2) - 9y^2 = 36,$$

its graph is a surface of revolution obtained by rotating the curve

(1) $x^2 - 9y^2 = 36$

in the xy-plane about the y-axis. This surface, obtained by rotating the hyperbola (1) about an axis, is called a hyperboloid of revolution.   Incidentally, the surface may also be generated by rotating the hyperbola

$$z^2 - 9y^2 = 36$$

in the yz-plane about the y-axis.

■ ■ ■ EXERCISES

Discuss and sketch the graph in space of each of the following equations.

1. $x^2 + y^2 = 9$.   2. $y^2 + z^2 = 4$.

3. $x^2 = 8z$.   4. $x^2 - y^2 = 1$.

5. $x^2 + y^2 + 9z^2 = 9$.   6. $y^2 + z^2 = \sin x$.

7. $y^2 = x^2 + z^2$.   8. $xz = 1$.

9. $x^2 = y^2$.   10. $x^2 + y^2 = 4z$.

11. $x^2(y^2 + z^2) = 1$.   12. $4x^2 + y^2 + 4z^2 = 16$.

13. $y^2 + z^2 = e^x$.   14. $y = 9 - x^2$.

15. $y^2 = 4 + z^2$.   16. $x^2 - y^2 - z^2 = 1$.

17. Find an equation of the ellipsoid of revolution obtained by rotating the ellipse $x^2/a^2 + y^2/b^2 = 1$ in the xy-plane about the x-axis; the y-axis. Sketch.

18. Find an equation of the hyperboloid of revolution obtained by rotating the hyperbola $x^2/a^2 - y^2/b^2 = 1$ in the xy-plane about the x-axis; the y-axis.   Sketch.

19. Find an equation of the paraboloid of revolution obtained by rotating the parabola $y^2 = 4px$ about the x-axis.   Sketch.

20. Find an equation of the cone obtained by rotating the curve $|y| = mx$ about the x-axis.   Sketch.

7. Quadric surfaces

The graph of a second-degree equation in x, y, and z is called a *quadric surface*.   We shall give some standard forms of equations of quadric surfaces in this section.

The graph of an equation of the form

17.13
$$\frac{x^2}{a^2} + \frac{y^2}{b^2} + \frac{z^2}{c^2} = 1$$

is called an *ellipsoid*.   If $a^2 = b^2 = c^2$, 17.13 is an equation of a sphere. If $a^2 = b^2$ (or $b^2 = c^2$, or $a^2 = c^2$), 17.13 is an equation of an ellipsoid of revolution as discussed in the previous section.

If we let $z = 0$ in 17.13, we get

$$\frac{x^2}{a^2} + \frac{y^2}{b^2} = 1$$

as the equation of the trace of the ellipsoid in the xy-plane. Clearly this trace is an ellipse. The traces of 17.13 in the other coordinate planes are easily seen to be ellipses also.

Letting $z = k$ in 17.13, we get the equation

$$\frac{x^2}{a^2} + \frac{y^2}{b^2} = 1 - \frac{k^2}{c^2}$$

of the trace of the ellipsoid in the plane $z = k$, a plane parallel to the xy-plane. This trace again is an ellipse if $k^2 < c^2$. Similar statements may be made for traces in planes parallel to the other coordinate planes. The graph of 17.13 is sketched in Figure 17.18.

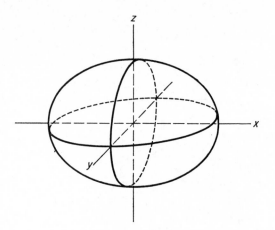

Figure 17.18

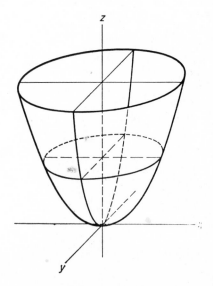

Figure 17.19

The graph of an equation of the form

17.14
$$\frac{x^2}{a^2} + \frac{y^2}{b^2} = cz$$

is called an *elliptic paraboloid*, so named because each trace of the surface in a plane $z = k$ is an ellipse (if $ck > 0$) while each trace in a plane $x = k$ or $y = k$ is a parabola. If $a^2 = b^2$, 17.14 is an equation of a paraboloid of revolution with the z-axis as axis of revolution. If $c > 0$, the graph of 17.14 is as sketched in Figure 17.19.

The quadric surface with equation of the form

17.15
$$\frac{x^2}{a^2} - \frac{y^2}{b^2} = cz$$

is called a *hyperbolic paraboloid*. It is the saddle-shaped surface sketched

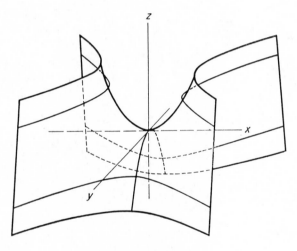

Figure 17.20

in Figure 17.20 if $c > 0$. We note that if $z = 0$, the trace consists of the lines

$$\frac{x}{a} = \pm\frac{y}{b},$$

whereas if $z = k$, $k \neq 0$, the trace is a hyperbola. The traces in planes parallel to the xz- and yz-planes are parabolas.

Quadric surfaces with equations of the form

17.16
$$\frac{x^2}{a^2} + \frac{y^2}{b^2} - \frac{z^2}{c^2} = 1,$$

or

17.17
$$\frac{x^2}{a^2} + \frac{y^2}{b^2} - \frac{z^2}{c^2} = -1$$

are called *hyperboloids*.   For each surface, the trace in a plane $z = k$ is an ellipse, and the traces in the planes $x = k$ and $y = k$ are hyperbolas. If $a^2 = b^2$, these surfaces are hyperboloids of revolution.   The graph of 17.16, sketched in Figure 17.21, is called a *hyperboloid of one sheet*.   The graph of 17.17, sketched in Figure 17.22, is called a *hyperboloid of two sheets*.

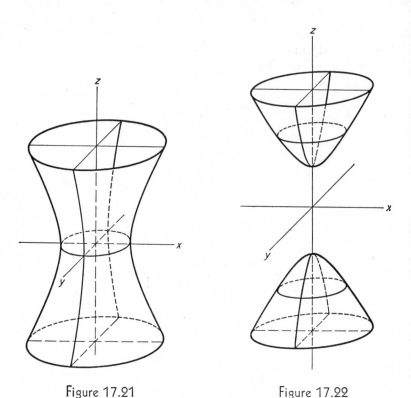

Figure 17.21   Figure 17.22

Closely related to the hyperboloids is the quadric surface with equation

17.18 $$\frac{x^2}{a^2} + \frac{y^2}{b^2} - \frac{z^2}{c^2} = 0.$$

This surface is related to each of the hyperboloids as the asymptotes are to a hyperbola.   It is an *elliptic cone*, frequently called the asymptotic cone of each of the hyperboloids 17.16 and 17.17.   For $z = k$, the trace of 17.18 is an ellipse; for $x = k$ or $y = k$, the trace is a hyperbola if $k \neq 0$ and a pair of lines intersecting at the origin if $k = 0$.

A cone may be thought of as a surface generated by a line moving along a given plane curve and passing through a fixed point, called the *vertex* of the cone.   Thus, if V is the vertex of a cone and P is any point on the cone, every point on the line through V and P also is on the cone.   The most common cone is the right circular cone generated by a line moving along a circle (17.18 if $a^2 = b^2$).

We may prove that 17.18 is a cone as follows. If $P(x_0, y_0, z_0)$ is any point on the graph of 17.18 other than the origin O, then the line L on P and O has parametric equations

$$x = x_0 t, \quad y = y_0 t, \quad z = z_0 t.$$

Each point on L is also on the graph of 17.18, since

$$\frac{(x_0 t)^2}{a^2} + \frac{(y_0 t)^2}{b^2} - \frac{(z_0 t)^2}{c^2} = t^2 \left(\frac{x_0^2}{a^2} + \frac{y_0^2}{b^2} - \frac{z_0^2}{c^2} \right) = 0.$$

Thus the graph of 17.18 is a cone.

■ ■ ■ EXERCISES

Name and sketch the graph of each of the following equations.

1. $x^2 + 4y^2 + 9z^2 = 36.$ 2. $x^2 + 4y^2 = 4z.$

3. $x^2 - y^2 + 4z^2 = 4.$ 4. $x^2 - y^2 - 4z^2 = 4.$

5. $x^2 = z^2 + 4y.$ 6. $16x^2 + y^2 = 64 - 4z^2.$

7. $4x^2 + 8y + z^2 = 0.$ 8. $x^2 + 9y^2 = z^2.$

9. $16x^2 - 9y^2 - z^2 - 144 = 0.$ 10. $36 + 4y^2 = x^2 + 9z^2.$

11. $x^2 + 25z^2 = 9y^2.$ 12. $y^2 = 4x + 4z^2.$

13. $x^2 + 25y^2 - 50z = 0.$ 14. $x^2 + 4y^2 = 4z.$

15. $x^2 + y^2 = 4x.$ 16. $x^2 + y^2 = 1 + z.$

8. Curves

A space curve may be described in many ways, one of which is as the curve of intersection of two surfaces. For example, two planes intersect in a straight line, and a plane and an ellipsoid intersect in an ellipse. A curve lying completely in a plane is called a *plane curve*. Every other curve not lying in any plane is called a *twisted curve*.

As an example of a twisted curve, consider the curve of intersection of the sphere

$$x^2 + y^2 + z^2 = 4$$

and the right circular cylinder

$$(x - 2)^2 + y^2 = 4.$$

We may visualize this curve by cutting a cylindrical piece out of the side (to the center) of an apple. The curve in question is then the closed curve on the surface of the apple along the edge of the cut. A quarter of this curve is sketched in Figure 17.23.

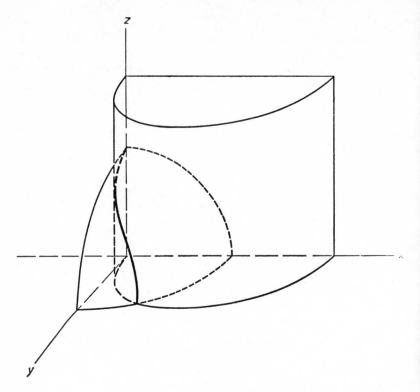

Figure 17.23

Another common way of describing a space curve is parametrically, as the locus of all points $P(x,y,z)$ obtained by giving t values in the equations

$$x = x(t), \quad y = y(t), \quad z = z(t),$$

where x, y, and z are functions. We have already seen how to describe a line parametrically.

The screwthread on a bolt is an interesting example of a twisted curve. The wire holding together the pages of a spiral notebook has the same shape. This curve, called a *circular helix*, may be described as follows.

The trace of the cylinder $x^2 + y^2 = r^2$ in the xy-plane is a circle with parametric equations

$$x = r \cos t, \quad y = r \sin t, \quad z = 0.$$

Now imagine a space curve starting from the point $(r,0,0)$ where $t = 0$, and winding about the given cylinder in such a way that the point $P(x,y,z)$ on the curve has a z-coordinate proportional to t when $x = r \cos t$ and $y = r \sin t$. That is, the point P has coordinates

17.19 $x = r \cos t, \quad y = r \sin t, \quad z = at$

for some positive constant a (Figure 17.24). These are parametric equations of a circular helix. The helix is above the xy-plane if $t > 0$, and below the xy-plane if $t < 0$.

Many of the applications of the calculus to plane curves carry over with

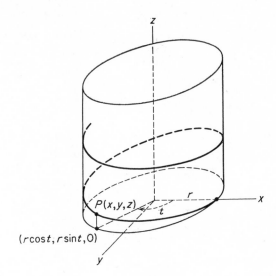

Figure 17.24

but little change to space curves. We shall consider two of these, namely, the applications to the finding of tangent lines and length of arc.

Let a space curve be given parametrically by the equations

$$x = x(t), \quad y = y(t), \quad z = z(t),$$

where x, y, and z are differentiable functions. We shall define the tangent line T to this curve at the point $P(x(t),y(t),z(t))$ much as we did for a plane curve by considering a secant line S on P and some other point $Q(x(t + \Delta t),y(t + \Delta t),z(t + \Delta t))$ (Figure 17.25). The numbers Δx, Δy, and Δz defined by

$$\Delta x = x(t + \Delta t) - x(t), \quad \Delta y = y(t + \Delta t) - y(t), \quad \Delta z = z(t + \Delta t) - z(t)$$

are direction numbers of the secant line S, as are also the numbers

$$\frac{\Delta x}{\Delta t}, \quad \frac{\Delta y}{\Delta t}, \quad \frac{\Delta z}{\Delta t}.$$

The limits of these direction numbers of S as Δt approaches 0 are dx/dt, dy/dt, and dz/dt, and are defined to be direction numbers of the tangent line T.

17.20 Definition. The tangent line to the space curve

$$x = x(t), \quad y = y(t), \quad z = z(t),$$

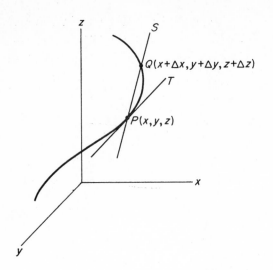

Figure 17.25

at the point $P(x,y,z)$ is the line on P with direction numbers

$$\frac{dx}{dt}, \quad \frac{dy}{dt}, \quad \frac{dz}{dt},$$

if these three derivatives exist and are not all zero.

Example 1. Find the tangent line T to the helix 17.19 at the point P where $t = 0$.

Solution: Since

$$\frac{dx}{dt} = -r \sin t, \quad \frac{dy}{dt} = r \cos t, \quad \frac{dz}{dt} = a,$$

we have that 0, r, and a are direction numbers of the tangent line T at the point $P(r,0,0)$. Hence

$$x = r, \quad y = rs, \quad z = as$$

are parametric equations (with parameter s) of T.

Example 2. Find the tangent line T to the *twisted cubic*

$$x = t^2, \quad y = t, \quad z = t^3$$

at the point P where $t = 1$.

Solution: We have

$$\frac{dx}{dt} = 2t, \quad \frac{dy}{dt} = 1, \quad \frac{dz}{dt} = 3t^2,$$

so that the tangent line T at $P(1,1,1)$ has direction numbers 2, 1, and 3. Hence

$$x = 1 + 2s, \quad y = 1 + s, \quad z = 1 + 3s$$

are parametric equations of T. The twisted cubic and its tangent line T are sketched in Figure 17.26.

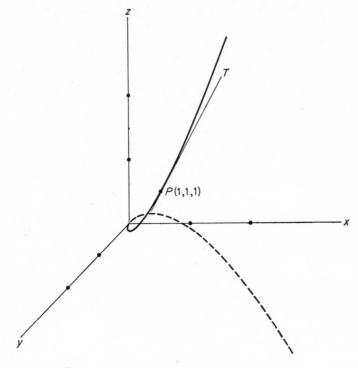

Figure 17.26

The length of an arc of a space curve may be found by precisely the same argument as given for a plane curve. Such an argument leads us to make the following definition.

17.21 Definition. If a space curve has equations
$$x = x(t), \quad y = y(t), \quad z = z(t),$$
where the functions x, y, and z have continuous derivatives, and if an arc of the curve is traced out once as t varies from t_0 to t_1, then the length of this arc is given by
$$L = \int_{t_0}^{t_1} \sqrt{x'^2 + y'^2 + z'^2} \, dt.$$

Example 3. Find the length of arc L of the helix 17.19 between $t = 0$ and $t = \theta$.

Solution: By 17.21,
$$L = \int_0^\theta \sqrt{(-r \sin t)^2 + (r \cos t)^2 + a^2} \, dt$$
$$= \int_0^\theta \sqrt{r^2 + a^2} \, dt = \sqrt{r^2 + a^2} \, \theta.$$

Thus, as might be expected, the length of arc of the helix is just a constant $\sqrt{r^2 + a^2}$ times the angle θ swept out in tracing the arc. In one revolution, for example, the arc has length $2\pi \sqrt{r^2 + a^2}$.

Example 4. Find the length of arc L of the twisted cubic of Example 2 between $t = 0$ and $t = 1$.

Solution: By 17.21,

$$L = \int_0^1 \sqrt{4t^2 + 1 + 9t^4}\, dt.$$

We cannot evaluate this integral by use of the integration formulas at our disposal. However, using Simpson's rule (13.3) with $n = 4$, we may approximate L as follows:

$$L \doteq \frac{1}{12}\left(1 + 4(1.13) + 2(1.60) + 4(2.47) + 3.74\right) \doteq 1.86.$$

■ ■ ■ EXERCISES

Find parametric equations of the tangent line to each of the following space curves at the indicated point. Sketch.

1. $x = 2\cos t$, $y = 2\sin t$, $z = t$; $t = \pi$.

2. $x = t^2$, $y = t$, $z = t^3$; $t = 0$.

3. $x = e^t$, $y = e^{-t}$, $z = t$; $t = 0$.

4. $x = t^2$, $y = t$, $z = 1/t$; $t = 1$.

5. $x = t^3$, $y = t$, $z = t^4$; $t = 1$.

6. $x = 2\sin t$, $y = 3\cos t$, $z = 4t$; $t = \pi/2$.

7. Find equations of the tangent lines to the twisted cubic $x = t^2$, $y = t$, $z = t^3$ at the points of intersection of this curve with the plane $x + 6y = z$.

8. Show that the twisted cubic $x = t^2$, $y = t$, $z = t^3$ is the curve of intersection of the two cylinders $x = y^2$ and $z = y^3$. Sketch.

9. Find the tangent line to the curve of Figure 17.23 at the point $(\frac{1}{2}, \sqrt{7}/2, \sqrt{2})$ by first finding parametric equations of the part of the curve in the first octant.

10. A conical helix is traced out by a point P starting from the vertex V of the cone $x^2 + y^2 = z^2$ and moving around the cone so that the z-coordinate of P is proportional to the angle through which the projection of P in the xy-plane has turned. Show that

$$x = at\cos t, \quad y = at\sin t, \quad z = at$$

are parametric equations of this conical helix.

Find the length of the specified arc of each of the following curves:

11. $x = 2t$, $y = t$, $z = t^2$; between $t = 0$ and $t = 2$.

12. $x = t$, $y = 2t\sqrt{t}$, $z = 3t$; between $t = 0$ and $t = 4$.

13. $x = t\cos t$, $y = t\sin t$, $z = t$; between $t = 0$ and $t = \pi$.

14. $x = e^t$, $y = e^{-t}$, $z = \sqrt{2}t$; between $t = 0$ and $t = 1$.

15. $x = t^2/\sqrt{2}$, $y = t$, $z = t^3/3$; between $t = 0$ and $t = 3$.

16. $x = \ln t$, $y = 2t$, $z = t^2$; between $t = 1$ and $t = 3$.

17. The wire of a spiral notebook has the shape of a helix. If the diameter

of the helix is $\frac{1}{2}$ in. and the helix has 5 turns per inch, and if the notebook is 9 in. high, find the length of the wire.

18. Show that the tangent line to the helix 17.19 makes a constant angle $\sin^{-1}(a/\sqrt{r^2 + a^2})$ with the xy-plane.

19. The description of motion in a plane given in Section 5 of Chapter 15 can be extended to the description of motion in space as is indicated by the following exercises.

   (a) Let $P(x_1, y_1, z_1)$ and $Q(x_2, y_2, z_2)$ be the initial and terminal points of the vector $\overrightarrow{PQ}$. Give the x-, y-, and z-components of $\overrightarrow{PQ}$. (See Figure 17.3.)

   (b) If at the time t the point P has coordinates given by $x = x(t)$, $y = y(t)$ and $z = z(t)$, define the velocity and acceleration vectors of P at the time t.

   (c) In each of Exercises 1–6 determine the velocity and acceleration vectors at the given time.

9. Cylindrical and spherical coordinate systems

There are two common generalizations in space of the polar coordinate system in a plane.

The basis of a *cylindrical coordinate system* is a plane p with a polar coordinate system on it and a z-axis perpendicular to p with the origin of the z-axis at the pole of p. Each point P in space then has coordinates (r, θ, z), where (r, θ) are the polar coordinates of the projection Q of P on p, and z is the coordinate of the projection R of P on the z-axis (Figure 17.27).

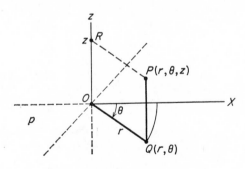

Figure 17.27

The graph of an equation of the form

$$r = c,$$

c a constant, is a right circular cylinder of radius c having the z-axis as its axis. This is the reason for the name "cylindrical" coordinate system. The graph of

$$\theta = c$$

is a plane containing the z-axis; the graph of

$$z = c$$

is a plane parallel to the given polar-coordinate plane p.

If a rectangular coordinate system and a cylindrical coordinate system are placed in space as in Figure 17.28, with the cylindrical coordinate

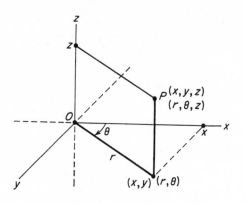

Figure 17.28

system having the xy-plane as its polar plane and the positive x-axis as its polar axis, then each point P has two sets of coordinates (x,y,z) and (r,θ,z) related by the equations

17.22 $\qquad x = r \cos \theta, \quad y = r \sin \theta, \quad z = z.$

This is evident from 15.6.

For a *spherical coordinate system*, we start off with a plane p having a polar coordinate system on it and a z-axis perpendicular to p with the origin of the z-axis meeting the plane p at the pole. Each point P in space has coordinates (ρ,θ,ϕ), where

$$\rho = |OP|,$$

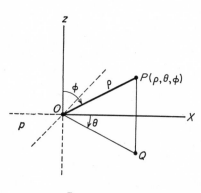

Figure 17.29

θ is the polar angle associated with the projection Q of P on plane p, and ϕ is the direction angle of the half-line from the pole through P relative to the z-axis (Figure 17.29). The origin has coordinates $(0,\theta,\phi)$ for any θ and ϕ. If $P(\rho,\theta,\phi)$ is a point different from the origin, then necessarily $\rho > 0$ and $0 \leq \phi \leq \pi$, with $\phi = 0$ if P is on the positive z-axis and $\phi = \pi$ if P is on the negative z-axis. There are no restrictions on the angle θ.

The graph of

$$\rho = c,$$

c a positive constant, is a sphere of radius c with center at the pole; hence the name "spherical" coordinate system. The graph of

$$\theta = c$$

is a plane containing the z-axis, and the graph of

$$\phi = c$$

is a right circular cone having the z-axis as its axis and the pole as its vertex.

If we place a rectangular coordinate system and a spherical coordinate system together as indicated in Figure 17.30, then each point P in space

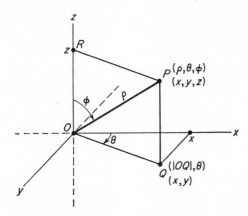

Figure 17.30

has two sets of coordinates (x,y,z) and (ρ,θ,ϕ). By 17.22, with $r = |OQ|$, we have

$$x = |OQ| \cos \theta, \qquad y = |OQ| \sin \theta.$$

Since $|OQ| = |PR| = \rho \sin \phi$ and $z = \rho \cos \phi$, we obtain

17.23 $x = \rho \sin \phi \cos \theta, \quad y = \rho \sin \phi \sin \theta, \quad z = \rho \cos \phi$

as the equations relating x, y, and z to ρ, θ, and ϕ.

■ ■ ■ EXERCISES

1. Find parametric equations in cylindrical coordinates of the helix 17.19.
2. Find parametric equations in spherical coordinates of the conical helix (Exercise 10 of the preceding section).
3. Given a curve $r = r(t)$, $\theta = \theta(t)$, $z = z(t)$ in cylindrical coordinates, find a formula for the length of the arc of this curve between $t = t_0$ and $t = t_1$.
4. Given a curve $\rho = \rho(t)$, $\theta = \theta(t)$, $\phi = \phi(t)$ in spherical coordinates, find a formula for the length of the arc of this curve between $t = t_0$ and $t = t_1$.

18

Vectors

■ ■ ■ ■ ■   Two-dimensional vectors were introduced in Chapter 15 and were used to study the motion of a point in a plane. Three-dimensional vectors will be studied in the present chapter. Much of the analytic geometry of the preceding chapter will be reformulated in terms of vectors.

1. The algebra of vectors

A three-dimensional vector is an ordered triple of numbers (x,y,z). Unless otherwise specified, a vector will always be three-dimensional in this chapter. We shall use our previous notation of boldface letters such as a and b to designate vectors.

Operations of addition, subtraction, scalar multiple, and dot product may be defined for three-dimensional vectors analogously to the way they were for two-dimensional vectors. Thus, if

$$a = (a_1, a_2, a_3), \qquad b = (b_1, b_2, b_3),$$

then

$$a + b = (a_1 + b_1, \ a_2 + b_2, \ a_3 + b_3),$$

$$a - b = (a_1 - b_1, \ a_2 - b_2, \ a_3 - b_3),$$

$$ca = (ca_1, ca_2, ca_3),$$

$$a \cdot b = a_1 b_1 + a_2 b_2 + a_3 b_3.$$

The vector

$$0 = (0,0,0)$$

is called the zero vector. The length $|a|$ of the vector a is defined by

$$|a| = \sqrt{a \cdot a} = \sqrt{a_1^2 + a_2^2 + a_3^2}.$$

These vector operations have the same properties as stated in Chapter 15, Section 3, for two-dimensional vectors. We list these properties below for the convenience of the reader.

$$a + b = b + a, \qquad a + (b + c) = (a + b) + c,$$
$$a + 0 = a, \qquad a - a = 0,$$
$$c(a + b) = ca + cb, \qquad (c + d)a = ca + da,$$
$$(cd)a = c(da), \qquad (-c)a = -(ca),$$
$$1a = a, \qquad 0a = 0, \qquad c0 = 0,$$
$$a \cdot b = b \cdot a, \qquad (a + b) \cdot c = a \cdot c + b \cdot c,$$
$$(ka) \cdot b = a \cdot (kb) = k(a \cdot b),$$
$$0 \cdot a = 0, \qquad a \cdot a > 0 \quad \text{if } a \neq 0.$$

We recall that a vector of length 1 is called a unit vector. Unit vectors of particular importance to us are

$$i = (1,0,0), \quad j = (0,1,0), \quad k = (0,0,1).$$

Every vector may be written as a sum of scalar multiples of i, j, and k as follows:

$$(a_1,a_2,a_3) = a_1 i + a_2 j + a_3 k.$$

Another vector operation that holds for three-dimensional vectors only is the so-called *cross product* (or vector product). The cross product of two vectors is a vector, unlike the dot product of two vectors, which is a number. We first define the cross product of the unit vectors i, j, and k as follows:

$$i \times i = 0, \qquad j \times j = 0, \qquad k \times k = 0,$$
$$i \times j = k, \qquad j \times k = i, \qquad k \times i = j,$$
$$j \times i = -k, \qquad k \times j = -i, \qquad i \times k = -j.$$

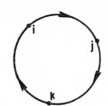

Figure 18.1

These may be remembered with the aid of Figure 18.1. If we move around the circle in the indicated direction, the cross product of two consecutive ones is the next one (i.e., if we encounter the vectors a, b, c in order, then $a \times b = c$). If we move around the circle in the opposite direction, the cross product of two consecutive ones is the negative of the next one. Finally, the cross product of a vector with itself is the zero vector.

The cross product of any two vectors a and b will be defined by expressing each in terms of i, j, and k and then assuming that the usual rules for multiplying two polynomials hold.

For example, the cross product of vectors $(2,0,-1)$ and $(0,-3,2)$ is found as follows:

$$(2,0,-1) \times (0,-3,2) = (2i - k) \times (-3j + 2k)$$
$$= -6(i \times j) + 4(i \times k) + 3(k \times j) - 2(k \times k)$$
$$= -6k - 4j - 3i - 20$$
$$= (-3,-4,-6).$$

In general, if

$$a = (a_1,a_2,a_3) = a_1i + a_2j + a_3k,$$
$$b = (b_1,b_2,b_3) = b_1i + b_2j + b_3k,$$

then

$$a \times b = (a_1i + a_2j + a_3k) \times (b_1i + b_2j + b_3k)$$
$$= a_1b_1(i \times i) + a_1b_2(i \times j) + a_1b_3(i \times k) + a_2b_1(j \times i)$$
$$\quad + a_2b_2(j \times j) + a_2b_3(j \times k) + a_3b_1(k \times i) + a_3b_2(k \times j)$$
$$\quad + a_3b_3(k \times k)$$
$$= (a_2b_3 - a_3b_2)i + (a_3b_1 - a_1b_3)j + (a_1b_2 - a_2b_1)k.$$

Thus, the cross product of two vectors is defined by

18.1 $(a_1,a_2,a_3) \times (b_1,b_2,b_3) = (a_2b_3 - a_3b_2, a_3b_1 - a_1b_3, a_1b_2 - a_2b_1).$

For example,

$$(2,-1,3) \times (3,4,-6) = (6 - 12, 9 + 12, 8 + 3) = (-6,21,11).$$

The cross product operation has the following properties. For any vectors a, b, and c and any number k,

$$a \times b = -b \times a, \qquad (ka) \times b = a \times (kb) = k(a \times b),$$
$$(a + b) \times c = a \times c + b \times c, \qquad c \times (a + b) = c \times a + c \times b,$$
$$a \times a = 0, \qquad 0 \times a = a \times 0 = 0,$$
$$a \cdot (b \times c) = (a \times b) \cdot c, \qquad a \times (b \times c) = (a \cdot c)b - (a \cdot b)c.$$

Note that the cross product is not commutative, i.e., $a \times b \neq b \times a$ in general. The cross product is also nonassociative, i.e.,

$$a \times (b \times c) \neq (a \times b) \times c$$

in general. For example,

$$i \times (i \times j) = i \times k = -j, \qquad (i \times i) \times j = 0 \times j = 0$$

and $i \times (i \times j) \neq (i \times i) \times j.$

The properties listed above can be proved by straightforward calculations. We shall prove two of them as illustrations of this method.

Proof that $(k\boldsymbol{a}) \times \boldsymbol{b} = k(\boldsymbol{a} \times \boldsymbol{b})$: If we let $\boldsymbol{a} = (a_1, a_2, a_3)$ and $\boldsymbol{b} = (b_1, b_2, b_3)$, then

$$
\begin{aligned}
(k\boldsymbol{a}) \times \boldsymbol{b} &= (ka_1, ka_2, ka_3) \times (b_1, b_2, b_3) \\
&= (ka_2b_3 - ka_3b_2, \ ka_3b_1 - ka_1b_3, \ ka_1b_2 - ka_2b_1) \\
&= k(a_2b_3 - a_3b_2, \ a_3b_1 - a_1b_3, \ a_1b_2 - a_2b_1) \\
&= k(\boldsymbol{a} \times \boldsymbol{b}).
\end{aligned}
$$

Proof that $\boldsymbol{a} \cdot (\boldsymbol{b} \times \boldsymbol{c}) = (\boldsymbol{a} \times \boldsymbol{b}) \cdot \boldsymbol{c}$: Let $\boldsymbol{a} = (a_1, a_2, a_3)$, $\boldsymbol{b} = (b_1, b_2, b_3)$, and $\boldsymbol{c} = (c_1, c_2, c_3)$. Then

$$\boldsymbol{a} \cdot (\boldsymbol{b} \times \boldsymbol{c}) = a_1(b_2c_3 - b_3c_2) + a_2(b_3c_1 - b_1c_3) + a_3(b_1c_2 - b_2c_1),$$

$$(\boldsymbol{a} \times \boldsymbol{b}) \cdot \boldsymbol{c} = (a_2b_3 - a_3b_2)c_1 + (a_3b_1 - a_1b_3)c_2 + (a_1b_2 - a_2b_1)c_3.$$

It is easily verified that the numbers on the right side of these two equations are equal.

■ ■ ■ EXERCISES

1. Prove that $\boldsymbol{a} \times \boldsymbol{b} = -\boldsymbol{b} \times \boldsymbol{a}$ and that $\boldsymbol{a} \times \boldsymbol{a} = \boldsymbol{0}$ for any vectors $\boldsymbol{a}$ and $\boldsymbol{b}$.

2. Prove the distributive law $(\boldsymbol{a} + \boldsymbol{b}) \times \boldsymbol{c} = \boldsymbol{a} \times \boldsymbol{c} + \boldsymbol{b} \times \boldsymbol{c}$. Show that the other distributive law listed above follows from this one and Ex. 1.

3. Prove that $\boldsymbol{a} \times (\boldsymbol{b} \times \boldsymbol{c}) = (\boldsymbol{a} \cdot \boldsymbol{c})\boldsymbol{b} - (\boldsymbol{a} \cdot \boldsymbol{b})\boldsymbol{c}$.

4. Prove that $\boldsymbol{a} \cdot (\boldsymbol{a} \times \boldsymbol{b}) = \boldsymbol{b} \cdot (\boldsymbol{a} \times \boldsymbol{b}) = 0$.

5. Prove that $\boldsymbol{a} \times (\boldsymbol{b} \times \boldsymbol{c}) = (\boldsymbol{a} \times \boldsymbol{b}) \times \boldsymbol{c}$ if and only if $(\boldsymbol{a} \times \boldsymbol{c}) \times \boldsymbol{b} = \boldsymbol{0}$.

6. Prove that $|\boldsymbol{a} \times \boldsymbol{b}|^2 = |\boldsymbol{a}|^2|\boldsymbol{b}|^2 - (\boldsymbol{a} \cdot \boldsymbol{b})^2$.

7. If $\boldsymbol{a}$ and $\boldsymbol{b}$ are nonzero vectors, prove that $\boldsymbol{a} \times \boldsymbol{b} = \boldsymbol{0}$ if and only if $\boldsymbol{b}$ is a scalar multiple of $\boldsymbol{a}$. (*Hint:* If $\boldsymbol{a} \times \boldsymbol{b} = \boldsymbol{0}$, then $\boldsymbol{a} \times (\boldsymbol{a} \times \boldsymbol{b}) = (\boldsymbol{a} \cdot \boldsymbol{b})\boldsymbol{a} - (\boldsymbol{a} \cdot \boldsymbol{a})\boldsymbol{b} = \boldsymbol{0}$ from Ex. 3. Solve this equation for $\boldsymbol{b}$.)

8. Prove Schwarz's inequality: for any numbers x_1, x_2, x_3, y_1, y_2, y_3,

$$(x_1y_1 + x_2y_2 + x_3y_3)^2 \le (x_1^2 + x_2^2 + x_3^2)(y_1^2 + y_2^2 + y_3^2).$$

9. Prove the Jacobi identity:

$$(\boldsymbol{a} \times \boldsymbol{b}) \times \boldsymbol{c} + (\boldsymbol{b} \times \boldsymbol{c}) \times \boldsymbol{a} + (\boldsymbol{c} \times \boldsymbol{a}) \times \boldsymbol{b} = \boldsymbol{0}.$$

10. Prove the Lagrange identity:

$$(\boldsymbol{a} \times \boldsymbol{b}) \cdot (\boldsymbol{c} \times \boldsymbol{d}) = (\boldsymbol{a} \cdot \boldsymbol{c})(\boldsymbol{b} \cdot \boldsymbol{d}) - (\boldsymbol{a} \cdot \boldsymbol{d})(\boldsymbol{b} \cdot \boldsymbol{c}).$$

2. *The geometry of vectors*

A three-dimensional vector may be represented by a directed line segment in space just as a two-dimensional vector was in the plane. Thus, the vector $\boldsymbol{a} = (a_1, a_2, a_3)$ may be represented by a directed line segment $\overrightarrow{PQ}$ having any point $P(x, y, z)$ as its initial point and $Q(x + a_1, y + a_2, z + a_3)$

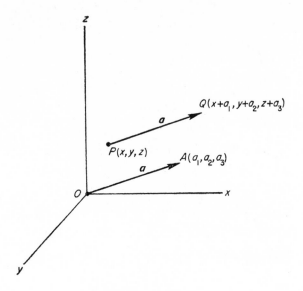

Figure 18.2

as its endpoint. If it is represented by a line segment $\overrightarrow{OA}$ having initial
point the origin O and endpoint $A(a_1,a_2,a_3)$, a is called a *position vector*
(Figure 18.2). In any case, a_1, a_2, a_3 are direction numbers of the line
segment representing a.

If $a = \overrightarrow{PQ}$, then it is clear that $|a|$ is the actual length of the segment PQ.
In case a is a unit vector, so that $|a| = 1$, then a_1, a_2, a_3 are the direction
cosines of the half-line having endpoint P and passing through Q.

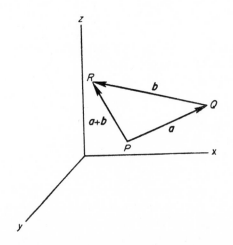

Figure 18.3

If $a = \overrightarrow{PQ}$ and $b = \overrightarrow{QR}$, then $a + b = \overrightarrow{PR}$ just as was the case in the plane (Figure 18.3). Also, the scalar multiple ka of a is just an elongation or contraction of a.

We shall again use the notation (a,b) to designate the angle of least positive measure between the nonzero vectors a and b (which are assumed to have the same initial point). By the same method as given in Chapter 15, we may show that

18.2 $$a \cdot b = |a|\,|b|\cos(a,b).$$

If a and b are nonzero vectors, then $a \cdot b = 0$ if and only if $\cos(a,b) = 0$. i.e., $(a,b) = \pi/2$. This proves the following theorem.

18.3 Theorem. The nonzero vectors a and b (having the same initial point) are perpendicular if and only if $a \cdot b = 0$.

By Exercise 6 of the preceding section,

$$|a \times b|^2 = |a|^2|b|^2 - (a \cdot b)^2.$$

Hence, using 18.2,

$$\begin{aligned}|a \times b|^2 &= |a|^2|b|^2 - |a|^2|b|^2\cos^2(a,b)\\ &= |a|^2|b|^2\sin^2(a,b).\end{aligned}$$

Since $\sin\theta \geq 0$ if $0 \leq \theta \leq \pi$, we may take square roots of the quantities above to obtain

18.4 $$|a \times b| = |a|\,|b|\sin(a,b).$$

It is clear from this equation that if a and b are nonzero vectors, then $|a \times b| = 0$ (and hence $a \times b = 0$) if and only if the angle between the vectors a and b is 0 or π. This proves the following result.

18.5 Theorem. The nonzero vectors a and b are parallel if and only if $a \times b = 0$.

Since $a \cdot (a \times b) = (a \times a) \cdot b = 0 \cdot b = 0$, the vectors a and $a \times b$ are perpendicular by 18.3. Similarly, b and $a \times b$ may be shown to be perpendicular. Thus, if $a \times b \neq 0$, the vector $a \times b$ is perpendicular to both a and b and hence to the plane of a and b (assuming a, b, and $a \times b$ have the same initial point).

Of the two possible directions that $a \times b$ might have, knowing only that it is a vector perpendicular to both a and b, the correct one may be shown to be found as follows. Representing i, j, and k as position vectors (Figure 18.4), a rotation through an angle $\pi/2$ that carries i into j is a clockwise rotation when viewed from the endpoint of k. We recall that $k = i \times j$. Similarly, a rotation through an angle (a,b) that carries a into b must be a clockwise rotation when viewed from the endpoint of $a \times b$ (Figure 18.4). This same rotation is counterclockwise when viewed from the endpoint of $b \times a$.

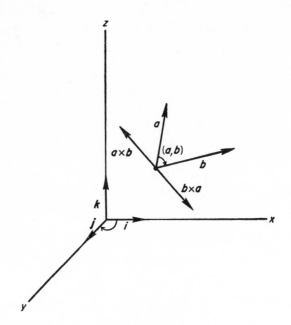

Figure 18.4

It is sometimes desirable to find the projection of a vector a on a line L. Assuming that the initial point of a is on L, then the *projection* of a on L is the vector a_L of Figure 18.5. The length of a_L is given by

$$|a_L| = |a| \cos \theta,$$

where θ is the angle (a, a_L). A convenient way of expressing a_L is as follows.

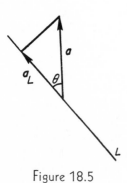

Figure 18.5

Let b be a unit vector on L having the same initial point as a, and having the same direction as a_L. Then

$$a \cdot b = |a| \cos \theta$$

by 18.2. Thus $a \cdot b$ is the length of a_L, and since a_L is just a scalar multiple of b, $a_L = (a \cdot b)b$. Incidentally, this is true even if the vector b has direction opposite to that of a_L. We have proved the following result.

18.6 Theorem. If a is a nonzero vector and b is a unit vector on the line L, then the projection a_L of a on L is given by

$$a_L = (a \cdot b)b.$$

■ ■ ■ EXERCISES

1. Show that $|a \times b|$ is the area of the parallelogram having nonparallel sides a and b.

2. If $a = \overrightarrow{PQ}$ and $b = \overrightarrow{PR}$, and if b is a unit vector, show that $|a \times b|$ is the distance between point Q and the line L on vector b (Figure 18.6).

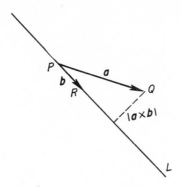

Figure 18.6

3. Find the distance between the point $(2,5,-1)$ and the line L passing through the two points $(1,-2,-3)$ and $(4,3,1)$. (*Hint:* Use Ex. 2.)

4. Find the distance between the point $(1,-1,2)$ and the line L passing through the points $(0,1,1)$ and $(1,-1,0)$.

5. Show that $(a \times b) \cdot c$ is the volume of the parallelopiped having vectors a, b, and c as the three edges at a vertex. (*Hint:* Volume equals $|a \times b|$ times the length of the projection of c on $a \times b$.)

6. If vector $a = \overrightarrow{PQ}$, $b = \overrightarrow{PR}$, and $c = \overrightarrow{PS}$, then the length of the projection of a on the line L containing the vector $b \times c$ is the distance between the point P and the plane p containing vectors b and c.
   (a) Find the distance between the point $(7,1,5)$ and the plane passing through the points $(1,-1,1)$, $(2,1,-1)$ and $(1,3,-2)$.
   (b) Find the distance between the point $(-3,1,4)$ and the plane passing through the points $(0,1,1)$, $(1,0,-1)$, and $(1,1,1)$.

7. Let lines K and L be two nonintersecting and nonparallel lines in space, and let A and B be two points on K and let C and D be two points on L. If $a = \overrightarrow{AB}$, $b = \overrightarrow{CD}$, $c = \overrightarrow{AC}$, let d be a unit vector on $a \times b$. Show that $|c \cdot d|$ is the minimum distance between lines K and L.

3. *Equations of lines and planes*

A plane p is determined by a point $P_0(x_0,y_0,z_0)$ on it and direction numbers a, b, c of a normal line to it. If we let

$$r = (x,y,z), \qquad r_0 = (x_0,y_0,z_0)$$

be position vectors and

$$n = (a,b,c)$$

be a normal vector of p with initial point P_0, as in Figure 18.7, then the

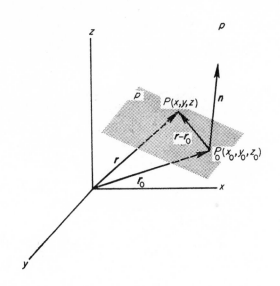

Figure 18.7

point $P(x,y,z)$ is on plane p if and only if the vectors n and $r - r_0$ are perpendicular, i.e., if and only if

$$n \cdot (r - r_0) = 0.$$

This equation may be put into the form

$$n \cdot r = n \cdot r_0.$$

If we let

$$d = n \cdot r_0$$

then we have proved the following result.

18.7 Theorem.   A plane having n as a normal vector has an equation of the form

$$n \cdot r = d.$$

That is, the position vector r has its endpoint on the plane if and only if r satisfies this equation.   The constant $d = n \cdot r_0$, where r_0 is some vector having its endpoint on the plane.

This equation for a plane is recognized to be 17.10 (with $-d$ in place of d)

when multiplied out:

$$(a,b,c) \cdot (x,y,z) = d,$$
$$ax + by + cz = d.$$

If a line L is parallel to a nonzero vector $n = (a,b,c)$, so that a, b, c are direction numbers of L, and if the endpoint of the position vector $r_0 =$

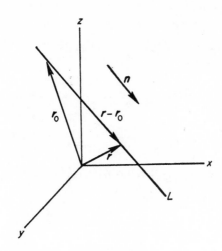

Figure 18.8

(x_0, y_0, z_0) is on L, then the position vector $r = (x,y,z)$ has its endpoint on L if and only if the vectors n and $r - r_0$ are parallel (Figure 18.8). By 18.5, this is the case if and only if

$$n \times (r - r_0) = 0,$$

or

$$n \times r = n \times r_0.$$

This proves the following result.

18.8 Theorem.   If the vector n is parallel to line L, then

$$n \times r = d$$

is an equation of L. That is, the position vector r has its endpoint on L if and only if r satisfies this equation. The constant vector $d = n \times r_0$, where r_0 is some vector having its endpoint on L.

Example.   Find an equation of the plane p and of the line L, given that L has direction numbers -1, 2, 2 and that L is perpendicular to p, meeting p at the point $(3, -1, 4)$.

Solution: Plane p has vector equation

$$(-1,2,2) \cdot (x,y,z) = d$$

for some constant d. Since $(3,-1,4)$ is a point on p,

$$d = (-1,2,2) \cdot (3,-1,4) = 3.$$

Thus,

$$(-1,2,2) \cdot (x,y,z) = 3$$

is an equation of p.

Line L has vector equation

$$(-1,2,2) \times (x,y,z) = \boldsymbol{d}$$

for some constant vector $\boldsymbol{d}$. Since $(3,-1,4)$ is a point on L,

$$\boldsymbol{d} = (-1,2,2) \times (3,-1,4) = (10,10,-5).$$

Thus,

$$(-1,2,2) \times (x,y,z) = (10,10,-5)$$

is an equation of L.

■ ■ ■ EXERCISES

1. Prove that the line $\boldsymbol{a} \times \boldsymbol{r} = \boldsymbol{b}$ intersects the plane $\boldsymbol{n} \cdot \boldsymbol{r} = d$ in the position vector $\boldsymbol{r} = (\boldsymbol{b} \times \boldsymbol{n} + d\boldsymbol{a})/(\boldsymbol{a} \cdot \boldsymbol{n})$, assuming $\boldsymbol{a} \cdot \boldsymbol{n} \neq 0$. What happens if $\boldsymbol{a} \cdot \boldsymbol{n} = 0$?

2. Find the point of intersection of the line $(-2,1,1) \times \boldsymbol{r} = (1,2,0)$ and the plane $(1,-1,1) \cdot \boldsymbol{r} = 3$.

3. If $\boldsymbol{b}$ and $\boldsymbol{d}$ are nonzero vectors, prove that $\boldsymbol{b} \times \boldsymbol{r} = \boldsymbol{d}$ is an equation of a line if and only if $\boldsymbol{b} \cdot \boldsymbol{d} = 0$.

4. Vector functions

Three-dimensional vector functions are defined just as were two-dimensional vector functions in Chapter 15, Section 5. If

$$\boldsymbol{r}(t) = (x(t),y(t),z(t))$$

is a three-dimensional vector function, then the derivatives of $\boldsymbol{r}$ are as defined previously,

$$\boldsymbol{r}'(t) = (x'(t),y'(t),z'(t)), \qquad \boldsymbol{r}''(t) = (x''(t),y''(t),z''(t)),$$

and so on.

Given vector functions $\boldsymbol{r}$ and $\boldsymbol{s}$ and a number c, the following differentiation formulas may be established.

18.9 $\qquad D_t[\boldsymbol{r}(t) + \boldsymbol{s}(t)] = D_t\boldsymbol{r}(t) + D_t\boldsymbol{s}(t).$

18.10 $\qquad D_t[f(t)\boldsymbol{r}(t)] = f(t)D_t\boldsymbol{r}(t) + f'(t)\boldsymbol{r}(t)$

18.11 $\qquad D_t[\boldsymbol{r}(t) \cdot \boldsymbol{s}(t)] = \boldsymbol{r}(t) \cdot D_t\boldsymbol{s}(t) + D_t\boldsymbol{r}(t) \cdot \boldsymbol{s}(t).$

18.12 $\qquad D_t[\boldsymbol{r}(t) \times \boldsymbol{s}(t)] = \boldsymbol{r}(t) \times D_t\boldsymbol{s}(t) + D_t\boldsymbol{r}(t) \times \boldsymbol{s}(t).$

These formulas are easily proved by differentiating each vector function coordinatewise. For example, if

$$r(t) = (x_1(t), y_1(t), z_1(t)), \qquad s(t) = (x_2(t), y_2(t), z_2(t)),$$

then

$$f(t) = y_1(t)z_2(t) - z_1(t)y_2(t)$$

is the first coordinate of $r(t) \times s(t)$. Now

$$
\begin{aligned}
f'(t) &= y_1(t)z_2'(t) + y_1'(t)z_2(t) - z_1(t)y_2'(t) - z_1'(t)y_2(t) \\
&= [y_1(t)z_2'(t) - z_1(t)y_2'(t)] + [y_1'(t)z_2(t) - z_1'(t)y_2(t)],
\end{aligned}
$$

that is, the first coordinate of $D_t[r(t) \times s(t)]$ is the sum of the first co-ordinates of $r(t) \times D_t s(t)$ and $D_t r(t) \times s(t)$. Carrying out a similar process for each coordinate, we establish 18.12.

The proofs of 18.9–18.11 are left to the reader.

If

$$r(t) = (x(t), y(t), z(t))$$

is the position vector of a moving point in space, then (the endpoint of) $r(t)$ generates a space curve C as indicated in Figure 18.9. The vector $r'(t)$,

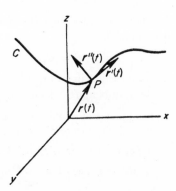

Figure 18.9

taken with its initial point at the endpoint P of $r(t)$, lies on the tangent line to C at P according to Section 8 of the preceding chapter.

In case t is interpreted as the time the moving point is at P, then $r'(t)$ is the *velocity vector* and $r''(t)$ is the *acceleration vector* of the moving point at time t. Again, $|r'(t)|$ is the *speed* of the moving point at time t.

Many of the problems of analysis and mechanics have a compact formulation using vectors. For this reason, vectors are widely used in mechanics, engineering, and even in parts of pure mathematics. Some examples of the usefulness of vectors will be given here and in succeeding chapters of the book.

The length of arc L of a space curve C (as in Figure 18.9) generated by $r(t)$ between $t = t_0$ and $t = t_1$ is given by

$$L = \int_{t_0}^{t_1} |r'(t)|\, dt$$

according to 18.21.   That is, the distance traveled by the moving point $r(t)$ between $t = t_0$ and $t = t_1$ is found by integrating the speed of the moving point between t_0 and t_1.

If the vector function

$$r(t) = (x(t),y(t),z(t))$$

is such that

$$|r(t)| = c, \text{ a constant,}$$

for every t, then clearly

$$x^2(t) + y^2(t) + z^2(t) = c^2$$

and, differentiating implicitly,

$$2x(t)x'(t) + 2y(t)y'(t) + 2z(t)z'(t) = 0.$$

Thus $2r(t)\cdot r'(t) = 0$, or

$$r(t)\cdot r'(t) = 0.$$

This is not at all surprising once we realize that the space curve C generated by r lies on a sphere with equation

$$x^2 + y^2 + z^2 = c^2.$$

Each tangent line to C at a point P lies in a tangent plane of the sphere, and hence is perpendicular to the radius at P.   Hence $r(t)\cdot r'(t) = 0$.

Example 1.   Show that if a point moves at a constant speed, then the acceleration vector is perpendicular to the velocity vector of the moving point.

Solution: If $r(t)$ is the position vector of the moving point at time t, then

$$|r'(t)| = c, \text{ a constant,}$$

by assumption.   Hence

$$x'^2(t) + y'^2(t) + z'^2(t) = c^2,$$

and, differentiating implicitly,

$$2x'(t)x''(t) + 2y'(t)y''(t) + 2z'(t)z''(t) = 0.$$

This shows that

$$r'(t)\cdot r''(t) = 0,$$

and hence that r' and r'' are perpendicular.

Example 2.   The satellite problem.   A satellite is moving freely around the earth. Describe its path.

Solution: Select a coordinate system having the center E of the earth at the origin, and let $r(t)$ be the position vector of the satellite at time t (Figure 18.10).   Then

$$v(t) = r'(t), \qquad a(t) = r''(t)$$

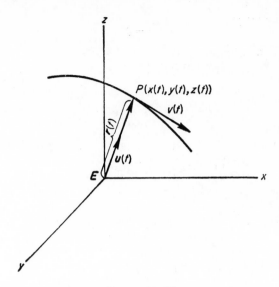

Figure 18.10

are its velocity and acceleration vectors. Let us designate the length of vector r by r,

$$r = |r|,$$

so that $r(t)$ is the distance of the satellite P from the center of the earth E at time t. Also, let

$$u = \frac{1}{r}\,r,$$

a unit vector (i.e., $|u| = 1$) directed along r. Since $|u(t)| = 1$ for every t,

$$u \cdot u' = 0$$

by our remarks before Example 1.

Let m be the mass of the satellite and M that of the earth. Assuming that the earth is a homogeneous sphere, we may use Newton's law of universal gravitation. This states that the force vector ma acting on the satellite P is directed toward the center of the earth E and has magnitude directly proportional to mM and inversely proportional to r^2, the square of the distance between P and E. That is,

$$ma = -k\,\frac{mM}{r^2}\,u$$

for some constant $k > 0$. Hence

(1)
$$a = -\frac{kM}{r^2}\,u$$

is the differential equation describing the motion of the satellite. Let us solve this differential equation for r.

Since r and a are parallel,
$$r \times a = 0$$
by 18.5. Now, according to 18.12,
$$D_t r \times v = r \times a + v \times v,$$
and therefore $D_t r \times v = 0$ since $r \times a = 0$ and $v \times v = 0$. If the derivative of a vector function is 0, then the vector function must be a constant, i.e.,

(2) $\qquad\qquad\qquad r \times v = b,\quad b$ a constant vector.

The constant vector b, being the cross product of r and v, is perpendicular to $r(t)$ (and $v(t)$) for every time t. Since the position vectors all have point E in common and are all perpendicular to b, they all lie in a plane containing E and perpendicular to b. This shows that the path of the satellite is a plane curve.

We can express (2) in a somewhat more useful form if we note that (using 18.10)
$$v = D_t(ru) = ru' + r'u.$$
Hence
$$\begin{aligned} r \times v &= r \times (ru' + r'u) \\ &= r(r \times u') + r'(r \times u) \\ &= r(r \times u') \end{aligned}$$
since $r \times u = 0$. Replacing r by ru and substituting this back in (2), we obtain

(3) $\qquad\qquad\qquad r^2(u \times u') = b.$

From (1) and (3) we derive
$$\begin{aligned} b \times a &= \left[r^2(u \times u') \right] \times \left[-\frac{kM}{r^2}\, u \right] \\ &= -kM[(u \times u') \times u] \\ &= -kM[(u \cdot u)u' - (u \cdot u')u]. \end{aligned}$$
Now $u \cdot u = 1$ and $u \cdot u' = 0$, and therefore we have proved that
$$b \times a = -kMu'.$$
This equation may be integrated, yielding

(4) $\qquad\qquad\qquad b \times v = -kM(u + c),$

c a constant vector. Since $u + c$ is a scalar multiple of $b \times v$, $u + c$ is perpendicular to b. Thus both u and $u + c$ are perpendicular to b, and their difference c must also be perpendicular to b. Hence vector c is in the plane of the path of the satellite.

Since $b = r \times v$ by (2),
$$\begin{aligned} b \cdot b &= b \cdot (r \times v) \\ &= -b \cdot (v \times r) \\ &= -(b \times v) \cdot r. \end{aligned}$$
Hence, using (4),
$$\begin{aligned} b \cdot b &= kM(u + c) \cdot r \\ &= kM(u \cdot r + c \cdot r), \end{aligned}$$

and therefore

$$|b|^2 = kM(r + c \cdot r)$$

since $u \cdot r = u \cdot (ru) = r(u \cdot u) = r$. If θ is the angle between r and the constant vector c (Figure 18.11), then

$$c \cdot r = r|c| \cos \theta.$$

Thus

$$|b|^2 = kMr(1 + |c| \cos \theta),$$

and, solving for r,

(5) $\qquad r = \dfrac{d}{1 + |c| \cos \theta}, \quad$ where $d = \dfrac{|b|^2}{kM}.$

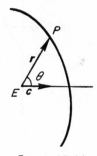

We recognize (5) to be the polar equation of a conic section (see Section 7, Chapter 15) having a focus at E. The nature of the physical problem is such that this conic section must be a closed curve, and therefore an ellipse (which is the case if $|c| < 1$). The perigee of the satellite orbit (i.e., the point nearest the earth) occurs when $\cos \theta = 1$, that is, when $\theta = 0$ and r is along c. The apogee of its orbit (i.e., the point farthest from the earth) occurs when $\cos \theta = -1$, that is, when $\theta = \pi$ and r has opposite direction to c.

Figure 18.11

The example above constitutes a proof of one of Kepler's three laws of planetary motion if we imagine that E is the sun and P is a planet. Kepler's first law states that the planets have elliptical orbits with the sun at a focus. Kepler's second law is contained in the following example (again thinking of E as the sun and P as a planet). We shall not discuss Kepler's third law.

Example 3. Show that the area of the sector of the ellipse swept out by the position vector r in t time units depends only on t and not on the position of r.

Solution: Let us superimpose a rectangular coordinate system on the polar coordinate system of Figure 18.11, taking the origin as E and the plane of the ellipse as the xy-plane with the positive x-axis along the vector c, as indicated in Figure 18.12. The coordinates of P in this plane are $(r \cos \theta, r \sin \theta, 0)$; thus, $r = (r \cos \theta, r \sin \theta, 0) = r(\cos \theta, \sin \theta, 0)$ in this plane. It is clear that $(\cos \theta, \sin \theta, 0)$ is just the unit vector u,

$$u = (\cos \theta, \sin \theta, 0).$$

Both θ and r are functions (of t). Evidently

$$u' = (-\theta' \sin \theta, \theta' \cos \theta, 0) = \theta'(-\sin \theta, \cos \theta, 0).$$

We recall that u and u' are perpendicular. Hence, by 18.4,

$$|u \times u'| = |u||u'| = \theta',$$

assuming $\theta' > 0$. If we go back to Equation (3) of the preceding example, we have

$$|b| = r^2|u \times u'| = r^2\theta',$$

or

$$r^2\theta' = c, \text{ a constant.}$$

If $\theta_1 = \theta(t_1)$ and $\theta_2 = \theta(t_1 + t)$, then the area of the sector swept out by r between times t_1 and $t_1 + t$ (the shaded region of Figure 18.13) is given in polar coordinates by

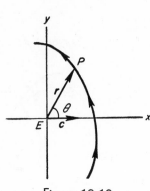

Figure 18.12   Figure 18.13

$$A = \int_{\theta_1}^{\theta_2} r^2 \, d\theta.$$

Changing variables,

$$\theta = \theta(t), \quad d\theta = \theta' \, dt$$

this becomes

$$A = \int_{t_1}^{t_1+t} r^2 \theta' \, dt = \int_{t_1}^{t_1+t} c \, dt = ct \Big|_{t_1}^{t_1+t} = ct.$$

Thus we have proved that the area of the sector swept out by r in t time units is the same for any choice of the initial vector $r(t_1)$.

■ ■ ■ EXERCISES

1. Prove 18.9.
2. Prove 18.10.
3. Prove 18.11.

In each of the following exercises find the distance traveled by a point P whose position vector is $r(t)$ from t_1 to t_2.

4. $r(t) = (t, t, t^2)$; $t_1 = 0$, $t_2 = 2$.
5. $r(t) = (2t, t^2, \frac{1}{3}t^3)$; $t_1 = 0$, $t_2 = 1$.
6. $r(t) = (\cos t, \sin t, t)$; $t_1 = 0$, $t_2 = 2\pi$.
7. $r(t) = (t, \sqrt{3}\, t, \frac{2}{3}t^{3/2})$; $t_1 = 0$, $t_2 = 5$.
8. (a) Prove that if $D_t r(t) = 0$, then $r(t) = c$ where c is a constant vector.
   (b) The *momentum* of a moving point P of mass m is defined to be $mr'(t)$ where $r(t)$ is the position vector of P. Show that the derivative of momentum is the force acting on P. Show that if the force acting on P is zero, then the momentum is a constant, and P is either at rest or P is moving in a straight line with constant velocity. (This is Newton's *law of inertia*.)
9. If the position vector of a point P of mass m is $r(t)$, then $k(t) = \frac{1}{2}m(r'(t) \cdot r'(t)) = \frac{1}{2}m|r'(t)|^2$ is called the *kinetic energy* of P. Show that
$$k'(t) = m(r'(t) \cdot r''(t)).$$
10. For each of exercises 4–7 above compute the kinetic energy and verify the equation for $k'(t)$, given in Exercise 9.

19

Partial differentiation

■ ■ ■ ■ ■ LIMITS AND DERIVATIVES of functions of several variables
are discussed in this chapter. The results obtained are
applied to the problems of finding tangent planes to surfaces and extrema of functions of several variables. Many
topics of this chapter serve as preparation for the remaining two chapters of the book.

1. Functions of several variables

A correspondence f that associates with each pair (x,y)
of real numbers in some set D of number-pairs one and
only one real number $f(x,y)$ is called a *function of two
variables*. The set D is called the *domain* of f, and the
set of all real numbers $f(x,y)$, (x,y) taken in D, is called
the *range* of f.

If we consider each number-pair (x,y) in the domain D
of a function f as the coordinates of a point in a rectangular
coordinate plane, then the domain D of f may be represented as a region in the plane. For example, if

$$f(x,y) = \sqrt{4 - x^2 - y^2},$$

then D is the set of all number-pairs (x,y) such that
$x^2 + y^2 \leq 4$ and D may be represented as the set of all
points on or interior to the circle $x^2 + y^2 = 4$.

We may also consider each number-pair in the domain
of a function as a point in a polar coordinate plane. For

523

example, if

$$f(r,\theta) = \sin \theta \sqrt{r-1},$$

then necessarily $r \geq 1$ and the domain of f is represented as the set of all points in a polar plane on or outside of the unit circle $r = 1$.

A correspondence F that associates with each triple (x,y,z) of real numbers in some set D of number-triples one and only one number $F(x,y,z)$ is called a *function of three variables*, and D is called the domain of F. The domain D of F may be represented as a region in a rectangular coordinate space. For example, if

$$F(x,y,z) = \frac{x}{y-z},$$

the domain of D may be represented as the set of all points in space except those on the plane $y - z = 0$.

The definition of a function of four or more variables is clear, although the geometric interpretation of the domain is no longer evident.

Functions of several variables may be combined just as functions (of one variable) are combined in Chapter 3. For example, if

$$f(x,y) = x + e^y, \qquad g(x,y) = \sin (xy),$$

then the sum of f and g is the function F defined by

$$F(x,y) = x + e^y + \sin (xy);$$

the product of f and g is the function G defined by

$$G(x,y) = (x + e^y) \sin (xy);$$

and similarly for the difference and quotient of two functions.

There are many ways of forming composites of functions of several variables, a few of which we now illustrate. If the functions f and g are as defined above, and if

$$h(x,y) = \sqrt{x} + \ln y,$$

then the composite of h by f and g is the function H defined by

$$H(x,y) = h(f(x,y),g(x,y))$$
$$= \sqrt{f(x,y)} + \ln g(x,y)$$
$$= \sqrt{x + e^y} + \ln \sin (xy).$$

As another example of a composite of functions of several variables, let

$$f(x,y,z) = \frac{x+y}{z}, \qquad g(x,y,z) = xe^{yz},$$

and

$$h(x,y) = x^2 y + \ln x.$$

The composite of h by f and g is the function H defined by

$$H(x,y,z) = h(f(x,y,z),g(x,y,z))$$
$$= \left(\frac{x+y}{z}\right)^2 xe^{yz} + \ln \left(\frac{x+y}{z}\right).$$

As a final example of a composite of functions, let

$$f(t) = \frac{1}{t}, \quad g(t) = e^t, \quad h(t) = t + \sin t,$$

and $F(x,y,z) = x^2 + y^2 - 2xy \cos z.$

The composite of F by f, g, and h is the function G (of one variable) defined by

$$G(t) = F(f(t),g(t),h(t))$$

$$= \frac{1}{t^2} + e^{2t} - \frac{2e^t}{t} \cos (t + \sin t).$$

2. Partial derivatives

The partial derivatives of a function of several variables may be defined as they were for a function of two variables in Section 15 of Chapter 10. For example, the three partial derivatives of a function f of three variables are defined as follows:

$$f_x(x,y,z) = \lim_{h \to 0} \frac{f(x + h,y,z) - f(x,y,z)}{h},$$

$$f_y(x,y,z) = \lim_{k \to 0} \frac{f(x,y + k,z) - f(x,y,z)}{k},$$

$$f_z(x,y,z) = \lim_{j \to 0} \frac{f(x,y,z + j) - f(x,y,z)}{j}.$$

We might equally well have defined

$$f_x(a,b,c) = \lim_{x \to a} \frac{f(x,b,c) - f(a,b,c)}{x - a},$$

and similarly for the other partial derivatives (cf. 4.24, 4.25). This form of the definition of f_x shows clearly that a partial derivative is just an ordinary derivative with all but one of the variables of the function held constant.

Other notations for partial derivatives are

$$f_x(x,y,z) = \frac{\partial}{\partial x} f(x,y,z) = \frac{\partial f}{\partial x},$$

or, if $w = f(x,y,z)$,

$$\frac{\partial w}{\partial x} = f_x(x,y,z),$$

and so on.

Each partial derivative of a function of several variables might in turn have partial derivatives, called second partial derivatives of the given function. Higher-order partial derivatives can be defined similarly.

A function f of two variables has four possible second partial derivatives, designated by

$$f_{xx}(x,y) = \frac{\partial}{\partial x} f_x(x,y) = \frac{\partial^2 f}{\partial x^2}, \qquad f_{yy}(x,y) = \frac{\partial}{\partial y} f_y(x,y) = \frac{\partial^2 f}{\partial y^2},$$

$$f_{xy}(x,y) = \frac{\partial}{\partial y} f_x(x,y) = \frac{\partial^2 f}{\partial y \, \partial x}, \qquad f_{yx}(x,y) = \frac{\partial}{\partial x} f_y(x,y) = \frac{\partial^2 f}{\partial x \, \partial y}.$$

As we shall prove in the next section, $f_{xy}(x,y) = f_{yx}(x,y)$ if these functions are continuous.

There are eight possible third partial derivatives of a function of two variables, among which are

$$f_{xxx}(x,y) = \frac{\partial}{\partial x} f_{xx}(x,y) = \frac{\partial^3 f}{\partial x^3},$$

$$f_{xyy}(x,y) = \frac{\partial}{\partial y} f_{xy}(x,y) = \frac{\partial^3 f}{\partial y^2 \, \partial x}.$$

Usually only four of the third partial derivatives are distinct, namely, f_{xxx}, f_{xxy}, f_{xyy}, and f_{yyy}.

A function f of three variables has nine possible second partial derivatives (of which usually only six are distinct) and twenty-seven possible third partial derivatives (of which usually only ten are distinct).

Example. If $f(x,y,z) = xe^{yz} + yze^x$, find f_{yxz} and $\partial^3 f / \partial x^2 \, \partial y$.

Solution: We have, holding x and z constant,

$$f_y(x,y,z) = \frac{\partial}{\partial y} (xe^{yz} + yze^x) = xze^{yz} + ze^x.$$

Next, holding y and z constant,

$$f_{yx}(x,y,z) = \frac{\partial}{\partial x} \left(\frac{\partial f}{\partial y} \right) = \frac{\partial}{\partial x} (xze^{yz} + ze^x) = ze^{yz} + ze^x.$$

Hence

$$f_{yxz}(x,y,z) = \frac{\partial}{\partial z} f_{yx}(x,y,z) = \frac{\partial}{\partial z} (ze^{yz} + ze^x) = e^{yz} + yze^{yz} + e^x,$$

and

$$\frac{\partial^3 f}{\partial x^2 \, \partial y} = \frac{\partial}{\partial x} \left(\frac{\partial^2 f}{\partial x \, \partial y} \right) = \frac{\partial}{\partial x} (ze^{yz} + ze^x) = ze^x.$$

A function f of two variables has a graph in space, defined as the graph of the equation

$$z = f(x,y).$$

For example, if $f(x,y) = x^2 + y^2$, the graph of f is the paraboloid of revolution with equation

$$z = x^2 + y^2.$$

Geometric interpretations of the partial derivatives of a function f of two variables may be given that are similar to those of a function of one variable. Thus the graph of f is the surface with equation

$$z = f(x,y),$$

and for a fixed $y = b$,

$$z = f(x,b)$$

is the equation of the trace of this surface in the plane $y = b$. Hence $f_x(a,b)$ is the slope of the tangent line to this curve in the plane $y = b$ at the point $(a,b,f(a,b))$. Similarly, $f_y(a,b)$ is the slope of the tangent line

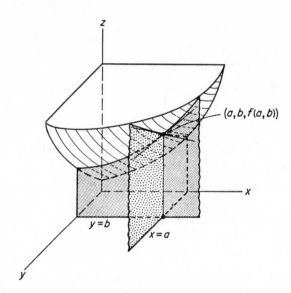

Figure 19.1

to the trace of the surface in the plane $x = a$ at the same point. These curves and tangent lines are shown in Figure 19.1. The second partial derivatives $f_{xx}(a,b)$ and $f_{yy}(a,b)$ measure the concavity of these curves.

■ ■ ■ EXERCISES

In each of the following exercises, find the domain of the given function. Also find the first and second partial derivatives of the function.

1. $f(x,y) = \sqrt{y - x}$.

2. $F(x,y) = \sqrt{x^2 - 1} + \sqrt{y^2 - 1}$.

3. $g(x,y) = e^{x/y}$.

4. $G(x,y) = x \ln y$.

5. $F(r,\theta) = \sqrt{1 - r}\, e^{\theta}$.

6. $f(r,\theta) = \sqrt{r} - \sin \theta$.

7. $G(x,y) = \dfrac{x - y}{x + y}$.

8. $g(u,v) = uv + \tan uv$.

Find the domain and first partial derivatives of each of the following functions.

9. $f(x,y,z) = \sqrt{4 - x^2 - y^2 - z^2}$.

10. $g(x,y,z) = \dfrac{x + y}{z}$.

11. $F(x,y,z) = \tan(x - 2y + 3z)$.   **12.** $G(r,\theta,z) = \sqrt{1 - r}\cos\dfrac{\theta}{z}$.

Find the second partial derivatives of each of the following functions.

13. $g(x,y,z) = x^2 y \sin z$.   **14.** $F(x,y,z) = \ln(x + y + z)$.

15. $G(u,v,w) = \tan^{-1}(uv + w)$.   **16.** $f(\rho,\theta,\phi) = \rho \sin \dfrac{\theta}{1 + \phi}$.

17. If $G(x,y,z) = x^2 + y^2 - 2xy \cos z$, find $\dfrac{\partial^3 G}{\partial y\,\partial z\,\partial x}$ and $\dfrac{\partial^3 G}{\partial z^2\,\partial y}$.

18. If $f(x,y,z,w) = \dfrac{xy}{z + w}$, find $\dfrac{\partial^4 f}{\partial x\,\partial y\,\partial z\,\partial w}$.

19. If $f(x,y) = x^2 + xy$, $g(x,y) = \dfrac{1}{x}\sec y$, $h(x,y) = xe^{xy}$, and $F(x,y) = h(f(x,y),g(x,y))$, find $\dfrac{\partial F}{\partial x}$ and $\dfrac{\partial F}{\partial y}$.

20. If $f(t) = t^2 + 1$, $g(t) = \tan^{-1} t$, $h(x,y) = \dfrac{x}{y} + \dfrac{y}{x}$, and $F(t) = h(f(t),g(t))$, find $F'(t)$.

21. If $f(r,s) = 3r + s$, $g(r,s) = \dfrac{r}{r - s}$, $h(r,s) = \dfrac{r - s}{rs}$, $H(x,y,z) = \dfrac{x^2 y}{z}$, and $F(r,s) = H(f(r,s),g(r,s),h(r,s))$, find $\dfrac{\partial F}{\partial r}$ and $\dfrac{\partial F}{\partial s}$.

22. If $F(x,y) = (y + ax)^2 e^{y + ax}$, show that $\dfrac{\partial^2 F}{\partial x^2} = a^2 \dfrac{\partial^2 F}{\partial y^2}$.

A function f of two variables is said to be harmonic if

$$\frac{\partial^2 f}{\partial x^2} + \frac{\partial^2 f}{\partial y^2} = 0.$$

Show that each of the following functions is harmonic.

23. $f(x,y) = e^x \sin y$.   **24.** $g(x,y) = \ln(x^2 + y^2)$.

25. $F(x,y) = 3x^2 y - y^3$.   **26.** $G(x,y) = \sin x \cosh y$.

27. If $M(x,y,z) = \sin yz$, $N(x,y,z) = xz \cos yz$, $P(x,y,z) = xy \cos yz$, show that

$$\frac{\partial M}{\partial y} = \frac{\partial N}{\partial x}, \quad \frac{\partial N}{\partial z} = \frac{\partial P}{\partial y}, \quad \frac{\partial P}{\partial x} = \frac{\partial M}{\partial z}.$$

28. Show that

$$x = a + t, \quad y = b, \quad z = c + f_x(a,b)t,$$

are parametric equations of the tangent line to the trace of the surface $z = f(x,y)$ in the plane $y = b$ at the point (a,b,c) on the surface. Show that

$$x = a, \quad y = b + t, \quad z = c + f_y(a,b)t$$

are parametric equations of the tangent line to the trace in the plane $x = a$ at the same point.

Using the preceding exercise, find parametric equations of the tangent lines to the traces of each of the following surfaces in the planes $x = a$ and $y = b$ at the point (a,b,c) on the surface. Sketch.

29. $z = x^2 + y^2$; $a = 2$, $b = 3$.   **30.** $z = 4 - 4x^2 + y^2$; $a = 1$, $b = 2$.

3. Limits of functions of several variables

Ordinary limits of functions of one variable were used in defining the partial derivatives of a function of several variables. In this section, the limit concept will be extended to functions of several variables.

Intuitively,

$$\underset{(x,y)\to(a,b)}{\text{limit}} \ f(x,y) = c,$$

read "the limit of f as (x,y) approaches (a,b) equals c," if $f(x,y)$ is close to c when the point (x,y) is close to the point (a,b). A more precise definition is as follows.

19.1 Definition. If f is a function of two variables, then

$$\underset{(x,y)\to(a,b)}{\text{limit}} \ f(x,y) = c$$

if for every number $\epsilon > 0$ there exists a number $\delta > 0$ such that

$$|f(x,y) - c| < \epsilon$$

for every number-pair (x,y), other than (a,b), satisfying

$$|x - a| < \delta, \qquad |y - b| < \delta.$$

Interpreted geometrically, the conditions $|x - a| < \delta$ and $|y - b| < \delta$ mean that the point (x,y) is within the square of Figure 19.2. Thus

$$\underset{(x,y)\to(a,b)}{\text{limit}} \ f(x,y) = c$$

if for every $\epsilon > 0$ there exists a square with center at (a,b) and with sides parallel to the coordinate axes such that $|f(x,y) - c| < \epsilon$ at every point (x,y) [other than (a,b)] within the square.

This definition extends to a function of three or more variables.

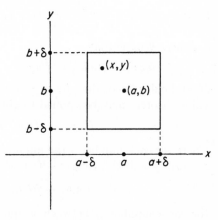

Figure 19.2

All the limit theorems for functions of one variable are equally valid for functions of several variables. However, we shall not formally state or prove these theorems in this book.

The concept of continuity easily extends to functions of several variables. Thus, for functions of two variables, the definition of continuity is as follows.

19.2 Definition. The function f of two variables is continuous at the number pair (a,b) if

$$\underset{(x,y)\to(a,b)}{\text{limit}} \ f(x,y) = f(a,b).$$

It may be shown that the sum, difference, and product of two continuous functions are continuous, as is the quotient if the denominator is nonzero at the number pair in question. An immediate consequence of the definition of limit is that if the function f of two variables is continuous at (a,b) and if $f(a,b) > 0$, then there exists a square region of the plane containing the point (a,b) such that $f(x,y) > 0$ at every point (x,y) within the square.

Another fact that we shall have occasion to use is that any composite of continuous functions is continuous. This is proved in 4.20 for functions of one variable.

The mean value theorem (6.11) for a function of one variable has the following analogue for functions of two variables.

19.3 Theorem. If f is a function of two variables for which f_x and f_y are continuous in a rectangular region R of the plane and if (a,b) is a point in R, then there exist functions θ_1 and θ_2 of two variables defined in R and having limit zero at (a,b),

$$\lim_{(x,y)\to(a,b)} \theta_1(x,y) = \lim_{(x,y)\to(a,b)} \theta_2(x,y) = 0,$$

such that at every point (x,y) in R,

$$f(x,y) - f(a,b) = f_x(a,b)(x - a) + f_y(a,b)(y - b) + \theta_1(x,y)(x - a)$$
$$+ \theta_2(x,y)(y - b).$$

Proof: We see that

$$f(x,y) - f(a,b) = [f(x,y) - f(a,y)] + [f(a,y) - f(a,b)].$$

If we hold y fixed, then $f(x,y) - f(a,y)$ depends only on x, and the mean value theorem may be applied to obtain

$$f(x,y) - f(a,y) = f_x(z_1,y)(x - a),$$

where for each number y the number z_1 is between x and a (with $z_1 = a$ if $x = a$). Similarly, $f(a,y) - f(a,b)$ depends only on y, and we have

$$f(a,y) - f(a,b) = f_y(a,z_2)(y - b)$$

for some number z_2 between y and b (with $z_2 = b$ if $y = b$). On substituting these values in the first equation, we get

(1) $$f(x,y) - f(a,b) = f_x(z_1,y)(x - a) + f_y(a,z_2)(y - b).$$

Let us define the functions θ_1 and θ_2 as follows:

$$\theta_1(x,y) = f_x(z_1,y) - f_x(a,b), \qquad \theta_2(x,y) = f_y(a,z_2) - f_y(a,b).$$

Since the functions f_x and f_y are continuous in R, and

$$\lim_{(x,y)\to(a,b)} z_1 = a, \qquad \lim_{(x,y)\to(a,b)} z_2 = b,$$

clearly

$$\lim_{(x,y)\to(a,b)} \theta_1(x,y) = \lim_{(x,y)\to(a,b)} \theta_2(x,y) = 0.$$

If we replace $f_x(z_1,y)$ and $f_y(a,z_2)$ in (1) by their values in terms of θ_1 and θ_2, we obtain

$$f(x,y) - f(a,b) = [f_x(a,b) + \theta_1(x,y)](x - a) + [f_y(a,b) + \theta_2(x,y)](y - b),$$

which easily reduces to the desired result.

An immediate corollary of 19.3 is that

$$\lim_{(x,y)\to(a,b)} [f(x,y) - f(a,b)] = 0.$$

Hence if the function f has continuous first partial derivatives in some region of the plane, necessarily the function f itself is continuous in the region. It is not true, however, that the mere existence of first partial derivatives of a function of several variables implies that the function is continuous. (See Exercises 6, 7 at the end of this section.)

We remarked in the previous section that the "mixed" partial derivatives f_{xy} and f_{yx} are equal under certain general conditions. Let us now prove this result.

19.4 Theorem. If f is a function of two variables for which f_{xy} and f_{yx} are continuous functions in a rectangular region R of the plane, then $f_{xy} = f_{yx}$ within R.

Proof: Let (a,b) be an interior point of R and let h and k be nonzero numbers such that the points $(a + h, b + k)$, $(a, b + k)$, and $(a + h, b)$ also are in R. Since

(1)
$$\frac{f_x(a,b + k) - f_x(a,b)}{k}$$

has as its limit $f_{xy}(a,b)$ as k approaches 0, and in turn

(2)
$$\frac{f(a + h, b + k) - f(a, b + k)}{h}, \qquad \frac{f(a + h, b) - f(a,b)}{h}$$

have as their limits $f_x(a, b + k)$ and $f_x(a,b)$, respectively, as h approaches 0, we might suspect on substituting the quantities in (2) for $f_x(a, b + k)$ and $f_x(a,b)$ in (1) that

(3)
$$\frac{f(a + h, b + k) - f(a, b + k) - f(a + h, b) + f(a,b)}{hk}$$

has as its limit $f_{xy}(a,b)$ as (h,k) approaches $(0,0)$. By similar reasoning, starting with

$$\frac{f_y(a + h, b) - f_y(a,b)}{h},$$

we would suspect that (3) has as its limit $f_{yx}(a,b)$ as (h,k) approaches $(0,0)$. It seems reasonable therefore that $f_{xy}(a,b) = f_{yx}(a,b)$. Let us now make our arguments mathematically valid.

If we let

$$H(h,k) = f(a + h, b + k) - f(a, b + k) - f(a + h, b) + f(a,b)$$

and
$$F(y) = f(a + h, y) - f(a,y),$$

then it is easily verified that

$$H(h,k) = F(b + k) - F(b).$$

Hence, by the mean value theorem,

$$H(h,k) = kF'(y_1) = k[f_y(a + h, y_1) - f_y(a, y_1)]$$

for some number y_1 between b and $b + k$. By another application of the mean value theorem,

$$f_y(a + h, y_1) - f_y(a, y_1) = hf_{yx}(x_1, y_1)$$

for some number x_1 between a and $a + h$. Therefore

(4) $$H(h,k) = hkf_{yx}(x_1, y_1).$$

On the other hand, if we let

$$G(x) = f(x, b + k) - f(x, b),$$

then $H(h,k) = G(a + h) - G(a)$ and

$$H(h,k) = hG'(x_2) = h[f_x(x_2, b + k) - f_x(x_2, b)] = hkf_{xy}(x_2, y_2)$$

for some numbers x_2 between a and $a + h$, and y_2 between b and $b + k$. Thus $hkf_{yx}(x_1, y_1) = hkf_{xy}(x_2, y_2)$ and

$$f_{yx}(x_1, y_1) = f_{xy}(x_2, y_2)$$

for some numbers x_1, x_2 between a and $a + h$, and y_1, y_2 between b and $b + k$. Since f_{yx} and f_{xy} are continuous, we may take limits of $f_{yx}(x_1, y_1)$ and $f_{xy}(x_2, y_2)$ as (h,k) approaches $(0,0)$, thereby obtaining

$$f_{yx}(a, b) = f_{xy}(a, b).$$

This proves the theorem.

A consequence of this theorem is that the order of differentiation may be interchanged for a function of several variables. For example, if f is a function of two variables having continuous partial derivatives in some region, then

$$f_{yxx} = f_{xyx} = f_{xxy}, \qquad f_{yyxx} = f_{yxyx} = f_{xyyx},$$

and so on.

If Δx and Δy are increments of x and y, then the corresponding increment Δf of a function f of two variables is defined by

$$\Delta f = f(x + \Delta x, y + \Delta y) - f(x, y).$$

The *total differential* of f, designated by df, is defined to be

$$df = \frac{\partial f}{\partial x} \Delta x + \frac{\partial f}{\partial y} \Delta y.$$

If $\partial f/\partial x$ and $\partial f/\partial y$ are continuous in some region containing the point (x,y), then according to 19.3 (with $x - a = \Delta x$, $y - b = \Delta y$),

$$\Delta f = df + \theta_1 \Delta x + \theta_2 \Delta y,$$

where θ_1 and θ_2 have limit 0 as $(\Delta x, \Delta y)$ approaches $(0,0)$. A function f of two variables is said to be *differentiable* at (x,y) if Δf can be expressed in the above form for some functions θ_1 and θ_2 with limit 0 as $(\Delta x, \Delta y)$ approaches $(0,0)$. Thus, by 19.3, a function with continuous first partial derivatives is differentiable.

■ ■ ■ EXERCISES

1. State the definitions of limit and continuity for a function of three variables. Also give each definition in geometric terms.

2. State a theorem analogous to 19.3 for a function of three variables, and indicate its proof.

3. Verify that if $f(x,y) = x \ln \sqrt{x^2 + y^2} - x + y \tan^{-1} \frac{x}{y}$, then $f_{xy} = f_{yx}$.

4. Verify that if $F(x,y,z) = x \sin y + z^2 \ln x$, then $F_{xy} = F_{yx}$, $F_{yz} = F_{zy}$, and $F_{xz} = F_{zx}$.

5. Verify that if $G(x,y,z) = xy + yz^2 + xyz^3$, then

$$\frac{\partial^3 G}{\partial z \, \partial y \, \partial x} = \frac{\partial^3 G}{\partial y \, \partial z \, \partial x} = \frac{\partial^3 G}{\partial x \, \partial y \, \partial z}.$$

6. If $f(x,y) = \dfrac{2xy}{x^2 + y^2}$, $(x,y) \neq (0,0)$, and $f(0,0) = 0$, prove that

$$\lim_{(x,y) \to (0,0)} f(x,y)$$

does not exist. Hence conclude that f is not continuous at $(0,0)$. [*Hint:* $f(x,0) = 0$ for every x, whereas $f(x,x) = 1$ for every $x \neq 0$.]

7. For the function f of the preceding exercise, find f_x and f_y at $(x,y) \neq (0,0)$. By going back to the definition of derivative, show that

$$f_x(0,0) = f_y(0,0) = 0.$$

Hence conclude that the first partial derivatives of f exist everywhere.

8. State a theorem analogous to 19.4 for a function f of three variables. Is the proof any different?

9. If $g(x,y) = \dfrac{xy(x^2 - y^2)}{x^2 + y^2}$, $(x,y) \neq (0,0)$ and $g(0,0) = 0$, show that

$$g_y(x,0) = \lim_{y \to 0} \frac{g(x,y) - g(x,0)}{y} = x$$

and similarly that $g_x(0,y) = -y$. Hence show that $g_{yx}(0,0) = 1$ and $g_{xy}(0,0) = -1$. Does this example contradict 19.4? Explain.

10. If θ_1 and θ_2 are the functions of 19.3, and if

$$\theta(h,k) = \frac{\theta_1(h,k)h + \theta_2(h,k)k}{\sqrt{h^2 + k^2}}, \qquad (h,k) \neq (0,0),$$

show that $0 \leq |\theta(h,k)| \leq |\theta_1(h,k)| + |\theta_2(h,k)|$ and hence that

$$\lim_{(h,k) \to (0,0)} \theta(h,k) = 0.$$

11. If the function f of two variables is differentiable, prove that $\Delta f \doteq df$ in

the sense that $\displaystyle\lim_{(\Delta x, \Delta y) \to (0,0)} \frac{\Delta f - df}{\sqrt{(\Delta x)^2 + (\Delta y)^2}} = 0.$

12. Using the fact that $\Delta f \doteq df$ for a differentiable function f, approximate the volume and surface area of a box with dimensions $x = 2 \pm .01$, $y = 3 \pm .02$, $z = 7 \pm .05$.

13. Assuming that f'' is continuous at a, prove that

$$\lim_{(h,k)\to(0,0)} \frac{f(a+h+k) - f(a+k) - f(a+h) + f(a)}{hk} = f''(a).$$

14. Prove that the function f of Exercise 6 above is not differentiable at $(0,0)$.

4. The chain rule

We recall that for functions of one variable, the chain rule gives us a method of differentiating the composite of two functions,

$$D_x f(g(x)) = f'(g(x))g'(x).$$

This rule will be extended to functions of several variables in what follows.

The chain rule for functions of two variables may be stated in the following way. If the functions f and g are continuous and possess first partial derivatives at (u,v), and if the function F has continuous first partial derivatives in some rectangular region containing the point $(f(u,v),g(u,v))$, then:

$$\frac{\partial}{\partial u} F(f(u,v),g(u,v)) = F_x(f(u,v),g(u,v))f_u(u,v)$$

19.5
$$+ F_y(f(u,v),g(u,v))g_u(u,v)$$

$$\frac{\partial}{\partial v} F(f(u,v),g(u,v)) = F_x(f(u,v),g(u,v))f_v(u,v)$$

$$+ F_y(f(u,v),g(u,v))g_v(u,v).$$

Proof: By definition,

$$\frac{\partial}{\partial u} F(f(u,v),g(u,v)) = \lim_{h\to 0} \frac{F(f(u+h,v),g(u+h,v)) - F(f(u,v),g(u,v))}{h}.$$

We may use 19.3 with $x = f(u+h,v)$, $a = f(u,v)$, $y = g(u+h,v)$, and $b = g(u,v)$ to obtain

$$\frac{F(f(u+h,v),g(u+h,v)) - F(f(u,v),g(u,v))}{h} =$$

$$F_x(f(u,v),g(u,v)) \frac{f(u+h,v) - f(u,v)}{h} + F_y(f(u,v),g(u,v)) \frac{g(u+h,v) - g(u,v)}{h}$$

$$+ \theta_1(f(u+h,v),g(u+h,v)) \frac{f(u+h,v) - f(u,v)}{h}$$

$$+ \theta_2(f(u+h,v),g(u+h,v)) \frac{g(u+h,v) - g(u,v)}{h}.$$

Since θ_1 and θ_2 have limit zero as h approaches 0 by 19.3, the first equation of 19.5 follows immediately on taking the limit of the above equation as h approaches 0. The proof of the second equation of 19.5 is similar and hence is omitted.

Example 1. The area of a rectangle is given by the formula

$$A = xy,$$

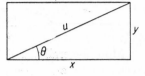

Figure 19.3

where x and y are the lengths of its sides. If u and θ are as indicated in Figure 19.3, then

$$x = u \cos \theta, \qquad y = u \sin \theta,$$

and A can be expressed in terms of u and θ. Find $\partial A/\partial u$ and $\partial A/\partial \theta$.

Solution: We are given $A = F(x,y) = xy$ and in turn

$$x = f(u,\theta) = u \cos \theta, \qquad y = g(u,\theta) = u \sin \theta.$$

Hence $A = F(f(u,\theta),g(u,\theta))$ and according to 19.5,

$$\frac{\partial A}{\partial u} = F_x(u \cos \theta, u \sin \theta)f_u(u,\theta) + F_y(u \cos \theta, u \sin \theta)g_u(u,\theta).$$

Since $F_x(x,y) = y$ and $F_y(x,y) = x$, and $f_u(u,\theta) = \cos \theta$ and $g_u(u,\theta) = \sin \theta$, we have

$$\frac{\partial A}{\partial u} = (u \sin \theta) \cos \theta + (u \cos \theta) \sin \theta$$

$$= 2u \sin \theta \cos \theta = u \sin 2\theta.$$

Similarly,

$$\frac{\partial A}{\partial \theta} = F_x(u \cos \theta, u \sin \theta)f_\theta(u,\theta) + F_y(u \cos \theta, u \sin \theta)g_\theta(u,\theta)$$

$$= (u \sin \theta)(-u \sin \theta) + (u \cos \theta)(u \cos \theta)$$

$$= u^2(\cos^2 \theta - \sin^2 \theta) = u^2 \cos 2\theta.$$

In this example, of course, we could have expressed A in the form

$$A = (u \cos \theta)(u \sin \theta) = \frac{1}{2} u^2 \sin 2\theta,$$

and then found $\partial A/\partial u$ and $\partial A/\partial \theta$ directly.

If we let $x = x(u,v)$ and $y = y(u,v)$, and $z = F(x,y)$, then 19.5 can be written in the form

19.6

$$\frac{\partial z}{\partial u} = \frac{\partial z}{\partial x}\frac{\partial x}{\partial u} + \frac{\partial z}{\partial y}\frac{\partial y}{\partial u}$$

$$\frac{\partial z}{\partial v} = \frac{\partial z}{\partial x}\frac{\partial x}{\partial v} + \frac{\partial z}{\partial y}\frac{\partial y}{\partial v}.$$

However, when using 19.6, the relations between z, x, y, u, and v must be kept clearly in mind.

There is a chain rule for functions of three or more variables similar to the one above for functions of two variables. For example, if

$$w = F(x,y,z), \quad x = x(u,v), \quad y = y(u,v), \quad z = z(u,v),$$

and if each of these functions has first partial derivatives with those of F being continuous, then it may be proved that

$$\frac{\partial w}{\partial u} = \frac{\partial w}{\partial x}\frac{\partial x}{\partial u} + \frac{\partial w}{\partial y}\frac{\partial y}{\partial u} + \frac{\partial w}{\partial z}\frac{\partial z}{\partial u}$$

$$\frac{\partial w}{\partial v} = \frac{\partial w}{\partial x}\frac{\partial x}{\partial v} + \frac{\partial w}{\partial y}\frac{\partial y}{\partial v} + \frac{\partial w}{\partial z}\frac{\partial z}{\partial v}.$$

More generally, if F is a function of n variables, designated for convenience by $x_1, x_2, \cdots, x_n$, and in turn, if each x_i is a function of m variables, designated by $u_1, u_2, \cdots, u_m$,

$$x_i = x_i(u_1, u_2, \cdots, u_m), \qquad i = 1, 2, \cdots, n,$$

then if $w = F(x_1, x_2, \cdots, x_n)$,

19.7 $$\frac{\partial w}{\partial u_j} = \sum_{i=1}^{n} \frac{\partial w}{\partial x_i}\frac{\partial x_i}{\partial u_j}, \qquad j = 1, 2, \cdots, m.$$

Thus 19.7 is a set of m equations, one for each variable u_j, and each equation is a sum of n terms, one for each variable x_i.

Example 2. If
$$w = x^2y + y^2z,$$

and w is changed into spherical coordinates according to 17.23, find the first partial derivatives of w with respect to ρ, θ, and ϕ.

Solution: Since

$$x = \rho \sin\phi \cos\theta, \quad y = \rho \sin\phi \sin\theta, \quad z = \rho \cos\phi,$$

we have by 19.7 (letting $x_1 = x$, $x_2 = y$, $x_3 = z$, $u_1 = \rho$, $u_2 = \theta$, $u_3 = \phi$),

$$\frac{\partial w}{\partial \rho} = \frac{\partial w}{\partial x}\frac{\partial x}{\partial \rho} + \frac{\partial w}{\partial y}\frac{\partial y}{\partial \rho} + \frac{\partial w}{\partial z}\frac{\partial z}{\partial \rho}$$

$$= 2xy \sin\phi \cos\theta + (x^2 + 2yz) \sin\phi \sin\theta + y^2 \cos\phi,$$

$$\frac{\partial w}{\partial \theta} = \frac{\partial w}{\partial x}\frac{\partial x}{\partial \theta} + \frac{\partial w}{\partial y}\frac{\partial y}{\partial \theta} + \frac{\partial w}{\partial z}\frac{\partial z}{\partial \theta}$$

$$= -2xy\rho \sin\phi \sin\theta + (x^2 + 2yz)\rho \sin\phi \cos\theta,$$

$$\frac{\partial w}{\partial \phi} = \frac{\partial w}{\partial x}\frac{\partial x}{\partial \phi} + \frac{\partial w}{\partial y}\frac{\partial y}{\partial \phi} + \frac{\partial w}{\partial z}\frac{\partial z}{\partial \phi}$$

$$= 2xy\rho \cos\phi \cos\theta + (x^2 + 2yz)\rho \cos\phi \sin\theta - y^2\rho \sin\phi.$$

In each of these equations, x, y, and z can be replaced by the appropriate quantity in terms of ρ, θ, and ϕ.

An interesting special case of 19.7 is that in which each x_i is a function of one variable. For example, if

$$z = F(x, y), \quad x = x(t), \quad y = y(t),$$

then 19.7 becomes ($u_1 = t$, $x_1 = x$, $x_2 = y$)

$$\frac{dz}{dt} = \frac{\partial z}{\partial x}\frac{dx}{dt} + \frac{\partial z}{\partial y}\frac{dy}{dt}.$$

Note that $z = F(x(t),y(t)) = G(t)$, so that the derivative of z with respect to t is a total derivative, and not a partial derivative. Similarly, dx/dt and dy/dt are total derivatives.

Example 3. If $z = x^2 + ye^x$, $x = t \sin t$, and $y = t \cos t$, find dz/dt.

Solution: We have

$$\frac{dz}{dt} = \frac{\partial z}{\partial x}\frac{dx}{dt} + \frac{\partial z}{\partial y}\frac{dy}{dt}$$

$$= (2x + ye^x)(t \cos t + \sin t) + e^x\,(-t \sin t + \cos t).$$

If we let $x = t \sin t$ and $y = t \cos t$ in this equation, we obtain dz/dt in terms of t alone.

The notation

$$\left(\frac{\partial z}{\partial u}\right)_v$$

is sometimes used to indicate the partial derivative of a function (of u and v) with respect to u, holding v constant. The notation is useful in that it points out that $z = F(u,v)$. With this notation, the first equation of 19.6 has the form

$$\left(\frac{\partial z}{\partial u}\right)_v = \left(\frac{\partial z}{\partial x}\right)_y\left(\frac{\partial x}{\partial u}\right)_v + \left(\frac{\partial z}{\partial y}\right)_x\left(\frac{\partial y}{\partial u}\right)_v.$$

Either $(\partial z/\partial x)_y$ or $(\partial z/\partial y)_x$ indicates that there is a function G such that $z = G(x,y)$, and $(\partial x/\partial u)_v$ and $(\partial y/\partial u)_v$ indicates that there are functions f and g such that $x = f(u,v)$ and $y = g(u,v)$. Then $(\partial z/\partial u)_v$ indicates that we wish to find the partial derivative with respect to u of the composite function of G by f and g.

■ ■ ■ EXERCISES

Find $\partial z/\partial u$ and $\partial z/\partial v$, given:

1. $z = x^2 + y^2$, $x = u \cos v$, $y = u \sin v$.
2. $z = xe^y + ye^x$, $x = u \ln v$, $y = v \ln u$.
3. $z = \sin^{-1} xy$, $x = u + v$, $y = u - v$.
4. $z = \sqrt{x^2 + y^2}$, $x = u \cos v$, $y = u \sin v$.
5. $z = e^{x/y}$, $x = 2u - v$, $y = u + 2v$.
6. $z = \tan^{-1}\dfrac{y}{x}$, $x = u + \sin v$, $y = u - \cos v$.

Find $\partial w/\partial r$, $\partial w/\partial s$, and $\partial w/\partial t$, given:

7. $w = \dfrac{x + y}{z}$, $x = r - 2s + t$, $y = 2r + s - 3t$, $z = r^2 + s^2 + t^2$.

8. $w = xy + yz + zx$, $x = r \cos s$, $y = r \sin t$, $z = st$.

Find $\partial w/\partial u$ and $\partial w/\partial v$, given:

9. $w = \sqrt{x^2 + y^2 + z^2}$, $x = u \sin v$, $y = u \cos v$, $z = uv$.

10. $w = \dfrac{x^2 + y^2}{y^2 + z^2}$, $x = ue^v$, $y = ve^u$, $z = \dfrac{1}{u}$.

Find dw/dt, given:

11. $w = x^2 + y^2$, $x = \dfrac{t-1}{t}$, $y = \dfrac{t}{t+1}$.

12. $w = x \sin y + y \sin z$, $x = t^2$, $y = e^{2t}$, $z = \dfrac{1}{t}$.

13. $w = t \sin xy$, $x = \ln t$, $y = t^3$.

14. $w = x \tan y + y \tan x$, $x = te^t$, $y = te^{-t}$.

15. If $z = F(x,y)$, $x = f(u,v)$, and $y = g(u,v)$, show that

$$\frac{\partial^2 z}{\partial u^2} = \frac{\partial^2 z}{\partial x^2}\left(\frac{\partial x}{\partial u}\right)^2 + \left(\frac{\partial^2 z}{\partial y \, \partial x} + \frac{\partial^2 z}{\partial x \, \partial y}\right)\frac{\partial x}{\partial u}\frac{\partial y}{\partial u} + \frac{\partial^2 z}{\partial y^2}\left(\frac{\partial y}{\partial u}\right)^2 + \frac{\partial z}{\partial x}\frac{\partial^2 x}{\partial u^2}$$
$$+ \frac{\partial z}{\partial y}\frac{\partial^2 y}{\partial u^2}.$$

16. If $z = F(x,y)$, $x = f(u,v)$, and $y = g(u,v)$, find a formula for $\partial^2 z/\partial v \, \partial u$ analogous to that of the preceding exercise.

17. If $z = x + f(u)$ and $u = xy$, show that

$$x\frac{\partial z}{\partial x} - y\frac{\partial z}{\partial y} = x.$$

18. If $z = f(u/v)/v$, show that $v\dfrac{\partial z}{\partial v} + u\dfrac{\partial z}{\partial u} + z = 0$.   [*Hint:* Let $x = u/v$ and $y = 1/v$, so that $z = yf(x)$.]

19. If $z = f(u^2 + v^2)$, show that $u\dfrac{\partial z}{\partial v} - v\dfrac{\partial z}{\partial u} = 0$.   (*Hint:* Let $x = u^2 + v^2$.)

20. If $z = f(x,y)$, $x = r \cos \theta$, and $y = r \sin \theta$, show that

$$\left(\frac{\partial z}{\partial r}\right)^2 + \frac{1}{r^2}\left(\frac{\partial z}{\partial \theta}\right)^2 = \left(\frac{\partial z}{\partial x}\right)^2 + \left(\frac{\partial z}{\partial y}\right)^2.$$

21. If $F(x,y) = f(y + ax) + g(y - ax)$, show that

$$\frac{\partial^2 F}{\partial x^2} = a^2\frac{\partial^2 F}{\partial y^2}.$$

22. If $z = F(u,v)$ and $u = g(x,v)$, find $\left(\dfrac{\partial z}{\partial x}\right)_v$ and $\left(\dfrac{\partial z}{\partial v}\right)_x$.

23. If $H = E + PV$ and $E = g(P,V)$, find $\left(\dfrac{\partial H}{\partial V}\right)_P$.

24. If $E = G(V,T)$ and $PV = k$, where k is a constant, find

$$\left(\frac{\partial E}{\partial P}\right)_T \quad \text{and} \quad \left(\frac{\partial E}{\partial T}\right)_P.$$

5. Implicit differentiation

The method of implicit differentiation was used in Chapter 5 to find the derivative of a function defined implicitly by an equation. We shall see in this section how the derivative of an implicitly defined function may be found using partial derivatives.

Let F be a function of two variables having continuous first partial derivatives, and let f be a differentiable function of one variable such that

$$F(x,f(x)) = 0$$

for every x in the domain of f. We may use the chain rule 19.7 (with $x_1 = x$, $x_2 = y$, $u_1 = x$) to obtain

$$0 = D_xF(x,f(x)) = \frac{\partial F}{\partial x}\frac{dx}{dx} + \frac{\partial F}{\partial y}\frac{dy}{dx}.$$

On solving this equation for dy/dx, we get

19.8
$$\frac{dy}{dx} = -\frac{\partial F/\partial x}{\partial F/\partial y}$$

at every x in the domain of f for which $F_y(x,f(x)) \neq 0$.

Example 1. If f is a differentiable function such that $y = f(x)$ satisfies the equation

$$x^3 + x^2y^2 - x - 2y + 1 = 0,$$

find dy/dx.

Solution: If $F(x,y) = x^3 + x^2y^2 - x - 2y + 1$, then

$$\frac{\partial F}{\partial x} = 3x^2 + 2xy^2 - 1, \qquad \frac{\partial F}{\partial y} = 2x^2y - 2,$$

and, by 19.8,

$$\frac{dy}{dx} = -\frac{3x^2 + 2xy^2 - 1}{2x^2y - 2}.$$

This example was solved by implicit differentiation in Section 6 of Chapter 5.

A function of several variables might be defined implicitly by an equation or a set of equations. For example, an equation

$$F(x,y,z) = 0$$

might be satisfied by

$$z = f(x,y),$$

where F and f are functions possessing continuous first partial derivatives. Since $F(x,y,f(x,y)) = 0$, we have by 19.7 (with $x_1 = x$, $x_2 = y$, $x_3 = z$, $u_1 = x$, $u_2 = y$),

$$0 = \frac{\partial}{\partial x}F(x,y,f(x,y)) = \frac{\partial F}{\partial x}\frac{\partial x}{\partial x} + \frac{\partial F}{\partial y}\frac{\partial y}{\partial x} + \frac{\partial F}{\partial z}\frac{\partial z}{\partial x}.$$

This equation may be solved for $\partial z/\partial x$, remembering that $\partial x/\partial x = 1$ and

$\partial y / \partial x = 0$, to yield

$$\frac{\partial z}{\partial x} = -\frac{\partial F/\partial x}{\partial F/\partial z}.$$

Similarly, we find

$$\frac{\partial z}{\partial y} = -\frac{\partial F/\partial y}{\partial F/\partial z}.$$

Note the similarity of these equations to 19.8.

Example 2.   Find $\partial z/\partial x$ and $\partial z/\partial y$ if $z = f(x,y)$ satisfies the equation

$$xy^2 + yz^2 + z^3 + x^3 - 4 = 0.$$

Solution: If $F(x,y,z) = xy^2 + yz^2 + z^3 + x^3 - 4$, then

$$\frac{\partial F}{\partial x} = y^2 + 3x^2, \quad \frac{\partial F}{\partial y} = 2xy + z^2, \quad \frac{\partial F}{\partial z} = 2yz + 3z^2,$$

and

$$\frac{\partial z}{\partial x} = -\frac{y^2 + 3x^2}{2yz + 3z^2}, \quad \frac{\partial z}{\partial y} = -\frac{2xy + z^2}{2yz + 3z^2}.$$

6. Directional derivatives

For a function f of two variables, it was pointed out that $f_x(a,b)$ is the slope of the tangent line at the point $(a,b,f(a,b))$ to the trace of the surface

$$z = f(x,y)$$

in the plane $y = b$, and similarly for $f_y(a,b)$ in the plane $x = a$. We might well call $f_x(a,b)$ the derivative, or rate of change, of f in the direction of the x-axis and $f_y(a,b)$ the derivative, or rate of change, of f in the direction of the y-axis at (a,b).

With this in mind, it is possible to define the derivative, or rate of change, of f in every direction from the point (a,b) as follows. Let L_θ be the line in the xy-plane and on the point $(a,b,0)$ that makes an angle θ with the positive x-axis. Clearly,

$$x = a + t \cos \theta, \quad y = b + t \sin \theta, \quad z = 0$$

are parametric equations of L_θ, and the plane parallel to the z-axis containing L_θ intersects the surface $z = f(x,y)$ in a curve C_θ having parametric equations (Figure 19.4)

$$x = a + t \cos \theta, \quad y = b + t \sin \theta, \quad z = f(a + t \cos \theta, b + t \sin \theta).$$

If we think of L_θ as the t-axis [with $(a,b,0)$ as the origin] and the vertical line through $(a,b,0)$ as the z-axis, then dz/dt is just the slope of the tangent line to the curve C_θ in the tz-plane. By the chain rule,

$$\frac{dz}{dt} = f_x(a + t \cos \theta, b + t \sin \theta) \cos \theta + f_y(a + t \cos \theta, b + t \sin \theta) \sin \theta.$$

The value of dz/dt at $t = 0$ is called the rate of change, or *directional derivative*, of f in the direction θ, and is designated by $D_\theta f(a,b)$. Thus, a

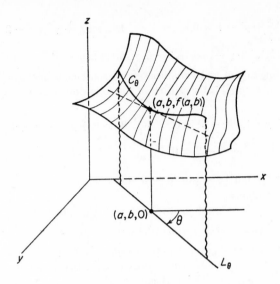

Figure 19.4

function f of two variables having continuous first partial derivatives has a directional derivative $D_\theta f(a,b)$ in the direction θ at (a,b) given by

19.9 $D_\theta f(a,b) = f_x(a,b) \cos \theta + f_y(a,b) \sin \theta.$

We note that in the direction $\theta = 0$, $D_0 f(a,b) = f_x(a,b)$, and in the direction $\theta = \pi/2$, $D_{\pi/2} f(a,b) = f_y(a,b)$.

Example. Find the maximum and minimum directional derivatives of f at $(1,-1)$, if $f(x,y) = x^2 + xy$.

Solution: We have $f_x(x,y) = 2x + y$ and $f_y(x,y) = x$. Hence $f_x(1,-1) = 1$ and $f_y(1,-1) = 1$, and

$$D_\theta f(1,-1) = \cos \theta + \sin \theta.$$

The function g defined by

$$g(\theta) = \cos \theta + \sin \theta$$

has derivative

$$g'(\theta) = -\sin \theta + \cos \theta.$$

If $g'(\theta) = 0$, then $\tan \theta = 1$ and $\theta = \pi/4$ or $5\pi/4$. These are the critical numbers of g. Since $g''(\theta) = -(\cos \theta + \sin \theta)$, $g''(\pi/4) < 0$ and $g''(5\pi/4) > 0$. Thus $g(\pi/4) = \sqrt{2}$ is the maximum directional derivative and $g(5\pi/4) = -\sqrt{2}$ is the minimum directional derivative.

■ ■ ■ EXERCISES

Find the derivative of each differentiable function f such that $y = f(x)$ satisfies each equation.

1. $x + y^2 + \sin xy = 0.$ 2. $x \ln x - ye^y + 3 = 0.$

3. $\tan^{-1}\dfrac{x}{y} + y^3 - 1 = 0.$ 4. $x \sec y + y \sec x - 2 = 0.$

5. $x^3 - 2x^2y^2 + y^3 - 3xy + 1 = 0.$ 6. $x^2 \ln y - y^3 + e^x = 0.$

If f is a function of two variables having continuous first partial derivatives such that $z = f(x,y)$ satisfies each of the following equations, find $\partial z/\partial x$ and $\partial z/\partial y$.

7. $x^2z + yz^2 + xy^2 - z^3 = 0.$ 8. $xe^{yz} + ye^{zz} - y^2 + 3 = 0.$

9. $\dfrac{x^3 + y^3}{z^3} + \dfrac{x + y}{z} - 2 = 0.$

10. $\tan^{-1} x + \tan^{-1} y + \tan^{-1} z - 3 = 0.$

11. The equations

$$xu + yv + x^2u^2 + y^2v^2 - 3 = 0$$
$$xu^2 + x^2u - yv^2 - y^2v - 2 = 0$$

can be solved simultaneously to yield $x = f(u,v)$ and $y = g(u,v)$. Find $\partial x/\partial u$, $\partial x/\partial v$, $\partial y/\partial u$, and $\partial y/\partial v$ without actually solving the equations, by use of implicit differentiation.

12. If F and G are functions of three variables and f and g are functions of one variable such that

$$F(x,f(x),g(x)) = 0, \qquad G(x,f(x),g(x)) = 0,$$

express $f'(x)$ and $g'(x)$ in terms of partial derivatives of F and G.

13. If F and G are functions of four variables and f and g are functions of two variables such that

$$F(x,y,f(x,y),g(x,y)) = 0, \qquad G(x,y,f(x,y),g(x,y)) = 0,$$

express the partial derivatives of f and g in terms of partial derivatives of F and G.

14. If F is a function of two variables and f is a function of one variable such that $F(x,f(x)) = 0$, express $f''(x)$ in terms of partial derivatives of F.

15. If the equations for changing from spherical coordinates to rectangular coordinates (17.23),

$$x = \rho \sin \phi \cos \theta, \quad y = \rho \sin \phi \sin \theta, \quad z = \rho \cos \phi,$$

could be solved for ρ, ϕ, and θ in terms of x, y, and z, then the partial derivatives of ρ, ϕ, and θ with respect to x, y, and z could be found. Show how to find these partial derivatives without actually solving the equations above.

16. If $f(x,y) = xe^y$, find $D_0f(x,y)$, $D_{\pi/2}f(1,1)$, and $D_{\pi/3}f(1,-1)$.

17. If $f(x,y) = e^x \sin y$, find $D_{\pi/2}f(0,\pi)$, $D_{\pi/4}f(1,0)$, and $D_{3\pi/2}f(1,\pi/3)$.

18. Let $f(x,y) = x^2 + 4y^2$.
   (a) In what direction is $D_\theta f(4,1) = 0$?
   (b) In what direction is $D_\theta f(4,1)$ a maximum or a minimum?

19. Let $g(x,y) = x^2 - 2y^2$.
   (a) In what direction is $D_{\theta}g(2\sqrt{3},1) = 0$?
   (b) In what direction is $D_{\theta}g(2\sqrt{3},1)$ a maximum or a minimum?

20. Let $F(x,y) = \sqrt{4 - x^2 - y^2}$.
   (a) In what direction is $D_\theta F(1,-1) = 0$?
   (b) In what direction is $D_\theta F(1,-1)$ a maximum or a minimum?

7. Tangent planes

Let f be a function of two variables having continuous first partial derivatives in some region of the plane containing the point (a,b). We shall show in this section that the surface

$$z = f(x,y)$$

has a *tangent plane* at the point $P(a,b,f(a,b))$ with equation

19.10 $z - f(a,b) = f_x(a,b)(x - a) + f_y(a,b)(y - b)$.

The proof that 19.10 is the tangent plane to the surface will consist of showing that for every curve C on the surface that passes through the point P, the tangent line T to C at P lies in the plane 19.10.

To this end, let C have parametric equations

$$x = x(t), \quad y = y(t), \quad z = z(t),$$

where the functions x, y, and z are differentiable, and let t_0 be the value of the parameter that gives the point P:

$$a = x(t_0), \quad b = y(t_0), \quad f(a,b) = z(t_0).$$

We shall also assume that $x'(t_0)$, $y'(t_0)$, and $z'(t_0)$ are not all equal to zero. Since the curve C is on the given surface,

$$z(t) = f(x(t),y(t))$$

for every value of t. By the chain rule,

$$z'(t) = f_x(x(t),y(t))x'(t) + f_y(x(t),y(t))y'(t),$$

and, in particular,

$$z'(t_0) = f_x(a,b)x'(t_0) + f_y(a,b)y'(t_0).$$

According to 17.20, the tangent line T to the curve C at the point $P(a,b,f(a,b))$ has direction numbers $x'(t_0)$, $y'(t_0)$, and $z'(t_0)$. Hence T has parametric equations

$$x = a + sx'(t_0), \quad y = b + sy'(t_0), \quad z = f(a,b) + sz'(t_0).$$

Thus

$$z - f(a,b) = sz'(t_0)$$
$$= s[f_x(a,b)x'(t_0) + f_y(a,b)y'(t_0)]$$
$$= f_x(a,b)sx'(t_0) + f_y(a,b)sy'(t_0)$$
$$= f_x(a,b)(x - a) + f_y(a,b)(y - b)$$

for every point (x,y,z) on the tangent line T, and T lies on the plane 19.10.

Example 1. Find an equation of the tangent plane to the surface $z = x^2 + y^2$ at the point $(2,1,5)$.

Solution: Since $f(x,y) = x^2 + y^2$ in this example,

$$f_x(x,y) = 2x, \qquad f_y(x,y) = 2y,$$

and $f_x(2,1) = 4; f_y(2,1) = 2$. Hence

$$z - 5 = 4(x - 2) + 2(y - 1)$$

or
$$4x + 2y - z - 5 = 0,$$

is an equation of the tangent plane at the point $(2,1,5)$.

If the equation of the surface is given in the form

$$F(x,y,z) = 0,$$

then by exactly the same argument as above, the tangent plane to the surface at the point $P(a,b,c)$ can be shown to have equation

19.11　$F_x(a,b,c)(x - a) + F_y(a,b,c)(y - b) + F_z(a,b,c)(z - c) = 0.$

If $F(x,y,z) = z - f(x,y)$, 19.11 reduces to 19.10.

Example 2. Find an equation of the tangent plane to the ellipsoid

$$4x^2 + 9y^2 + z^2 = 17$$

at the point $(-1,1,2)$.

Solution: If we let $F(x,y,z) = 4x^2 + 9y^2 + z^2 - 17$, then

$$F_x(x,y,z) = 8x, \quad F_y(x,y,z) = 18y, \quad F_z(x,y,z) = 2z$$

and　　$F_x(-1,1,2) = -8, \quad F_y(-1,1,2) = 18, \quad F_z(-1,1,2) = 4.$

Hence the tangent plane has equation

$$-8(x + 1) + 18(y - 1) + 4(z - 2) = 0,$$

or
$$4x - 9y - 2z + 17 = 0.$$

An interesting vector representation of the tangent plane may be given using the concept of the gradient. If F is a function of three variables, then the vector function (F_x, F_y, F_z) is called the *gradient* of F and is designated by ∇F (read "del F"):

$$\nabla F = \left(\frac{\partial F}{\partial x}, \frac{\partial F}{\partial y}, \frac{\partial F}{\partial z} \right).$$

If we formally think of ∇ as the "vector"

$$\nabla = \left(\frac{\partial}{\partial x}, \frac{\partial}{\partial y}, \frac{\partial}{\partial z} \right),$$

then ∇F is the result of applying the vector operator ∇ to F.

If $r(t)$ is the position vector of a point moving on the surface with equation

$$F(x,y,z) = 0,$$

then $F(x(t),y(t),z(t)) = 0$ for every number t and

$$\frac{\partial F}{\partial x} x'(t) + \frac{\partial F}{\partial y} y'(t) + \frac{\partial F}{\partial z} z'(t) = 0$$

by the chain rule.   Hence

$$\nabla F \cdot r'(t) = 0,$$

and the vector ∇F is perpendicular to the tangent vector $r'(t)$ at each point on the path of the moving point.

By the argument of the preceding paragraph the gradient ∇F at a point P on the surface $F(x,y,z) = 0$ is perpendicular to the tangent line of every curve on the surface passing through P.   Therefore ∇F is perpendicular to the tangent plane of the surface at P; i.e., ∇F is a normal vector of the surface at P.

If we let $(\nabla F)_0$ designate the gradient of F at the point $P_0(x_0,y_0,z_0)$ on the surface $F(x,y,z) = 0$ and $r = (x,y,z)$, then

$$(\nabla F)_0 \cdot r = d$$

is an equation of the tangent plane to the surface at P_0.   If we let $r_0 = (x_0,y_0,z_0)$, then

$$d = (\nabla F)_0 \cdot r_0.$$

■ ■ ■ EXERCISES

Find the tangent plane to each of the following surfaces at the indicated point.

1. $z = 4x^2 + y^2$, $(-1,2,8)$.   2. $z = x^2 + 3y^2$, $(3,-1,12)$.
3. $x^2 + y^2 + z^2 = 9$, $(1,2,2)$.   4. $x^2 + 4y^2 + 9z^2 = 17$, $(2,-1,-1)$.
5. $z = x^2 - 4y^2$, $(2,1,0)$.   6. $z^2 = x^2 + y^2$, $(3,3,3\sqrt{2})$.
7. $x = y^2 + 9z^2$, $(13,-2,1)$.   8. $xy + yz + zx + 1 = 0$, $(-1,1,-1)$.
9. $x^2 + y^2 - 4z^2 = 4$, $(2,-2,1)$.   10. $9x^2 - y^2 - 4z^2 = 1$, $(1,-2,1)$.

A line perpendicular to the tangent plane at a given point on a surface is called a *normal line* of the surface.

11. Given the surface $z = f(x,y)$, prove that the normal line at the point $(a,b,f(a,b))$ has parametric equations

$$x = a + tf_x(a,b), \quad y = b + tf_y(a,b), \quad z = f(a,b) - t.$$

12. Given the surface $F(x,y,z) = 0$, prove that 19.11 is the equation of its tangent plane at the point $P(a,b,c)$.

13. Given the surface $F(x,y,z) = 0$, prove that the normal line at the point (a,b,c) has parametric equations

$$x = a + tF_x(a,b,c), \quad y = b + tF_y(a,b,c), \quad z = c + tF_z(a,b,c).$$

14. Prove that every normal line of the sphere $x^2 + y^2 + z^2 = r^2$ passes through the center of the sphere.

If a curve is given as the curve of intersection of two surfaces, then the tangent line to the curve at a point is the line of intersection of the two tangent planes of the surfaces at that point.   Use this fact to find the tangent line of each of the following curves at the indicated point.

15. $x^2 + y^2 + z^2 = 9$, $(x - 2)^2 + y^2 = 5$; $(1,2,2)$.
16. $x^2 + 4y^2 + z^2 = 33$, $z = x^2 + y^2$; $(-2,1,5)$.

17. $x + y + z + 2 = 0$, $x^2 + y^2 + z^2 = 9$; $(-2,1,-1)$.

18. $z = 4x^2 + y^2$, $x^2 - 4y^2 + z^2 = 49$; $(-1,-2,8)$.

If
$$a = (a_1(x,y,z), a_2(x,y,z), a_3(x,y,z)),$$
then a is a vector function of three variables. The number $\nabla \cdot a$ is defined by
$$\nabla \cdot a = \frac{\partial a_1}{\partial x} + \frac{\partial a_2}{\partial y} + \frac{\partial a_3}{\partial z}$$
and is called *the divergence* of a. On the other hand, $\nabla \times a$ is the vector defined by
$$\nabla \times a = \left(\frac{\partial a_3}{\partial y} - \frac{\partial a_2}{\partial z}, \frac{\partial a_1}{\partial z} - \frac{\partial a_3}{\partial x}, \frac{\partial a_2}{\partial x} - \frac{\partial a_1}{\partial y} \right)$$
is called the *curl* of a.

For each of the following vector functions find the divergence and the curl.

19. $a = (x,y,z)$.

20. $b = (x^2, y^2, z^2)$.

21. $c = (\sin x, \cos y, x + y + z)$.

22. $v = (2x + 2y, 2x - z^3, -3yx^2)$.

23. $f = (xe^y, ye^z, ze^x)$.

8. *Extrema of a function of two variables*

The concept of an extremum of a function of one variable easily extends to a function of several variables, as we shall indicate in this section for functions of two variables.

The number $f(a,b)$ is called the *maximum value* of the function f in a region R if $f(a,b) \geq f(x,y)$ for every point (x,y) in R. The number $f(a,b)$ is called a *relative maximum value* of f if there exists a rectangular region R of the plane containing (a,b) as an interior point such that $f(a,b)$ is the maximum value of f in R. Relative minimum values of a function are defined similarly. If $f(a,b)$ is either a relative maximum or a relative minimum value of f, then $f(a,b)$ is called a *relative extremum* of the function f.

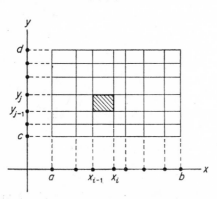

Figure 19.5

When we speak of a *rectangular region* of the plane, we always mean to imply that the rectangle has its sides parallel to the axes of a rectangular coordinate plane and that the region includes its boundary. Thus a rectangular region R of the plane is bounded by lines $x = a$, $x = b$, $y = c$, and $y = d$. By a *partition* of R we understand a subdivision of R into smaller rectangular regions. If $a = x_0 < x_1 < x_2 < \cdots < x_n = b$ and $c = y_0 < y_1 < y_2 < \cdots < y_m = d$, then the numbers $x_0, x_1, \cdots, x_n, y_0, y_1, \cdots, y_m$ define a partition p of R into mn smaller rectangles. The i,jth subrectangle of p is bounded by the lines $x = x_{i-1}$, $x = x_i$, $y = y_{j-1}$, and $y = y_j$ as indicated in Figure 19.5.

We shall have need for the following two-variable analogue of Theorem 14.1.

19.12 Theorem. If the function f of two variables is continuous in a rectangular region R, then for every number $\epsilon > 0$ there exists a partition p of R such that

$$|f(x',y') - f(x'',y'')| < \epsilon$$

for every pair (x',y'), (x'',y'') of points in the same subrectangle of p.

The proof of 19.12 proceeds in a similar way to that of 14.1. Thus, if the theorem is false for R, it is also false in one of the quarters of R formed by cutting R with the lines $x = (a + b)/2$ and $y = (c + d)/2$. Proceeding with the argument as before, we reach a contradiction of the continuity of f in R. We leave the details of the proof for the reader.

In the same way that 14.2 follows from 14.1, we have that every function f of two variables that is continuous in a rectangular region R also is bounded in R. Then the following analogue of 14.3 may be shown to hold.

19.13 Theorem. If the function f of two variables is continuous in a rectangular region R, then there exist points (u',v') and (u'',v'') in R such that $f(u',v')$ is the minimum value and $f(u'',v'')$ is the maximum value of f in R.

The extrema of a function f of two variables occur at the "mountain peaks" and "valley bottoms" of the graph of f. Let us now show how the extrema of a function of two variables are found.

In the first place, if $f(a,b)$ is a maximum value of f, then $(a,b,f(a,b))$ must be a maximum point on the trace of the graph of f in each of the planes $x = a$ and $y = b$, and similarly for minimum values of f. Thus, if $f(a,b)$ is a relative extremum of f and if f has first partial derivatives at (a,b), then necessarily

$$f_x(a,b) = 0, \quad f_y(a,b) = 0.$$

Hence, as is intuitively evident, the tangent plane at a relative extremum is parallel to the xy-plane.

The procedure to be followed in finding the extrema of a function f of two variables is clear from our remarks above. We find the simultaneous solutions of the equations

$$f_x(x,y) = 0, \quad f_y(x,y) = 0,$$

and then test each of these solutions to see if the function has a maximum or minimum value there. An extremum might occur at a number pair (a,b) at which the partial derivatives do not exist, but we shall not consider such here.

Example 1. If $f(x,y) = 4 - x^2 - y^2$, find the extrema of f.

Solution: We have $f_x(x,y) = -2x$ and $f_y(x,y) = -2y$. The only solution of the equations

$$-2x = 0, \qquad -2y = 0$$

is $x = 0$ and $y = 0$. Thus $f(0,0)$ is the only possible extremum of f. Since $4 - x^2 - y^2 < 4$ if $(x,y) \neq (0,0)$, $f(0,0) = 4$ is a maximum value of f.

Example 2. If $g(x,y) = 4 + x^2 - y^2$, find the extrema of g.

Solution: We have $g_x(x,y) = 2x$, $g_y(x,y) = -2y$, so that again $g(0,0)$ is the only possible extremum of g. The trace

$$z = 4 + x^2$$

of the surface $z = 4 + x^2 - y^2$ in the xz-plane has a minimum point at $(0,0,4)$, whereas the trace

$$z = 4 - y^2$$

of this surface in the yz-plane has a maximum point at $(0,0,4)$. Therefore it is evident that $g(0,0) = 4$ is neither a maximum nor a minimum value of g. The point $(0,0,4)$ is called a *saddle point* of the surface, and resembles the origin on the surface in Figure 17.20. The function g has no extrema.

For a more complicated example than those above, it might be very difficult to decide whether or not a given number pair at which the first partial derivatives of f are zero leads to an extremum of f. Therefore we shall give a test, corresponding to the second derivative test for functions of one variable, for extrema of a function of two variables.

If $f_x(a,b) = 0$ and $f_y(a,b) = 0$, and if the second partial derivatives $f_{xx}(a,b)$ and $f_{yy}(a,b)$ exist and are nonzero, then the traces of $z = f(x,y)$ in the planes $x = a$ and $y = b$ must be concave downward and we must have

$$f_{xx}(a,b) < 0, \qquad f_{yy}(a,b) < 0,$$

if $f(a,b)$ is a maximum value of f. Similarly, if $f(a,b)$ is a minimum value of f,

$$f_{xx}(a,b) > 0, \qquad f_{yy}(a,b) > 0.$$

If $f_{xx}(a,b)$ and $f_{yy}(a,b)$ differ in sign, then $f(a,b)$ cannot be an extremum of f.

19.14 Test for extrema. If f is a function of two variables having continuous second partial derivatives in a rectangular region R of the plane, if (a,b) is an interior point of R at which

$$f_x(a,b) = 0, \qquad f_y(a,b) = 0,$$

and if

$$D(x,y) = f_{xx}(x,y)f_{yy}(x,y) - f_{xy}^2(x,y),$$

then:

(1) $f(a,b)$ is a maximum value of f if $D(a,b) > 0$ and $f_{xx}(a,b) < 0$.
(2) $f(a,b)$ is a minimum value of f if $D(a,b) > 0$ and $f_{xx}(a,b) > 0$.
(3) $f(a,b)$ is not an extremum of f if $D(a,b) < 0$.

If $D(a,b) > 0$, then evidently the first term of D must be positive, $f_{xx}(a,b)f_{yy}(a,b) > 0$. Hence $f_{xx}(a,b)$ and $f_{yy}(a,b)$ must agree in sign, and $f_{xx}(a,b)$ can be replaced by $f_{yy}(a,b)$ in either part (1) or part (2) of the test.

The above theorem gives no information about $f(a,b)$ if $D(a,b) = 0$. In such a case, a direct analysis (as in Examples 1 and 2) must be made to determine if $f(a,b)$ is an extremum of f.

Before proving the theorem above, an example will be given to illustrate its use.

Example 3.   Find the extrema of the function f defined by

$$f(x,y) = x^3 - 12xy + 8y^3.$$

Solution: Evidently

$$f_x(x,y) = 3x^2 - 12y, \qquad f_y(x,y) = -12x + 24y^2.$$

The two equations

$$3x^2 - 12y = 0, \qquad -12x + 24y^2 = 0$$

have as their simultaneous solutions $(0,0)$ and $(2,1)$. The second partial derivatives of f are as follows:

$$f_{xx}(x,y) = 6x, \quad f_{xy}(x,y) = -12, \quad f_{yy}(x,y) = 48y.$$

We easily compute

$$D(0,0) = -144, \qquad D(2,1) = 432.$$

Since $D(0,0) < 0$, $f(0,0)$ is not an extremum of f by 19.14(3). And since $D(2,1) > 0$ and $f_{xx}(2,1) > 0$, $f(2,1) = -8$ is a minimum value of f by 19.14(2). This is the only extremum of f.

Proof of 19.14(1): Since the functions f_{xx} and D are continuous and $D(a,b) > 0$, $f_{xx}(a,b) < 0$, there exists a rectangle R' contained in R and containing (a,b) as an interior point such that

$$D(x,y) > 0, \qquad f_{xx}(x,y) < 0,$$

for every point (x,y) in R'.

Let $(a + h, b + k)$ be any point in R' distinct from (a,b). If $0 \le t \le 1$, the point $(a + ht, b + kt)$ is on the line segment joining (a,b) to $(a + h, b + k)$, and hence is in R'. We define the function F of one variable as follows:

$$F(t) = f(a + ht, b + kt) - f(a,b), \qquad 0 \le t \le 1.$$

By the chain rule, the first two derivatives of F are as follows:

$$F'(t) = hf_x(a + ht, b + kt) + kf_y(a + ht, b + kt),$$
$$F''(t) = h^2 f_{xx} + hk f_{xy} + hk f_{yx} + k^2 f_{yy}$$
$$= h^2 f_{xx} + 2hk f_{xy} + k^2 f_{yy},$$

where each second partial derivative is evaluated at $(a + ht, b + kt)$. Evidently $F(0) = 0$ and $F'(0) = hf_x(a,b) + kf_y(a,b) = 0$.

We may use Maclaurin's formula (14.15) for the function F with $n = 1$, obtaining

$$F(t) = F(0) + F'(0)t + \frac{F''(z)}{2} t^2$$

for some z, $0 < z < t$. If $t = 1$, this yields

$$(1) \qquad f(a + h, b + k) - f(a,b) = \frac{1}{2}(h^2 f_{xx} + 2hk f_{xy} + k^2 f_{yy}),$$

where each second partial derivative is evaluated at $(a + hz, b + kz)$ for some number z, $0 < z < 1$. By a process of completing squares, we may put (1) in the form

$$f(a + h, b + k) - f(a,b) = \frac{f_{xx}}{2}\left[\left(h + \frac{f_{xy}}{f_{xx}}k\right)^2 + \frac{f_{xx}f_{yy} - f_{xy}^2}{f_{xx}^2}k^2\right],$$

or

$$(2) \quad f(a + h, b + k) - f(a,b) = \frac{f_{xx}}{2}\left[\left(h + \frac{f_{xy}}{f_{xx}}k\right)^2 + \frac{D}{f_{xx}^2}k^2\right].$$

The part of (2) in brackets is a positive number, since

$$D(a + hz, b + hz) > 0.$$

Even if $k = 0$, the first term is $h^2 > 0$. Since

$$f_{xx}(a + hz, b + kz) < 0,$$

$f(a + h, b + k) - f(a,b) < 0$ and we have proved that

$$f(a + h, b + k) < f(a,b)$$

for every point $(a + h, b + k) \neq (a,b)$ in R'. Hence $f(a,b)$ is a maximum value of f.

The proof of 19.14(2) is similar to the proof of 19.14(1) and hence is omitted. We shall leave the proof of 19.14(3) as an exercise for the reader.

Example 4. A rectangular box without top is to have a given volume. How should the box be made so as to use the least amount of material?

Solution: Let k designate the volume of the box. Hence, if the base of the box is x by y units and the altitude is z units,

$$k = xyz.$$

The surface area S of the box is given by

$$S = xy + 2xz + 2yz.$$

Since $z = k/xy$, we may express S in the form

$$S = xy + \frac{2k}{y} + \frac{2k}{x}.$$

The problem is to find the minimum value of S. Hence we solve simultaneously the equations

$$S_x = y - \frac{2k}{x^2} = 0, \qquad S_y = x - \frac{2k}{y^2} = 0.$$

Since $x^2 y = 2k$ and $xy^2 = 2k$, clearly $x = y$ and $x^3 = y^3 = 2k$. It is easily established that $D(\sqrt[3]{2k}, \sqrt[3]{2k}) > 0$ and $S_{xx} > 0$, so that $(\sqrt[3]{2k}, \sqrt[3]{2k})$ gives a minimum value for S. We have

$$z = \frac{k}{xy} = \frac{kx}{x^3} = \frac{x}{2},$$

and therefore we conclude that the box should have a square base and an altitude half the length of the base.

■ ■ ■ EXERCISES

Find the extrema of each of the following functions.

1. $f(x,y) = x^2 + xy + y^2$.   **2.** $g(x,y) = x^2 - xy + y^2 + 6x$.

3. $F(x,y) = x^3 - 12x + y^2$.   **4.** $G(x,y) = x^3 + x^2 - y^3 + y^2$.

5. $g(x,y) = x^2 - 2xy + y^2 - y^3$.   **6.** $f(x,y) = (2x - y)^2 - x^3$.

7. $f(x,y) = \dfrac{1}{x} + xy - \dfrac{8}{y}$.   **8.** $F(x,y) = xy(4 - x - y)$.

9. $F(x,y) = x^2 + \dfrac{2}{xy^2} + y^2$.

10. $g(x,y) = \sin x + \sin y + \sin (x + y)$.

11. Find the minimum distance between the point $(1,-1,2)$ and the plane $3x + y - 2z = 4$. [*Hint:* Express the distance between the point $(1,-1,2)$ and the point (x,y,z) on the plane in terms of x and y.]

12. Find the minimum distance between the point $(0,-2,-4)$ and the plane $x + y - 4z = 5$.

13. Show that the volume of the largest rectangular parallelopiped that can be inscribed in the ellipsoid

$$\frac{x^2}{a^2} + \frac{y^2}{b^2} + \frac{z^2}{c^2} = 1$$

is $8abc/3\sqrt{3}$.

14. Find the minimum distance between the lines with parametric equations $x = t$, $y = 3 - 2t$, $z = 1 + 2t$ and $x = -1 - s$, $y = s$, $z = 4 - 3s$.

15. A rectangular box without top is to be made from A sq ft of material. Prove that the box should have a square base and altitude half the length of the base if it is to have a maximum volume.

16. Let $z = f(x,y)$ be a surface and $P(a,b,c)$ be a point not on the surface. Making all the necessary assumptions about the function f, prove that the minimum distance from P to the surface is measured along a normal line of the surface.

17. A rectangular parallelopiped has three of its faces in the coordinate planes and its vertex opposite to the origin in the first octant and on the plane $2x + y + 3z = 6$. Find the maximum volume that this box can have.

18. Find the point on the plane $ax + by + cz + d = 0$ that is nearest to the origin.

19. Indicate the changes that must be made in the proof of 19.14, (1) to give the proof of 19.14, (2).

20. Prove 19.14 (3). [*Hint:* If $g(h,k) = h^2 f_{xx}(a,b) + 2hk f_{xy}(a,b) + k^2 f_{yy}(a,b)$, then in any rectangle R' containing (a,b) it is possible to find a point $(a + h, b + k)$ at which $g(h,k) > 0$ and another point $(a + h, b + k)$ at which $g(h,k) < 0$.]

9. Complex polynomials

We shall develop a few of the properties of complex polynomials in this section in preparation for a proof of one of the celebrated theorems of mathematics, the fundamental theorem of algebra.*

We recall that a complex number has the form $a + bi$, where a and b are real numbers and $i^2 = -1$. Complex numbers are added and multiplied as follows:

$$(a + bi) + (c + di) = (a + c) + (b + d)i,$$
$$(a + bi)(c + di) = (ac - bd) + (ad + bc)i.$$

The operations of addition and multiplication so defined for the system of complex numbers have all the properties of the corresponding operations in the real number system stated at the bottom of page 2.

Associated with each complex number $a + bi$ is a vector (a,b); conversely, associated with each vector (a,b) is a complex number $a + bi$. The sum of two complex numbers $a + bi$ and $c + di$, being equal to $(a + c) + (b + d)i$ is associated with the sum $(a + c, b + d)$ of the two vectors (a,b) and (c,d). The operations of complex numbers and of vectors have the same properties. In this way, the system of complex numbers can be represented geometrically as the system of all two-dimensional position vectors.

The *absolute value* of a complex number $z = a + bi$ is defined by

$$|z| = \sqrt{a^2 + b^2}.$$

We note that this is just the length of the vector (a,b) associated with z. If w and z are two complex numbers, then it may be shown that

$$|wz| = |w||z|, \quad |w + z| \le |w| + |z|.$$

In terms of vectors, the second inequality above states that the length of a side of a triangle is less than or equal to the sum of the lengths of the other two sides.

If

$$p(z) = (1 + i)z^2 + (2 - 3i)z + 5,$$

then $p(z)$ is an example of a complex polynomial in z. If we let

$$z = x + yi,$$

then

$$p(z) = p(x + yi) = (1 + i)(x + yi)^2 + (2 - 3i)(x + yi) + 5$$
$$= (1 + i)(x^2 - y^2 + 2xyi) + (2 - 3i)(x + yi) + 5$$
$$= (x^2 - y^2 - 2xy + 2x + 3y + 5) + (x^2 - y^2 + 2xy - 3x + 2y)i.$$

---

* Throughout the history of mathematics, one of the central problems has been the solution of polynomial equations. The solution of the quadratic equation dates back to antiquity. Higher degree equations were solved in the 16th century. The first rigorous proof of the fundamental theorem of algebra, which asserts that every polynomial equation has a root, was given by the great German mathematician Gauss in his doctor's dissertation in 1799.

That is to say,

$$p(z) = u(x,y) + v(x,y)i,$$

where

$$u(x,y) = x^2 - y^2 - 2xy + 2x + 3y + 5,$$
$$v(x,y) = x^2 - y^2 + 2xy - 3x + 2y.$$

We may verify that

$$u_x(x,y) = 2x - 2y + 2, \qquad u_y(x,y) = -2y - 2x + 3,$$
$$v_x(x,y) = 2x + 2y - 3, \qquad v_y(x,y) = -2y + 2x + 2.$$

Note that

$$u_x(x,y) = v_y(x,y), \qquad u_y(x,y) = -v_x(x,y).$$

In general, if

$$p(z) = \alpha_0 z^n + \alpha_1 z^{n-1} + \cdots + \alpha_{n-1} z + \alpha_n,$$

where $\alpha_0, \alpha_1, \cdots, \alpha_n$ are complex numbers and $\alpha_0 \neq 0$, then $p(z)$ is called a *complex polynomial* in z of degree n. If we replace z by $x + yi$ in this polynomial as we did in the preceding example, then we obtain as before

$$p(x + yi) = u(x,y) + v(x,y)i,$$

where $u(x,y)$ and $v(x,y)$ are real polynomials in the real variables x and y. Let us prove that the functions u and v satisfy the differential equations

19.15 $$u_x(x,y) = v_y(x,y), \qquad u_y(x,y) = -v_x(x,y),$$

as they did in the preceding example.

Equations 19.15 are called the *Cauchy-Riemann* equations in honor of the two mathematicians who founded the theory of functions of complex variables.

To prove that 19.15 hold for any polynomial function

$$p(x + yi) = u(x,y) + v(x,y)i,$$

we first observe that they hold for the constant polynomial

$$p(z) = \alpha = a + bi.$$

For then $u(x,y) = a$, $v(x,y) = b$, and the first partial derivatives of u and v are all zero. Next, if

$$p(z) = z = x + yi,$$

then

$$u(x,y) = x, \qquad v(x,y) = y,$$

and $u_x = 1 = v_y$, $u_y = 0 = -v_x$. Hence Equations 19.15 hold for the polynomial $p(z) = z$.

If we can prove that the sum or product of two polynomials in z satisfies 19.15 if the individual polynomials do, then we will have proved that 19.15 holds for any polynomial. This is so since every polynomial is a sum of terms, each term being a product of a constant polynomial and some z's.

The constant polynomial α and the polynomial z satisfy 19.15 by the preceding paragraph.

Thus, let

$$p_1(z) = u_1(x,y) + v_1(x,y)i, \qquad p_2(z) = u_2(x,y) + v_2(x,y)i$$

be any two polynomials satisfying 19.15. Their sum has the form

$$p(z) = u(x,y) + v(x,y)i,$$

where

$$u(x,y) = u_1(x,y) + u_2(x,y), \qquad v(x,y) = v_1(x,y) + v_2(x,y).$$

Hence

$$u_x = u_{1x} + u_{2x}, \qquad v_y = v_{1y} + v_{2y},$$

and $u_x = v_y$ since $u_{1x} = v_{1y}$ and $u_{2x} = v_{2y}$. It is evident, in a similar way, that $u_y = -v_x$. Therefore the sum $p(z) = p_1(z) + p_2(z)$ satisfies 19.15. We leave it for the reader to verify that the product

$$p_1(z)p_2(z) = (u_1u_2 - v_1v_2) + (u_1v_2 + v_1u_2)i$$

also satisfies 19.15. This proves the following result.

19.16 Theorem. If $p(z) = u(x,y) + v(x,y)i$ is a complex polynomial, then the functions u and v satisfy the Cauchy-Riemann equations.

The real polynomials u and v possess continuous derivatives of all orders, and therefore the mixed partial derivatives such as u_{xy} and u_{yx} are equal by 19.4. Starting with the Cauchy-Riemann equations, we may further differentiate them as follows:

$$u_{xx}(x,y) = v_{yx}(x,y), \qquad u_{yy}(x,y) = -v_{xy}(x,y).$$

Since $v_{yx} = v_{xy}$, we have proved that

$$u_{xx}(x,y) + u_{yy}(x,y) = 0.$$

A function u satisfying this partial differential equation is called *harmonic*. Similarly, it may be shown that v is harmonic.

We leave it for the reader to prove the following theorem using the Cauchy-Riemann equations and the harmonic properties of u and v.

19.17 Theorem. If $p(z) = u(x,y) + v(x,y)i$ is a complex polynomial and if

$$f(x,y) = |p(z)|^2 = u^2(x,y) + v^2(x,y),$$

then

$$f_x^2(x,y) + f_y^2(x,y) = f(x,y)[f_{xx}(x,y) + f_{yy}(x,y)].$$

As a final theorem of this section, let us prove that $|p(z)|$ is large when $|z|$ is large. To be more specific, let us prove the following result.

19.18 Theorem. If $p(z)$ is a complex polynomial of positive degree and k is any positive real number, there exists a positive real number r such that

$$|p(z)| \geq k \quad \text{if} \quad |z| \geq r.$$

Proof: If $p(z) = \alpha_0 z^n + \alpha_1 z^{n-1} + \cdots + \alpha_n,\ \alpha_0 \neq 0,$ then $\alpha_0 z^n = p(z)$
$- \alpha_1 z^{n-1} - \cdots - \alpha_n$ and

(1) $$|\alpha_0||z|^n \leq |p(z)| + |\alpha_1||z|^{n-1} + \cdots + |\alpha_n|$$

by repeated use of the properties of the absolute value. Let b be the largest of the real numbers $|\alpha_1|, |\alpha_2|, \cdots, |\alpha_n|$. Then

(2) $$|\alpha_1||z|^{n-1} + |\alpha_2||z|^{n-2} + \cdots + |\alpha_n| \leq b(|z|^{n-1} + |z|^{n-2} + \cdots + 1).$$

If we choose $|z| \geq 1$, then

$$|z|^{n-1} \geq |z|^{n-2} \geq \cdots \geq |z| \geq 1$$

and

(3) $$b(|z|^{n-1} + |z|^{n-2} + \cdots + 1) \leq b(|z|^{n-1} + |z|^{n-2} + \cdots |z|^{n-1})$$
$$\leq nb|z|^{n-1}.$$

On combining (1), (2), and (3), we have

$$|\alpha_0||z|^n \leq |p(z)| + nb|z|^{n-1},$$

or

(4) $$|p(z)| \geq |z|^n \left(|\alpha_0| - \frac{nb}{|z|}\right) \geq |z| \left(|\alpha_0| - \frac{nb}{|z|}\right).$$

Now

$$\frac{nb}{|z|} \leq \frac{|\alpha_0|}{2} \quad \text{if} \quad |z| \geq \frac{2nb}{|\alpha_0|},$$

and therefore

$$|\alpha_0| - \frac{nb}{|z|} \geq \frac{|\alpha_0|}{2} \quad \text{if} \quad |z| \geq \frac{2nb}{|\alpha_0|}.$$

Thus, from (4),

(5) $$|p(z)| \geq \frac{|\alpha_0|}{2}|z|$$

if $|z| \geq 1$ and $|z| \geq 2nb/|\alpha_0|$.

We see by (5) that $|p(z)|$ is large when $|z|$ is large. If, for example, $|z| \geq 1, |z| \geq 2nb/|\alpha_0|,$ and $|z| \geq 2k/|\alpha_0|,$ then

$$|p(z)| \geq \frac{|\alpha_0|}{2} \frac{2k}{|\alpha_0|} = k.$$

This proves 19.18, using as r the largest of the three numbers

$$1, \quad \frac{2nb}{|\alpha_0|}, \quad \frac{2k}{|\alpha_0|}.$$

■ ■ ■ EXERCISES

1. Verify that $|z_1 z_2| = |z_1||z_2|$, and show that $|z^n| = |z|^n$.

In each of Exercises 2–7, find $u(x,y)$ and $v(x,y)$ such that $p(x + yi) = u(x,y) + v(x,y)i$ and verify the Cauchy-Riemann equations for u and v.

2. $p(z) = z^2 + (1 + i)z - 5i$.

3. $p(z) = z^3 + 5z + 7$.

4. $p(z) = iz^2 - 2z + i$.

5. $p(z) = (2 - i)z^2 + (\sqrt{2} + 3i)z + (2 + i)$.

6. $p(z) = z^4 - i$.

7. $p(z) = z^3 - (1 + i)z$.

8. If $p(z) = z^2 + (1 + i)z - i$, find $u(x,y)$ and $v(x,y)$ such that $p(x + yi) = u(x,y) + v(x,y)i$, find $f(x,y) = u^2(x,y) + v^2(x,y)$, and verify Theorem 19.17 by direct computation.

9. Prove Theorem 19.17.

10. If $p(z) = z^2 - (1 + i)z + (2 + 3i)$, find $|p(x + yi)|$.

11. Show that $a + bi = 0$ if and only if $|a + bi|^2 = 0$.

10. Fundamental theorem of algebra

A complex number $a + bi$ is called a root of the complex polynomial $p(z)$ if $p(a + bi) = 0$. That every polynomial of positive degree has a root is the important theorem we are about to prove.

If $p(z) = u(x,y) + v(x,y)i$ and f is the function of two real variables associated with $p(z)$,

$$f(x,y) = |p(z)|^2 = u^2(x,y) + v^2(x,y),$$

then $a + bi$ is a root of $p(z)$ if and only if

$$f(a,b) = 0.$$

We shall prove that $p(z)$ has a root by showing that $f(a,b) = 0$ for some number pair (a,b).

18.19 Fundamental Theorem of Algebra.[*] If $p(z)$ is a complex polynomial of positive degree, then $p(z)$ has a root.

Proof: Let the function f be as defined above and let

$$f(0,0) = c.$$

By 18.18, corresponding to the positive number $k = 1 + c$ is a positive number r such that

$$|p(z)| \geq 1 + c \quad \text{if} \quad |z| \geq r.$$

Since $f(x,y) = |p(z)|^2$, evidently we also have

$$f(x,y) \geq 1 + c \quad \text{if} \quad |z| \geq r.$$

If S is a square region of the plane with vertices $(\pm r, \pm r)$, then

$$f(x,y) \geq 1 + c$$

for every point (x,y) on the boundary (and outside) of S, since $|z| = x^2 + y^2 \geq r$ for every point (x,y) more than r units from the origin.

---

[*] This proof is due to R. Redheffer, *Amer. Math. Monthly*, Vol. 64 (8), 1957, p. 582.

The function f is continuous in the square S, and therefore there exists a point (a,b) in S such that $f(a,b)$ is the minimum value of f in S by 19.13. Clearly $f(a,b) \geq 0$ by the definition of f. We will have proved the theorem when we have shown that $f(a,b) = 0$.

With this end in mind, let h be any real number such that

$$0 < h < \frac{1}{r^2},$$

that is,

$$0 < hr^2 < 1,$$

and let g be the function defined by

$$g(x,y) = f(x,y) - hx^2.$$

Evidently

$$g(0,0) = f(0,0) = c.$$

If point (x,y) is on the boundary of S, then $x^2 \leq r^2$, $hx^2 \leq hr^2 < 1$, and

$$g(x,y) \geq (1 + c) - hx^2 > c$$

since $f(x,y) \geq 1 + c$ and $1 - hx^2 > 0$.

The function g is continuous in S. Therefore, by 19.13, there exists a point (x',y') in S such that $g(x',y')$ is the minimum value of g in S. Since $g(0,0) = c$ and $g(x,y) > c$ if point (x,y) is on the boundary of S, it is clear that the point (x',y') is not on the boundary of S. Thus $g(x',y')$ is a relative minimum value of g, and we must have

$$g_x(x',y') = 0, \qquad g_y(x',y') = 0,$$
$$g_{xx}(x',y') \geq 0, \qquad g_{yy}(x',y') \geq 0.$$

Since

$$g_x(x,y) = f_x(x,y) - 2hx, \qquad g_{xx}(x,y) = f_{xx}(x,y) - 2h,$$

and so on, we must have

$$f_x(x',y') = 2hx', \qquad f_y(x',y') = 0,$$
$$f_{xx}(x',y') \geq 2h, \qquad f_{yy}(x',y') \geq 0.$$

If we use these equations and inequalities with 19.17, we obtain

$$f_x^2(x',y') + f_y^2(x',y') = 4h^2x'^2 = f(x',y')[f_{xx}(x',y') + f_{yy}(x',y')]$$

and therefore

$$4h^2x'^2 \geq 2h\, f(x',y').$$

On solving for $f(x',y')$, we have

$$f(x',y') \leq 2hx'^2.$$

The point (x',y') is interior to S, so that $x'^2 < r^2$. Thus we have proved that to each positive number $h < 1/r^2$, there corresponds a point (x',y') in S such that

$$f(x',y') < 2hr^2.$$

We recall that $f(a,b)$ is the minimum value of f in S, and therefore

$$f(a,b) < 2hr^2$$

for every positive number $h < 1/r^2$. Since $f(a,b) \geq 0$ and

$$\lim_{h \to 0} 2hr^2 = 0,$$

necessarily $f(a,b) = 0$. This proves the fundamental theorem of algebra.

■ ■ ■ EXERCISES

1. (a) Let $q(z) = \beta_0 z^n + \cdots + \beta_{n-1} z + \beta_n$, $n \geq 1$, be a complex polynomial. Show that $q(0) = 0$ if and only if $q(z) = z\, r(z)$ for some polynomial $r(z)$.

   (b) Let $p(z) = \alpha_0 z^n + \cdots + \alpha_{n-1} z + \alpha_n$, $n \geq 1$, and let w be a complex number such that $p(w) = 0$. Show that $p(z) = (z - w)s(z)$ for some polynomial $s(z)$. (*Hint:* Consider $q(z') = p(z' + w)$ where $z' = z - w$.)

2. (a) Use the fundamental theorem of algebra and the preceding exercise to prove that if $p(z)$ is a complex polynomial of degree $n \geq 1$, then there exist complex numbers $w_1, w_2, \cdots, w_n$ such that $p(z) = \alpha_0(z - w_1)(z - w_2) \cdots (z - w_n)$, where α_0 is the coefficient of z^n in $p(z)$.

   (b) Prove that $p(z)$ has at most n roots. (*Hint:* Let w be a root of $p(z)$. Show that $w = w_i$ for some integer i, $i = 1, 2, \cdots, n$).

3. (a) Let $q(z) = cz^m$ where $m \geq 0$ and c is a real number. If $q(x + yi) = u(x,y) + v(x,y)i$, prove that $u(x,-y) = u(x,y)$ and $v(x,-y) = -v(x,y)$. (*Hint:* Consider $m = 0$ and $m = 1$ separately. For $m \geq 2$ expand $(x + yi)^m$ by the binomial theorem.)

   (b) Let $p(z) = a_0 z^n + \cdots + a_{n-1} z + a_n$ where $a_0, \cdots, a_{n-1}, a_n$ are real numbers: $p(z)$ is called a real polynomial. Use Part (a) to show that if $p(z) = u(x,y) + v(x,y)i$, then $u(x,-y) = u(x,y)$ and $v(x,-y) = -v(x,y)$.

   (c) If $w = a + bi$ is a complex number, then $w^* = a - bi$ is called the *complex conjugate* of w. The number w is nonreal if $b \neq 0$. Use Part (b) to show that if w is a root of the real polynomial $p(z)$, then so is w^*.

4. (a) Show that if w is a nonreal complex number, then $(z - w)(z - w^*)$ is a real polynomial.

   (b) Use Exercises 2(a), 3(c), and 4(a) to show that every real polynomial can be factored into a product of real polynomials of degree less than or equal to 2.

5. Use Exercise 4(b) to show that every real polynomial of odd degree $n \geq 1$ has a real root.

6. Show that the factorization in Exercise 2(a) is unique except for the order of factors.

11. *Uniform continuity*

Let R be a rectangular region of the plane bounded by the lines $x = a$, $x = b$, $y = c$, and $y = d$. If p is a partition of R defined by the partitions $[x_0, x_1, \cdots, x_n]$ and $[y_0, y_1, \cdots, y_m]$ of $[a,b]$ and $[c,d]$, respectively, then the largest of the numbers Δx_1, Δx_2, $\cdots$, Δx_n, Δy_1, Δy_2, $\cdots$, Δy_m (where $\Delta x_i = x_i - x_{i-1}$, etc.) is called the *norm* of partition p.

If f is a continuous function of two variables in a rectangular region R, then, according to 19.12, for each number $\epsilon > 0$ there exists at least one partition p of R (having sufficiently small norm) such that

$$|f(x',y') - f(x'',y'')| < \epsilon$$

provided that the points (x',y') and (x'',y'') are in the same subrectangle of p. Let us now prove the following stronger result, which essentially states that f possesses this property for every partition of sufficiently small norm.

19.20 Theorem. If the function f of two variables is continuous in a rectangular region R, then for every number $\epsilon > 0$ there exists a number $\delta > 0$ such that for every pair of points (x',y'), (x'',y'') of R,

$$|f(x',y') - f(x'',y'')| < \epsilon$$

provided that

$$|x' - x''| < \delta, \qquad |y' - y''| < \delta.$$

Proof: Corresponding to the positive number $\epsilon/2$ is some partition $p = [x_0, x_1, \cdots, x_n; y_0, y_1, \cdots, y_m]$ of R such that

$$|f(z',w') - f(z'',w'')| < \frac{\epsilon}{2}$$

provided that the points (z',w') and (z'',w'') are in the same subrectangle of p by 19.12. Let δ be the smallest of the numbers Δx_1, Δx_2, $\cdots$, Δx_n; Δy_1, Δy_2, $\cdots$, Δy_m.

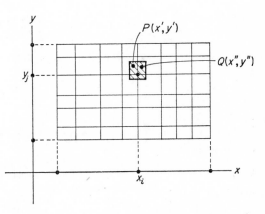

Figure 19.6

If $P(x',y')$ and $Q(x'',y'')$ are any points of R such that

$$|x' - x''| < \delta, \qquad |y' - y''| < \delta,$$

then P and Q lie in a square S whose sides have length δ. By the choice of δ, the square S will be contained in no more than four subrectangles of p, as indicated in Figure 19.6. Thus there must exist a point (x_i, y_j) of the partition such that (x',y') and (x_i, y_j) lie in the same subrectangle of p, and also (x'',y'') and (x_i,y_j) lie in the same subrectangle of p. Hence, by the property of p,

$$|f(x',y') - f(x'',y'')| = |f(x',y') - f(x_i,y_j) + f(x_i,y_j) - f(x'',y'')|$$
$$\leq |f(x',y') - f(x_i,y_j)| + |f(x_i,y_j) - f(x'',y'')|$$
$$< \frac{\epsilon}{2} + \frac{\epsilon}{2} = \epsilon,$$

and the theorem is proved.

The property of a function f contained in the conclusion of Theorem 19.20 is called *uniform continuity*. According to this theorem, any function continuous in a rectangular region R is uniformly continuous in R. We shall use the uniform continuity of a continuous function to establish the following result on differentiating an integral of a function of two variables.

19.21 Theorem. If the function f of two variables has continuous first partial derivatives in a rectangular region R, then

$$D_y \int_a^b f(x,y)\, dx = \int_a^b f_y(x,y)\, dx$$

in R.

Proof: By definition,

$$D_y \int_a^b f(x,y)\, dx = \lim_{k \to 0} \frac{1}{k}\left[\int_a^b f(x,y+k)\, dx - \int_a^b f(x,y)\, dx\right]$$
$$= \lim_{k \to 0} \int_a^b \frac{f(x,y+k) - f(x,y)}{k}\, dx.$$

If we use the mean value theorem on the integrand, we get

$$\frac{f(x,y+k) - f(x,y)}{k} = f_y(x,z) = f_y(x,y) + [f_y(x,z) - f_y(x,y)]$$

for some number z between y and $y + k$.

By uniform continuity, for every number $\epsilon > 0$ there exists a number $\delta > 0$ such that for all x,

(1) $|f_y(x,z) - f_y(x,y)| < \epsilon$

provided that $|z - y| < \delta$. If we choose k so that $|k| < \delta$, then $|z - y| < \delta$ and (1) holds. Therefore (assuming $a < b$),

$$\left|\int_a^b [f_y(x,z) - f_y(x,y)]\, dx\right| \leq \int_a^b |f_y(x,z) - f_y(x,y)|\, dx$$
$$< \int_a^b \epsilon\, dx = \epsilon(b - a)$$

if $|k| < \delta$. Since $\epsilon(b - a)$ can be made as small as we please, we have proved that

$$\lim_{k \to 0} \int_a^b [f_y(x,z) - f_y(x,y)]\, dx = 0.$$

Thus

$$D_y \int_a^b f(x,y) \, dx = \lim_{k \to 0} \left\{ \int_a^b f_y(x,y) \, dx + \int_a^b [f_y(x,z) - f_y(x,y)] \, dx \right\}$$

$$= \int_a^b f_y(x,y) \, dx,$$

and the theorem is proved.

The theorem above on the derivative of an integral is valid for functions of three or more variables by a similar argument.

An integral of the form

$$\int_a^x f(x,y) \, dx \qquad \left(= \int_a^x f(u,y) \, du \right)$$

defines a function F of two variables as follows,

$$F(x,y) = \int_a^x f(x,y) \, dx.$$

We may find the first partial derivatives of F by use of the fundamental theorem of the calculus and the above theorem. Thus

$$\frac{\partial}{\partial x} \int_a^x f(x,y) \, dx = f(x,y), \qquad \frac{\partial}{\partial y} \int_a^x f(x,y) \, dx = \int_a^x f_y(x,y) \, dx.$$

In like manner,

$$\frac{\partial}{\partial x} \int_b^y f(x,y) \, dy = \int_b^y f_x(x,y) \, dy, \qquad \frac{\partial}{\partial y} \int_b^y f(x,y) \, dy = f(x,y).$$

If there exist functions f, M, and N of two variables such that $f_x(x,y) = M(x,y)$ and $f_y(x,y) = N(x,y)$, then $M_y(x,y) = N_x(x,y)$, since $f_{xy}(x,y) = f_{yx}(x,y)$. Conversely, we have the following theorem.

19.22 Theorem. If M and N are functions of two variables having continuous first partial derivatives in a rectangular region R, and if

$$M_y(x,y) = N_x(x,y)$$

in R, then there exists a function f such that

$$f_x(x,y) = M(x,y), \qquad f_y(x,y) = N(x,y)$$

in R.

Proof: Let us define the function f by

$$f(x,y) = \int_a^x M(x,y) \, dx + \int_b^y N(a,y) \, dy,$$

(x,y) and (a,b) in R. Then

$$f_x(x,y) = \frac{\partial}{\partial x} \int_a^x M(x,y) \, dx + \frac{\partial}{\partial x} \int_b^y N(a,y) \, dy$$

$$= M(x,y) + 0,$$

and

$$f_y(x,y) = \frac{\partial}{\partial y} \int_a^x M(x,y)\, dx + \frac{\partial}{\partial y} \int_b^y N(a,y)\, dy$$

$$= \int_a^x M_y(x,y)\, dx + N(a,y) = \int_a^x N_x(x,y)\, dx + N(a,y)$$

$$= N(x,y) \Big|_a^x + N(a,y) = N(x,y) - N(a,y) + N(a,y) = N(x,y).$$

This proves the theorem.

Example 1. If $M(x,y) = 3x^2 + 2x + y^2$ and $N(x,y) = 2xy + y^3$, then

$$\frac{\partial M}{\partial y} = 2y = \frac{\partial N}{\partial x}.$$

Find a function f such that $f_x = M$ and $f_y = N$.

Solution: As in the proof of 19.22 (with $a = 0$, $b = 0$), let

$$f(x,y) = \int_0^x (3x^2 + 2x + y^2)\, dx + \int_0^y y^3\, dy$$

$$= x^3 + x^2 + xy^2 + \frac{1}{4} y^4.$$

It is easily verified that $f_x = M$ and $f_y = N$.

Frequently a function f satisfying the conclusions of 19.22 can be determined by inspection. For example, if

$$M(x,y) = x + y, \qquad N(x,y) = x - y,$$

then $M_y = N_x = 1$ and there exists some function f such that

$$f_x(x,y) = x + y, \qquad f_y(x,y) = x - y$$

according to the above theorem. The function f must have at least the terms $x^2/2 + xy$ in order that $f_x(x,y) = x + y$; and it must have at least the terms $xy - y^2/2$ in order that $f_y(x,y) = x - y$. Hence, if

$$f(x,y) = \frac{1}{2} x^2 + xy - \frac{1}{2} y^2,$$

then $f_x(x,y) = x + y$ and $f_y(x,y) = x - y$.

Another method of determining the function f of 19.22 is illustrated in the following example.

Example 2. If
$$M(x,y) = \sin y, \qquad N(x,y) = x \cos y + 3,$$

find a function f such that $f_x = M$ and $f_y = N$.

Solution: We easily verify that $M_y(x,y) = N_x(x,y) = \cos y$, so that such a function f exists by Theorem 19.22. A function f for which $f_x(x,y) = \sin y$ might be expected to have the form

$$f(x,y) = x \sin y + g(y)$$

for some function g, since then

$$f_x(x,y) = \sin y + \frac{\partial}{\partial x} g(y) = \sin y.$$

If f has this form, then

$$f_y(x,y) = x \cos y + g'(y) = x \cos y + 3,$$

since $f_y = N$. Evidently we must have $g'(y) = 3$, and therefore we may choose

$$g(y) = 3y.$$

Thus, if

$$f(x,y) = x \sin y + 3y,$$

then $f_x = M$ and $f_y = N$.

■ ■ ■ EXERCISES

1. If $M(x,y) = \tan y$ and $N(x,y) = x \sec^2 y$, find F and G where

$$F(x,y) = \int_0^x M(x,y)\, dx + \int_0^y N(0,y)\, dy,$$

$$G(x,y) = \int_1^x M(x,y)\, dx + \int_{\pi/4}^y N(1,y)\, dy.$$

Verify that $F_x = G_x = M$ and $F_y = G_y = N$.

2. If $M(x,y) = \sin y$ and $N(x,y) = x \cos y + 3$, find a function f such that $f_x = M$ and $f_y = N$ by using the proof of 19.22 with $a = 1$ and $b = 1$. Compare with the solution of Example 2 above.

In each of the following, verify that $M_y = N_x$ and find a function f such that $f_x = M$ and $f_y = N$. Solve by inspection or by the method of Example 2 of the text.

3. $M(x,y) = y \sec x \tan x$, $N(x,y) = \sec x$.

4. $M(x,y) = 3x^2 + 8xy - 2$, $N(x,y) = 4x^2 - 2y + 3$.

5. $M(x,y) = \sqrt{1 - y^2}$, $N(x,y) = \dfrac{1 - xy}{\sqrt{1 - y^2}}$.

6. $M(x,y) = e^y$, $N(x,y) = xe^y$.

7. $M(x,y) = y \cos(x + y)$, $N(x,y) = y \cos(x + y) + \sin(x + y)$.

8. $M(x,y) = ye^x$, $N(x,y) = e^x + 2y$.

9. $M(x,y) = \ln y$, $N(x,y) = \dfrac{x}{y}$.

10. $M(x,y) = \ln \sqrt{x^2 + y^2}$, $N(x,y) = \tan^{-1} \dfrac{x}{y}$.

11. Find F and G if

$$F(x,y) = \int_a^x f_{yx}(x,y)\, dx, \qquad G(x,y) = \int_a^x f_{xy}(x,y)\, dx.$$

Hence prove 19.4.

12. If M, N, and P are functions of three variables with continuous first partial derivatives and if $M_y = N_x$, $N_z = P_y$, and $P_x = M_z$, show that there

exists a function F such that $F_x = M, F_y = N$, and $F_z = P$. (*Hint:* Look at the proof of 19.22.)

13. Find a function F such that $F_x = M$, $F_y = N$, and $F_z = P$, where $M(x,y,z) = y + z, N(x,y,z) = x + z, P(x,y,z) = x + y$.

12. *Line integrals*

Let M and N be functions of two variables having continuous first partial derivatives in a rectangular region R, and let C be a curve in R having parametric equations

$$x = x(t), \quad y = y(t), \qquad t_0 \le t \le t_1,$$

where x' and y' are continuous in $[t_0,t_1]$. The integral

19.23 $$\int_{t_0}^{t_1} [M(x(t),y(t))x'(t) + N(x(t),y(t))y'(t)]\, dt$$

is called the *line integral* of M and N along the curve C. We shall not do so, but it may be shown that the value of 19.23 is independent of the choice of parametric equations for C. For this reason, the line integral of M and N along the curve C is frequently designated by

$$\int_C M\, dx + N\, dy.$$

Example 1. If $M(x,y) = 2x + y$ and $N(x,y) = x - y$, and if C has parametric equations

$$x = t - 1, \quad y = t^2, \qquad 0 \le t \le 2,$$

find the line integral of M and N along C.

Solution: We have

$$\int_C M\, dx + N\, dy = \int_0^2 \{[2(t-1) + t^2] \cdot 1 + [(t-1) - t^2]2t\}\, dt$$

$$= \int_0^2 (-2t^3 + 3t^2 - 2)\, dt = \left(-\frac{1}{2}t^4 + t^3 - 2t\right)\Big|_0^2 = -4.$$

If $$M_y(x,y) = N_x(x,y),$$

then by 19.22 there exists a function f such that

$$f_x(x,y) = M(x,y), \qquad f_y(x,y) = N(x,y).$$

By the chain rule,

$$D_t f(x(t),y(t)) = f_x(x(t),y(t))x'(t) + f_y(x(t),y(t))y'(t)$$
$$= M(x(t),y(t))x'(t) + N(x(t),y(t))y'(t),$$

and hence $f(x(t),y(t))$ is an antiderivative of the integrand of the line integral 19.23. Thus, if

$$x(t_0) = a, \quad y(t_0) = b, \quad x(t_1) = c, \quad y(t_1) = d,$$

we have

$$\int_C M\,dx + N\,dy = f(x(t),y(t))\,\Big|_{t_0}^{t_1} = f(c,d) - f(a,b).$$

Now if C' is another curve in R joining the points (a,b) and (c,d) (Figure 19.7), then by the same reasoning as above,

$$\int_{C'} M\,dx + N\,dy = f(c,d) - f(a,b).$$

That is, the line integral is independent of the path C joining the points

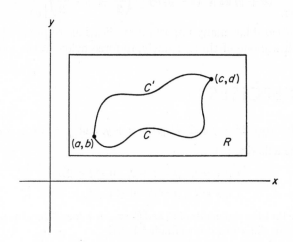

Figure 19.7

(a,b) and (c,d).   Since it is independent of the path, the line integral in this case is designated by

$$\int_{(a,b)}^{(c,d)} M\,dx + N\,dy.$$

We have proved the following theorem.

19.24 Theorem. If the functions of two variables M and N have continuous first partial derivatives in a rectangular region R, if (a,b) and (c,d) are points of R, and if

$$M_y(x,y) = N_x(x,y)$$

in R, then

$$\int_{(a,b)}^{(c,d)} M\,dx + N\,dy = f(c,d) - f(a,b)$$

where f is any function such that $f_x(x,y) = M(x,y)$ and $f_y(x,y) = N(x,y)$.

This theorem on line integrals is analogous to the fundamental theorem of the calculus for ordinary integrals.

Example 2. Find $\displaystyle\int_{(0,1)}^{(2,3)} (x+y)\,dx + (x-y)\,dy.$

Solution: If $M(x,y) = x + y$ and $N(x,y) = x - y$, then

$$M_y(x,y) = 1 = N_x(x,y).$$

Thus there exists a function f such that $f_x(x,y) = M(x,y)$ and $f_y(x,y) = N(x,y)$. Such a function f is defined by

$$f(x,y) = \frac{x^2}{2} + xy - \frac{y^2}{2}.$$

Hence

$$\int_{(0,1)}^{(2,3)} (x + y)\, dx + (x - y)\, dy = \left(\frac{x^2}{2} + xy - \frac{y^2}{2}\right)\bigg|_{(0,1)}^{(2,3)} = 4.$$

The line integral has many important applications to physical problems. We shall indicate one of these, namely, to force fields, in the next section.

■ ■ ■ EXERCISES

1. If $M(x,y) = 2x - y$ and $N(x,y) = x + y$, find $\int_C M\, dx + N\, dy$ for each of the following paths.

$$C_1: x = t, \quad y = t + 2, \quad 0 \le t \le 2.$$
$$C_2: x = t, \quad y = t^2, \quad 0 \le t \le 2.$$

Note that the end points of C_1 and C_2 are the same. Does the fact that the integrals differ in value contradict 19.24?

2. Show that $\int_C M\, dx + N\, dy = 0$ when $M(x,y) = x$, $N(x,y) = y$, and C is given by $x = \cos\theta, y = \sin\theta, 0 \le \theta \le 2\pi$. What properties of M, N, and C make the integral vanish?

Show that each of the following integrals exists and evaluate each of them.

3. $\int_{(-1,2)}^{(3,4)} (x^2 + y)\, dx + (y^2 + x)\, dy.$

4. $\int_{(0,0)}^{(1,1)} e^y\, dx + xe^y\, dy.$

5. $\int_{(0,1)}^{(\pi,2)} y \cos x\, dx + \sin x\, dy.$

6. $\int_{(1,1)}^{(1,e)} \ln y\, dx + \frac{x}{y}\, dy.$

7. If M, N, P are functions of three variables, define the line integral $\int_C M\, dx + N\, dy + P\, dz$. State conditions under which this integral is independent of the path, and prove the conditions sufficient. (*Hint:* See Exercise 12 of Section 11.)

8. Find

$$\int_{(0,0,0)}^{(1,1,\pi)} \sin yz\, dx + xz \cos yz\, dy + xy \cos yz\, dz.$$

13. Work as a line integral

We shall consider in this section motion in the xy-plane. The generalization of our results to three dimensions will be evident.

Let $\overrightarrow{AB}$ be a vector indicating the motion of a point P along the line segment AB from A to B. If A and B have position vectors r and s respectively, then $s - r = \overrightarrow{AB}$, and $s - r$ is called a *displacement vector* or simply *displacement*. Let f be a constant force acting on P during this motion. The projection of f on $\overrightarrow{AB}$ is $|f| \cos \theta$ where θ is the angle between f and $\overrightarrow{AB}$. The work done by f as P moves from A to B is then $|f| \cos \theta \, |s - r| = f \cdot (s - r)$ by 18.2. That is to say, work (with constant force) is the dot product of force by displacement.

It is, however, possible that force is not a constant and that the path of P is not a line segment.

If the force f is defined at every point (x,y) in a region R of the plane,

$$f = (M(x,y), N(x,y)),$$

where M and N have continuous first partial derivatives in R, then f determines a *force field* in R. For example,

$$f = (-kx/(x^2 + y^2)^{3/2}, \; -ky/(x^2 + y^2)^{3/2})$$

determines the force field of Newtonian gravity in a plane. (See Exercise 1 below.)

If the point P moving in the region R has position vector $r(t) = (x(t), y(t))$ at the time t, let C be the path of P between $t = a$ and $t = b$. The force acting on P at the time t will be written

$$f(t) = (M(x(t), y(t)), N(x(t), y(t))).$$

Let $[t_0, t_1, \cdots, t_n]$ be a partition of the time interval $[a,b]$. The work done by the force field on the point P in the time interval $[t_{i-1}, t_i]$ is approximated by

$$W_i = f(t_{i-1}) \cdot (r(t_i) - r(t_{i-1})).$$

By the mean value theorem

$$\begin{aligned} r(t_i) - r(t_{i-1}) &= (x(t_i) - x(t_{i-1}), \, y(t_i) - y(t_{i-1})) \\ &= (x'(u_i), y'(v_i))(t_i - t_{i-1}) \end{aligned}$$

for some numbers u_i and v_i in (t_{i-1}, t_i). Thus

$$W_i = [f(t_{i-1}) \cdot (x'(u_i), y'(v_i))](t_i - t_{i-1}),$$

and the work done by f as P traces the path C is approximated by $\sum_{i=1}^{n} W_i$.

If we consider a sequence of partitions of $[a,b]$ whose norms approach zero, we see that the corresponding sequences of sums ΣW_i will approach the integral

$$\int_b^a f(t) \cdot r'(t)\, dt.$$

This is just the line integral 19.23 defined in the previous section. If we write $dr = r'(t)\, dt = (dx, dy)$, then dr may be called the displacement differential. For the force f and the path C we make the following definition of work W.

19.25 $$W = \int_C f \cdot dr.$$

That is to say, work is the line integral of the dot product of force and the displacement differential.

If $M_y = N_x$, then by the preceding sections there is a function F such that $F_x = M$, $F_y = N$, and

$$\int_C f \cdot dr = F(x(b), y(b)) - F(x(a), y(a)).$$

If $p(x,y) = -F(x,y)$, p is called a *potential function* of the force field. Hence $p_x = -M$, $p_y = -N$, and in the notation of gradient, $\nabla p = -f$, and

$$W = -\int_C \nabla p \cdot dr.$$

If a force field possesses a potential function, the field is said to be *conservative*.

If we consider $p(x,y)$ to be the potential of the point $P(x,y)$ in the force field then we may prove the *conservation of energy theorem*:

19.26 Theorem. In a conservative force field the sum of the kinetic and potential energies of a point of mass m is a constant.

Proof: By definition (Exercise 9, p. 522) the kinetic energy is $\frac{1}{2}m|r'(t)|^2$. Let $G(t) = \frac{1}{2}m|r'(t)|^2 + p(x(t), y(t))$. Then

$$G'(t) = m(r'(t) \cdot r''(t)) + \nabla p \cdot r'(t)$$
$$= [mr''(t) - f(t)] \cdot r'(t).$$

But $f(t) = mr''(t)$, and hence $G'(t) = 0$, or $G(t)$ is a constant.

■ ■ ■ EXERCISES

1. If a mass m is concentrated at the origin 0 of a plane rectangular system, a particle of mass 1 at a point $P(x,y)$ distinct from 0 will experience a gravitation force whose components are $M(x,y) = -kx/(x^2 + y^2)^{3/2}$ and $N(x,y) = -ky/(x^2 + y^2)^{3/2}$, where k is some positive constant.
   (a) Show that this gravitational field is conservative in any region not containing the origin.
   (b) Find a function F such that $F_x = M$ and $F_y = N$.

(c) Find the work done by the force field if P moves from $A(4,0)$ to $B(0,1)$.

(d) Show that the work done by the force field if P moves from $A(a_1,b_1)$ to $B(a_2,b_2)$ is $k\left(\dfrac{1}{|OB|} - \dfrac{1}{|OA|}\right)$.

2. If W is a charged wire of infinite length perpendicular to the xy-plane at the origin and if a unit charge of the same sign as W is at the point $P(x,y)$, then P experiences a force whose components are $M(x,y) = \dfrac{kx}{x^2 + y^2}$ and $N(x,y) = \dfrac{ky}{x^2 + y^2}$ for some constant k.

   (a) Show that this force field is conservative in any region not containing the origin.

   (b) Find the work done by the force field if the point P moves from $A(a_1,b_1)$ to $B(a_2,b_2)$.

3. Let the x- and y-axes be positively charged wires of infinite length. If a unit positive charge is placed at the point $P(x,y)$, $x \neq 0$ and $y \neq 0$, then P experiences a force $\boldsymbol{f} = (k/x,k/y)$ for some positive number k. Find a potential function for $\boldsymbol{f}$, and find the work done by $\boldsymbol{f}$ when P moves from $A(x_1,y_1)$ to $B(x_2,y_2)$.

4. The *equipotential lines* of a force field in a plane are defined to be those curves along which the potential remains a constant. Find the equipotential lines in each of Exercises 1, 2, 3 above.

5. If $\boldsymbol{f} = (M(x,y,x),\ N(x,y,z),\ P(x,y,z))$, then $\boldsymbol{f}$ defines a force field in three dimensions. Prove that this force field is conservative (i.e., possesses a potential function) if $\Delta \times \boldsymbol{f} = \boldsymbol{0}$.

6. Solve Exercise 1 in three dimensions.

20

Multiple integration

■ ■ ■ ■ ■   THE CONCEPT OF an integral of a function of one variable given in Chapter 8 may be extended to a function of several variables, as we shall demonstrate in the present chapter. For a function of two or three variables, analogous geometrical and physical applications will be shown to hold for this so-called multiple integral.

1. Double integrals

Let R be a rectangular region of the plane bounded by the lines $x = a$, $x = b$, $y = c$, and $y = d$, and let f be a function of two variables that is continuous in R. The integral of f over R will be defined in this section.

If $p = [x_0, x_1, \cdots, x_n; y_0, y_1, \cdots, y_m]$ is a partition of R into mn subrectangles, let R_{ij} designate the i,jth subrectangle of p, bounded by the lines $x = x_{i-1}$, $x = x_i$, $y = y_{j-1}$, and $y = y_j$, and let m_{ij} and M_{ij} designate, respectively, the minimum and maximum values of f in R_{ij}. The area of R_{ij}, designated by ΔR_{ij}, is given by

$$\Delta R_{ij} = \Delta x_i \, \Delta y_j,$$

where $\Delta x_i = x_i - x_{i-1}$ and $\Delta y_j = y_j - y_{j-1}$. The area A of R is given by $(b - a)(d - c)$; clearly A is the sum of the areas of the subrectangles R_{ij},

$$A = \sum_{i=1}^{n} \sum_{j=1}^{m} \Delta R_{ij}.$$

570

We now form the lower sum L_p and the upper sum U_p of f relative to the partition p of R in an analogous way to that in Section 3 of Chapter 8. Thus L_p is a sum of mn terms of the form $m_{ij} \Delta R_{ij}$, and similarly for U_p. Using the sigma notation,

$$L_p = \sum_{i=1}^{n} \sum_{j=1}^{m} m_{ij} \Delta R_{ij}, \qquad U_p = \sum_{i=1}^{n} \sum_{j=1}^{m} M_{ij} \Delta R_{ij}.$$

If m and M designate, respectively, the minimum and maximum values of f in R, then clearly $m \leq m_{ij} \leq M$ for each i and j. Hence

$$mA = \sum_{i=1}^{n} \sum_{j=1}^{m} m \, \Delta R_{ij} \leq \sum_{i=1}^{n} \sum_{j=1}^{m} m_{ij} \, \Delta R_{ij} = L_p,$$

and, similarly, $U_p \leq MA$; thus

$$mA \leq L_p \leq U_p \leq MA.$$

The set of all lower sums L_p of f over R has an upper bound MA by the above inequality. Therefore the set of all lower sums has a least upper bound by the completeness property of the real number system. This least upper bound, designated by

$$\underline{\iint_R} f,$$

is called the *lower integral* of f over R. In turn, the set of all upper sums U_p of f over R has a lower bound mA and hence a greatest lower bound designated by

$$\overline{\iint_R} f$$

and called the *upper integral* of f over R.

It follows immediately from the definitions that

$$L_p \leq \underline{\iint_R} f, \qquad U_p \geq \overline{\iint_R} f$$

for every partition p of R. Also, for every number $\epsilon > 0$, there exists a partition q of R such that

$$L_q + \frac{\epsilon}{2} \geq \underline{\iint_R} f, \qquad U_q - \frac{\epsilon}{2} \leq \overline{\iint_R} f.$$

From the inequalities above, we have

$$0 \leq U_q - L_q \leq \overline{\iint_R} f - \underline{\iint_R} f + \epsilon,$$

and

$$\overline{\iint_R} f \leq \underline{\iint_R} f + \epsilon.$$

Since this latter inequality holds for every number $\epsilon > 0$, evidently

$$\underline{\iint_R} f \leq \overline{\iint_R} f.$$

Since the function f is continuous in R, it is uniformly continuous in R and for every number $\epsilon > 0$, there exists a partition $p = [x_0, x_1, \cdots, x_n; y_0, y_1, \cdots, y_m]$ of R by 19.13 such that

$$0 \le M_{ij} - m_{ij} < \frac{\epsilon}{A}$$

for every choice of i and j.   Hence

$$U_p - L_p = \sum_{i=1}^{n} \sum_{j=1}^{m} (M_{ij} - m_{ij}) \, \Delta R_{ij} < \sum_{i=1}^{n} \sum_{j=1}^{m} \frac{\epsilon}{A} \, \Delta R_{ij} = \epsilon,$$

and

$$0 \le \overline{\iint_R} f - \underline{\iint_R} f \le U_p - L_p < \epsilon.$$

Since

$$0 \le \overline{\iint_R} f - \underline{\iint_R} f < \epsilon$$

for every positive number ϵ, it follows that

$$\underline{\iint_R} f = \overline{\iint_R} f.$$

We may therefore make the following definition.

20.1 Definition.   If f is a continuous function of two variables in a rectangular region R, then the common value of the lower and upper integrals of f over R is called the *double integral* of f over R and is designated by

$$\iint_R f(x,y) \, dR.$$

Methods of evaluating double integrals will be given in the next section.

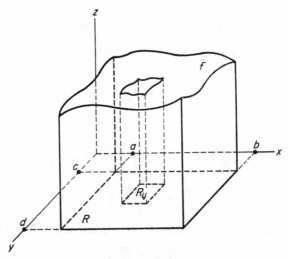

Figure 20.1

If the continuous function f is nonnegative in R, that is, $f(x,y) \geq 0$ for every (x,y) in R, then the surface

$$z = f(x,y)$$

and the planes $x = a$, $x = b$, $y = c$, $y = d$, and $z = 0$ bound a solid (Figure 20.1). Let us show that the double integral of f over R may be interpreted as the volume of this solid.

Each term $m_{ij} \Delta R_{ij}$ of the lower sum L_p of f over R is the volume of a parallelopiped with base R_{ij} and height m_{ij}. Since m_{ij} is the minimum value of f in R_{ij}, this parallelopiped is completely contained in the solid of Figure 20.1. Hence L_p is the volume of a solid made up of mn parallelopipeds and completely contained in the solid in question. Thus, if the solid of Figure 20.1 is to have a volume V, we would desire that $V \geq L_p$. A similar argument would lead us to desire that $V \leq U_p$, so that $L_p \leq V \leq U_p$ for every partition p of R. Hence

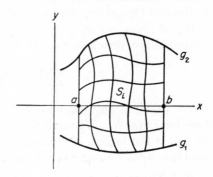

$$L_p \leq \iint_R f \leq V \leq \iint_R f \leq U_p.$$

There is a unique number V having this property, namely, the double integral of f over R. Therefore we shall define the volume V of this solid to be

Figure 20.2

$$V = \iint_R f(x,y) \, dR.$$

The double integral of a function f may be defined over a more general region of the plane than a rectangle, such as, for example, the region S of Figure 20.2. This region is bounded by the graphs of the continuous functions* g_1 and g_2, and the lines $x = a$ and $x = b$, with $g_1(x) \leq g_2(x)$ if $a \leq x \leq b$. We may partition S into n subregions S_i, each with area ΔS_i, and form the sums

$$L = \sum_{i=1}^{n} m_i \Delta S_i, \qquad U = \sum_{i=1}^{n} M_i \Delta S_i,$$

where m_i and M_i are the minimum and the maximum values, respectively, of f in S_i. Although we shall not prove it here, it may be shown that the least upper bound of the set of all lower sums L and the greatest lower bound of the set of all upper sums U are equal. Their common value is

---

* It is assumed that the arcs of the graphs of g_1 and g_2 between $x = a$ and $x = b$ have length. Such will be the case, according to 15.14, if the functions g_1 and g_2 have continuous derivatives in the interval $[a,b]$.

designated by

$$\iint_S f(x,y) \, dS,$$

and is called the double integral of f over S. If f is nonnegative in S, this double integral may be interpreted as the volume of the solid bounded by the surface $z = f(x,y)$, the cylinders $y = g_1(x)$ and $y = g_2(x)$, the planes $x = a$ and $x = b$, and the xy-plane.

Just as an integral of a function of one variable may be given as a limit of a sequence of Riemann sums (Chapter 9), so can a double integral of a function of two variables be represented as a limit of a sequence of double sums. We shall indicate below how this is done. The proofs, being similar to those of Chapter 9, will not be given.

If $p = [x_0, x_1, \cdots, x_n; y_0, y_1, \cdots, y_m]$ is a partition of rectangle R as described above, then a sum of the form

$$\sum_{i=1}^{n} \sum_{j=1}^{m} f(x_i', y_j') \, \Delta x_i \, \Delta y_j,$$

where (x_i', y_j') is any point in R_{ij}, will be called a *Riemann sum* of the function f over R. We recall that the norm of the partition p, designated by $|p|$, is the largest of the numbers $\Delta x_1, \cdots, \Delta x_n, \Delta y_1, \cdots, \Delta y_m$. The double integral analogue of Theorem 9.11 may be stated as follows.

20.2 Theorem. If f is a continuous function of two variables over a rectangular region R, and if $p_1, p_2, \cdots, p_n, \cdots$ is a sequence of partitions of R for which

$$\lim_{n \to \infty} |p_n| = 0,$$

then if $S_1, S_2, \cdots, S_n, \cdots$ is any sequence of Riemann sums of f associated with the given sequence of partitions,

$$\lim_{n \to \infty} S_n = \iint_R f(x,y) \, dR.$$

■ ■ ■ EXERCISES

In each of the following, R is the rectangular region bounded by the lines $x = 0$, $x = 4$, $y = 0$, and $y = 2$, and p_n is the regular partition of R defined by $p_n = [0, \Delta x_n, 2\Delta x_n, \cdots, 4; 0, \Delta y_n, 2\Delta y_n, \cdots, 2]$, $\Delta x_n = 4/n$, $\Delta y_n = 2/n$. Also, for a given function f, the numbers L_n and U_n are the lower and upper sums, respectively, of f relative to p_n.

1. If $f(x,y) = 2x + y$, find L_2, L_4, U_2, and U_4. Also find L_n in terms of n, and find the double integral of f over R.

2. If $f(x,y) = 4 - x - y$, find L_3 and U_3. Also find U_n in terms of n, and find the double integral of f over R.

3. If $f(x,y) = x^2 + y$, find L_4 and U_4. Also find L_n in terms of n, and find the double integral of f over R.

4. If $f(x,y) = xy$, find L_3 and U_3. Also find U_n in terms of n, and find the double integral of f over R.

2. Repeated integrals

If the function f of two variables is continuous in the rectangular region R bounded by the lines $x = a$, $x = b$, $y = c$, and $y = d$, then the function F defined by

$$F(x) = \int_c^d f(x,y)\, dy$$

may be shown to be continuous in the interval $[a,b]$ by an argument similar to that in the proof of 19.21. Hence the integral of F exists in $[a,b]$; it is designated by

$$\int_a^b F(x)\, dx = \int_a^b \left[\int_c^d f(x,y)\, dy \right] dx = \int_a^b dx \int_c^d f(x,y)\, dy.$$

Such an integral of a function of two variables is called a *repeated integral* (or iterated integral). By reversing the roles of x and y, we may define a second repeated integral

$$\int_c^d dy \int_a^b f(x,y)\, dx = \int_c^d \left[\int_a^b f(x,y)\, dx \right] dy.$$

It is the aim of this section to show that each of the above repeated integrals equals the double integral of f over R.

Example 1. Find $\displaystyle \int_{-1}^2 dx \int_0^4 (x - 2y + x^2 y)\, dy$.

Solution: Letting x be a constant,

$$\int_0^4 (x - 2y + x^2 y)\, dy = xy - y^2 + \frac{1}{2} x^2 y^2 \Big|_0^4 = 4x - 16 + 8x^2.$$

Therefore

$$\int_{-1}^2 dx \int_0^4 (x - 2y + x^2 y)\, dy = \int_{-1}^2 (4x - 16 + 8x^2)\, dx$$

$$= 2x^2 - 16x + \frac{8}{3} x^3 \Big|_{-1}^2 = -18.$$

20.3 Theorem. If the function f of two variables is continuous in the rectangular region R bounded by the lines $x = a$, $x = b$, $y = c$, and $y = d$, then

$$\iint_R f(x,y)\, dR = \int_a^b dx \int_c^d f(x,y)\, dy = \int_c^d dy \int_a^b f(x,y)\, dx.$$

Proof: If $p = [x_0, x_1, \cdots, x_n; y_0, y_1, \cdots, y_m]$ is any partition of R, let m_{ij} and M_{ij} designate the minimum and maximum values, respectively, of f in the i,jth subrectangle R_{ij} of p, and let $\Delta R_{ij} = (x_i - x_{i-1})(y_j - y_{j-1}) = \Delta x_i \, \Delta y_j$, the area of R_{ij}.

For a fixed number x in the interval $[x_{i-1}, x_i]$, we have $m_{ij} \leq f(x,y) \leq M_{ij}$ for every number y in $[y_{j-1}, y_j]$, and therefore

$$m_{ij} \, \Delta y_j \leq \int_{y_{i-1}}^{y_i} f(x,y) \, dy \leq M_{ij} \, \Delta y_j.$$

Hence

$$\sum_{j=1}^{m} m_{ij} \, \Delta y_j \leq \sum_{j=1}^{m} \int_{y_{i-1}}^{y_i} f(x,y) \, dy \leq \sum_{j=1}^{m} M_{ij} \, \Delta y_j,$$

and, since

$$\sum_{j=1}^{m} \int_{y_{i-1}}^{y_i} f(x,y) \, dy = \int_{c}^{d} f(x,y) \, dy,$$

evidently

(1) $$\sum_{j=1}^{m} m_{ij} \, \Delta y_j \leq \int_{c}^{d} f(x,y) \, dy \leq \sum_{j=1}^{m} M_{ij} \, \Delta y_j.$$

According to (1), the function g defined by

$$g(x) = \int_{c}^{d} f(x,y) \, dy, \qquad x_{i-1} \leq x \leq x_i,$$

has its values between two constants k_i and K_i, where

$$k_i = \sum_{j=1}^{m} m_{ij} \, \Delta y_j, \qquad K_i = \sum_{j=1}^{m} M_{ij} \, \Delta y_j.$$

Therefore

$$k_i \, \Delta x_i \leq \int_{x_{i-1}}^{x_i} g(x) \, dx \leq K_i \, \Delta x_i,$$

and

$$\sum_{i=1}^{n} k_i \, \Delta x_i \leq \int_{a}^{b} g(x) \, dx \leq \sum_{i=1}^{n} K_i \, \Delta x_i,$$

or

(2) $$\sum_{i=1}^{n} \sum_{j=1}^{m} m_{ij} \, \Delta x_i \, \Delta y_j \leq \int_{a}^{b} dx \int_{c}^{d} f(x,y) \, dy \leq \sum_{i=1}^{n} \sum_{j=1}^{m} M_{ij} \, \Delta x_i \, \Delta y_j.$$

We recognize the extremities of (2) as being the lower sum L_p and upper sum U_p of f relative to the partition p as defined in the previous section. Thus (2) may be written in the form

(3) $$L_p \leq \int_{a}^{b} dx \int_{c}^{d} f(x,y) \, dy \leq U_p.$$

Since the double integral of f over R is the least upper bound of the set of all L_p and the greatest lower bound of the set of all U_p, (3) implies that

$$\int_{a}^{b} dx \int_{c}^{d} f(x,y) \, dy = \iint_{R} f(x,y) \, dR.$$

This proves one part of 20.3. The proof of the other part, being similar, is omitted.

A device for recalling the repeated integral equal to a given double integral is to imagine that the rectangle R is cut into strips parallel to an

axis.   A representative strip parallel to the y-axis is shown in Figure 20.3.
A Riemann sum approximating the double integral over R has the form

$$\sum\left[\sum f(x,y)\,\Delta y\right]\Delta x.$$

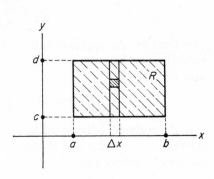

As an intermediate step we think of
each $\sum f(x,y)\,\Delta y$ as being approximated by the integral $\int_c^d f(x,y)\,dy$,
the result of integrating in the
direction of the y-axis.   The double
integral of f over R is then approximated by

$$\sum \int_c^d f(x,y)\,dy\,\Delta x$$

where each term of the sum is approximately the double integral of f

Figure 20.3

over one of the strips.   Summing the integrals over the various strips between $x = a$ and $x = b$ and taking the limit as Δx approaches 0 we should
obtain

$$\iint_R f(x,y)\,dR = \int_a^b dx \int_c^d f(x,y)\,dy.$$

Had R been cut into strips parallel to the x-axis, we would have obtained

$$\iint_R f(x,y)\,dR = \int_c^d dy \int_a^b f(x,y)\,dx.$$

The double integral of a continuous function f over a region S other
than a rectangle may again be evaluated by a repeated integral.   If S is
bounded by the curves $y = g_1(x)$ and $y = g_2(x)$, and the lines $x = a$ and
$x = b$ as in Figure 20.4 (assuming that $g_1(x) \leq g_2(x)$ and that the functions
g_1 and g_2 have continuous derivatives), then we may imagine the region S

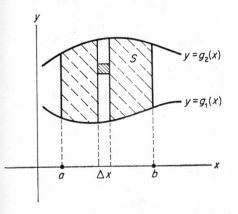

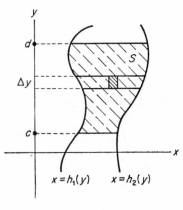

Figure 20.4   Figure 20.5

cut into strips parallel to the y-axis. The double integral of f over a representative strip (Figure 20.4) is approximately equal to

$$\Delta x \int_{g_1(x)}^{g_2(x)} f(x,y) \, dy.$$

The limit (as Δx approaches 0) of the sum of these double integrals for the strips of S between $x = a$ and $x = b$ should give the double integral of f over S; hence

$$\iint_S f(x,y) \, dS = \int_a^b dx \int_{g_1(x)}^{g_2(x)} f(x,y) \, dy.$$

If the region S is bounded by the curves $x = h_1(y)$ and $x = h_2(y)$, and the lines $y = c$ and $y = d$ (Figure 20.5), then a similar intuitive argument leads us to believe that

$$\iint_S f(x,y) \, dS = \int_c^d dy \int_{h_1(y)}^{h_2(y)} f(x,y) \, dx.$$

The informal arguments above for the equality of a double integral and a repeated integral can be made mathematically rigorous, but we shall not attempt to do so in this book.

Example 2.   If

$$f(x,y) = \sqrt{x} + y - 3x^2y,$$

and if R is the rectangular region of the plane bounded by the lines $x = 0$, $x = 1$, $y = 1$, and $y = 3$, find

$$\iint_R f(x,y) \, dR.$$

Solution: By 20.3,

$$\iint_R (\sqrt{x} + y - 3x^2y) \, dR = \int_0^1 dx \int_1^3 (\sqrt{x} + y - 3x^2y) \, dy$$

$$= \int_0^1 (\sqrt{x}\,y + \frac{1}{2}\,y^2 - \frac{3}{2}\,x^2y^2) \Big|_{y=1}^{y=3} dx$$

$$= \int_0^1 (2\sqrt{x} + 4 - 12x^2) \, dx$$

$$= \left(\frac{4}{3}\,x^{3/2} + 4x - 4x^3 \right) \Big|_0^1 = \frac{4}{3}.$$

We also have, by 20.3,

$$\iint_R (\sqrt{x} + y - 3x^2y) \, dR = \int_1^3 dy \int_0^1 (\sqrt{x} + y - 3x^2y) \, dx$$

$$= \int_1^3 \left(\frac{2}{3}\,x^{3/2} + xy - x^3y \right) \Big|_{x=0}^{x=1} dy$$

$$= \int_1^3 \frac{2}{3} \, dy = \frac{2}{3}\,y \Big|_1^3 = \frac{4}{3}.$$

Example 3.   If

$$f(x,y) = \frac{2y - 1}{x + 1},$$

and if the region S is bounded by $x = 0$, $y = 0$, and $2x - y - 4 = 0$, find the double integral of f over S.

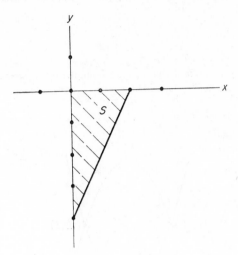

Figure 20.6

Solution: The region S (Figure 20.6) may be thought of as being bounded by the curves $y = 0$ and $y = 2x - 4$ between $x = 0$ and $x = 2$.   Hence

$$\iint_S \frac{2y - 1}{x + 1}\, dS = \int_0^2 dx \int_0^{2x-4} \frac{2y - 1}{x + 1}\, dy = \int_0^2 \frac{y^2 - y}{x + 1}\Bigg|_{y=0}^{y=2x-4} dx$$

$$= \int_0^2 \frac{4x^2 - 16x + 16 - 2x + 4}{x + 1}\, dx$$

$$= 2 \int_0^2 \left(2x - 11 + \frac{21}{x + 1} \right) dx$$

$$= 2(x^2 - 11x + 21 \ln (x + 1))\Big|_0^2 = 6(7 \ln 3 - 9).$$

We could think of the region S as being bounded by the curves $x = 0$ and $x = (y + 4)/2$ between $y = -4$ and $y = 0$, in which case

$$\iint_S \frac{2y - 1}{x + 1}\, dS = \int_{-4}^0 dy \int_0^{(y+4)/2} \frac{2y - 1}{x + 1}\, dx$$

$$= \int_{-4}^0 (2y - 1) \ln (x + 1)\Big|_{x=0}^{x=(y+4)/2} dy$$

$$= \int_{-4}^0 (2y - 1) \ln \frac{y + 6}{2}\, dy,$$

and so on.   It is clear that the integration is easier in the first case.

If $f(x,y) = 1$ everywhere in the region S bounded by the curves $y = g_1(x)$ and $y = g_2(x)$, and the lines $x = a$ and $x = b$ (Figure 20.4), then

$$\int_a^b dx \int_{g_1(x)}^{g_2(x)} f(x,y)\, dy = \int_a^b [g_2(x) - g_1(x)]\, dx.$$

This latter integral is just the area of the region S. Thus,

$$\iint_S dS$$

is the area of region S.

Example 4. Find the area of the region S bounded by the parabolas $y = x^2$ and $y = 4 - x^2$ (Figure 20.7).

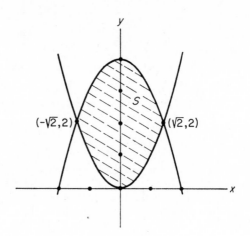

Figure 20.7

Solution: The area is given by

$$\iint_S dS = \int_{-\sqrt{2}}^{\sqrt{2}} dx \int_{x^2}^{4-x^2} dy = \int_{-\sqrt{2}}^{\sqrt{2}} (4 - x^2 - x^2)\, dx = \frac{16}{3}\sqrt{2}.$$

■ ■ ■ EXERCISES

By the use of repeated integrals, find the double integral of each of the following functions over the given region S of the plane, and sketch the region S.

1. $f(x,y) = 2x - y + 4$; S bounded by $x = 1$, $x = 4$, $y = -1$, $y = 2$.
2. $g(x,y) = 3x - y + 2xy$; S bounded by $x = -2$, $x = 0$, $y = 0$, $y = 3$.
3. $F(x,y) = y \sin x - xe^y$; S bounded by $x = \pi/2$, $x = 0$, $y = -1$, $y = 1$.
4. $G(x,y) = \dfrac{y^2}{1 + x^2}$; S bounded by $x = -1$, $x = 1$, $y = 0$, $y = 2$.
5. $g(x,y) = 3x - y + 1$; S bounded by $x = 0$, $y = 0$, $x + 3y - 3 = 0$.

6. $f(x,y) = 2x + 2y - 1$; S bounded by $x = y$, $x + y - 4 = 0$, $x = 0$.

7. $G(x,y) = xy - x^2 + 1$; S bounded by $x - 2y + 2 = 0$, $x + 3y - 3 = 0$, $y = 0$.

8. $F(x,y) = 2x^2y - x + 3$; S bounded by $3y = x$, $x + y - 4 = 0$, $y = -1$.

9. $f(x,y) = \dfrac{2y - 1}{x^2 + 1}$; S bounded by $y = 4 - x^2$, $y = 0$.

10. $g(x,y) = 2xy - 3x^2$; S bounded by $y = \ln |x|$, $y = 0$, $y = -2$.

By the use of repeated integrals, find the area of the region bounded by the following curves.

11. $x = y^2$, $x - y - 2 = 0$.

12. $y = x^3 - x$, $x = -1$, $2x + y - 2 = 0$.

13. $y = \sin \pi x$, $y = x^2 - x$.

14. $y = \ln x$, $2x + y - 2 = 0$, $y = 2$.

15. $y = |x|$, $4y = 4x^2 + 1$.

16. $x^2 + 4y^2 = 16$, $x^2 = 12y$. (Smaller region.)

3. Volumes

We indicated in the first section how the double integral could be interpreted as the volume of a solid. Thus, if f is a continuous function of two variables in a region S of the type discussed in previous sections and if $f(x,y) \geq 0$ in S, then the volume of the solid bounded above by the

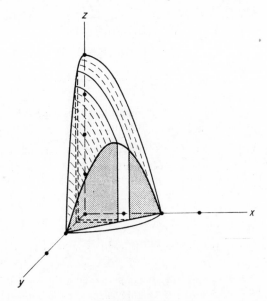

Figure 20.8

surface

$$z = f(x,y),$$

below by the xy-plane, and laterally by the cylinder whose directrix is the boundary of S and whose generator is parallel to the z-axis is given by

$$V = \iint_S f(x,y) \ dS.$$

We shall speak of this solid as the solid under the surface $z = f(x,y)$ and above the region S of the xy-plane.

Example 1.   Find the volume of the solid under the surface

$$z = 4 - x^2 - 4y^2$$

and above the region S of the xy-plane bounded by $x = 0$, $y = 0$, and $x + 2y - 2 = 0$ (Figure 20.8).

Solution: The volume V of this solid is given by

$$V = \iint_S (4 - x^2 - 4y^2) \ dS.$$

We evaluate this double integral by a repeated integral:

$$V = \int_0^1 dy \int_0^{2-2y} (4 - x^2 - 4y^2) \ dx.$$

For a given y, the inner integral

$$\int_0^{2-2y} (4 - x^2 - 4y^2) \ dx = 8(1 - y) - \frac{8}{3} (1 - y)^3 - 8y^2 + 8y^3$$

is the area of a section of the solid parallel to the xz-plane, as indicated in Figure 20.8.   Then the volume V can be interpreted as the sum of the volumes of all slices between $y = 0$ and $y = 1$.   Continuing the integration, we obtain,

$$V = \int_0^1 \left[8(1 - y) - \frac{8}{3} (1 - y)^3 - 8y^2 + 8y^3 \right] dy = \frac{8}{3}.$$

Example 2.   Find the volume of the solid under the plane $z = x + 2y$ and over the quarter circle of radius 2 in the first quadrant of the xy-plane (Figure 20.9).

Solution: The quarter circle may be described as the region S bounded by the curves $y = 0$ and $y = \sqrt{4 - x^2}$ between $x = 0$ and $x = 2$.   Hence the volume V of the solid under the plane $z = x + 2y$ and above S is given by

$$V = \iint_S (x + 2y) \ dS = \int_0^2 dx \int_0^{\sqrt{4-x^2}} (x + 2y) \ dy$$

$$= \int_0^2 (x\sqrt{4 - x^2} + 4 - x^2) \ dx = \left(-\frac{1}{3} (4 - x^2)^{3/2} + 4x - \frac{1}{3} x^3 \right) \Big|_0^2 = 8.$$

Again, the inner integral is the area of a section of the solid, this time parallel to the yz-plane, as indicated in Figure 20.9, and the outer integral sums up the volumes of the slices from $x = 0$ to $x = 2$.

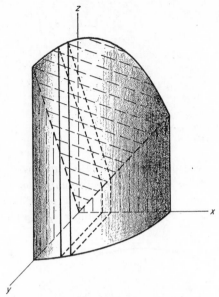

Figure 20.9

■ ■ ■ EXERCISES

1. Find the volume of the solid under the plane $z = 2x + y + 1$ and above the region bounded by $x = 0$, $y = 0$, and $x + 3y - 3 = 0$. Sketch the solid, and describe an alternate way of finding its volume.

2. Find the volume of the solid under the plane $x - z + y + 2 = 0$ and above the region bounded by $y = x$, $x + 2y = 2$, and $y = 1$. Sketch.

3. Find the volume of the solid under the plane $z = 3x + y$ and above the part of the ellipse $4x^2 + 9y^2 = 36$ in the first quadrant. Sketch.

4. Find the volume of the solid under the plane $z = 2x + y + 10$ and above the circle $x^2 + y^2 = 16$. Sketch.

5. Find the volume of the solid under the plane $z = 2y$ and above the region bounded by $y = x^2$, $y = 0$, and $x = 2$. Sketch.

6. Find the volume of the solid in the first octant bounded by the cylinder $y^2 + z^2 = 4$, the plane $y = x$, and the xy-plane. Sketch.

7. Find the volume of the solid in the first octant bounded by the paraboloid $z = 16 - x^2 - 4y^2$. Sketch.

8. Find the volume of the solid in the first octant bounded by the cylinder $z = x^2$ and the planes $x = 2y$ and $x = 2$. Sketch.

9. Find the volume of the solid in the first octant bounded by the two cylinders $x^2 + y^2 = r^2$ and $y^2 + z^2 = r^2$. Sketch.

10. Find the volume of the solid in the first octant bound by the two cylinders $z = 4 - x^2$ and $y = 4 - x^2$. Sketch.

Describe and sketch the solid whose volume is given by each of the following repeated integrals. Find each volume.

11. $\int_0^2 dx \int_0^3 x\, dy.$

12. $\int_1^3 dy \int_1^4 (2 + x + y)\, dx.$

13. $\int_0^r dy \int_0^y \sqrt{r^2 - y^2}\, dx.$

14. $\int_0^1 dx \int_{-3x}^{\sqrt{1-x^2}} (3x + y)\, dy.$

15. $\int_0^2 dx \int_0^{\sqrt{4-x^2}} (x^2 + 4y^2)\, dy.$

16. $\int_0^2 dy \int_{2-y}^{2y+2} (x^2 + 4y^2)\, dx.$

4. Polar coordinates

Let us show in this section how a double integral over a region of a polar coordinate plane can be defined and represented as a repeated integral.

Let R be the region on a polar coordinate plane bounded by the lines $\theta = \alpha$ and $\theta = \beta$, and the circles $r = a$ and $r = b$. The region R may be

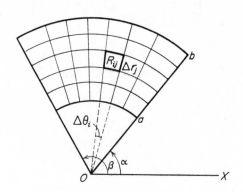

Figure 20.10

divided into mn subregions by a partition $p = [\theta_0, \theta_1, \cdots, \theta_n; r_0, r_1, \cdots, r_m]$. The i,jth subregion R_{ij} of p is bounded by the lines $\theta = \theta_{i-1}$ and $\theta = \theta_i$, and the circles $r = r_{j-1}$ and $r = r_j$ (Figure 20.10). The area ΔR_{ij} of R_{ij} is given by

$$\Delta R_{ij} = \frac{1}{2} \Delta\theta_i (r_j^2 - r_{j-1}^2) = \bar{r}_j\, \Delta r_j\, \Delta\theta_i,$$

where $\Delta\theta_i = \theta_i - \theta_{i-1}$, $\Delta r_j = r_j - r_{j-1}$, and $\bar{r}_j = (r_{j-1} + r_j)/2$.

If f is a continuous function of two variables in R, then relative to a partition p of R we can define a Riemann sum S_p of f as follows:

$$S_p = \sum_{i=1}^n \sum_{j=1}^m f(r_j', \theta_i') \bar{r}_j\, \Delta r_j\, \Delta\theta_i,$$

where (r_j', θ_i') is any point of R_{ij}. By taking a sequence of partitions of R with norms approaching 0, the limit of the corresponding sequence of Riemann sums of f will be the double integral of f over R, just as in 20.2 for a rectangular coordinate plane. In turn, this double integral of f over

R may be shown to equal a repeated integral having one of two possible forms:

20.4 $$\iint_R f(r,\theta)\, dR = \int_\alpha^\beta d\theta \int_a^b f(r,\theta)r\, dr = \int_a^b dr \int_\alpha^\beta f(r,\theta)r\, d\theta.$$

Note that the integrand in each repeated integral is not just $f(r,\theta)$, but r times $f(r,\theta)$.

The double integral of a continuous function f of two variables can be defined over regions of the polar coordinate plane other than the ones described above. If, for example, the region S is bounded by the graphs of the curves $r = g_1(\theta)$ and $r = g_2(\theta)$, and the lines $\theta = \alpha$ and $\theta = \beta$ (Figure 20.11), where g_1' and g_2' are continuous functions and $g_1(\theta) \le g_2(\theta)$ in $[\alpha,\beta]$, then it may be shown that the double integral of f over S exists and equals a repeated integral as follows:

20.5 $$\iint_S f(r,\theta)\, dS = \int_\alpha^\beta d\theta \int_{g_1(\theta)}^{g_2(\theta)} f(r,\theta)r\, dr.$$

If the region S is bounded by the curves $\theta = h_1(r)$ and $\theta = h_2(r)$, and the circles $r = a$ and $r = b$ as in Figure 20.12, where the functions h_1' and h_2' are continuous and $h_1(r) \le h_2(r)$ in $[a,b]$, then

20.6 $$\iint_S f(r,\theta)\, dS = \int_a^b dr \int_{h_1(r)}^{h_2(r)} f(r,\theta)r\, d\theta.$$

We may figure out which of the above evaluations of a double integral

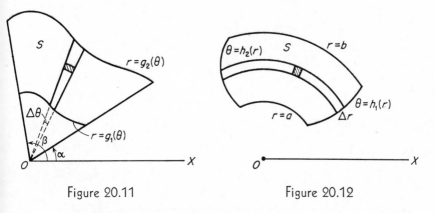

Figure 20.11   Figure 20.12

of f over a region S to use by a device similar to that used for a rectangular coordinate plane. Thus, if we can cut S into strips by lines drawn through the pole, then

$$\Delta\theta \int_{g_1(\theta)}^{g_2(\theta)} f(r,\theta)r\, dr$$

is approximately equal to the double integral of f over the strip at θ (shown in Figure 20.11), where $g_1(\theta)$ and $g_2(\theta)$ are the values of r at each end of the strip. On summing up the double integrals over all the strips and taking a limit, we obtain 20.5.

If the region S can be cut into strips by circles with centers at the pole, as in Figure 20.12, then the double integral of f over S will be evaluated by 20.6 above. In many examples, either of 20.5 or 20.6 may be used.

The double integral of a function f over a region S of a polar coordinate plane may be interpreted as a volume of a solid in a cylindrical coordinate space. Thus it may be shown that the volume of the solid under the surface

$$z = f(r,\theta)$$

and above the region S of the polar coordinate plane is given by

$$V = \iint_S f(r,\theta) \, dS.$$

Example 1.   Find the volume of the solid under the surface $z = 4 - r^2$ and above the region S bounded by the circle $r = 1$.

Solution: The surface $z = 4 - r^2$ is a paraboloid of revolution about the z-axis, so that the solid is a circular cylinder with a parabolic top. Its volume is given by

$$V = \iint_S (4 - r^2) \, dS$$

$$= \int_0^1 dr \int_0^{2\pi} (4 - r^2) r \, d\theta$$

$$= 2\pi \int_0^1 (4r - r^3) \, dr = \frac{7}{2} \pi.$$

Example 2.   Find the volume of the solid bounded by the cylinder $r = 2 \cos \theta$, the cone $z = r$, $r \geq 0$, and the plane $z = 0$.

Solution: The solid in question is under the surface $z = r$, $r \geq 0$, and above the circular region S bounded by $r = 2 \cos \theta$. If we imagine the region S cut into strips by lines through the pole, then we may evaluate the volume of this solid as follows:

$$V = \iint_S r \, dS = \int_{-\pi/2}^{\pi/2} d\theta \int_0^{2 \cos \theta} r^2 \, dr = \frac{8}{3} \int_{-\pi/2}^{\pi/2} \cos^3 \theta \, d\theta = \frac{32}{9}.$$

■ ■ ■ EXERCISES

Find the volume of the solid bounded by the following surfaces.

1. The cylinder $r = 2$ and the sphere $z^2 + r^2 = 9$.
2. The cylinder $r = 2 \sin \theta$, the paraboloid $z = 4 - r^2$, and the plane $z = 0$.
3. The ellipsoid $z^2 + 4r^2 = 4$.
4. The ellipsoid $z^2 + 4r^2 = 4$ and the cylinder $r = \cos \theta$.
5. The cone $z = 2r$, $r \geq 0$, the cylinder $r = 1 - \cos \theta$, and the plane $z = 0$.
6. The cylinder $r = 1 + \cos \theta$, and the planes $z = r \cos \theta$ and $z = 0$, in the first octant.

5. *Center of gravity of a lamina*

Single integrals were used in Chapter 13 to find the center of gravity of a homogeneous lamina. We shall employ double integrals in the present section to find the center of gravity of any lamina, whether or not it is homogeneous.

Let a given lamina have the shape of region S in a rectangular coordinate plane, and let ρ be the weight density function of the lamina. Thus ρ is a continuous function of two variables in S, and the weight of any piece of the lamina of area ΔS lies between $\rho_m \, \Delta S$ and $\rho_M \, \Delta S$, where ρ_m is the minimum value and ρ_M is the maximum value of ρ in the piece. It is clear by the usual arguments that the weight W of the lamina is given by

$$W = \iint_S \rho(x,y) \, dS.$$

The moment of a piece of the lamina about the x-axis is between $y_m \rho_m \, \Delta S$ and $y_M \rho_M \, \Delta S$, where y_m is the minimum and y_M is the maximum y-coordinate of any point in the piece, and ρ and ΔS are as described above. Hence the moment about the x-axis of the whole lamina is given by

$$M_x = \iint_S y\rho(x,y) \, dS,$$

and, similarly, its moment about the y-axis is

$$M_y = \iint_S x\rho(x,y) \, dS.$$

The center of gravity of the lamina is the point $(\bar{x},\bar{y})$, where

$$\bar{x} = \frac{M_y}{W}, \qquad \bar{y} = \frac{M_x}{W}.$$

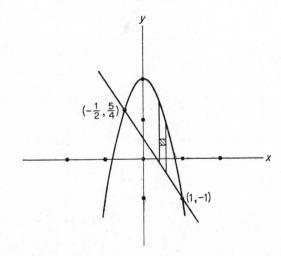

Figure 20.13

Each of the double integrals above may be evaluated by a repeated integral. We illustrate the method in the following examples.

Example 1. Find the center of gravity of a homogeneous lamina (of constant density ρ) having the shape of the region bounded by the parabola $y = 2 - 3x^2$ and the line $3x + 2y - 1 = 0$ (Figure 20.13).

Solution: It is easily verified that the parabola and the line meet at the points $(-\frac{1}{2}, \frac{5}{4})$ and $(1, -1)$. Integrating first with respect to y, we have

$$W = \int_{-1/2}^{1} dx \int_{(1-3x)/2}^{2-3x^2} \rho \, dy = \rho \int_{-1/2}^{1} \left[2 - 3x^2 - \frac{1}{2}(1 - 3x) \right] dx = \frac{27}{16} \rho,$$

$$M_x = \int_{-1/2}^{1} dx \int_{(1-3x)/2}^{2-3x^2} \rho y \, dy = \frac{\rho}{2} \int_{-1/2}^{1} \left[(2 - 3x^2)^2 - \frac{1}{4}(1 - 3x)^2 \right] dx = \frac{27}{20} \rho,$$

$$M_y = \int_{-1/2}^{1} dx \int_{(1-3x)/2}^{2-3x^2} \rho x \, dy = \rho \int_{-1/2}^{1} \left[2x - 3x^3 - \frac{1}{2}(x - 3x^2) \right] dx = \frac{27}{64} \rho.$$

Hence $\bar{x} = M_y/W = \frac{1}{4}$, $\bar{y} = M_x/W = \frac{4}{5}$, and the center of gravity of the lamina is the point $(\frac{1}{4}, \frac{4}{5})$.

Example 2. Find the center of gravity of a rectangular lamina $ABCD$ if the density of the lamina at any point P is the product of the distances of P from AB and BC.

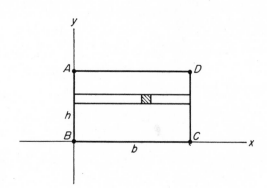

Figure 20.14

Solution: Let us choose coordinate axes as in Figure 20.14. By assumption, the density $\rho(x,y)$ at point (x,y) is given by

$$\rho(x,y) = xy.$$

Hence

$$W = \int_0^h dy \int_0^b xy \, dx = \frac{b^2}{2} \int_0^h y \, dy = \frac{b^2 h^2}{4},$$

$$M_x = \int_0^h dy \int_0^b xy^2 \, dx = \frac{b^2}{2} \int_0^h y^2 \, dy = \frac{b^2 h^3}{6},$$

$$M_y = \int_0^h dy \int_0^b x^2 y \, dx = \frac{b^3}{3} \int_0^h y \, dy = \frac{b^3 h^2}{6}.$$

Hence $(\bar{x}, \bar{y}) = (\frac{2}{3}b, \frac{2}{3}h)$ is the center of gravity.

The formulas for W, M_x, and M_y hold for a polar coordinate system, M_x being the moment of the lamina about the polar axis and M_y being the moment of the lamina about the line perpendicular to the polar axis at the pole. Thus, for a lamina having the shape of a region S of the polar coordinate plane and density function ρ,

$$W = \iint_S \rho(r,\theta) \, dS, \quad M_x = \iint_S \rho(r,\theta) r \sin \theta \, dS, \quad M_y = \iint_S \rho(r,\theta) r \cos \theta \, dS.$$

These integrals are equal to certain repeated integrals as shown in the previous section.

Example 3. Find the center of gravity of a semicircular lamina if the density of the lamina at any point P is proportional to the distance between P and the center of the circle.

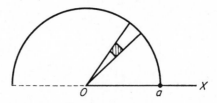

Figure 20.15

Solution: Let us choose a polar coordinate system as in Figure 20.15, with the semicircle having equation

$$r = a, \quad 0 \leq \theta \leq \pi.$$

The density $\rho(r,\theta)$ at point (r,θ) is given by

$$\rho(r,\theta) = kr$$

for some constant k. Hence (by 20.5)

$$W = \int_0^\pi d\theta \int_0^a (kr) r \, dr = \frac{ka^3}{3} \int_0^\pi d\theta = \frac{\pi ka^3}{3},$$

$$M_x = \int_0^\pi d\theta \int_0^a (kr)(r \sin \theta) r \, dr = \frac{ka^4}{4} \int_0^\pi \sin \theta \, d\theta = \frac{ka^4}{2},$$

$$M_y = \int_0^\pi d\theta \int_0^a (kr)(r \cos \theta) r \, dr = \frac{ka^4}{4} \int_0^\pi \cos \theta \, d\theta = 0,$$

and $\left(0, \dfrac{3a}{2\pi}\right)$ in rectangular coordinates, or $\left(\dfrac{3a}{2\pi}, \dfrac{\pi}{2}\right)$ in polar coordinates, is the center of gravity.

■ ■ ■ EXERCISES

Find the center of gravity of a lamina having density function ρ and the shape of a region bounded by the following curves. Sketch each region.

1. $y = \sqrt{x}, y = 0, x = 4$; ρ a positive constant.

2. $y = \sqrt{x}$, $y = 0$, $x = 4$; $\rho(x,y) = x + y$.

3. $y = 0$, $y = h$, $x = 0$, $x = b$; $\rho(x,y) = kx$, h, b, k, positive constants.

4. $y = \ln x$, $y = 0$, $x = e$; $\rho(x,y) = y$.

5. $r = a$, $\theta = 0$, $\theta = \dfrac{\pi}{2}$; $\rho(r,\theta) = \theta$, a a positive constant.

6. $r = 1 + \cos \theta$, $\theta = 0$, $\theta = \dfrac{\pi}{2}$; $\rho(r,\theta) = r \sin \theta$.

7. $x^2 - y^2 = 1$, $x = 3$; $\rho(x,y) = x$.

8. $y = \sin x$, $y = 0$, $x = 0$, $x = \pi$; $\rho(x,y) = ky$, k a positive constant.

9. $r = \cos 2\theta$, $\theta = -\dfrac{\pi}{4}$, $\theta = \dfrac{\pi}{4}$; $\rho(r,\theta) = r$.

10. $r = \cos 2\theta$, $\theta = 0$, $\theta = \dfrac{\pi}{4}$; $\rho(r,\theta) = r\theta$.

11. The density at a point P of a triangular lamina with base of length b and altitude h is proportional to the distance of P from the base. Find the distance from the base to the center of gravity of the lamina.

12. A lamina has the shape of the region cut off from a parabola by its latus rectum. If the density at point P of the lamina is proportional to the distance of P from the latus rectum, find the center of gravity of the lamina.

13. The density of a semicircular lamina at any point P is proportional to the square of the distance of P from the center of the circle. Find the center of gravity of the lamina.

14. The density of a lamina in the shape of a quarter of an ellipse (bounded by the semimajor and semiminor axes) at any point P equals the sum of its distances from the axes. Find the center of gravity of the lamina.

6. Moments of inertia

If a particle of mass m is d units from a line L (Figure 20.16), then the number md^2 is called the *moment of inertia* of the particle about L. The moment of a particle studied in the preceding section is frequently called the *first moment*, and the moment of inertia the *second moment*, of the particle about L.

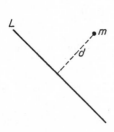

A system of n particles of masses $m_1, m_2, \cdots,$ m_n and at distances $d_1, d_2, \cdots, d_n$ units, respectively, from a line L has a moment of inertia I defined as the sum of the moments of the individual particles:

Figure 20.16

$$I = \sum_{i=1}^{n} m_i d_i^2.$$

It is clear that by our usual limiting process, the moment of inertia of a lamina having the shape of a plane region S and mass density function ρ can be found about any line L. In particular, it is clear that the moments of inertia I_x and I_y of the lamina about the x- and y-axes, respectively, are given by

$$I_x = \iint_S \rho(x,y)y^2 \, dS, \qquad I_y = \iint_S \rho(x,y)x^2 \, dS.$$

Example 1. Find I_x and I_y for the homogeneous lamina having the shape of the region S bounded by the curve $y = \sqrt{x}$, and the lines $y = 0$ and $x = 4$ (Figure 20.17).

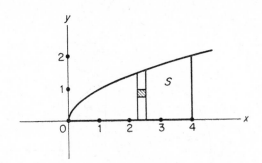

Figure 20.17

Solution: Since ρ is a constant by assumption, we have

$$I_x = \iint_S \rho y^2 \, dS = \int_0^4 dx \int_0^{\sqrt{x}} \rho y^2 \, dy = \frac{\rho}{3} \int_0^4 x^{3/2} \, dx = \frac{64}{15} \rho,$$

$$I_y = \iint_S \rho x^2 \, dS = \int_0^4 dx \int_0^{\sqrt{x}} \rho x^2 \, dy = \rho \int_0^4 x^{5/2} \, dx = \frac{256}{7} \rho.$$

The physical meaning of the moment of inertia is to be found in the study of the *kinetic energy* of a moving particle. A particle of mass m moving at a speed v has kinetic energy

$$K = \frac{1}{2} mv^2.$$

If a particle of mass m at a distance of d units from a line L is rotating about L with an angular velocity of ω radians per unit of time, then $|\omega d|$ is the speed of the particle and

$$K = \frac{1}{2} m(\omega d)^2 = \frac{1}{2} I\omega^2$$

is its kinetic energy, where I is the moment of inertia of the particle. Noting the similarity between $\frac{1}{2}I\omega^2$ and $\frac{1}{2}mv^2$, we can say that I is the "rotational mass" of the particle. Similarly, if I is the moment of inertia of a system of particles about L, $\frac{1}{2}I\omega^2$ is again the kinetic energy of the system when rotated about L with an angular velocity of ω.

A lamina (or system of particles) of total mass m and moment of inertia I about a line L has *radius of gyration* d defined by the equation

$$I = md^2.$$

Accordingly, a particle of mass m located d units from L has the same moment of inertia as the given lamina; that is, the mass of the lamina may be considered to be concentrated at a point d units from L in computing the moment of inertia of the lamina.

Example 2.   Find the radius of gyration about its diameter of a semicircular lamina, if the density of the lamina at a point is proportional to the distance of the point from the diameter.

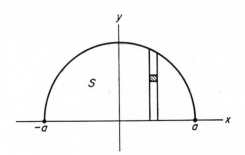

Figure 20.18

Solution: If we select the coordinate axes as in Figure 20.18, the density of the lamina at point (x,y) is given by $\rho(x,y) = ky$, k a positive constant.   Evidently

$$I_x = \iint_S ky^3 \, dS = \int_{-a}^{a} dx \int_{0}^{\sqrt{a^2 - x^2}} ky^3 \, dy = \frac{k}{4} \int_{-a}^{a} (a^2 - x^2)^2 \, dx = \frac{4}{15} ka^5.$$

The mass M of the lamina is given by

$$M = \iint_S ky \, dS = \int_{-a}^{a} dx \int_{0}^{\sqrt{a^2 - x^2}} ky \, dy = \frac{k}{2} \int_{-a}^{a} (a^2 - x^2) \, dx = \frac{2}{3} ka^3.$$

Hence the radius of gyration d of the lamina satisfies the equation

$$\frac{4}{15} ka^5 = \left(\frac{2}{3} ka^3\right) d^2,$$

from which we conclude that $d = (\sqrt{10}/5)a \doteq .63a$.

If a lamina has the shape of a region S of the polar coordinate plane, then its moment of inertia about the polar axis is given by

$$I_x = \iint_S \rho(r,\theta) r^2 \sin^2 \theta \, dS,$$

where ρ is the mass density function of the lamina, and its moment of inertia about the axis perpendicular to the polar axis at the pole (the "y-axis") is given by

$$I_y = \iint_S \rho(r,\theta) r^2 \cos^2 \theta \, dS.$$

Since the distance of a point (x,y) in the xy-plane from the z-axis is $\sqrt{x^2 + y^2}$, the moment of inertia of a particle of mass m at (x,y) about the x-axis is $m(x^2 + y^2)$. Similarly, a lamina having the shape of a region S of the xy-plane and density function ρ will have

$$I_z = \iint_S \rho(x,y)(x^2 + y^2) \, dS$$

as its moment of inertia about the z-axis. Clearly

$$I_z = I_x + I_y.$$

If the region S is in the polar coordinate plane of a cylindrical coordinate system, then

$$I_z = \iint_S \rho(r,\theta) r^2 \, dS.$$

Example 3. Find I_z for the lamina of Example 2.

Solution: We are assuming that the z-axis is perpendicular to the plane of the semicircle at the origin. In polar coordinates, the semicircle has equation $r = a, 0 \le \theta \le \pi$, and $\rho = kr \sin \theta$. Hence

$$I_z = \iint_S (kr \sin \theta) \, r^2 \, dS = k \int_0^\pi d\theta \int_0^a r^4 \sin \theta \, dr = \frac{2}{5} ka^5.$$

Example 4. Find the radius of gyration d of a homogeneous lamina in the shape of a right triangle about an axis perpendicular to the plane of the triangle at the vertex of the right angle.

Solution: If the coordinate axes are chosen as in Figure 20.19, the hypotenuse has equation

$$y = -\frac{a}{b} x + a$$

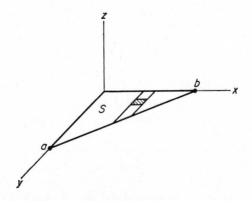

Figure 20.19

in the xy-plane.   Hence (with ρ the constant density)

$$I_z = \rho \iint_S (x^2 + y^2)\, dS = \rho \int_0^b dx \int_0^{-ax/b+a} (x^2 + y^2)\, dy$$

$$= \rho \int_0^b \left[x^2 \left(-\frac{a}{b}x + a \right) + \frac{1}{3}\left(-\frac{a}{b}x + a \right)^3 \right] dx = \frac{1}{12}\,\rho ab(a^2 + b^2).$$

The mass of the lamina is $\rho ab/2$, and therefore

$$\frac{1}{12}\,\rho ab(a^2 + b^2) = \frac{1}{2}\,\rho ab\, d^2,$$

and $d = \sqrt{a^2 + b^2}/\sqrt{6}$.

■ ■ ■ EXERCISES

A rectangular lamina $ABCD$ has density function ρ.   Find the radius of gyration of the lamina about:

1. AB if ρ is a constant.

2. AB if the density at a point P is the sum of the distances of P from AB and BC.

3. The line perpendicular to the lamina at B if ρ is a constant.

4. The line perpendicular to the lamina at B if the density at a point P is the sum of the distances of P from AB and BC.

5. The line perpendicular to the lamina at its center of gravity if ρ is a constant.

6. The line perpendicular to the lamina at its geometric center O if the density at a point P is proportional to the distance $|OP|$.

A circular lamina with center O and radius a has density function ρ.   Find the radius of gyration of the lamina about:

7. A diameter if ρ is a constant.

8. A line perpendicular to the lamina at O if ρ is a constant.

9. A tangent line if ρ is a constant.

10. A diameter if the density at P is proportional to the distance of point P from the diameter.

11. A line perpendicular to the lamina at O if the density at P is proportional to the distance of point P from O.

12. A tangent line if the density at P is proportional to the distance of P from the point of tangency.

13. A lamina has the shape of a triangle with sides of lengths a, b, and c. Assuming ρ is a constant, find the moment of inertia of the lamina about the side of length c.

14. Find the moment of inertia of the preceding exercise in case the density at point P is proportional to the distance of P from the side of length c.

15. A homogeneous lamina is bounded by one loop of the curve $r^2 = \cos 2\theta$ in the polar plane.   Find its radius of gyration about an axis perpendicular to the polar plane at the pole.

16. A homogeneous lamina is bounded by the curve $r = 1 + \cos \theta$ in the polar plane. Find the radius of gyration of the lamina about an axis perpendicular to the polar plane at the pole.

7. *Triple integrals*

A region R of rectangular coordinate space bounded by the planes $x = a_1$, $x = a_2$, $y = b_1$, $y = b_2$, $z = c_1$, and $z = c_2$ will again be called a *rectangular region*. Clearly R is a rectangular parallelopiped with edges parallel to the coordinate axes. If f is a continuous function of three variables in R, then we shall define in this section the triple integral of f over R.

Let $p = [x_0, x_1, \cdots, x_n; y_0, y_1, \cdots, y_m; z_0, z_1, \cdots, z_s]$ be a partition of R into mns subregions, and let R_{ijk} designate the i,j,kth subregion of p, bounded by the planes $x = x_{i-1}$, $x = x_i$, $y = y_{j-1}$, $y = y_j$, $z = z_{k-1}$, and $z = z_k$. The volume of R_{ijk} is designated by ΔR_{ijk}, and equals

$$\Delta R_{ijk} = \Delta x_i \, \Delta y_j \, \Delta z_k,$$

where $\Delta x_i = x_i - x_{i-1}$, and so on.

It may be shown as in Section 11 of the previous chapter that a continuous function f of three variables assumes a minimum value m_{ijk} and a maximum value M_{ijk} in each subregion R_{ijk} of p. The lower sum L_p of f relative to the partition p of R is a sum of mns terms, one associated with each subregion of p, as follows:

$$L_p = \sum_{i=1}^{n} \sum_{j=1}^{m} \sum_{k=1}^{s} m_{ijk} \, \Delta R_{ijk}.$$

The upper sum U_p is defined similarly, with each m_{ijk} of L_p replaced by M_{ijk}.

By arguments entirely analogous to those of Section 1 for double integrals, it may be shown that the least upper bound of the set of all lower sums L_p equals the greatest lower bound of the set of all upper sums U_p. Their common value is called the *triple integral* of f over R, and is designated by

$$\iiint_R f(x,y,z) \, dR.$$

A sum of the form

$$S_p = \sum_{i=1}^{n} \sum_{j=1}^{m} \sum_{k=1}^{s} f(x_i', y_j', z_k') \, \Delta x_i \, \Delta y_j \, \Delta z_k,$$

where (x_i', y_j', z_k') is a point in R_{ijk}, is called a *Riemann sum* of f over R. If $p_1, p_2, \cdots, p_n, \cdots$ is a sequence of partitions of p for which

$$\lim_{n \to \infty} |p_n| = 0,$$

where the norm of p_n, $|p_n|$, is defined as expected, and if $S_1, S_2, \cdots, S_n, \cdots$

is any associated sequence of Riemann sums of f, then it may be shown that

$$\lim_{n \to \infty} S_n = \iiint_R f(x,y,z)\ dR.$$

By analogous arguments to those used in the proof of 20.3, the triple integral may be expressed in terms of a repeated integral. Thus if f is a continuous function of three variables in a region R bounded by the planes $x = a_1$, $x = a_2$, $y = b_1$, $y = b_2$, $z = c_1$, and $z = c_2$,

$$\iiint_R f(x,y,z)\ dR = \int_{a_1}^{a_2} dx \int_{b_1}^{b_2} dy \int_{c_1}^{c_2} f(x,y,z)\ dz.$$

In all, there are six possible repeated integrals equal to the triple integral of f over R corresponding to the six permutations of the three single integrals.

Example 1. If $f(x,y,z) = 3(x^2 y + y^2 z)$, find the triple integral of f over the rectangular region R bounded by the planes $x = 1$, $x = 3$, $y = -1$, $y = 1$, $z = 2$, and $z = 4$.

Solution: We have

$$\iiint_R 3(x^2 y + y^2 z)\ dR = \int_2^4 dz \int_{-1}^1 dy \int_1^3 3(x^2 y + y^2 z)\ dx$$

$$= \int_2^4 dz \int_{-1}^1 (x^3 y + 3xy^2 z)\ \Big|_{x=1}^{x=3} dy$$

$$= \int_2^4 dz \int_{-1}^1 (26y + 6y^2 z)\ dy = \int_2^4 (13y^2 + 2y^3 z)\ \Big|_{y=-1}^{y=1} dz$$

$$= \int_2^4 4z\ dz = 24.$$

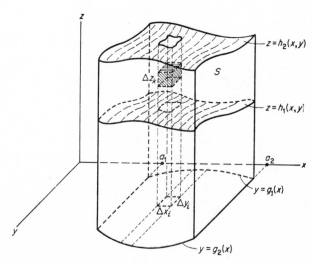

Figure 20.20

We could equally well have started with

$$\iiint_R 3(x^2y + y^2z)\, dR = \int_{-1}^{1} dy \int_{2}^{4} dz \int_{1}^{3} 3(x^2y + y^2z)\, dx,$$

or any other one of the six possible threefold repeated integrals.

The triple integral of a continuous function f of three variables may be defined over a region of space other than a rectangular parallelopiped. For example, it can be defined over the region S of Figure 20.20, a region bounded below by the surface $z = h_1(x,y)$, above by $z = h_2(x,y)$, and laterally by the cylinders $y = g_1(x)$ and $y = g_2(x)$, and the planes $x = a_1$ and $x = a_2$, where the functions involved have continuous derivatives. It may be shown that

$$\iiint_S f(x,y,z)\, dS = \int_{a_1}^{a_2} dx \int_{g_1(x)}^{g_2(x)} dy \int_{h_1(x,y)}^{h_2(x,y)} f(x,y,z)\, dz.$$

The region S might be oriented differently with respect to the axes, in which case the repeated integral might have to be taken in a different order. If $f(x,y,z) = 1$ throughout the region S, then the triple integral of f over S is just the volume V of the region S:

$$V = \iiint_S dS.$$

Example 2. Find the volume of the solid bounded above by the paraboloid $z = 4 - x^2 - y^2$ and below by the plane $z = 4 - 2x$.

Solution: The solid is sketched in Figure 20.21. If we eliminate z between the two given equations, we obtain $4 - 2x = 4 - x^2 - y^2$, or

$$y^2 = 2x - x^2$$

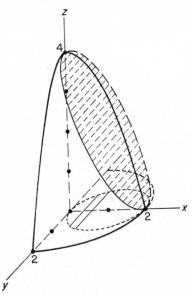

Figure 20.21

as the equation of a cylinder containing the curve of intersection of the given paraboloid and plane. Thus $y = -\sqrt{2x - x^2}$ and $y = \sqrt{2x - x^2}$ are the y-limits of integration, and the volume of the solid is given by

$$
\begin{aligned}
V &= \int_0^2 dx \int_{-\sqrt{2x-x^2}}^{\sqrt{2x-x^2}} dy \int_{4-2x}^{4-x^2-y^2} dz \\
&= \int_0^2 dx \int_{-\sqrt{2x-x^2}}^{\sqrt{2x-x^2}} [(4 - x^2 - y^2) - (4 - 2x)] \, dy \\
&= \int_0^2 \left(-x^2 y - \frac{1}{3} y^3 + 2xy \right) \Big|_{y=-\sqrt{2x-x^2}}^{y=\sqrt{2x-x^2}} dx \\
&= \frac{4}{3} \int_0^2 (2x - x^2)^{3/2} \, dx = \frac{\pi}{2}.
\end{aligned}
$$

■ ■ ■ EXERCISES

Find the volume of each of the following regions of space, and also find the value of the triple integral of the given function f over this region. Sketch each region.

1. Region S bounded by the planes $x = -1$, $x = 2$, $y = 0$, $y = 3$, $z = 1$, and $z = 4$: $f(x,y,z) = x - 2y + z$.

2. Region S bounded by the planes $x = 0$, $x = 1$, $y = -1$, $y = 2$, $z = 0$, and $z = 5$: $f(x,y,z) = 3xyz$.

3. Region S bounded by the cylinder $x^2 + y^2 = 16$ and the planes $z = 0$ and $z = 3$: $f(x,y,z) = xz + yz$.

4. Region S bounded by the cylinder $y^2 + z^2 = 9$ and the planes $x = 0$ and $x + z = 3$: $f(x,y,z) = 3y + yz$.

5. Region S bounded by the cylinders $x^2 = z$ and $x^2 = 4 - z$, and the planes $y = 0$ and $z + 2y = 4$: $f(x,y,z) = 2x - z$.

6. Region S bounded by the cylinder $x = \sqrt{4 + y^2}$ and the planes $z = 0$ and $x + 2z = 4$: $f(x,y,z) = xy$.

7. Region S bounded by the surface $z = \dfrac{y}{1 + x^2}$ and the planes $x = 0$, $y = 0$, $z = 0$, and $x + y = 1$: $f(x,y,z) = y + x^2 y$.

8. Region S bounded by the surface $y^2 + z^2 = 2x$ and the plane $x + y = 1$: $f(x,y,z) = 3z$.

9. Region S in the first octant bounded by the cylinders $x^2 + y^2 = a^2$ and $y^2 + z^2 = a^2$: $f(x,y,z) = xyz$.

10. Region S bounded by the ellipsoid $x^2/a^2 + y^2/b^2 + z^2/c^2 = 1$: $f(x,y,z) = xz$.

8. Physical applications of triple integrals

If a material object has the shape of a region S of space and has a constant density ρ, then the weight W of the object is given by

$$
W = \iiint_S \rho \, dS.
$$

It could be argued that W is the weight of the object even if ρ is variable, but we shall not consider such a possibility here.

A particle of weight w located at the point (x,y,z) has moments wx, wy, and wz with respect to the yz-, xz-, and xy-planes, respectively. Using familiar arguments, the moments with respect to the coordinate planes of a homogeneous material object of density ρ and having the shape of a region S of space are given by

$$M_{xy} = \iiint_S \rho z \, dS, \quad M_{xz} = \iiint_S \rho y \, dS, \quad M_{yz} = \iiint_S \rho x \, dS.$$

The center of gravity of the object is the point $(\bar{x}, \bar{y}, \bar{z})$, where

$$\bar{x} = \frac{M_{yz}}{W}, \quad \bar{y} = \frac{M_{xz}}{W}, \quad \bar{z} = \frac{M_{xy}}{W}.$$

Example 1. Find the center of gravity of a homogeneous material object bounded by the coordinate planes, the plane $x + y = 1$, and the paraboloid

$$z = 4 - x^2 - 4y^2.$$

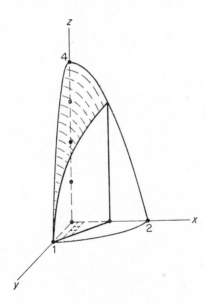

Figure 20.22

Solution: The object is sketched in Figure 20.22. Evidently

$$W = \int_0^1 dx \int_0^{1-x} dy \int_0^{4-x^2-4y^2} \rho \, dz,$$

and we easily show that

$$W = \frac{19}{12} \rho.$$

Also,

$$M_{xy} = \int_0^1 dx \int_0^{1-x} dy \int_0^{4-x^2-4y^2} \rho z \, dz,$$

which may be evaluated to yield

$$M_{xy} = \frac{95}{36} \rho.$$

Similarly,

$$M_{xz} = \int_0^1 dx \int_0^{1-x} dy \int_0^{4-x^2-4y^2} \rho y \, dz = \frac{9}{20} \rho,$$

$$M_{yz} = \int_0^1 dx \int_0^{1-x} dy \int_0^{4-x^2-4y^2} \rho x \, dz = \frac{11}{20} \rho.$$

Thus $(\frac{33}{95}, \frac{27}{95}, \frac{5}{3})$ is the center of gravity of the object.

We may use triple integrals to find the moment of inertia of a material object about some line. Since a particle of mass m located at the point (x,y,z) in space has $m(y^2 + z^2)$ as its moment of inertia about the x-axis, it seems reasonable that the moment of inertia about the x-axis of a material object of constant mass density ρ having the shape of region S of space is given by

$$I_x = \iiint_S \rho(y^2 + z^2) \, dS.$$

Similarly,

$$I_y = \iiint_S \rho(x^2 + z^2) \, dS, \qquad I_z = \iiint_S \rho(x^2 + y^2) \, dS.$$

Example 2. Find the moment of inertia and radius of gyration about the z-axis of the homogeneous solid of density ρ bounded by the coordinate planes and the plane

$$\frac{x}{a} + \frac{y}{b} + \frac{z}{c} = 1, \qquad a, b, c \text{ positive.}$$

Solution: The solid is a tetrahedron as sketched in Figure 20.23. Since the trace of the given plane in the xy-plane has equation

$$y = b - \frac{b}{a} x,$$

we have

$$I_z = \int_0^a dx \int_0^{b-bx/a} dy \int_0^{c-cx/a-cy/b} \rho(x^2 + y^2) \, dz$$

$$= \rho c \int_0^a dx \int_0^{b-bx/a} (x^2 + y^2)\left(1 - \frac{1}{a}x - \frac{1}{b}y\right) dy$$

$$= \rho bc \int_0^a \left[\frac{1}{2} x^2 - \frac{1}{a} x^3 + \frac{1}{2a^2} x^4 + \frac{b^2}{12}\left(1 - \frac{1}{a}x\right)^4\right] dx$$

$$= \frac{\rho abc}{60} (a^2 + b^2).$$

The volume of the given solid is $abc/6$, and therefore its mass is $\rho abc/6$. Hence

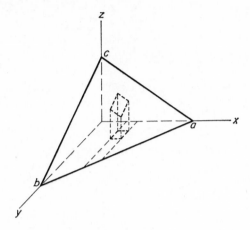

Figure 20.23

the radius r of gyration is given by

$$\frac{\rho abc}{60}(a^2 + b^2) = \frac{\rho abc}{6}r^2.$$

and $r = \sqrt{a^2 + b^2}/\sqrt{10}$.

■ ■ ■ EXERCISES

Find the center of gravity of the homogeneous solid having the shape of:

1. The tetrahedron with vertices $(0,0,0)$, $(a,0,0)$, $(0,b,0)$, $(0,0,c)$.
2. An octant of a sphere, bounded by the coordinate axes and the sphere $x^2 + y^2 + z^2 = a^2$ in the first octant. (*Hint*: $\bar{x} = \bar{y} = \bar{z}$ by symmetry.)
3. The region bounded by the xy-plane and the paraboloid $z = 1 - \dfrac{x^2}{a^2} - \dfrac{y^2}{b^2}$.
4. The region in the first octant bounded by the cylinder $x = y^2$ and the planes $x = 4$, $z = 0$, and $z = 2$.
5. Region S of Exercise 4, p. 598.
6. Region S of Exercise 5, p. 598.
7. Region S of Exercise 6, p. 598.
8. Region S of Exercise 8, p. 598.
9. Region S of Exercise 9, p. 598.
10. An octant of the ellipsoid $x^2/a^2 + y^2/b^2 + z^2/c^2 = 1$.

Set up an integral for I_z for each of the following homogeneous solids.

11. A hemisphere, z the axis of symmetry.
12. The solid bounded by the plane $z = h$ and the paraboloid $z = x^2/a^2 + y^2/b^2$.
13. The solid bounded by the plane $z = h$ and the paraboloid $z = x^2 + y^2$.

14. A right circular cylinder of radius r and altitude h, z the axis of symmetry.

15. The solid having the shape of region S of Exercise 7 above.

16. The solid having the shape of region S of Exercise 9 above.

17. A rectangular parallelopiped of length a, width b, and height c, the z-axis along an edge of length c. (Compute.)

18. The rectangular parallelopiped of the preceding exercise along a diagonal.

9. Cylindrical and spherical coordinates

Triple integrals may be defined for continuous functions of three variables over regions of a cylindrical or spherical coordinate space much as they are over regions of a rectangular coordinate space. We shall indicate in this section how such triple integrals may be evaluated by repeated integrals.

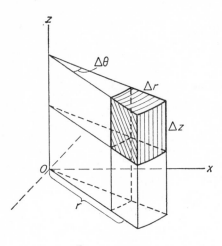

Figure 20.24

A region R of cylindrical coordinate space bounded by the curves $r = a_1$, $r = a_2$, $\theta = b_1$, $\theta = b_2$, $z = c_1$, and $z = c_2$ may be partitioned into subregions of the same type. One such subregion is sketched in Figure 20.24. This subregion is a cylinder having its generator parallel to the z-axis. Hence its volume, ΔR, is the product of the area of its base, $r\,\Delta r\,\Delta\theta$, and its altitude Δz,

$$\Delta R = r\,\Delta r\,\Delta\theta\,\Delta z,$$

where r is the average radius of its base.

If f is a continuous function of three variables over R, then the triple integral of f over R may be defined as usual in terms of the least upper bound of the set of all lower sums of f over partitions of R. Then it may be shown that the triple integral of f over R can be expressed in the form

$$\iiint_R f(r,\theta,z)\,dR = \int_{a_1}^{a_2} dr \int_{b_1}^{b_2} d\theta \int_{c_1}^{c_2} f(r,\theta,z)r\,dz.$$

Again, there are six possible permutations of the single integrals on the right side of the above equation.

The usual modifications of the limits of integration must be made if the triple integral of f is taken over a region S of space not bounded by coordinate surfaces like the region R described above. Centers of gravity and moments of inertia of an object may be found if the formulas of the preceding section are modified in the obvious way.

Example 1. Find the center of gravity and moment of inertia about the z-axis of the homogeneous solid bounded by the cylinder $r = a$, the cone $z = r$, and the plane $z = 0$.

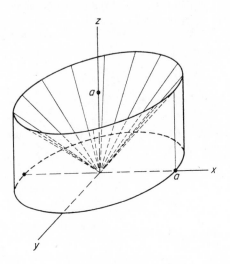

Figure 20.25

Solution: This solid S is a right circular cylinder with a cone hollowed out of it, as sketched in Figure 20.25. If ρ designates its constant density, then its weight is given by

$$W = \rho \left(\pi a^3 - \frac{1}{3} \pi a^3 \right) = \frac{2}{3} \rho \pi a^3.$$

It is clear by symmetry that the center of gravity of the solid is on the z-axis. The moment M_p of the solid with respect to the polar coordinate plane p is given by

$$M_p = \iiint_S \rho z \, dS = \int_0^{2\pi} d\theta \int_0^a dr \int_0^r zr \, dz$$

$$= \frac{\rho}{2} \int_0^{2\pi} d\theta \int_0^a r^3 \, dr = \frac{\rho}{8} \int_0^{2\pi} a^4 \, d\theta = \frac{\rho}{4} \pi a^4.$$

Hence $\bar{z} = M_p/W = 3a/8$, and the point $\left(0, 0, \frac{3a}{8} \right)$ is the center of gravity of the solid.

A particle of mass m located at the point (r, θ, z) is r units from the z-axis. Hence mr^2 is its moment of inertia about the z-axis. Therefore it is clear that the moment of inertia of the solid of Figure 20.25 about the z-axis is given by (ρ is now taken as the mass density)

$$I_z = \iiint_S (r^2) \rho \, dS = \rho \int_0^{2\pi} d\theta \int_0^a dr \int_0^r r^3 \, dz$$

$$= \rho \int_0^{2\pi} d\theta \int_0^a r^4 \, dr = \frac{\rho}{5} \int_0^{2\pi} a^5 \, d\theta = \frac{2}{5} \rho \pi a^5.$$

The basic region of spherical coordinate space is the region R bounded by the spheres $\rho = a_1$ and $\rho = a_2$, the planes $\theta = b_1$ and $\theta = b_2$, and the cones $\phi = c_1$ and $\phi = c_2$. If such a region is partitioned into subregions in the usual way, then one such subregion is sketched in Figure 20.26.

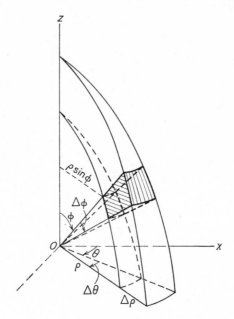

Figure 20.26

The volume ΔR of this subregion may be shown by geometry to be approximately equal to

$$\Delta R = \rho^2 \sin \phi \, \Delta\rho \, \Delta\theta \, \Delta\phi.$$

Although we shall not prove it, we can imagine that the triple integral of a continuous function f over R is given by

$$\iiint_R f(\rho,\theta,\phi) \, dR = \int_{a_1}^{a_2} d\rho \int_{b_1}^{b_2} d\theta \int_{c_1}^{c_2} f(\rho,\theta,\phi)\rho^2 \sin \phi \, d\phi.$$

There are six possible permutations of the single integrals in the above repeated integral.

An application of spherical coordinates to the problem of finding the center of gravity and moment of inertia of a solid is indicated in the following example.

Example 2. Find the volume, center of gravity, and moment of inertia about the axis of symmetry of the solid (of constant density 1) bounded above by the sphere $\rho = a$ and below by the cone $\phi = k$.

Solution: The solid is a cone with a spherical top; a quarter of it is sketched in Figure 20.27. The volume of the solid is given by

$$V = \int_0^{2\pi} d\theta \int_0^k d\phi \int_0^a \rho^2 \sin\phi \, d\rho = \frac{2}{3}\pi a^3(1 - \cos k),$$

and its moment about the polar coordinate plane p by (recalling that $z = \rho \cos\phi$),

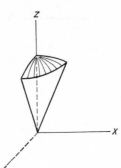

$$M_p = \int_0^{2\pi} d\theta \int_0^k d\phi \int_0^a (\rho\cos\phi)\,\rho^2 \sin\phi \, d\rho$$

$$= \frac{a^4}{4} \int_0^{2\pi} d\theta \int_0^k \sin\phi \cos\phi \, d\phi$$

$$= \frac{a^4}{8} \sin^2 k \int_0^{2\pi} d\theta = \frac{1}{4}\pi a^4 \sin^2 k.$$

By symmetry, the center of gravity is on the vertical z-axis above the pole at a distance of

$$\bar{z} = \frac{M_p}{V} = \frac{3}{8} a(1 + \cos k).$$

Figure 20.27

Thus $(\frac{3}{8}a(1 + \cos k),0,0)$ is the center of gravity of the solid. Note that if $k = \pi/2$, we obtain $(\frac{3}{8}a,0,0)$ as the center of gravity of a hemisphere.

The distance r of a point (ρ,θ,ϕ) from the vertical z-axis is given by $r = \rho \sin\phi$. Hence the moment of inertia about the z-axis of a particle of mass m located at the point (ρ,θ,ϕ) is $m\rho^2\sin^2\phi$. With this in mind, evidently the moment of inertia about the z-axis of the given solid is (assuming a constant density of 1),

$$I_z = \int_0^{2\pi} d\theta \int_0^k d\phi \int_0^a (\rho^2 \sin^2\phi)\,\rho^2 \sin\phi \, d\rho$$

$$= \frac{a^5}{5} \int_0^{2\pi} d\theta \int_0^k \sin^3\phi \, d\phi$$

$$= \frac{2}{15}\pi a^5 (\cos^3 k - 3\cos k + 2).$$

■ ■ ■ EXERCISES

1. Given a right circular cone having radius of base a and altitude h, find:
   (a) Its center of gravity.
   (b) Its moment of inertia about the axis of symmetry.
   (c) Its moment of inertia about a diameter of the base.
2. Given a right circular cylinder of diameter a and altitude h, find:
   (a) Its moment of inertia about the axis of symmetry.
   (b) Its moment of inertia about a generator.
   (c) Its moment of inertia about a diameter of the base.
3. A hemispherical shell has inner radius a and outer radius b. Find:
   (a) Its center of gravity.
   (b) Its moment of inertia about the axis of symmetry.
   (c) Its moment of inertia about a diameter of the base.

4. The cone $\phi = k$ (spherical coordinates) is cut out of the solid hemisphere $\rho = a, 0 \leq \phi \leq \pi/2$.   Find:
   (a) The center of gravity of the solid left.
   (b) Its moment of inertia about the axis of symmetry.
   (c) Its moment of inertia about a diameter of the base.

5. A solid is bounded by the cylinder $r = a \cos \theta$, the paraboloid $z = br^2$, and the plane $z = 0$ (cylindrical coordinates).   Find:
   (a) Its volume.
   (b) Its center of gravity.

21

Differential equations

■ ■ ■ ■ ■ THE THEORY OF differential equations is a large part of
mathematics, and the application of the results of this
theory constitutes a strong tool of science. Parts of the
brief treatment of the subject of this chapter suggest the
character of the general theory. A surprising number of
applications may be made of the limited set of topics
covered.

1. Introduction

If G is a function of $n + 2$ variables, the equation

$$G(x,y,y',y'', \cdots ,y^{[n]}) = 0,$$

where y', y'', $\cdots$, $y^{[n]}$ formally designate the first, second,
$\cdots$, nth derivative of y at x, is called an *ordinary differential equation of order n*. A function f is a *solution* of
this equation if

$$G(x,f(x),f'(x),f''(x), \cdots ,f^{[n]}(x)) = 0$$

for every x in the domain of f.

The separable differential equation

21.1 $$M(x) + N(y)y' = 0$$

studied in Chapter 11 is an example of an ordinary differential equation of order 1.

The equation

$$y'' - 4y = 0$$

607

is an example of an ordinary differential equation of order 2. It is easily verified that the function f defined by $f(x) = e^{2x}$ is a solution of this equation.

In contrast to ordinary differential equations, an equation such as

$$\frac{\partial^2 z}{\partial x^2} = \frac{\partial^2 z}{\partial y^2}$$

is called a *partial differential equation*. A function f of two variables is a solution of this equation if

$$\frac{\partial^2 f}{\partial x^2} = \frac{\partial^2 f}{\partial y^2}.$$

We shall focus our attention in this book on ordinary differential equations of the more elementary types and of order 1 or 2.

If M and N are continuous functions, then it was shown in **11.27** that the separable differential equation **21.1** has solution

21.2 $$\int M(x)\,dx + \int N(y)\,dy = C.$$

That is, every solution f (with continuous derivative) of **21.1** satisfies **21.2** for some constant C, and vice versa.

For example, the differential equation

(1) $$3x^2 + 1 + e^y y' = 0$$

has solution

(2) $$x^3 + x + e^y = C$$

by **21.2**. Thus, each differentiable function f that is a solution of (1) satisfies (2) [with $y = f(x)$] for some constant C, and vice versa. Equation (2) is called an *implicit solution* of (1). We may solve (2) for y, thereby obtaining an explicit solution

$$y = \ln(C - x^3 - x)$$

of (1). The function f defined by $f(x) = \ln(C - x^3 - x)$ is a solution of (1) for every constant C.

Equation (2) is typical of the solution of a differential equation of order 1 in that it contains one arbitrary parameter C. Such a description of the solution of a differential equation in terms of one or more parameters is called the *general solution* of the equation.

For example, the differential equation

(3) $$y'' - 4y = 0$$

may be shown to have the general solution

(4) $$y = C_1 e^{2x} + C_2 e^{-2x}.$$

We note in this example that the differential equation is of order 2 and the general solution has two parameters C_1 and C_2.

On the other hand, the second-order partial differential equation

$$\frac{\partial^2 z}{\partial x^2} = \frac{\partial^2 z}{\partial y^2}$$

has solutions described in terms of two arbitrary *functions* f and g:

$$z = f(x - y) + g(x + y).$$

Example 1. Verify that for any constants C_1 and C_2, Equation (4) above is a solution of (3).

Solution: If y is as given in (4), then

$$y' = 2C_1 e^{2x} - 2C_2 e^{-2x}, \qquad y'' = 4C_1 e^{2x} + 4C_2 e^{-2x},$$

and $y'' = 4y$. Thus (4) is a solution of (3) for any constants C_1 and C_2.

In this example, the solution of the differential equation is given explicitly, so that we might verify it by direct computation of y' and y'' and subsequent substitution of these functions into the given differential equation. If the solution of a differential equation is given implicitly, then the solution may be verified by implicit differentiation as illustrated in the following example.

Example 2. Show that for every constant C,

$$x^2 - 2xy + y^4 = C$$

is a solution of the differential equation

$$x - y + (2y^3 - x)y' = 0.$$

Solution: If f is a differentiable function such that $y = f(x)$ satisfies

$$x^2 - 2xy + y^4 = C$$

for some constant C, then we have by implicit differentiation that

$$2x - 2y + (-2x + 4y^3)y' = 0$$

or

$$x - y + (2y^3 - x)y' = 0.$$

Example 3. Find the general solution of the differential equation

$$\frac{1}{x} + \frac{y'}{y} = 0.$$

Solution: This separable differential equation has the general solution

$$\int \frac{1}{x} \, dx + \int \frac{1}{y} \, dy = C_1,$$

or

(1) $$\ln |x| + \ln |y| = C_1,$$

where C_1 is a parameter. That is to say, a function f is a solution of the given differential equation if and only if $y = f(x)$ is a solution of Equation (1) for some constant C_1. It is evident that the solution (1) may be put in the form $\ln |xy| = C_1$, or

(2) $$|xy| = e^{C_1} = C_2.$$

We can show, moreover, that

(3) $$xy = C$$

(where $C = \pm C_2$) also is a solution for each nonzero C.   Thus

$$y = \frac{C}{x}$$

is an explicit solution of the given equation.

   That (2) implies (3) is a consequence of the following remarks.   If the function G is continuous in an interval $[a,b]$ and if $G(x) \neq 0$ in this interval, then either $G(x) > 0$ or $G(x) < 0$ in $[a,b]$.   Hence either $|G(x)| = G(x)$ or $|G(x)| = -G(x)$ in $[a,b]$.

■ ■ ■ EXERCISES

Verify that if C, C_1, C_2 are any constants, then the given relation between x and y satisfies the corresponding differential equation.

1. $y = Ce^{2x}; y' = 2y.$ **2.** $y = Ce^{x^2}; y' = 2xy.$

3. $y = C_1 + C_2x; y'' = 0.$

4. $y = C_1 \sin x + C_2 \cos x; y'' + y = 0.$

5. $xy + \cos x = C; xy' + y = \sin x.$

6. $y = \dfrac{C + x}{x^2 + 1}; y' = \dfrac{1 - 2xy}{x^2 + 1}.$

7. $y = C_1(x^2 + C_2); y' = y''x.$

8. Show that if f and g are any functions possessing second derivatives and if $z = f(x - y) + g(x + y)$, then $\dfrac{\partial^2 z}{\partial x^2} = \dfrac{\partial^2 z}{\partial y^2}.$

Find the general solution of the following differential equations.

9. $x - yy' = 0.$ **10.** $\sin x - (\sin y)y' = 0.$

11. $\dfrac{dy}{dx} = y/x.$ **12.** $x + y(1 + x^2) D_xy = 0.$

13. $xy' = 2y.$ **14.** $y' = x^{-2}.$

15. $y'' = x^{-1}.$ **16.** $y''' = x.$

2. Families of curves

The differential equation

$$y' = 2$$

has the general solution

$$y = 2x + C.$$

We may interpret this solution as the set, or *family*, of all straight lines in the plane each having slope 2 (Figure 21.1).

Similarly, the equation

$$xy' + y = 0$$

has the general solution

$$xy = C,$$

which may be interpreted as the family of all hyperbolas in the plane, each having the coordinate axes as asymptotes. Note that in these examples, the parameter C of the general solution of a differential equation is the parameter of the family of curves.

It is true, conversely, that a family of curves described with one parameter may often be shown to be the general solution of a first-order differential equation. For example, the equation

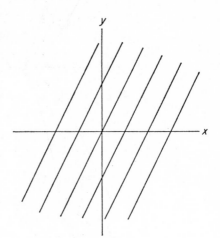

(1) $$y = Cx^2$$

describes the family of parabolas, each of which has its vertex at the origin and axis along the y-axis (Figure 21.2). If we differentiate (1), we obtain

Figure 21.1

(2) $$y' = 2Cx.$$

We may eliminate C between (1) and (2), thereby getting the differential equation

(3) $$xy' = 2y.$$

It is easily shown that (1) is the general solution of (3), so that (3) is completely descriptive of the given family of parabolas.

According to (3), $y' = 2y/x$; that is, at each point (x,y) (other than the origin) on each of the parabolas of the given family, the slope of the tangent line to that parabola is $2y/x$. Therefore this is a property of every member of the family. Equation (2), on the other hand, expresses a property of a particular member of the family.

Example 1. Find a differential equation describing the family of hyperbolas

(1) $$xy = Cx - 1.$$

Solution: We may differentiate (1), obtaining

(2) $$xy' + y = C.$$

On eliminating C between (1) and (2), we get

$$xy = (xy' + y)x - 1,$$

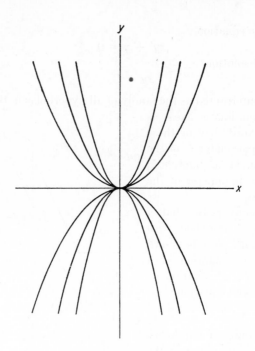

Figure 21.2

or $$x^2 y' = 1,$$

as the differential equation of the family of hyperbolas.

Example 2. Each member of a family of curves has the property that its slope is $-x/y$ at each point (x,y), $y \neq 0$, on the curve. Find an equation describing this family.

Solution: By assumption, the family is described by the differential equation $y' = -x/y$, or

$$x + yy' = 0.$$

This separable differential equation has the solution

$$x^2 + y^2 = C,$$

which is therefore an equation of the given family of curves. Clearly this family consists of all circles in the plane, each with center at the origin.

3. Boundary conditions

It was shown above that the differential equation $x + yy' = 0$ has a family of circles $x^2 + y^2 = C$ as its general solution. There is one and only one circle of this family passing through a given point of the plane. For example, to find the circle passing through the point $(2,1)$, we must determine the value of C such that $2^2 + 1^2 = C$. Clearly $C = 5$, and

$$x^2 + y^2 = 5$$

is the particular circle of the family passing through the point (2,1).

The equation $x^2 + y^2 = 5$ is called a *particular solution* of $x + yy' = 0$ as distinguished from the general solution $x^2 + y^2 = C$. It is the unique solution satisfying the condition $y = 1$ when $x = 2$. Such a condition is called a *boundary condition* of the given differential equation.

A differential equation of order 1 has one parameter in its general solution, and one boundary condition suffices to determine a particular solution. For a differential equation of order 2, two boundary conditions are needed to determine a particular solution (for example, $y = b$ and $y' = c$ when $x = a$). Similar remarks may be made for higher order equations.

Example 1. Determine the member of the family of parabolas $y = Cx^2$ that passes through the point $(10, -3)$.

Solution: On substituting $x = 10$ and $y = -3$ in $y = Cx^2$, we get $-3 = 100C$ and hence $C = -.03$. Thus

$$y = -.03x^2$$

is the parabola desired.

Example 2. Find the particular solution of the differential equation

$$(1 - \tan^2 \theta) + 2r \tan \theta \frac{d\theta}{dr} = 0$$

satisfying the boundary condition $r = 1$ when $\theta = \pi/8$.

Solution: The given differential equation may be put in the form

$$\frac{1}{r} + \frac{2 \tan \theta}{1 - \tan^2 \theta} \frac{d\theta}{dr} = 0,$$

or

$$\frac{1}{r} + \tan 2\theta \frac{d\theta}{dr} = 0.$$

Its general solution is therefore

$$\ln |r| + \frac{1}{2} \ln |\sec 2\theta| = C_1,$$

or

$$r^2 = C \cos 2\theta.$$

If $\theta = \pi/8$ and $r = 1$, we find $C = \sqrt{2}$. Hence

$$r^2 = \sqrt{2} \cos 2\theta$$

is the desired particular solution.

Example 3. Find a function f that is a solution of the differential equation

$$x + e^x + 3y^2y' = 0$$

and is such that $f(0) = 3$.

Solution: We are asked to find an explicit solution $y = f(x)$ of the equation satisfying the boundary condition $y = 3$ when $x = 0$. The given differential equation has the general solution

$$\frac{1}{2} x^2 + e^x + y^3 = C,$$

or

$$y = \sqrt[3]{C - \frac{1}{2} x^2 - e^x}.$$

If $y = 3$ when $x = 0$, then $C = 28$. Hence

$$f(x) = \sqrt[3]{28 - \frac{1}{2} x^2 - e^x}$$

defines the solution for which $f(0) = 3$.

■ ■ ■ EXERCISES

Sketch four different members of each of the following families of curves, and find a differential equation of the family.

1. $y = Cx.$ 2. $y^2 = x - C.$

3. $y = x^2 + C.$ 4. $\dfrac{x^2}{4} + \dfrac{y^2}{9} = C.$

5. $x^2 - y^2 = C.$ 6. $x^2 + (y - C)^2 = 1.$

7. $(x - C)^2 + (y - C)^2 = C^2.$ 8. $\dfrac{x^2}{C^2} + \dfrac{y^2}{9} = 1.$

Solve each of the following differential equations, and sketch that member of the family of solutions passing through the given point.

9. $y' = 2x;\ (-2,0).$ 10. $y' = -3;\ (1,-1).$

11. $xy' + y = 0;\ (-1,3).$ 12. $y' = 2\sqrt{y};\ (2,4).$

13. $yy' + x - 2 = 0;\ (0,0).$ 14. $(y - 1)y' = x;\ (0,1).$

Find the particular solution of each of the following differential equations that satisfies the given boundary condition.

15. $r^2 \dfrac{dr}{d\theta} = \sin \theta;\ r = 1$ when $\theta = \pi/4.$

16. $\dfrac{dz}{du} = \ln u;\ z = 2$ when $u = e.$

17. $yy' = x + 1;\ y = 3$ when $x = 0.$

18. $e^{y-x}y' + x = 0;\ y = 2$ when $x = 2.$

19. Show that $y'' = 0$ is the differential equation of the family of curves $y = C_1 x + C_2.$ Interpret this result geometrically.

20. Show that the particular solution of the differential equation

$$M(x) + N(y)y' = 0$$

satisfying the boundary condition $y = y_0$ when $x = x_0$ is given by

$$\int_{x_0}^{x} M(x)\, dx + \int_{y_0}^{y} N(y)\, dy = 0.$$

Solve Exercises 17 and 18 by this method.

21. If one family of curves has the differential equation $y' = G(x,y)$ and another family of curves has the differential equation $y' = -1/G(x,y)$, then each member of the first family is *orthogonal* to each member of the second family (i.e., they meet at right angles). The second family is called the set of *orthogonal trajectories* of the first family, and vice versa. Show that the two families with equations $y^2 = Cx^3$ and $2x^2 + 3y^2 = K$ are orthogonal trajectories of each other.

Find the orthogonal trajectories of each of the following families of curves. (*Hint:* Find the differential equation of the family, replace y' by $-1/y'$, and then solve the resulting differential equation.)

22. $y = Cx$.   **23.** $xy = Cx - 1$.

24. $y^2 = x^2 + C$.   **25.** $y^2 = Cx$.

26. Show that the family of curves $y^2 = 4C(x + C)$ is self-orthogonal; that is, each two members of the family that meet necessarily meet at right angles.

27. Show that the family of circles $(y - 1)^2 + (x - C)^2 = 1$ has the differential equation $y^2 - 2y + (y - 1)^2(y')^2 = 0$. Show that this differential equation also has the solutions $y = 0$ and $y = 2$. Explain this phenomenon geometrically.

4. Exact differential equations

We shall study in this section methods of solving a large class of differential equations of the first order, among which are the separable differential equations.

21.3 Definition. The differential equation

$$M(x,y) + N(x,y)y' = 0$$

is called *exact* if

$$\frac{\partial M}{\partial y} = \frac{\partial N}{\partial x}.$$

For example,

$$2x - y + (y^2 - x)y' = 0$$

is an exact differential equation, since

$$\frac{\partial}{\partial y}(2x - y) = -1 = \frac{\partial}{\partial x}(y^2 - x).$$

We shall always assume that the functions M and N of two variables have continuous first partial derivatives. Since $M_y = N_x$, there exists a function F of two variables according to 19.22 such that $F_x = M$ and $F_y = N$. Let us show that the differentiable function f (of one variable) is a solution of the exact differential equation

$$M(x,y) + N(x,y)y' = 0$$

if and only if f is a solution of the equation

$$F(x,y) = C$$

for some constant C.

In the first place, if

$$M(x,f(x)) + N(x,f(x))f'(x) = 0,$$

then, by the chain rule,

$$D_xF(x,f(x)) = F_x(x,f(x)) + F_y(x,f(x))f'(x)$$
$$= M(x,f(x)) + N(x,f(x))f'(x) = 0.$$

Hence $F(x,f(x)) = C$ for some constant C.

On the other hand, if $F(x,f(x)) = C$ for some constant C, then $D_xF(x,f(x)) = D_xC = 0$ and, since $F_x = M$ and $F_y = N$,

$$D_xF(x,f(x)) = M(x,f(x)) + N(x,f(x))f'(x) = 0.$$

Thus f is a solution of the given exact differential equation. We have therefore proved the following result:

21.4 Theorem. The exact differential equation

$$M(x,y) + N(x,y)y' = 0$$

has the general solution

$$F(x,y) = C,$$

where F is any function of two variables such that

$$F_x = M, \qquad F_y = N.$$

Methods of determining a function F that satisfies the requirements of 21.4 were given in Section 11 of Chapter 19. We shall review these methods in the following examples.

Example 1. Solve the differential equation

$$2x - y + (y^2 - x)y' = 0.$$

Solution: We verified above that this equation is exact. Its solution will be $F(x,y) = C$, where F is a function such that

(1) $$F_x(x,y) = 2x - y,$$

(2) $$F_y(x,y) = y^2 - x.$$

It follows from (1) by integration that

$$F(x,y) = x^2 - xy + g(y)$$

for some function g. Hence, by (2),

$$F_y(x,y) = -x + g'(y) = y^2 - x,$$

so that $g'(y) = y^2$ and $g(y) = y^3/3$. Thus

$$F(x,y) = x^2 - xy + \frac{1}{3}y^3,$$

and the given differential equation has general solution

$$x^2 - xy + \frac{1}{3} y^3 = C.$$

Example 2. Solve the differential equation

$$\sin y + (x \cos y + y \cos y + \sin y)y' = 0.$$

Solution: We easily verify that

$$\frac{\partial}{\partial y} \sin y = \cos y = \frac{\partial}{\partial x} (x \cos y + y \cos y + \sin y),$$

and hence that the given equation is exact. We wish to find a function F such that

(1) $$F_x(x,y) = \sin y,$$
(2) $$F_y(x,y) = x \cos y + y \cos y + \sin y.$$

We have from (1) that

$$F(x,y) = x \sin y + g(y)$$

for some function g. Therefore, using (2),

$$F_y(x,y) = x \cos y + g'(y) = x \cos y + y \cos y + \sin y,$$

and $$g'(y) = y \cos y + \sin y.$$

Hence (using Formula 51 of the *Table of Integrals*)

$$g(y) = \int (y \cos y + \sin y)\, dy = y \sin y,$$

and $F(x,y) = x \sin y + y \sin y$. Thus the given differential equation has general solution

$$x \sin y + y \sin y = C.$$

For the separable differential equation 21.1,

$$M(x) + N(y)y' = 0,$$

we clearly have $M_y(x) = N_x(y) = 0$. Thus this equation is exact, and if

$$F(x,y) = \int M(x)\, dx + \int N(y)\, dy,$$

evidently $F_x = M$ and $F_y = N$. Hence

$$\int M(x)\, dx + \int N(y)\, dy = C$$

is the general solution of 21.1, and we have another proof of 11.27.

5. The differential notation

The first-order differential equation

$$R(x,y) + S(x,y) \frac{dy}{dx} = 0$$

is equivalent to the equation

$$R(x,y) \, dx + S(x,y) \, dy = 0$$

if we use the differential notation. That is, letting $dy = y' \, dx$, $y = f(x)$ is a solution of the first equation above if and only if it is a solution of the second one when $dx \neq 0$. This second equation is called the *symmetric form* of the given differential equation.

Example 1. Solve the equation $y' = \dfrac{2xy}{y^2 - x^2}$.

Solution: If we let $y' = dy/dx$, this equation has symmetric form

$$2xy \, dx + (x^2 - y^2) \, dy = 0.$$

We recognize the equation above as an exact differential equation. If

$$F(x,y) = x^2 y - \frac{1}{3} y^3,$$

then $F_x(x,y) = 2xy$ and $F_y(x,y) = x^2 - y^2$. Hence

$$x^2 y - \frac{1}{3} y^3 = C$$

is the general solution of the given equation.

Example 2. Find the particular solution of the equation

$$(\sin y + y \sin x) \, dx + (x \cos y - \cos x) \, dy = 0$$

that satisfies the boundary condition $y = \pi/2$ when $x = \pi$.

Solution: The given equation is exact. If

$$F(x,y) = x \sin y - y \cos x,$$

then $F_x(x,y) = \sin y + y \sin x$ and $F_y(x,y) = x \cos y - \cos x$. Hence

$$x \sin y - y \cos x = C$$

is the general solution of the given differential equation. If $y = \pi/2$ when $x = \pi$, then $C = 3\pi/2$, and

$$x \sin y - y \cos x = \frac{3\pi}{2}$$

is the desired particular solution.

■ ■ ■ EXERCISES

Solve the following differential equations.

1. $(x + y) \, dx + (x + 2y) \, dy = 0.$ **2.** $1 + r \cos \theta + \sin \theta \dfrac{dr}{d\theta} = 0.$

3. $ye^x - x + (e^x + 1)y' = 0.$ **4.** $ye^x - y + (e^x + 1)y' = 0.$

5. $(x \sin y - y)y' = \cos y.$ **6.** $(x \sin y - x)y' = \cos y.$

7. $(ye^{xy} + 2xy) \, dx + (xe^{xy} + x^2) \, dy = 0.$

8. $(r + e^\theta) \, d\theta + (\theta + e^r) \, dr = 0.$ **9.** $y \sec^2 x \, dx + \tan x \, dy = 0.$

10. $y' = \dfrac{x(6xy + 2)}{3y - 2x^3}$. **11.** $(e^x \sin y + y)y' = e^x \cos y$.

12. $\ln (y^2 + 1) + \dfrac{2xy}{x^2 + 1}\, y' = 0$.

Find the particular solution satisfying the given boundary condition for each of the following equations.

13. $(x - y)\, dx + (2y^3 - x)\, dy = 0; y = 1$ when $x = 2$.
14. $y \cos xy + (1 + x \cos xy)y' = 0; y = -1$ when $x = \pi/4$.
15. Show that if $M(x,y)\, dx + N(x,y)\, dy = 0$ is an exact differential equation, then the equation

$$\int_{x_0}^{x} M(x,y)\, dx + \int_{y_0}^{y} N(x_0,y)\, dy = 0$$

is that solution of the differential equation which satisfies the boundary condition $y = y_0$ when $x = x_0$. Solve Exercises 13 and 14 by this method.

If $I(x,y)M(x,y)\, dx + I(x,y)N(x,y)\, dy = 0$ is an exact differential equation, then $I(x,y)$ is said to be an *integrating factor* for the equation

$$M(x,y)\, dx + N(x,y)\, dy = 0.$$

Show in each of the following exercises that $I(x,y)$ is an integrating factor, and solve the equation.

16. $y\, dx - x\, dy = 0; I(x,y) = y^{-2}$.
17. $y\, dx - x\, dy = 0; I(x,y) = x^{-2}$.
18. $y\, dx - x\, dy = 0; I(x,y) = \dfrac{1}{xy}$.
19. $x + y + y' = 0; I(x,y) = e^x$.
20. $xy' = x - 3y; I(x,y) = x^2$.
21. $(y + x)\, dx + (y - x)\, dy = 0; I(x,y) = (x^2 + y^2)^{-1}$.

6. Homogeneous equations

A function F of two variables is said to be *homogeneous of degree n* if

21.5 $\qquad F(tx,ty) = t^n F(x,y)$

for every number t and every number-pair (x,y) such that both (x,y) and (tx,ty) are in the domain of F.

The polynomial functions defined by

$$f(x,y) = ax + by,$$
$$g(x,y) = ax^2 + bxy + cy^2,$$
$$h(x,y) = ax^3 + bx^2y + cxy^2 + dy^3,$$

and so on, are examples of homogeneous functions, f of degree 1, g of degree 2, h of degree 3, and so on. As another example, the function F

defined by

$$F(x,y) = x^2 + \frac{x^3 + 2y^3}{y}$$

is homogeneous of degree 2, since

$$F(tx,ty) = (tx)^2 + \frac{(tx)^3 + 2(ty)^3}{ty} = t^2 F(x,y).$$

Also, the function G defined by

$$G(x,y) = \frac{1}{x+y} \sin \frac{x-y}{x+y}$$

is homogeneous of degree -1, since

$$G(tx,ty) = \frac{1}{tx+ty} \sin \frac{tx-ty}{tx+ty} = t^{-1} G(x,y).$$

The equation

21.6 $$R(x,y) + S(x,y)y' = 0$$

is called a *homogeneous differential equation* if the functions R and S are homogeneous of the same degree. Let us show how such an equation may be solved.

We shall seek a solution of 21.6 of the form

$$y = xg(x), \quad x \neq 0,$$

for some differentiable function g. If we let $v = g(x)$, then

$$y = xv, \quad y' = v + xv',$$

and 21.6 takes on the form

$$R(x,xv) + S(x,xv)(v + xv') = 0.$$

If R and S are homogeneous of degree n, then by 21.5,

$$R(x,xv) = x^n R(1,v), \quad S(x,xv) = x^n S(1,v),$$

and the above differential equation becomes (on dividing out x^n)

$$R(1,v) + S(1,v)(v + xv') = 0,$$

or

21.7 $$\frac{1}{x} + \frac{S(1,v)}{R(1,v) + vS(1,v)} v' = 0.$$

Retracing our steps, we see that if $v = g(x)$ is a solution of 21.7, then $y = xg(x)$ is a solution of 21.6.

Thus we are always able to transform a homogeneous differential equation 21.6 into a separable differential equation 21.7. The transformation $y = xv, v = g(x)$, is said to *reduce* 21.6 to the simpler form 21.7. Examples of reductions of other first- and second-order differential equations will be given in the exercises.

In the differential notation, the substitution

$$y = xv, \quad dy = x\,dv + v\,dx,$$

transforms the homogeneous differential equation

$$R(x,y) \, dx + S(x,y) \, dy = 0$$

into the separable differential equation

$$\frac{1}{x} \, dx + \frac{S(1,v)}{R(1,v) + vS(1,v)} \, dv = 0.$$

Example 1. Solve the differential equation

$$(y - 4x) \, dx + (y + 2x) \, dy = 0.$$

Solution: In this example,

$$R(x,y) = y - 4x, \qquad S(x,y) = y + 2x,$$

and R and S are homogeneous of degree 1. The substitution

$$y = xv, \qquad dy = x \, dv + v \, dx$$

changes the given equation into the form

$$(xv - 4x) \, dx + (xv + 2x)(x \, dv + v \, dx) = 0,$$

or, on dividing by $x \neq 0$,

$$(v - 4) \, dx + (v + 2)(x \, dv + v \, dx) = 0.$$

A separation of variables yields the equation

$$\frac{1}{x} \, dx + \frac{v + 2}{v^2 + 3v - 4} \, dv = 0,$$

whose solution is

$$\ln |x| + \frac{2}{5} \ln |v + 4| + \frac{3}{5} \ln |v - 1| = C_1.$$

This may be put into the form

$$\ln |x^5(v + 4)^2(v - 1)^3| = 5C_1,$$

$$x^5(v + 4)^2(v - 1)^3 = C,$$

or

$$(xv + 4x)^2(xv - x)^3 = C.$$

Since $xv = y$, we have

$$(y + 4x)^2(y - x)^3 = C$$

as the general solution of the given differential equation.

Example 2. Solve the differential equation

$$\left(x - y \tan \frac{y}{x} \right) dx + x \tan \frac{y}{x} \, dy = 0.$$

Solution: This equation again is homogeneous of degree 1. On substituting

$$y = xv, \qquad dy = x \, dv + v \, dx,$$

in this equation, we get the separable differential equation

$$\frac{1}{x} \, dx + \tan v \, dv = 0,$$

whose solution is

$$\ln |x| + \ln |\sec v| = C_1,$$

or

$$x \sec v = C.$$

Hence the original equation has solution

$$x \sec \frac{y}{x} = C.$$

■ ■ ■ EXERCISES

Solve each of the following equations.

1. $(x - 2y) \, dx + x \, dy = 0.$ **2.** $y' = \dfrac{x^2 + y^2}{x^2}.$

3. $(2ye^{y/x} - x) \, dy + (2x + y) \, dx = 0.$

4. $(y^2 - x^2 + 2xy) \, dx + (y^2 - x^2 - 2xy) \, dy = 0.$

Show that each of the following equations is both homogeneous and exact, and solve it by each of the corresponding methods.

5. $(x^2 + y^2) \, dx + 2xy \, dy = 0.$ **6.** $(2x + y) \, dx + (x + 3y) \, dy = 0.$

7. Let the point (h,k) be the point of intersection of the lines

$$4x + 3y + 1 = 0,$$
$$x + y + 1 = 0.$$

Show that the transformation

$$X = x - h, \quad dX = dx,$$
$$Y = y - k, \quad dY = dy,$$

reduces the equation

$$(4x + 3y + 1) \, dx + (x + y + 1) \, dy = 0$$

to a homogeneous equation, and solve.

8. Show that the transformation

$$z = 2x + y, \quad dz = 2 \, dx + dy$$

reduces the equation

$$(2x + y) \, dx + (1 - 4x - 2y) \, dy = 0$$

to a separable equation, and solve. Why does this problem require a solution different from that of Exercise 7?

Solve each of the following equations.

9. $(x + 2y + 1) \, dx + (x + y) \, dy = 0.$

10. $(2x + y + 1) \, dx + (2x + y) \, dy = 0.$

A second-order differential equation of the form $F(x,y',y'') = 0$ in which y is missing may be reduced to one of the first order by the transformation $p = y', \ p' = y''$. Solve each of the following equations.

11. $y'' = y'.$ **12.** $y'' = -2y'.$

13. $y'' = \sin x.$ **14.** $xy'' = y' + 1.$

15. $y'' = \sqrt{(y')^2 + 1}.$ **16.** $y'' - e^x y' = 0.$

7. First-order linear differential equations

The equation

21.8 $$y' + P(x)y = Q(x),$$

where P and Q are continuous functions, is called a *linear differential equation of the first order.* We shall show below how this equation can be solved.

If the function Q is zero, the resulting equation $y' + P(x)y = 0$ may be put in the form

$$\frac{1}{y} y' + P(x) = 0.$$

This separable differential equation has solution

$$y = Ce^{-\int P(x)dx},$$

or $$ye^{\int P(x)dx} = C.$$

To return to the solution of 21.8, we first note that

$$D_x y e^{\int P(x)dx} = y'e^{\int P(x)dx} + yP(x)e^{\int P(x)dx}.$$

Hence, if we multiply each side of 21.8 by $I(x)$, where

$$I(x) = e^{\int P(x)dx},$$

the left side becomes $D_x yI(x)$, and 21.8 has the form

$$D_x yI(x) = Q(x)I(x).$$

Integrating, we get

$$yI(x) = \int Q(x)I(x)\, dx + C,$$

or

21.9 $$y = e^{-\int P(x)dx} \left(\int Q(x)e^{\int P(x)dx}\, dx + C \right)$$

as the general solution of **21.8**. We call $I(x)$ an *integrating factor* for the equation 21.8.

Example 1. Solve the differential equation

$$y' + y = x.$$

Solution: This equation has the form 21.8 with $P(x) = 1$ and $Q(x) = x$. If we multiply each side of the equation by the integrating factor

$$I(x) = e^{\int P(x)dx} = e^x,$$

we obtain the equation

$$e^x y' + e^x y = xe^x,$$

or $$D_x ye^x = xe^x.$$

Hence

$$ye^x = \int xe^x\, dx + C = (x - 1)e^x + C,$$

and $$y = x - 1 + Ce^{-x}$$

is the general solution of the given equation.

The differential equation

21.10 $y' + R(x)y = S(x)y^k, \qquad k \neq 0, 1,$

is called a *Bernoulli equation*.* Since k is neither 0 nor 1, this equation is not linear. However, it may be reduced to a linear equation by a suitable transformation, as we now show.

Assuming that $y \neq 0$, let us multiply each side of 21.10 by $(1 - k)y^{-k}$ to obtain

$$(1 - k)y^{-k}y' + (1 - k)R(x)y^{1-k} = (1 - k)S(x).$$

If $v = y^{1-k}$, then $v' = (1 - k)y^{-k}y'$ and the above equation may be put in the form

$$v' + (1 - k)R(x)v = (1 - k)S(x),$$

which is a linear differential equation with $P(x) = (1 - k)R(x)$ and $Q(x) = (1 - k)S(x)$ (in 21.8). This equation may be solved, as in 21.9, for v. Then $y^{1-k} = v$ is a solution of 21.10.

Example 2. Solve the differential equation

$$y' + \frac{1}{x}y = x^5 y^4.$$

Solution: This is a Bernoulli equation (21.10) with $k = 4$. If we let $v = y^{-3}$ as above, and multiply each side of the given equation by $-3y^{-4}$, we obtain the equation

$$-3y^{-4}y' - \frac{3}{x}y^{-3} = -3x^5,$$

or

(1) $v' - \dfrac{3}{x}v = -3x^5, \qquad v = y^{-3}.$

This differential equation may be solved by multiplying each side by the integrating factor

$$I(x) = e^{\int -\frac{3}{x}dx} = e^{-3 \ln |x|} = |x|^{-3}.$$

Thus $I(x) = x^{-3}$ if $x > 0$, whereas $I(x) = -x^{-3}$ if $x < 0$. In either case, (1) becomes

$$x^{-3}v' - 3x^{-4}v = -3x^2,$$

$$D_x x^{-3}v = -3x^2,$$

and

$$x^{-3}v = -x^3 + C.$$

Hence

$$v = -x^6 + Cx^3$$

is the solution of (1), and

$$y^{-3} = -x^6 + Cx^3,$$

or

$$(-x^6 + Cx^3)y^3 = 1,$$

is the solution of the given equation.

* Jacob Bernoulli (1654–1705) proposed this equation for solution in 1695. The solution given here is that of Leibniz published in 1696. Jacob Bernoulli is credited with the first use of the word integral. He was a member of a very large and famous family of Swiss mathematicians.

■ ■ ■ EXERCISES

Solve each of the following differential equations.

1. $y' + xy = x$.
2. $y' - 2y = 3$.
3. $y' + by = c$; b, c constants.
4. $y' - y/x = \sin x$.
5. $y' + y \tan x = \sec x$.
6. $y' + y \tan x = \sin x$.
7. $y' = e^{2x} + 3y$.
8. $y' = e^{ix} + ay$, a constant.
9. $(x^2 + 1)y' = 2x(x^2 + 1)^2 + 2xy$.
10. $y' \sin x + y \cos x = 1$.
11. $y' + xy = xy^2$.
12. $y' = y^3 e^{2x} + 3y$.
13. $yy' - 2y^2 = e^x$.
14. $xy' + y = xe^x y^2$.

8. Applications

The solutions of many physical problems are naturally described by differential equations. For example, it was shown in Chapter 10 that the amount of a radioactive substance left after a period of time is given by the differential equation

$$\frac{dy}{dt} = ky.$$

Other examples are given in this section.

Example 1. A body of mass m falls from rest in a straight line toward the earth. Describe the motion of the body, assuming that the force due to air resistance on the body is proportional to its speed.

Solution: Let us choose an x-axis directed downward, with its origin at the point from which the body is dropped. Let $x = x(t)$ be the position of the body at time t, and let us assume that $x = 0$ when $t = 0$. Then $v = x'(t)$ is the velocity of the body at time t. By assumption, $x = 0$, and $v = 0$ when $t = 0$.

The weight of the body is mg, where g is the acceleration due to gravity. Thus mg is the force due to gravity acting on the body in the direction of the positive x-axis. The force due to air resistance on the body will be a vector directed upward (in direction opposite to that of the motion). By assumption, its magnitude is $-k_1 v$ for some number $k_1 > 0$. Hence the sum of the forces acting on the body is $mg - k_1 v$. By Newton's second law, this force equals ma where a is the acceleration of the body. Therefore

$$ma = mg - k_1 v.$$

It is convenient to let $k_1 = mk$, in which case the equation above yields $a = g - kv$, or

(1) $v' = g - kv$,

as the differential equation of the motion.

Equation (1) is separable and has the solution

$$-\frac{1}{k} \ln |g - kv| = t + C_1,$$

or
$$g - kv = Ce^{-kt}.$$

Since $v = 0$ when $t = 0$, we have $C = g$ and

(2)
$$v = \frac{g}{k}(1 - e^{-kt}).$$

We note in passing that the body has a limiting velocity given by

$$\underset{t \to \infty}{\text{limit}}\, v = \underset{t \to \infty}{\text{limit}}\, \frac{g}{k}(1 - e^{-kt}) = \frac{g}{k}.$$

Since $v(t) = x'(t)$, (2) is the differential equation

$$x' = \frac{g}{k}(1 - e^{-kt}).$$

This equation has the solution

$$x = \frac{g}{k}\left(t + \frac{1}{k}e^{-kt}\right) + C_2.$$

If we let $x = 0$ when $t = 0$, we get $C_2 = -g/k^2$. Hence

$$x = \frac{g}{k}t + \frac{g}{k^2}(e^{-kt} - 1)$$

is the equation of motion of the body.

It is interesting to note that $x'' = ge^{-kt}$, and that

$$\underset{t \to \infty}{\text{limit}}\, x'' = 0.$$

That is to say, the forces of gravity and air resistance tend to balance each other, giving rise to the limiting velocity mentioned above.

Example 2. (Catenary problem.) A flexible rope is suspended from two fixed points and hangs at rest under its own weight. Find the curve in which the rope hangs.

Partial solution: Let $Q(x_0, y_0)$ be any fixed point on the curve and let $P(x,y)$ be any other point on the curve (Figure 21.3). If H_0 and H are the horizontal

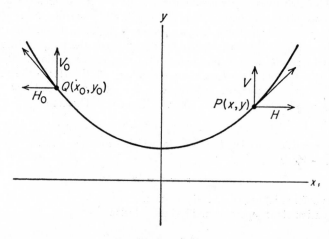

Figure 21.3

components of the forces acting at Q and P, respectively, then

$$H_0 = H$$

since the rope is at rest. We interpret the term "flexible rope" to mean that y' is continuous. Hence the length L of the rope between P and Q is given by

$$L = \int_{x_0}^{x} \sqrt{1 + y'^2}\, dx.$$

If w is the weight of a unit length of the rope, then wL is the weight of the rope between P and Q. The sum $V_0 + V$ of the vertical components of the forces acting at Q and P must be the weight of the rope between P and Q; that is,

(1) $$V_0 + V = w \int_{x_0}^{x} \sqrt{1 + y'^2}\, dx.$$

The force vector at P lies along the tangent line to the curve, and therefore

$$y' = \frac{V}{H}.$$

Hence $V = Hy' = H_0 y'$, and (1) becomes

(2) $$\frac{V_0}{H_0} + y' = k \int_{x_0}^{x} \sqrt{1 + y'^2}\, dx,$$

where $k = w/H_0$. We may differentiate each side of (2), obtaining the differential equation

(3) $$y'' = k\sqrt{1 + y'^2}.$$

One of the solutions of (3) has as its graph the curve in which the rope hangs. We may start solving (3) by letting $p = y'$, thereby obtaining the equation

$$p' = k\sqrt{1 + p^2},$$

which may be solved for p. In turn, this solution is a first-order differential equation which may be solved for y. It is convenient to choose $y' = 0$ and $y = 1/k$ when $x = 0$, as boundary conditions.

Example 3. A mirror has the shape of a surface of revolution. If there exists a point F on the axis of the mirror such that light emitted from this point will be reflected from the mirror in rays parallel to the axis, prove that the mirror is parabolic and that F is the focus of the generating parabola.

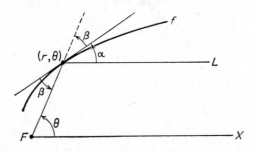

Figure 21.4

Partial solution 1. Let the surface be generated by rotating the curve $r = f(\theta)$ in a polar coordinate plane about the polar axis, and let F be at the pole. If L is a light ray reflected from the surface at the point (r,θ), so that $\alpha = \beta$ in Figure 21.4, then $\theta = \alpha + \beta = 2\alpha$ if L is parallel to the polar axis. By 15.10, $r' = r \cot(\alpha - \theta) = -r \cot(\theta/2)$, that is,

$$\cot \frac{\theta}{2} = -\frac{r'}{r}.$$

Since $\cot(\theta/2) = \sin\theta/(1 - \cos\theta)$, we have

$$\frac{r'}{r} = -\frac{\sin\theta}{1 - \cos\theta}$$

as the differential equation satisfied by $r = f(\theta)$. Each solution of this equation may be shown to be a parabola with focus at F.

Partial solution 2. Let the surface be generated by rotating the curve $y = g(x)$ in a rectangular coordinate plane about the x-axis, and let F be at the origin (Figure 21.5). If L is a light ray reflected from the surface at the point (x,y),

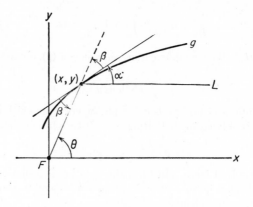

Figure 21.5

so that $\alpha = \beta$ in the figure, then $\theta = \alpha + \beta = 2\alpha$ if L is parallel to the x-axis. Evidently

$$\tan\theta = \frac{y}{x}$$

and $\tan\alpha = y'$. It is reasonable to assume that $y' > 0$ in solving the resulting differential equation satisfied by $y = g(x)$.

■ ■ ■ EXERCISES

1. An object falls from rest in a straight line toward the earth. The force of air resistance is proportional to the square of the velocity. Show that the differential equation of motion is $a = g - k^2v^2$ and solve the equation. It is convenient to let $r^2 = gk^2$ and to give the result in terms of r.

2. Complete the solution of Example 2.

3. Complete both solutions of Example 3.

In the circuit of Figure 21.6, R is the resistance, L is the inductance, and E is an impressed emf. If $I = I(t)$ is the current in the circuit at the time t, then $I(t)R$ is the voltage drop across the resistor and $I'(t)L$ is the voltage drop across the inductor. The sum of the voltage drops in the circuit must equal the impressed emf, that is,

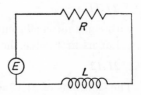

Figure 21.6

$$LI' + RI = E.$$

The numbers L and R are constants. If $I(0) = 0$, determine $I(t)$ in each of the following cases.

4. $L = 10, R = 5, E = 1.$ **5.** $L = 5, R = 20, E = 1.$

6. $L = 1, R = 2, E = \sin t.$

7. Solve the equation

$$LI' + RI = E(t).$$

Let A and B be chemical substances which combine to form a chemical substance C. If a and b are the amounts of A and B present at the time $t = 0$ and if $x = x(t)$ is the amount of C formed at the time t, then, under certain conditions, $a - x(t)$ and $b - x(t)$ will be the amounts of A and B, respectively, remaining at the time t. We assume $x(0) = 0$. If the rate of increase of $x(t)$ is proportional to the product of the amounts of A and B present at the time t, the chemical action is known as a *second-order process*, and the differential equation is

$$x' = k(a - x)(b - x).$$

Solve this equation in each of the following cases.

8. $a = 10, b = 5.$ **9.** $a = b = 10.$

10. $a \neq b.$ **11.** $a = b.$

12. A radioactive substance A changes into a substance B, which in turn changes into a substance C. Let a be the amount of A present at the time $t = 0$. Let $x(t)$ be the amount of B which has been formed up to the time t, and let $y(t)$ be the amount of C which has been formed up to the time t. Then $x(t) - y(t)$ is the amount of B present at the time t. Assuming that the radioactivity is proportional to the amount present at a given time, we get the equations

$$x' = k_1(a - x); \qquad y' = k_2(x - y).$$

Solve for $x(t)$ and $y(t)$.

9. Second-order linear differential equations

A differential equation of the form

$$y^{[n]} + a_1(x)y^{[n-1]} + \cdots + a_{n-1}(x)y' + a_n(x)y = G(x)$$

is called a *linear differential equation of order n*. We shall not study the general linear equation above, but rather shall limit our remarks to the second-order linear differential equation

21.11 $y'' + by' + cy = G(x)$

with constant coefficients b and c.

Let us first solve the so-called *homogeneous* linear differential equation

21.12 $y'' + by' + cy = 0.$

The solutions of 21.12 will be used in finding the solutions of 21.11.

21.13 Theorem. If $y = u(x)$ and $y = v(x)$ are solutions of 21.12, then so is $y = C_1 u(x) + C_2 v(x)$ for any numbers C_1 and C_2.

Proof: By assumption,

$$u''(x) + bu'(x) + cu(x) = 0,$$
$$v''(x) + bv'(x) + cv(x) = 0.$$

Hence

$$D_x^2[C_1 u(x) + C_2 v(x)] + bD_x[C_1 u(x) + C_2 v(x)] + c[C_1 u(x) + C_2 v(x)]$$
$$= C_1[u''(x) + bu'(x) + cu(x)] + C_2[v''(x) + bv'(x) + cv(x)] = 0,$$

and the theorem is proved.

This theorem will allow us to express the general solution of 21.12 in terms of two particular solutions.

We first inquire whether the exponential function defined by

$$y = e^{mx}$$

is a solution of 21.12. Since $D_x e^{mx} = me^{mx}$ and $D_x^2 e^{mx} = m^2 e^{mx}$, this function is a solution of 21.12 if and only if

$$m^2 e^{mx} + bme^{mx} + ce^{mx} = 0,$$

or, on dividing by the nonzero number e^{mx}, if and only if

21.14 $m^2 + bm + c = 0.$

Equation 21.14 is called the *characteristic equation*, or *auxiliary equation*, of 21.12.

The roots of 21.14 are given by

$$m = \frac{-b \pm \sqrt{b^2 - 4c}}{2}.$$

Let us consider three cases as follows.

Case 1. $b^2 - 4c > 0$. Then 21.14 has distinct real roots m_1 and m_2, and $y = e^{m_1 x}$ and $y = e^{m_2 x}$ are particular solutions of 21.12. The general solution is given by

21.15 $y = C_1 e^{m_1 x} + C_2 e^{m_2 x}.$

Case 2. $b^2 - 4c = 0$. Then 21.14 has a double root $m = -b/2$, and $y = e^{mx}$ is a particular solution of 21.12. It is easily verified that $y = xe^{mx}$

also is a solution:

$$D_x^2 x e^{mx} + b\, D_x x e^{mx} + c x e^{mx} = (m^2 x e^{mx} + 2m e^{mx}) + b(m x e^{mx} + e^{mx}) + c x e^{mx}$$
$$= (m^2 + bm + c)x e^{mx} + (2m + b)e^{mx} = 0.$$

Hence

21.16 $$y = C_1 e^{mx} + C_2 x e^{mx}$$

is the general solution of 21.12 in this case.

Case 3. $b^2 - 4c < 0$. Then 21.14 has distinct imaginary roots $\alpha + \beta i$ and $\alpha - \beta i$, where

$$\alpha = -\frac{b}{2}, \qquad \beta i = \frac{\sqrt{b^2 - 4c}}{2}.$$

We shall use the following argument to lead us to two particular solutions of 21.12.

The calculus can be extended to functions of complex variables, and

$$y = A_1 e^{(\alpha + \beta i)x} + A_2 e^{(\alpha - \beta i)x},$$

or

$$y = e^{\alpha x}(A_1 e^{\beta i x} + A_2 e^{-\beta i x}),$$

is a solution of 21.12 for any (complex) constants A_1 and A_2.

The theorems on real infinite series (Chapter 16) can be extended to complex series, and it can be shown that

$$e^{iz} = 1 + (iz) + \frac{(iz)^2}{2!} + \frac{(iz)^3}{3!} + \frac{(iz)^4}{4!} + \frac{(iz)^5}{5!} + \cdots$$

holds for every real number z. Since $i^2 = -1$, $i^3 = -i$, and so on, we may write the series above in the form

$$e^{iz} = \left(1 - \frac{z^2}{2!} + \frac{z^4}{4!} - \cdots\right) + i\left(z - \frac{z^3}{3!} + \frac{z^5}{5!} - \cdots\right).$$

Since the series in parentheses represent $\cos z$ and $\sin z$, respectively, we finally obtain the so-called *Euler's formula*

$$e^{iz} = \cos z + i \sin z.$$

With the aid of Euler's formula, we easily derive the formulas

$$\sin \beta x = \frac{e^{\beta i x} - e^{-\beta i x}}{2i}, \qquad \cos \beta x = \frac{e^{\beta i x} + e^{-\beta i x}}{2}.$$

Hence, by choosing $A_1 = A_2 = \frac{1}{2}$, we have that $y = e^{\alpha x} \cos \beta x$ is a particular solution of 21.12; and by choosing $A_1 = 1/2i$ and $A_2 = -1/2i$, we have that $y = e^{\alpha x} \sin \beta x$ also is a particular solution of 21.12. Thus, in Case 3, we expect that

21.17 $$y = e^{\alpha x}(C_1 \cos \beta x + C_2 \sin \beta x)$$

will be the general solution of 21.12.

Example 1. Solve the differential equation

$$y'' - y' - 6y = 0.$$

Solution: The characteristic equation

$$m^2 - m - 6 = 0$$

has roots $m_1 = 3$ and $m_2 = -2$. Hence the given equation has solution (21.15),

$$y = C_1e^{3x} + C_2e^{-2x}.$$

Example 2. Solve the differential equation

$$y'' + 2\sqrt{3}\,y' + 3 = 0.$$

Solution: The characteristic equation

$$m^2 + 2\sqrt{3}\,m + 3 = 0$$

has a double root $m = -\sqrt{3}$. Therefore

$$y = (C_1 + C_2x)e^{-\sqrt{3}x}$$

is the solution of the given equation by 21.16.

Example 3. Solve the differential equation

$$y'' - 6y' + 13y = 0.$$

Solution: The characteristic equation

$$m^2 - 6m + 13 = 0$$

has imaginary roots $3 \pm 2i$. Thus $\alpha = 3$ and $\beta = 2$ in 21.17, and

$$y = e^{3x}(C_1 \cos 2x + C_2 \sin 2x)$$

is the general solution of the given equation.

21.18 Theorem. Let $y = u(x)$ and $y = v(x)$ be solutions of the differential equation

$$y'' + by' + cy = 0$$

such that

$$u(x)v'(x) - v(x)u'(x) \neq 0$$

for all x. Then for any given numbers x_0, y_0, and y_1, there exists a solution

$$f(x) = C_1u(x) + C_2v(x)$$

of the given equation such that

$$f(x_0) = y_0, \qquad f'(x_0) = y_1.$$

Proof: We wish to show that the constants C_1 and C_2 can be determined so that $f(x_0) = y_0$ and $f'(x_0) = y_1$; that is, so that

$$y_0 = C_1u(x_0) + C_2v(x_0), \qquad y_1 = C_1u'(x_0) + C_2v'(x_0).$$

This pair of linear equations in C_1 and C_2 has the unique solution

$$C_1 = \frac{y_0v'(x_0) - y_1v(x_0)}{w}, \qquad C_2 = \frac{y_1u(x_0) - y_0u'(x_0)}{w},$$

where $w = u(x_0)v'(x_0) - v(x_0)u'(x_0) \neq 0$ by assumption. That $y = f(x)$ is a solution of the differential equation for this choice of C_1 and C_2 follows from 21.13.

In each of the three cases considered above, we have chosen the two solutions u and v so that the hypotheses of 21.18 are satisfied. For example, in Case 1, $u(x) = e^{m_1 x}$ and $v(x) = e^{m_2 x}$ with $m_1 \neq m_2$. Hence

$$u(x)v'(x) - v(x)u'(x) = (m_2 - m_1)e^{(m_1 + m_2)x} \neq 0.$$

That the hypotheses of 21.18 are satisfied in the other two cases will be left for the reader to verify.

We shall prove in a later section that if $y = f(x)$ and $y = g(x)$ are solutions of 21.12 such that

$$f(x_0) = g(x_0), \qquad f'(x_0) = g'(x_0)$$

for some number x_0, then $f(x) = g(x)$ for every x. Now if $y = g(x)$ is any solution of 21.12, there exists a solution of 21.12 of the form

$$f(x) = C_1 u(x) + C_2 v(x)$$

by 21.18 such that $f(x_0) = g(x_0)$, $f'(x_0) = g'(x_0)$. Hence it will follow that $g(x) = C_1 u(x) + C_2 v(x)$; that is, that $C_1 u(x) + C_2 v(x)$ is the general solution of 21.12 as we contended in each of the cases above.

■ ■ ■ EXERCISES

1. Prove that in each case $u(x)v'(x) - v(x)u'(x) \neq 0$.
    (a) $u(x) = e^{mx}, \qquad v(x) = xe^{mx}$.
    (b) $u(x) = e^{\alpha x} \cos \beta x, \qquad v(x) = e^{\alpha x} \sin \beta x, \beta \neq 0$.

Solve each of the following differential equations.

2. $y'' + 9y = 0$.
3. $y'' = 9y = 0$.
4. $y'' + 2y' + y = 0$.
5. $y'' + 2y' - y = 0$.
6. $y'' - y' - 6y = 0$.
7. $y'' - 3y' - 10y = 0$.
8. $y'' + y' = 0$.
9. $y'' + y' + 3y = 0$.
10. $y'' - 4y' + 29y = 0$.
11. $y'' - 2y' + 3y = 0$.
12. $y'' + 2y' + 3y = 0$.
13. $y'' + \sqrt{2}y' + 7y = 0$.
14. $6y'' + y' - 2y = 0$.
15. $3y'' - 2y' + 5y = 0$.
16. $y'' - 2y' + (1 - \pi)y = 0$.
17. $y'' - 2\sqrt{3}y' + (3 + \pi^2)y = 0$.

In each of the following exercises, find the particular solution of the equation satisfying the given boundary conditions.

18. $y'' + y = 0$; $y = 0$, $y' = 1$ when $x = 0$.
19. $y'' - 3y' + 5y = 0$; $y = 0$, $y' = 0$ when $x = 0$.
20. $y'' - 2y' - 8y = 0$; $y = 10$, $y' = 1$ when $x = 0$.
21. $y'' - 5y' + 6y = 0$; $y = 1$, $y' = 1$ when $x = 1$.
22. $y'' - 4y' + 4y = 0$; $y = 3$, $y' = 0$ when $x = 2$.
23. An object is suspended from a fixed standard by a spring. There is a point at which this system is in equilibrium. The resultant of the force of the spring and the weight of the object is proportional to the vertical

displacement of the object from the point of equilibrium. Describe the motion of the object.

10. Nonhomogeneous linear equations

We shall consider in this section the problem of solving the nonhomogeneous second-order linear differential equation

21.19 $$y'' + by' + cy = G(x),$$

where b and c are constants and G is a continuous function.

In discussing the solutions of 21.19, it is convenient to introduce the notation $L(y)$ for the left side of 21.19:

$$L(y) = y'' + by' + cy.$$

The "operator" L is linear in the sense that

$$L(y_1 \pm y_2) = L(y_1) \pm L(y_2).$$

Using the L notation, the function g is a solution of 21.19 if and only if $L(g(x)) = G(x)$.

Let g_p designate a particular solution of 21.19 and let g be any other solution. If $f(x) = g(x) - g_p(x)$, then

$$L(f(x)) = L(g(x)) - L(g_p(x)) = 0;$$

that is, f is a solution of the *complementary equation*

21.20 $$y'' + by' + cy = 0.$$

Conversely, if g_p is a particular solution of 21.19 and f is any solution of 21.20, then $g(x) = g_p(x) + f(x)$ also is a solution of 21.19. Consequently, the general solution of 21.19 has the form

$$y = g_p(x) + f_c(x),$$

where g_p is a particular solution of 21.19 and f_c is the general solution of 21.20. Since we can find the general solution of the homogeneous linear differential equation 21.20 by the methods of the preceding section, we can find the general solution of 21.19 provided we can find a particular solution of it. Various ways of finding particular solutions of 21.19 are given in the remainder of this section.

Example 1. Solve the differential equation

$$y'' + y = 2x.$$

Solution: We see by inspection that $y_p = 2x$ is a solution. The complementary equation $y'' + y = 0$ has general solution

$$y_c = C_1 \cos x + C_2 \sin x.$$

Hence

$$y = C_1 \cos x + C_2 \sin x + 2x$$

is the general solution of the given equation.

The following procedure, called the method of *variation of parameters*, will yield a particular solution of 21.19. Let

$$y_c = C_1 u(x) + C_2 v(x)$$

be the general solution of 21.20; $L(y_c) = 0$. We shall find functions u_1 and v_1 which, when put in place of C_1 and C_2 in y_c, will give a particular solution

$$y_p = u_1(x)u(x) + v_1(x)v(x)$$

of 21.19.

We first place the condition that

$$u_1'u + v_1'v = 0.$$

This condition simplifies subsequent computations. Now if $y = u_1 u + v_1 v$, then $y' = u_1 u' + u_1' u + v_1' v + v_1 v'$, and, using the condition above,

$$y' = u_1 u' + v_1 v'.$$

Hence
$$y'' = u_1 u'' + v_1 v'' + u_1' u' + v_1' v',$$

and $\quad L(u_1 u + v_1 v) = u_1 L(u) + v_1 L(v) + u_1' u' + v_1' v' = u_1' u' + v_1' v'.$

Therefore $L(u_1 u + v_1 v) = G(x)$ if and only if $u_1' u' + v_1' v' = G(x)$. Consequently, if the functions u_1 and v_1 are chosen so that

21.21 $\qquad u_1'u + v_1'v = 0, \qquad u_1'u' + v_1'v' = G(x),$

then $y_p = u_1 u + v_1 v$ is a particular solution of 21.19.

Equations 21.21 are two linear equations in the unknowns u_1' and v_1'. Since $uv' - vu' \neq 0$ by results of the preceding section, these equations may be solved for u_1' and v_1', yielding

$$u_1' = -\frac{vG(x)}{uv' - vu'}, \qquad v_1' = \frac{uG(x)}{uv' - vu'}.$$

Hence
$$u_1 = -\int \frac{vG(x)}{uv' - vu'}\, dx, \qquad v_1 = \int \frac{uG(x)}{uv' - vu'}\, dx$$

always exist.

Example 2. Solve the differential equation

$$y'' + y = \sec x.$$

Solution: The complementary equation $y'' + y = 0$ has general solution

$$y_c = C_1 \sin x + C_2 \cos x.$$

We wish to determine functions u_1 and v_1 such that

$$y_p = u_1(x)\sin x + v_1(x)\cos x$$

is a particular solution of the given equation. For this example, $G(x) = \sec x$, $u = \sin x$, $v = \cos x$, $u' = \cos x$, $v' = -\sin x$, and 21.21 becomes

$$u_1' \sin x + v_1' \cos x = 0; \qquad u_1' \cos x - v_1' \sin x = \sec x.$$

Solving for u_1' and v_1', we obtain

$$u_1' = 1, \qquad v_1' = -\sin x \sec x = -\tan x.$$

Hence

$$u_1 = x, \qquad v_1 = \ln |\cos x|,$$

and

$$y_p = x \sin x + (\ln |\cos x|) \cos x$$

is a particular solution. The general solution of the given equation is therefore $y_p + y_c$, or

$$y = (x + C_1) \sin x + (\ln |\cos x| + C_2) \cos x.$$

Another technique for finding a particular solution of 21.19, called the method of undetermined coefficients, is illustrated below.

Example 3. Determine A_1 and A_2 so that

$$y_p = A_1 \sin x + A_2 \cos x$$

is a particular solution of the differential equation

$$y'' - y' - 6y = \sin x.$$

Solution: Evidently

$$y_p' = A_1 \cos x - A_2 \sin x, \qquad y_p'' = -A_1 \sin x - A_2 \cos x,$$

so that

$$y_p'' - y_p' - 6y_p = (A_2 - 7A_1) \sin x + (-A_1 - 7A_2) \cos x.$$

Hence y_p is a solution if

$$(A_2 - 7A_1) \sin x + (-A_1 - 7A_2) \cos x = \sin x,$$

that is, if

$$A_2 - 7A_1 = 1, \qquad -A_1 - 7A_2 = 0.$$

Solving these equations for A_1 and A_2, we obtain

$$A_1 = -\frac{7}{50}, \qquad A_2 = \frac{1}{50}.$$

Thus

$$y_p = -\frac{7}{50} \sin x + \frac{1}{50} \cos x$$

is a particular solution of the given equation. The general solution is

$$y = C_1 e^{3x} + C_2 e^{-2x} - \frac{7}{50} \sin x + \frac{1}{50} \cos x.$$

■ ◻ ■ EXERCISES

1. If $L(y) = y'' - 3y'$, find $L(\sin x)$, $L(e^x)$, $L(e^{3x})$, $L(xe^{3x})$, $L(x)$.
2. If $L(y) = y'' + y$, find $L(e^x)$, $L(\sin x)$, $L(\cos x)$, $L(A_1x^2 + A_2x + A_3)$.
3. Determine A_1, A_2, A_3 so that

$$y_p = A_1 x^2 + A_2 x + A_3$$

is a solution of the equation

$$y'' - 2y' + 2y = x^2 - 1,$$

and find the general solution.

4. Find a particular solution $y_p = Ax + B$, and find the general solution of the equation

$$y'' - 2y' - 8y = x + 3.$$

5. If $L(y) = y'' + 2y' - 2y$, find $L(A \sin x + B \cos x)$ and hence solve the equation

$$y'' + 2y' - 2y = 2 \sin x - \cos x.$$

Use the method of variation of parameters to solve each of the following equations.

6. $y'' + y = \csc x.$ 7. $y'' + y = \tan x.$

8. $y'' - 4y' + 4y = x^2 e^{2x}.$ 9. $y'' - y = e^x \sin x.$

10. $y'' - y = \cos x.$ 11. $y'' + 2y' = xe^{-2x}.$

12. If $L(y) = y'' - 3y' + 2y$, find $L(e^x)$ and $L(xe^x)$. Hence solve the equation

$$y'' - 3y' + 2y = 3e^x.$$

13. If $L(y) = y'' + 4y$, find $L(x \sin 2x)$ and $L(x \cos 2x)$, and solve the equation

$$y'' + 4y = \cos 2x.$$

Solve by any method each of the following equations.

14. $y'' - 3y = x.$ 15. $y'' - 2y = 5x.$

16. $y'' - y' = 3x.$ 17. $y'' + y' = e^x.$

18. $y'' + y' + y = \sin x.$ 19. $y'' - 3y' - y = e^x.$

In the circuit of Figure 21.7 the current at the time t satisfies the equation

$$L \frac{dI}{dt} + RI + \frac{1}{C} \int I \, dt = E(t),$$

or

$$(1) \quad L \frac{d^2I}{dt^2} + R \frac{dI}{dt} + \frac{1}{C} I = E'(t),$$

where $E(t)$ is the impressed emf, L, R, and C are the constants of inductance, resistance, and capacitance, respectively. Solve equation (1) in each of the following cases:

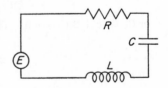

Figure 21.7

19. $R = 0, C = 1, L = 10, E = 5.$

20. $R = 10, C = \frac{1}{5}, L = 10, E = \sin t.$

21. $R = 1, C = 1, L = 1, E = 10 \sin 2t.$

22. Given that $m^3 - 6m^2 + 11m - 6 = (m - 1)(m - 2)(m - 3)$, solve the equation

$$y''' - 6y'' + 11y' - 6y = 0.$$

23. Solve the equation

$$y''' - 3y'' - y' + 3y = 0.$$

24. Solve the equation

$$y''' - 3y'' + y' - 3y = 0.$$

11. Solutions in series

The infinite series

$$f(x) = C_0 + C_1(x - x_0) + C_2(x - x_0)^2 + \cdots + C_n(x - x_0)^n + \cdots$$

defines a function f in the interval of convergence of the series. It is frequently possible to find solutions of differential equations in the form of infinite series, as is illustrated in the following example.

Example. Find an infinite series solution of the differential equation

$$y'' + xy' + y = 0.$$

Solution: If

$$y = \sum_{k=0}^{\infty} C_k x^k$$

is a solution, then (by 16.20),

$$y' = \sum_{k=1}^{\infty} kC_k x^{k-1}, \qquad y'' = \sum_{k=2}^{\infty} k(k-1)C_k x^{k-2} = \sum_{k=0}^{\infty} (k+2)(k+1)C_{k+2}x^k.$$

Hence

$$y'' + xy' + y = \sum_{k=0}^{\infty} [C_k + kC_k + (k+2)(k+1)C_{k+2}]x^k.$$

If y is to be a solution, the right side of the above equation must equal zero, and the coefficient of each power of x must be zero:

$$(1 + k)C_k + (k+2)(k+1)C_{k+2} = 0,$$

or $C_k + (k+2)C_{k+2} = 0$. Thus

$$C_{k+2} = -\frac{1}{k+2}C_k, \qquad k = 0, 1, 2, \cdots, n, \cdots.$$

In particular,

$$C_2 = -\frac{1}{2}C_0, \qquad\qquad C_3 = -\frac{1}{3}C_1,$$

$$C_4 = -\frac{1}{4}C_2 = \frac{1}{2\cdot4}C_0, \qquad C_5 = -\frac{1}{5}C_3 = \frac{1}{3\cdot5}C_1,$$

$$C_6 = -\frac{1}{6}C_4 = -\frac{1}{2\cdot4\cdot6}C_0, \qquad C_7 = -\frac{1}{7}C_5 = -\frac{1}{3\cdot5\cdot7}C_1,$$

and so on, with

$$C_{2n} = \frac{(-1)^n}{2\cdot4\cdot\ldots\cdot2n}C_0, \qquad C_{2n+1} = \frac{(-1)^n}{1\cdot3\cdot\ldots\cdot(2n+1)}C_1.$$

Thus y may be expressed as a sum of two series, one containing the even powers of x and the other containing the odd powers:

$$y = C_0\sum_{k=0}^{\infty}\frac{(-1)^k}{2\cdot4\cdot\ldots\cdot2k}x^{2k} + C_1\sum_{k=0}^{\infty}\frac{(-1)^k}{1\cdot3\cdot\ldots\cdot(2k+1)}x^{2k+1}.$$

The ratio test establishes that each of the series is convergent everywhere. This is the general solution of the given differential equation.

A function f which can be expressed as a power series in some interval is said to be *analytic* in that interval. Thus, we are seeking analytic solutions of differential equations in this section.

The theory of Taylor's series (Chapter 16) gives us a criterion for determining whether or not a function is analytic. Let us use the Taylor's theory to establish the following result.

21.22 Theorem. If f is a solution of the differential equation

$$y'' = ky$$

in an interval $[x_1, x_2]$, then f is analytic in this interval.

Proof: Since f is a solution of $y'' = ky$, then f' and f'' exist in $[x_1, x_2]$. Furthermore, $f''(x) = kf(x)$, $f'''(x) = kf'(x)$, $f^{iv}(x) = kf''(x) = k^2 f(x)$, and so on. That is, f possesses derivatives of every order in $[x_1, x_2]$.

By Taylor's formula (14.13),

$$f(x) = P_n(x) + R_n(x),$$

where

$$P_n(x) = \sum_{k=0}^{n} \frac{f^{[k]}(x_0)}{k!} (x - x_0)^k, \qquad R_n(x) = \frac{f^{[n+1]}(z_n)}{(n+1)!} (x - x_0)^{n+1},$$

for x_0 in $[x_1, x_2]$ and some z_n between x and x_0. If

$$\lim_{n \to \infty} R_n(x) = 0$$

for every x in $[x_1, x_2]$, then f is represented by its Taylor's series (i.e., f is analytic) in $[x_1, x_2]$,

$$f(x) = \sum_{k=0}^{\infty} \frac{f^{[k]}(x_0)}{k!} (x - x_0)^k,$$

according to 16.25.

Since f and f' are continuous in $[x_1, x_2]$, there exists a number M such that

$$|f(x)| \le M, \qquad |f'(x)| \le M$$

in $[x_1, x_2]$. Let $m = |k|$ if $|k| > 1$; $m = 1$ if $|k| \le 1$. Then

$$|f''(x)| = |kf(x)| \le Mm \le Mm^2,$$

$$|f'''(x)| = |kf'(x)| \le Mm \le Mm^3,$$

$$|f^{iv}(x)| = |kf''(x)| \le m|f''(x)| \le Mm^4,$$

and, in general,

$$|f^{[n]}(x)| \le Mm^n$$

for every x in $[x_1, x_2]$.   Hence

$$|R_n(x)| = \frac{|f^{[n+1]}(z_n)|}{(n+1)!} |x - x_0|^{n+1} \leq \frac{Mm^{n+1}}{(n+1)!} |x - x_0|^{n+1},$$

or $$|R_n(x)| \leq \frac{M}{(n+1)!} |m(x - x_0)|^{n+1}.$$

Now $$\lim_{n \to \infty} \frac{M}{(n+1)!} |m(x - x_0)|^{n+1} = 0,$$

and therefore $\lim\limits_{n \to \infty} R_n = 0$.   This proves the theorem.

Let us consider the possibility that the equation

$$y'' = ky$$

has two solutions g_1 and g_2 in a given interval such that

$$g_1(x_0) = g_2(x_0), \qquad g_1'(x_0) = g_2'(x_0)$$

at some number x_0 in the interval.   If we let

$$f(x) = g_1(x) - g_2(x),$$

then f is a solution of the given homogeneous linear differential equation such that

$$f(x_0) = 0, \qquad f'(x_0) = 0.$$

Since $f''(x_0) = kf(x_0)$, $f'''(x_0) = kf'(x_0)$, $f^{iv}(x_0) = k^2 f(x_0)$, and so on, it is clear that

$$f^{[n]}(x_0) = 0$$

for every n.

By the proof of 21.22, f is represented by its Taylor's series

$$f(x) = \sum_{k=0}^{\infty} \frac{f^{[k]}(x_0)}{k!} (x - x_0)^k$$

in the given interval.   Since each coefficient of this power series is zero, evidently $f(x) = 0$.   Hence

$$g_1(x) = g_2(x)$$

at every x in the interval.   In other words, the boundary conditions

$$y = y_0, \qquad y' = y_1, \qquad \text{when } x = x_0$$

determine a unique solution (see 21.18) of the differential equation $y'' = ky$.

Since the differential equation

$$w'' + bw' + cw = 0$$

can be reduced to the equation

$$y'' = ky$$

by the transformation

$$y = we^{bx/2},$$

we have established the uniqueness of the solution of any second order linear differential equation with constant coefficients.

■ ■ ■ EXERCISES

1. Prove that every solution of the equation $y''' = ky$ is analytic.

Find series solutions for each of the following equations, and determine the interval of convergence of the series.

2. $y' = y$.   3. $y' = xy$.

4. $y'' = xy$.   5. $y'' + x^2y' + xy = 0$.

6. $(x^2 + 1)y'' + xy' - y = 0$.

7. Solve the equation $y'' = y$ by infinite series to get the solution

$$y = A_1 \cosh x + A_2 \sinh x.$$

Show that this solution is equivalent to $y = C_1e^x + C_2e^{-x}$.

■ ■ ■ ■ ■

Facts and formulas
from trigonometry

IF ANGLE θ is placed in a rectangular coordinate plane as in Figure A.1, with its initial side on the positive x-axis, then the coordinates of the point on the terminal side of θ one unit from the origin are $\cos \theta$ and $\sin \theta$. The other trigonometric functions are defined as follows:

$$\tan \theta = \frac{\sin \theta}{\cos \theta}, \qquad \cot \theta = \frac{\cos \theta}{\sin \theta},$$

$$\sec \theta = \frac{1}{\cos \theta}, \qquad \csc \theta = \frac{1}{\sin \theta}.$$

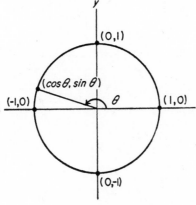

Figure A.1

The basic trigonometric identities are as follows:

$$\sin^2 \theta + \cos^2 \theta = 1, \qquad \tan^2 \theta + 1 = \sec^2 \theta$$

$$\sin (\theta \pm \phi) = \sin \theta \cos \phi \pm \cos \theta \sin \phi$$

$$\cos (\theta \pm \phi) = \cos \theta \cos \phi \mp \sin \theta \sin \phi$$

$$\tan (\theta \pm \phi) = \frac{\tan \theta \pm \tan \phi}{1 \mp \tan \theta \tan \phi}$$

$$\sin \theta \sin \phi = -\tfrac{1}{2} \left[\cos (\theta + \phi) - \cos (\theta - \phi) \right]$$

$$\sin \theta \cos \phi = \tfrac{1}{2} \left[\sin (\theta + \phi) + \sin (\theta - \phi) \right]$$

$$\cos \theta \cos \phi = \tfrac{1}{2} \left[\cos (\theta + \phi) + \cos (\theta - \phi) \right]$$

$$\sin 2\theta = 2 \sin \theta \cos \theta, \qquad \cos 2\theta = \cos^2 \theta - \sin^2 \theta$$

$$\sin^2 \frac{\theta}{2} = \frac{1 - \cos \theta}{2}, \qquad \cos^2 \frac{\theta}{2} = \frac{1 + \cos \theta}{2}.$$

If A, B, C are the angles of a triangle and a, b, c are the lengths of the respective opposite sides, then the following formulas hold:

Law of Sines:
$$\frac{\sin A}{a} = \frac{\sin B}{b}$$

Law of Cosines:
$$a^2 = b^2 + c^2 - 2bc \cos A.$$

Table of integrals

1. $\displaystyle\int x^n\, dx = \frac{1}{n+1} x^{n+1} + C, \quad n \neq -1.$

2. $\displaystyle\int \frac{1}{x}\, dx = \ln |x| + C.$

3. $\displaystyle\int \frac{1}{x^2 + a^2}\, dx = \frac{1}{a} \tan^{-1}\frac{x}{a} + C.$

4. $\displaystyle\int \frac{1}{x^2 - a^2}\, dx = \frac{1}{2a} \ln \left|\frac{x-a}{x+a}\right| + C.$

5. $\displaystyle\int x^m(ax + b)^n\, dx =$

$$\frac{1}{a(m+n+1)} \left\{ x^m(ax+b)^{n+1} - mb \int x^{m-1}(ax+b)^n\, dx \right\},$$
$$m > 0, \quad m+n+1 \neq 0.$$

6. $\displaystyle\int \frac{1}{(ax+b)(cx+d)}\, dx = \frac{1}{bc-ad} \ln \left|\frac{cx+d}{ax+b}\right| + C, \quad bc - ad \neq 0.$

7. $\displaystyle\int \frac{x}{(ax+b)(cx+d)}\, dx =$

$$\frac{1}{bc-ad} \left\{ \frac{b}{a} \ln |ax+b| - \frac{d}{c} \ln |cx+d| \right\} + C, \quad bc - ad \neq 0.$$

8. $\displaystyle\int \frac{1}{(ax+b)^2(cx+d)}\, dx =$

$$\frac{1}{bc-ad} \left\{ \frac{1}{ax+b} + \frac{c}{bc-ad} \ln \left|\frac{cx+d}{ax+b}\right| \right\} + C, \quad bc - ad \neq 0.$$

9. $\displaystyle\int \frac{x}{(ax+b)^2(cx+d)}\, dx =$

$$-\frac{1}{bc-ad}\left\{\frac{b}{a(ax+b)} + \frac{d}{bc-ad}\ln\left|\frac{cx+d}{ax+b}\right|\right\} + C, \quad bc-ad \ne 0.$$

10. $\displaystyle\int x\sqrt{ax+b}\, dx = \frac{2}{15a^2}(3ax-2b)(ax+b)^{3/2} + C.$

11. $\displaystyle\int x^n\sqrt{ax+b}\, dx =$

$$\frac{2}{a(2n+3)}\left\{x^n(ax+b)^{3/2} - nb\int x^{n-1}\sqrt{ax+b}\, dx\right\}, \quad n \ne -\frac{3}{2}.$$

12. $\displaystyle\int \frac{x}{\sqrt{ax+b}}\, dx = \frac{2}{3a^2}(ax-2b)\sqrt{ax+b} + C.$

13. $\displaystyle\int \frac{x^n}{\sqrt{ax+b}}\, dx = \frac{2}{a(2n+1)}\left\{x^n\sqrt{ax+b} - nb\int \frac{x^{n-1}}{\sqrt{ax+b}}\, dx\right\},$

$$n \ne -\frac{1}{2}.$$

14. $\displaystyle\int \frac{1}{x\sqrt{ax+b}}\, dx = \frac{1}{\sqrt{b}}\ln\left|\frac{\sqrt{ax+b}-\sqrt{b}}{\sqrt{ax+b}+\sqrt{b}}\right| + C, \quad b > 0.$

15. $\displaystyle\int \frac{1}{x\sqrt{ax+b}}\, dx = \frac{2}{\sqrt{-b}}\tan^{-1}\sqrt{\frac{ax+b}{-b}} + C, \quad b < 0.$

16. $\displaystyle\int \frac{1}{x^n\sqrt{ax+b}}\, dx =$

$$-\frac{1}{b(n-1)}\frac{\sqrt{ax+b}}{x^{n-1}} - \frac{(2n-3)a}{(2n-2)b}\int \frac{1}{x^{n-1}\sqrt{ax+b}}\, dx, \quad n \ne 1.$$

17. $\displaystyle\int \frac{\sqrt{ax+b}}{x}\, dx = 2\sqrt{ax+b} + b\int \frac{1}{x\sqrt{ax+b}}\, dx.$

18. $\displaystyle\int \sqrt{x^2 \pm a^2}\, dx = \frac{x}{2}\sqrt{x^2 \pm a^2} \pm \frac{a^2}{2}\ln|x + \sqrt{x^2 \pm a^2}| + C.$

19. $\displaystyle\int \frac{1}{\sqrt{x^2 \pm a^2}}\, dx = \ln|x + \sqrt{x^2 \pm a^2}| + C.$

20. $\displaystyle\int x^2\sqrt{x^2 \pm a^2}\, dx =$

$$\frac{x}{8}(2x^2 \pm a^2)\sqrt{x^2 \pm a^2} - \frac{a^4}{8}\ln|x + \sqrt{x^2 \pm a^2}| + C.$$

21. $\displaystyle\int \frac{x^2}{\sqrt{x^2 \pm a^2}}\, dx = \frac{x}{2}\sqrt{x^2 \pm a^2} \mp \frac{a^2}{2}\ln|x + \sqrt{x^2 \pm a^2}| + C.$

22. $\int (x^2 \pm a^2)^{3/2}\, dx = x(x^2 \pm a^2)^{3/2} - 3\int x^2\sqrt{x^2 \pm a^2}\, dx.$

23. $\int \dfrac{1}{(x^2 \pm a^2)^{3/2}}\, dx = \dfrac{\pm x}{a^2\sqrt{x^2 \pm a^2}} + C.$

24. $\int \dfrac{x^2}{(x^2 \pm a^2)^{3/2}}\, dx = -\dfrac{x}{\sqrt{x^2 \pm a^2}} + \ln|x + \sqrt{x^2 \pm a^2}| + C.$

25. $\int \dfrac{1}{x^2\sqrt{x^2 \pm a^2}}\, dx = \mp \dfrac{\sqrt{x^2 \pm a^2}}{a^2 x} + C.$

26. $\int \dfrac{\sqrt{x^2 \pm a^2}}{x^2}\, dx = -\dfrac{\sqrt{x^2 \pm a^2}}{x} + \ln|x + \sqrt{x^2 \pm a^2}| + C.$

27. $\int \dfrac{\sqrt{x^2 \pm a^2}}{x}\, dx = \sqrt{x^2 \pm a^2} \pm a^2 \int \dfrac{1}{x\sqrt{x^2 \pm a^2}}\, dx.$

28. $\int \dfrac{1}{x\sqrt{x^2 + a^2}}\, dx = -\dfrac{1}{a}\ln\left|\dfrac{a + \sqrt{x^2 + a^2}}{x}\right| + C.$

29. $\int \dfrac{1}{x\sqrt{x^2 - a^2}}\, dx = \dfrac{1}{a}\sec^{-1}\dfrac{x}{a} + C.$

30. $\int \sqrt{a^2 - x^2}\, dx = \dfrac{x}{2}\sqrt{a^2 - x^2} + \dfrac{a^2}{2}\sin^{-1}\dfrac{x}{a} + C.$

31. $\int \dfrac{1}{\sqrt{a^2 - x^2}}\, dx = \sin^{-1}\dfrac{x}{a} + C.$

32. $\int x^2\sqrt{a^2 - x^2}\, dx = -\dfrac{x}{4}(a^2 - x^2)^{3/2} + \dfrac{a^2}{4}\int \sqrt{a^2 - x^2}\, dx.$

33. $\int \dfrac{x^2}{\sqrt{a^2 - x^2}}\, dx = -\dfrac{x}{2}\sqrt{a^2 - x^2} + \dfrac{a^2}{2}\sin^{-1}\dfrac{x}{a} + C.$

34. $\int (a^2 - x^2)^{3/2}\, dx = \dfrac{x}{4}(a^2 - x^2)^{3/2} + \dfrac{3a^2}{4}\int \sqrt{a^2 - x^2}\, dx.$

35. $\int \dfrac{1}{(a^2 - x^2)^{3/2}}\, dx = \dfrac{x}{a^2\sqrt{a^2 - x^2}} + C.$

36. $\int \dfrac{x^2}{(a^2 - x^2)^{3/2}}\, dx = \dfrac{x}{\sqrt{a^2 - x^2}} - \sin^{-1}\dfrac{x}{a} + C.$

37. $\int \dfrac{1}{x\sqrt{a^2 - x^2}}\, dx = -\dfrac{1}{a}\ln\left|\dfrac{a + \sqrt{a^2 - x^2}}{x}\right| + C.$

38. $\int \dfrac{1}{x^2\sqrt{a^2 - x^2}}\, dx = -\dfrac{\sqrt{a^2 - x^2}}{a^2 x} + C.$

39. $\displaystyle \int \frac{\sqrt{a^2 - x^2}}{x} \, dx = \sqrt{a^2 - x^2} - a \ln \left| \frac{a + \sqrt{a^2 - x^2}}{x} \right| + C.$

40. $\displaystyle \int \frac{\sqrt{a^2 - x^2}}{x^2} \, dx = -\frac{\sqrt{a^2 - x^2}}{x} - \sin^{-1} \frac{x}{a} + C.$

41. $\displaystyle \int \frac{1}{(x^2 + a^2)^n} \, dx =$

$$\frac{1}{2(n-1)a^2} \left\{ \frac{x}{(x^2 + a^2)^{n-1}} + (2n - 3) \int \frac{1}{(x^2 + a^2)^{n-1}} \, dx \right\}, \quad n \neq 1.$$

42. $\displaystyle \int \sin x \, dx = -\cos x + C.$

43. $\displaystyle \int \sin^2 x \, dx = \frac{x}{2} - \frac{1}{4} \sin 2x + C.$

44. $\displaystyle \int \sin^n x \, dx = -\frac{1}{n} \sin^{n-1} x \cos x + \frac{n-1}{n} \int \sin^{n-2} x \, dx, \quad n \geq 2.$

45. $\displaystyle \int x \sin x \, dx = \sin x - x \cos x + C.$

46. $\displaystyle \int x^2 \sin x \, dx = 2x \sin x - (x^2 - 2) \cos x + C.$

47. $\displaystyle \int x^n \sin x \, dx = -x^n \cos x + nx^{n-1} \sin x - n(n - 1) \int x^{n-2} \sin x \, dx.$

48. $\displaystyle \int \cos x \, dx = \sin x + C.$

49. $\displaystyle \int \cos^2 x \, dx = \frac{x}{2} + \frac{1}{4} \sin 2x + C.$

50. $\displaystyle \int \cos^n x \, dx = \frac{1}{n} \sin x \cos^{n-1} x + \frac{n-1}{n} \int \cos^{n-2} x \, dx, \quad n \geq 2.$

51. $\displaystyle \int x \cos x \, dx = \cos x + x \sin x + C.$

52. $\displaystyle \int x^2 \cos x \, dx = 2x \cos x + (x^2 - 2) \sin x + C.$

53. $\displaystyle \int x^n \cos x \, dx = x^n \sin x + nx^{n-1} \cos x - n(n - 1) \int x^{n-2} \cos x \, dx.$

54. $\displaystyle \int \sin x \cos x \, dx = \frac{1}{2} \sin^2 x + C.$

55. $\displaystyle \int \sin^2 x \cos^2 x \, dx = \frac{x}{8} - \frac{1}{32} \sin 4x + C.$

56. $\int \sin^m x \cos^n x \, dx =$

$$\begin{cases} \dfrac{1}{m+n}\left[-\sin^{m-1} x \cos^{n+1} x + (m-1) \int \sin^{m-2} x \cos^n x \, dx \right] \\[2ex] \dfrac{1}{m+n}\left[\sin^{m+1} x \cos^{n-1} x + (n-1) \int \sin^m x \cos^{n-2} x \, dx \right], \\[2ex] \hspace{7cm} m \neq -n. \end{cases}$$

57. $\int \tan x \, dx = \ln |\sec x| + C.$

58. $\int \tan^2 x \, dx = \tan x - x + C.$

59. $\int \tan^n x \, dx = \dfrac{1}{n-1} \tan^{n-1} x - \int \tan^{n-2} x \, dx, \quad n \geq 2.$

60. $\int \cot x \, dx = \ln |\sin x| + C.$

61. $\int \cot^2 x \, dx = -\cot x - x + C.$

62. $\int \cot^n x \, dx = -\dfrac{1}{n-1} \cot^{n-1} x - \int \cot^{n-2} x \, dx, \quad n \geq 2.$

63. $\int \sec x \, dx = \ln |\sec x + \tan x| + C.$

64. $\int \sec^2 x \, dx = \tan x + C.$

65. $\int \sec^n x \, dx = \dfrac{1}{n-1} \left\{ \sec^{n-2} x \tan x + (n-2) \int \sec^{n-2} x \, dx \right\},$
$$n \geq 2.$$

66. $\int \csc x \, dx = \ln |\csc x - \cot x| + C.$

67. $\int \csc^2 x \, dx = -\cot x + C.$

68. $\int \csc^n x \, dx = \dfrac{1}{n-1} \left\{ -\csc^{n-2} x \cot x + (n-2) \int \csc^{n-2} x \, dx \right\},$
$$n \geq 2.$$

69. $\int \sec x \tan x \, dx = \sec x + C.$

70. $\displaystyle\int \csc x \cot x \, dx = -\csc x + C.$

71. $\displaystyle\int e^{ax} \, dx = \frac{1}{a} e^{ax} + C.$

72. $\displaystyle\int x e^{ax} \, dx = \frac{1}{a^2} (ax - 1) e^{ax} + C.$

73. $\displaystyle\int x^n e^{ax} \, dx = \frac{x^n}{a} e^{ax} - \frac{n}{a} \int x^{n-1} e^{ax} \, dx.$

74. $\displaystyle\int e^{ax} \sin bx \, dx = \frac{1}{a^2 + b^2} (a \sin bx - b \cos bx) e^{ax} + C.$

75. $\displaystyle\int e^{ax} \cos bx \, dx = \frac{1}{a^2 + b^2} (a \cos bx + b \sin bx) e^{ax} + C.$

76. $\displaystyle\int \ln |x| \, dx = x \ln |x| - x + C.$

77. $\displaystyle\int \ln^n |x| \, dx = x \ln^n |x| - n \int \ln^{n-1} |x| \, dx.$

78. $\displaystyle\int x^n \ln |x| \, dx = \frac{x^{n+1}}{n+1} \left(\ln |x| - \frac{1}{n+1} \right) + C, \quad n \ne -1.$

79. $\displaystyle\int \frac{\ln^n |x|}{x} \, dx = \frac{1}{n+1} \ln^{n+1} |x| + C, \quad n \ne -1.$

80. $\displaystyle\int \frac{1}{x \ln |x|} \, dx = \ln |\ln|x| \,| + C.$

81. $\displaystyle\int x^m \ln^n |x| \, dx = \frac{1}{m+1} \left\{ x^{m+1} \ln^n |x| - n \int x^m \ln^{n-1} |x| \, dx \right\},$

$$m \ne -1.$$

82. $\displaystyle\int \sin^{-1} x \, dx = x \sin^{-1} x + \sqrt{1 - x^2} + C.$

83. $\displaystyle\int x^n \sin^{-1} x \, dx = \frac{1}{n+1} \left\{ x^{n+1} \sin^{-1} x - \int \frac{x^{n+1}}{\sqrt{1 - x^2}} \, dx \right\}, \quad n \ne -1.$

84. $\displaystyle\int \tan^{-1} x \, dx = x \tan^{-1} x - \frac{1}{2} \ln (x^2 + 1) + C.$

85. $\displaystyle\int x^n \tan^{-1} x \, dx = \frac{1}{n+1} \left\{ x^{n+1} \tan^{-1} x - \int \frac{x^{n+1}}{x^2 + 1} \, dx \right\}, \quad n \ne -1.$

86. $\displaystyle\int \sec^{-1} x \, dx = x \sec^{-1} x - \ln |x + \sqrt{x^2 - 1}| + C.$

Numerical tables

TABLE I.   Logarithms to base 10

N	0	1	2	3	4	5	6	7	8	9
1.0	.0000	.0043	.0086	.0128	.0170	.0212	.0253	.0294	.0334	.0374
1.1	.0414	.0453	.0492	.0531	.0569	.0607	.0645	.0682	.0719	.0755
1.2	.0792	.0828	.0864	.0899	.0934	.0969	.1004	.1038	.1072	.1106
1.3	.1139	.1173	.1206	.1239	.1271	.1303	.1335	.1367	.1399	.1430
1.4	.1461	.1492	.1523	.1553	.1584	.1614	.1644	.1673	.1703	.1732
1.5	.1761	.1790	.1818	.1847	.1875	.1903	.1931	.1959	.1987	.2014
1.6	.2041	.2068	.2095	.2122	.2148	.2175	.2201	.2227	.2253	.2279
1.7	.2304	.2330	.2355	.2380	.2405	.2430	.2455	.2480	.2504	.2529
1.8	.2553	.2577	.2601	.2625	.2648	.2672	.2695	.2718	.2742	.2765
1.9	.2788	.2810	.2833	.2856	.2878	.2900	.2923	.2945	.2967	.2989
2.0	.3010	.3032	.3054	.3075	.3096	.3118	.3139	.3160	.3181	.3201
2.1	.3222	.3243	.3263	.3284	.3304	.3324	.3345	.3365	.3385	.3404
2.2	.3424	.3444	.3464	.3483	.3502	.3522	.3541	.3560	.3579	.3598
2.3	.3617	.3636	.3655	.3674	.3692	.3711	.3729	.3747	.3766	.3784
2.4	.3802	.3820	.3838	.3856	.3874	.3892	.3909	.3927	.3945	.3962
2.5	.3979	.3997	.4014	.4031	.4048	.4065	.4082	.4099	.4116	.4133
2.6	.4150	.4166	.4183	.4200	.4216	.4232	.4249	.4265	.4281	.4298
2.7	.4314	.4330	.4346	.4362	.4378	.4393	.4409	.4425	.4440	.4456
2.8	.4472	.4487	.4502	.4518	.4533	.4548	.4564	.4579	.4594	.4609
2.9	.4624	.4639	.4654	.4669	.4683	.4698	.4713	.4728	.4742	.4757
3.0	.4771	.4786	.4800	.4814	.4829	.4843	.4857	.4871	.4886	.4900
3.1	.4914	.4928	.4942	.4955	.4969	.4983	.4997	.5011	.5024	.5038
3.2	.5051	.5065	.5079	.5092	.5105	.5119	.5132	.5145	.5159	.5172
3.3	.5185	.5198	.5211	.5224	.5237	.5250	.5263	.5276	.5289	.5302
3.4	.5315	.5328	.5340	.5353	.5366	.5378	.5391	.5403	.5416	.5428
3.5	.5441	.5453	.5465	.5478	.5490	.5502	.5514	.5527	.5539	.5551
3.6	.5563	.5575	.5587	.5599	.5611	.5623	.5635	.5647	.5658	.5670
3.7	.5682	.5694	.5705	.5717	.5729	.5740	.5752	.5763	.5775	.5786
3.8	.5798	.5809	.5821	.5832	.5843	.5855	.5866	.5877	.5888	.5899
3.9	.5911	.5922	.5933	.5944	.5955	.5966	.5977	.5988	.5999	.6010
4.0	.6021	.6031	.6042	.6053	.6064	.6075	.6085	.6096	.6107	.6117
4.1	.6128	.6138	.6149	.6160	.6170	.6180	.6191	.6201	.6212	.6222
4.2	.6232	.6243	.6253	.6263	.6274	.6284	.6294	.6304	.6314	.6325
4.3	.6335	.6345	.6355	.6365	.6375	.6385	.6395	.6405	.6415	.6425
4.4	.6435	.6444	.6454	.6464	.6474	.6484	.6493	.6503	.6513	.6522
4.5	.6532	.6542	.6551	.6561	.6571	.6580	.6590	.6599	.6609	.6618
4.6	.6628	.6637	.6646	.6656	.6665	.6675	.6684	.6693	.6702	.6712
4.7	.6721	.6730	.6739	.6749	.6758	.6767	.6776	.6785	.6794	.6803
4.8	.6812	.6821	.6830	.6839	.6848	.6857	.6866	.6875	.6884	.6893
4.9	.6902	.6911	.6920	.6928	.6937	.6946	.6955	.6964	.6972	.6981
5.0	.6990	.6998	.7007	.7016	.7024	.7033	.7042	.7050	.7059	.7067
5.1	.7076	.7084	.7093	.7101	.7110	.7118	.7126	.7135	.7143	.7152
5.2	.7160	.7168	.7177	.7185	.7193	.7202	.7210	.7218	.7226	.7235
5.3	.7243	.7251	.7259	.7267	.7275	.7284	.7292	.7300	.7308	.7316
5.4	.7324	.7332	.7340	.7348	.7356	.7364	.7372	.7380	.7388	.7396
N	0	1	2	3	4	5	6	7	8	9

TABLE I. Logarithms to base 10 (*continued*)

N	0	1	2	3	4	5	6	7	8	9
5.5	.7404	.7412	.7419	.7427	.7435	.7443	.7451	.7459	.7466	.7474
5.6	.7482	.7490	.7497	.7505	.7513	.7520	.7528	.7536	.7543	.7551
5.7	.7559	.7566	.7574	.7582	.7589	.7597	.7604	.7612	.7619	.7627
5.8	.7634	.7642	.7649	.7657	.7664	.7672	.7679	.7689	.7694	.7701
5.9	.7709	.7716	.7723	.7731	.7738	.7745	.7752	.7760	.7767	.7774
6.0	.7782	.7789	.7796	.7803	.7810	.7818	.7825	.7832	.7839	.7846
6.1	.7853	.7860	.7868	.7875	.7882	.7889	.7896	.7903	.7910	.7917
6.2	.7924	.7931	.7938	.7945	.7952	.7959	.7966	.7973	.7980	.7987
6.3	.7993	.8000	.8007	.8014	.8021	.8028	.8035	.8041	.8048	.8055
6.4	.8062	.8069	.8075	.8082	.8089	.8096	.8102	.8109	.8116	.8122
6.5	.8129	.8136	.8142	.8149	.8156	.8162	.8169	.8176	.8182	.8189
6.6	.8195	.8202	.8209	.8215	.8222	.8228	.8235	.8241	.8248	.8254
6.7	.8261	.8267	.8274	.8280	.8287	.8293	.8299	.8306	.8312	.8319
6.8	.8325	.8331	.8338	.8344	.8351	.8357	.8363	.8370	.8376	.8328
6.9	.8388	.8395	.8401	.8407	.8414	.8420	.8426	.8432	.8439	.8445
7.0	.8451	.8457	.8463	.8470	.8476	.8482	.8488	.8494	.8500	.8506
7.1	.8513	.8519	.8525	.8531	.8537	.8543	.8549	.8555	.8561	.8567
7.2	.8573	.8579	.8585	.8591	.8597	.8603	.8609	.8615	.8621	.8627
7.3	.8633	.8639	.8645	.8651	.8657	.8663	.8669	.8675	.8681	.8686
7.4	.8692	.8698	.8704	.8710	.8716	.8722	.8727	.8733	.8739	.8475
7.5	.8751	.8756	.8762	.8768	.8774	.8779	.8785	.8791	.8797	.8802
7.6	.8808	.8814	.8820	.8825	.8831	.8837	.8842	.8848	.8854	.8859
7.7	.8865	.8871	.8876	.8882	.8887	.8893	.8899	.8904	.8910	.8915
7.8	.8921	.8927	.8932	.8938	.8943	.8949	.8954	.8960	.8965	.8971
7.9	.8976	.8982	.8987	.8993	.8998	.9004	.9009	.9015	.9020	.9025
8.0	.9031	.9036	.9042	.9047	.9053	.9058	.9063	.9069	.9074	.9079
8.1	.9085	.9090	.9096	.9101	.9106	.9112	.9117	.9122	.9128	.9133
8.2	.9138	.9143	.9149	.9154	.9159	.9165	.9170	.9175	.9180	.9186
8.3	.9191	.9196	.9201	.9206	.9212	.9217	.9222	.9227	.9232	.9238
8.4	.9243	.9248	.9253	.9258	.9263	.9269	.9274	.9279	.9284	.9289
8.5	.9294	.9299	.9304	.9309	.9315	.9320	.9325	.9330	.9335	.9340
8.6	.9345	.9350	.9355	.9360	.9365	.9370	.9375	.9380	.9385	.9390
8.7	.9395	.9400	.9405	.9410	.9415	.9420	.9425	.9430	.9435	.9440
8.8	.9445	.9450	.9455	.9460	.9465	.9469	.9474	.9479	.9484	.9489
8.9	.9494	.9499	.9504	.9509	.9513	.9518	.9523	.9528	.9533	.9538
9.0	.9542	.9547	.9552	.9557	.9562	.9566	.9571	.9576	.9581	.9586
9.1	.9590	.9595	.9600	.9605	.9609	.9614	.9619	.9624	.9628	.9633
9.2	.9638	.9643	.9647	.9652	.9657	.9661	.9666	.9671	.9765	.9680
9.3	.9685	.9689	.9694	.9699	.9703	.9708	.9713	.9717	.9722	.9727
9.4	.9731	.9736	.9741	.9745	.9750	.9754	.9759	.9763	.9768	.9773
9.5	.9777	.9782	.9786	.9791	.9795	.9800	.9805	.9809	.9814	.9818
9.6	.9823	.9827	.9832	.9836	.9841	.9845	.9850	.9854	.9859	.9863
9.7	.9868	.9872	.9877	.9881	.9886	.9890	.9894	.9899	.9903	.9908
9.8	.9912	.9917	.9921	.9926	.9930	.9934	.9939	.9943	.9948	.9952
9.9	.9956	.9961	.9965	.9969	.9974	.9978	.9983	.9987	.9991	.9996
N	0	1	2	3	4	5	6	7	8	9

TABLE II. Logarithms to base *e*

N	.0	.1	.2	.3	.4	.5	.6	.7	.8	.9
1	0.000	0.095	0.182	0.262	0.336	0.405	0.470	0.531	0.588	0.642
2	0.693	0.742	0.788	0.833	0.875	0.916	0.956	0.993	1.030	1.065
3	1.099	1.131	1.163	1.194	1.224	1.253	1.281	1.308	1.335	1.361
4	1.386	1.411	1.435	1.459	1.482	1.504	1.526	1.548	1.569	1.589
5	1.609	1.629	1.649	1.668	1.686	1.705	1.723	1.740	1.758	1.775
6	1.792	1.808	1.825	1.841	1.856	1.872	1.887	1.902	1.917	1.932
7	1.946	1.960	1.974	1.988	2.001	2.015	2.028	2.041	2.054	2.067
8	2.079	2.092	2.104	2.116	2.128	2.140	2.152	2.163	2.175	2.186
9	2.197	2.208	2.219	2.230	2.241	2.251	2.262	2.272	2.282	2.293
10	2.303	2.313	2.322	2.332	2.342	2.351	2.361	2.370	2.380	2.389

TABLE III. e^x and e^{-x}

x	e^x	e^{-x}	x	e^x	e^{-x}
0.0	1.00	1.00	3.1	22.2	.045
0.1	1.11	.905	3.2	24.5	.041
0.2	1.22	.819	3.3	27.1	.037
0.3	1.35	.741	3.4	30.0	.033
0.4	1.49	.670	3.5	33.1	.030
0.5	1.65	.607	3.6	36.6	.027
0.6	1.82	.549	3.7	40.4	.025
0.7	2.01	.497	3.8	44.7	.022
0.8	2.23	.449	3.9	49.4	.020
0.9	2.46	.407	4.0	54.6	.018
1.0	2.72	.368	4.1	60.3	.017
1.1	3.00	.333	4.2	66.7	.015
1.2	3.32	.301	4.3	73.7	.014
1.3	3.67	.273	4.4	81.5	.012
1.4	4.06	.247	4.5	90.0	.011
1.5	4.48	.223	4.6	99.5	.010
1.6	4.95	.202	4.7	110	.0091
1.7	5.47	.183	4.8	122	.0082
1.8	6.05	.165	4.9	134	.0074
1.9	6.69	.150	5.0	148	.0067
2.0	7.39	.135	5.1	164	.0061
2.1	8.17	.122	5.2	181	.0055
2.2	9.02	.111	5.3	200	.0050
2.3	9.97	.100	5.4	221	.0045
2.4	11.0	.091	5.5	245	.0041
2.5	12.2	.082	5.6	270	.0037
2.6	13.5	.074	5.7	299	.0033
2.7	14.9	.067	5.8	330	.0030
2.8	16.4	.061	5.9	365	.0027
2.9	18.2	.055	6.0	403	.0025
3.0	20.1	.050			

TABLE IV. Trigonometric functions

Degrees	Radians	Sin	Tan	Cot	Cos		Degrees
0°	.000	.000	.000		1.000	1.571	90°
1°	.017	.017	.017	57.29	1.000	1.553	89°
2°	.035	.035	.035	28.64	.999	1.536	88°
3°	.052	.052	.052	19.081	.999	1.518	87°
4°	.070	.070	.070	14.301	.998	1.501	86°
5°	.087	.087	.087	11.430	.996	1.484	85°
6°	.105	.105	.105	9.514	.995	1.466	84°
7°	.122	.122	.123	8.144	.993	1.449	83°
8°	.140	.139	.141	7.115	.990	1.431	82°
9°	.157	.156	.158	6.314	.988	1.414	81°
10°	.175	.174	.176	5.671	.985	1.396	80°
11°	.192	.191	.194	5.145	.982	1.379	79°
12°	.209	.208	.213	4.705	.978	1.361	78°
13°	.227	.225	.231	4.331	.974	1.344	77°
14°	.244	.242	.249	4.011	.970	1.326	76°
15°	.262	.259	.268	3.732	.966	1.309	75°
16°	.279	.276	.287	3.487	.961	1.292	74°
17°	.297	.292	.306	3.271	.956	1.274	73°
18°	.314	.309	.325	3.078	.951	1.257	72°
19°	.332	.326	.344	2.904	.946	1.239	71°
20°	.349	.342	.364	2.747	.940	1.222	70°
21°	.367	.358	.384	2.605	.934	1.204	69°
22°	.384	.375	.404	2.475	.927	1.187	68°
23°	.401	.391	.424	2.356	.921	1.169	67°
24°	.419	.407	.445	2.246	.914	1.152	66°
25°	.436	.423	.466	2.144	.906	1.134	65°
26°	.454	.438	.488	2.050	.899	1.117	64°
27°	.471	.454	.510	1.963	.891	1.100	63°
28°	.489	.469	.532	1.881	.883	1.082	62°
29°	.506	.485	.554	1.804	.875	1.065	61°
30°	.524	.500	.577	1.732	.866	1.047	60°
31°	.541	.515	.601	1.664	.857	1.030	59°
32°	.559	.530	.625	1.600	.848	1.012	58°
33°	.576	.545	.649	1.540	.839	.995	57°
34°	.593	.559	.675	1.483	.829	.977	56°
35°	.611	.574	.700	1.428	.819	.960	55°
36°	.628	.588	.727	1.376	.809	.942	54°
37°	.646	.602	.754	1.327	.799	.925	53°
38°	.663	.616	.781	1.280	.788	.908	52°
39°	.681	.629	.810	1.235	.777	.890	51°
40°	.698	.643	.839	1.192	.766	.873	50°
41°	.716	.656	.869	1.150	.755	.855	49°
42°	.733	.669	.900	1.111	.743	.838	48°
43°	.750	.682	.933	1.072	.731	.820	47°
44°	.768	.695	.966	1.036	.719	.803	46°
45°	.785	.707	1.000	1.000	.707	.785	45°
		Cos	Cot	Tan	Sin	Radians	Degrees

Supplementary exercises

■ ■ ■ CHAPTER 1

The statement "If a is non-negative, then $a + b$ is not less than b" can be translated into "If $a \geq 0$ then $a + b \geq b$." In Exercises 1 through 5 translate each statement into a statement concerning inequalities.

1. The number u does not exceed the number v.
2. c is at least as great as b.
3. x lies strictly between c and d.
4. x can never be greater than a.
5. No number in the interval $[a,b]$ exceeds c.
6. Prove that if a and b are non-negative, then $a^2 < b^2$ if and only if $a < b$.
7. Note that $|x|$ is always non-negative and that $x^2 = |x|^2$. Hence use the preceding exercise to solve each of the inequalities. (Use 1.9 or 1.10) In each case give the interval solution.
   a) $x^2 < 4$,   b) $x^2 \leq .01$,   c) $(x - 5)^2 < 1$,
   d) $x^2 + 4x + 4 < 7$,   e) $x^2 + 2x \leq 0$.
8. Prove that if a and b agree in sign, then $1/a < 1/b$ if and only if $a > b$. State and prove a corresponding theorem if a and b differ in sign.
9. Prove that if $a \leq A \leq B \leq b$, then $0 \leq B - A \leq b - a$. Interpret this result in terms of intervals and their lengths.
10. Let a, b, c, d be non-negative numbers. Prove that if $a > c$ and $b > d$, then $ab > cd$. What is the relation between ab and cd if b and c are negative, a and d any numbers, and $a > c$, $b > d$?
11. Let c and d be non-negative numbers. Prove that $\sqrt{c} < \sqrt{d}$ if and only if $c < d$. (Recall that $\sqrt{x}$ is non-negative.)
12. In each of the following find the smallest positive integer that satisfies the inequality.

a) $\dfrac{1}{100}N > 156.$

b) $\dfrac{1}{100}N > -2.$

c) $\dfrac{3}{N} < \dfrac{1}{16}.$

d) $\dfrac{2}{N^2} < \dfrac{1}{2}.$

e) $\dfrac{100}{N^2} < \dfrac{1}{1000}.$

f) $\dfrac{1}{2^N} < \dfrac{1}{64}.$

g) $(\tfrac{3}{2})^N \geq 5.$

13. Let m, n, p, q be integers with n and q positive. Prove that $\dfrac{m}{n} < \dfrac{p}{q}$ if and only if $mq < np$. Compare the rational numbers $a = 291/43$ and $b = 693/127$. Compare the numbers $c = -411/233$ and $d = -2.13$.

14. The temperature F in degrees Fahrenheit is related to the temperature C in degrees centigrade by the equation

$$C = \tfrac{5}{9}(F - 32).$$

Let F_1, F_2 be two Fahrenheit readings, and let C_1, C_2 be the corresponding centigrade readings. Prove that $F_1 < F_2$ if and only if $C_1 < C_2$.

15. Prove that $a^2 + ab + b^2 > 0$ unless $a = b = 0$. (Consider the various possible cases, and note that $a^2 + ab + b^2 = (a + b)^2 - ab$.) Hence prove that $a^3 < b^3$ if and only if $a < b$.

16. Solve the inequalities:
   a) $(x - 1)^3 < 27.$
   b) $(x^2 - 3)^3 < -8.$
   c) $(x^3 - 3)^3 \geq -8.$
   d) $(1 - x^2)^3 < -27.$

17. Prove that $\dfrac{a + b + |a - b|}{2}$ is the larger of a and b.

18. Give the interval solution of each of the inequalities:
   a) $|10^x - 55| < 45.$
   b) $|10^x - 505| < 495.$
   c) $|2^x - 5| < 3.$
   d) $|2^{-x} - 5| < 3.$

19. Prove that if $a < x < b$, then $|x|$ is less than the larger of $|a|$ and $|b|$.

20. If $|x - 2| < 1$ then $-1 < x - 2 < 1$ and $1 < x < 3$. In each of the following find c and d such that $|x - c| < d$ is equivalent to the given inequality.
   a) $5 < x < 7.$
   b) $-7 < x < 3.$
   c) $-1 < x < -\tfrac{1}{2}.$
   d) $0 < x - 3 < 14.$

■ ■ ■ CHAPTER 2

1. The distance from a point P to a line L is $|PQ|$ where Q is the foot of the perpendicular drawn from P to L. In each of the following find the distance from the given point to the given line. Sketch the figure.
   a) $3x + 4y = 12$; $(1,1)$.
   b) $3x + 4y = 12$; $(10,0)$.
   c) $2x - 4y - 5 = 0$; $(5,-1)$.
   d) $x + y - 3 = 0$; $(1,2)$.
   e) $x + y - 3 = 0$; $(0,0)$.

2. Given the points $A(-4,1)$, $B(2,-3)$, $C(1,-5)$ find:
   a) $|AB|$.
   b) An equation of the line on A and B.

c) An equation of the line perpendicular to AB at the point where AB crosses the y-axis.

d) An equation of the line on C and the mid-point of AB.

3. Let the line L have equation $2x - 7y = 4$.
   a) Write an equation of the line L_1 on the point $(-2,5)$ parallel to L.
   b) Write an equation of the line L_2 on the point $(-2,5)$ perpendicular to L.
   c) Find the area of the triangle formed by L_1, L_2 and the y-axis.
   d) Find the area of the triangle formed by L_1, L_2 and the x-axis.

4. Find the area of the triangle formed by the coordinate axes and the tangent line to the circle $x^2 + y^2 = 25$ at the point $(3,-4)$.

5. Let $A(-2,4)$, $B(6,3)$, $C(1,-4)$ be vertices of a triangle.
   a) Find the point of intersection of the three medians of the triangle.
   b) Find the point of intersection of the three altitudes of the triangle.

6. If $ab \neq 0$, show that $\dfrac{x}{a} + \dfrac{y}{b} = 1$ is an equation of the line whose x- and y-intercepts are a and b respectively.

7. Write equations of the circles whose diameters have the following pairs of end points.
   a) $(-6,1)$; $(0,5)$.   b) $(-1,-3)$; $(5,-5)$.   c) $(-1,4)$; $(3,6)$.

8. Sketch the circles with equations

$$x^2 + y^2 + 6x - 16 = 0,$$

$$x^2 + y^2 - 18x - 18y + 62 = 0.$$

   a) Show that these circles intersect in one and only one point, and find this point.
   b) Write an equation of the line on the centers of the circles.
   c) Write an equation of the line tangent to the circles at their point of intersection.

9. Find an equation of the circle which has center on the line $2x + y - 3 = 0$, lies in the first quadrant, and is tangent to both coordinate axes.

10. Prove that every triangle that is inscribed in a circle and has a diameter as one side is a right triangle. (Consider the semi-circle with equation $y = \sqrt{r^2 - x^2}$.)

11. Let $Ax + By + C = 0$ be an equation of a line. Show that the distance d from $P(h,k)$ to the line is given by the formula

$$d = \frac{|Ah + Bk + C|}{\sqrt{A^2 + B^2}}.$$

(Use the method of Exercise 1 above.)

12. Using the formula in the preceding exercise, find an equation of the circle with given point as center which is tangent to the line with given equation. Sketch.
   a) $3x - 4y - 12 = 0$; $(1,1)$.   b) $x + y + 1 = 0$; $(3,4)$.
   c) $2x - 3y = 0$; $(-1,4)$.   d) $2x + y = 4$; $(0,0)$.

13. Find the points of intersection of the graphs of the equations $x^2 = y + 1$ and $2x = y + 1$. Sketch the region enclosed by these graphs.

14. Graph each of the following equations:

a) $y = \dfrac{|x|}{x}$, $x \neq 0$.

b) $|x| + |y| = 0$.

c) $|x| - |y| = 0$.

d) $y = \dfrac{|x|}{x}(x - 1)$, $x \neq 0$.

e) $|y - x| = 1$.

f) $y = \dfrac{|x|}{x}(x^2 + 1)$, $x \neq 0$.

15. The point (x,y) lies above the graph of the equation $y = mx + b$ if and only if x and y are numbers such that $y > mx + b$. Thus the inequality $y > mx + b$ may be represented graphically by shading the region of the xy-plane above the line $y = mx + b$. Other inequalities have similar geometric interpretations. Graph the following inequalities:

a) $y > 2x - 3$.

b) $y > 5 - x$.

c) $y \leq x + 2$.

d) $2x + y \geq 2$.

e) $x^2 + y^2 > 25$.

f) $x^2 + y^2 \leq 4$.

g) $y > |x|$.

h) $y \geq x^2$.

16. Represent graphically the set of points (x,y) (if any) whose coordinates satisfy the following systems of inequalities:

a) $x > 1$, $y < -2$.

b) $2x - 5y + 10 < 0$, $2x - 3y + 6 > 0$, $y > 1$.

c) $y > 3$, $x^2 + y^2 < 25$.

d) $x^2 + y^2 < 25$, $x^2 + y^2 - 10x < 25$.

e) $y > x - 1$, $y < 2 - x$, $y + 2x > 0$.

f) $y > x + 3$, $y < 1 - x$, $2y + x > 6$.

g) $y > x^2$, $y - x < 2$.

17. Let r_1 and r_2 be non-zero numbers. Let $P_1(a_1,b_1)$ and $P_2(a_2,b_2)$ be distinct points. Derive a formula for the coordinates of the point $Q(c,d)$ which divides P_1P_2 in the ratio of r_1 to r_2. That is, find $Q(c,d)$ such that

$$\frac{\overline{P_1Q}}{\overline{QP_2}} = \frac{r_1}{r_2}.$$

Show that the mid-point of P_1P_2 is given by these formulas for proper choice of r_1, r_2.

18. Referring to the previous exercise, find coordinates of Q for each of the following cases:

a) $P_1(-1,0)$, $P_2(2,3)$; $r_1 = 1$, $r_2 = 2$.

b) $P_1(-1,0)$, $P_2(2,3)$; $r_1 = 2$, $r_2 = 1$.

c) $P_1(1,-5)$, $P_2(5,10)$; $r_1 = 1$, $r_2 = 4$.

d) $P_1(1,-5)$, $P_2(5,10)$; $r_1 = 3$, $r_2 = -2$.

e) $P_1(6,0)$, $P_2(0,6)$; $r_1 = 1$, $r_2 = -1$.

■ ■ ■ CHAPTER 3

1. Often, when a function is given by means of a formula or an equation, its domain is not explicitly stated. We then understand the domain to be the largest set of numbers for which the formula or equation is meaningful. For example, if f is defined by the equation $f(x) = 1/x$, we understand the domain of f to be the set of all non-zero numbers. For each of the functions defined below, state the implied domain.

a) $f(x) = \dfrac{1}{x+1}$.

b) $h(x) = \sqrt[3]{x}$.

c) $g(x) = \sqrt{x}$.

d) $F(x) = \sqrt{2x + 5}$.

e) $G(x) = \dfrac{x+1}{x^2 - 4}$.

f) $R(x) = \sqrt{x-2} + \sqrt{x+2}$.

g) $H(x) = \sqrt{x-1} - \sqrt{1-x}$.

h) $f(x) = \sqrt{x-2}\sqrt{x^2-1}$.

i) $G(x) = \sqrt{2x - x^2}$.

2. As in Exercise 1 state the implied domain of each function.

a) $f(x) = \sin x$.

b) $g(\theta) = \tan \theta$.

c) $F(\alpha) = \dfrac{1}{1 - 2\cos \alpha}$.

d) $R(x) = \sqrt{\sin x}$.

e) $H(x) = \sqrt{\csc x}$.

f) $G(x) = \sqrt{1 - \tan x}$.

3. For each of the following pairs of functions find $f(x) + g(x), f(x)\cdot g(x), f(x)/g(x)$, and $f(g(x))$.

a) $f(x) = x + 2, g(x) = -x + 5$.

b) $f(x) = x^2, g(x) = 2x - 3$.

c) $f(x) = \dfrac{1}{x^2 + 1}, g(x) = \dfrac{1}{x^2 - 1}$.

d) $f(x) = x^3 - 1, g(x) = x^3 - 1$.

4. For each of the following pairs of functions graph $y = f(x), y = g(x), y = f(x) + g(x)$ and $y = f(x) - g(x)$. Describe the method (addition and subtraction of ordinates) that is illustrated by this exercise.

a) $f(x) = x, g(x) = 2x$.

b) $f(x) = x^2, g(x) = x$.

c) $f(x) = x^2, g(x) = x^3$.

d) $f(x) = (x + 1)^2, g(x) = 2$.

e) $f(x) = x, g(x) = \sqrt{4 - x^2}, x$ in $[-2,2]$.

f) $f(x) = 1/x, g(x) = 2x + 4, x$ in $[-3,-1]$.

g) $f(x) = \sin x, g(x) = x$.

h) $f(x) = |\sin x|, g(x) = x$.

5. A function f is said to be *even* if $f(-x) = f(x)$ and *odd* if $f(-x) = -f(x)$ for every x in the domain of f. (It is understood that $-x$ is in the domain of f whenever x is.)

a) What can be said of the graph of f if f is even? If f is odd?

b) When is a polynomial function odd and when is it even?

c) Show that if f and g are both odd, then so are the sum and difference functions, but the product and quotient are even.

6. Using the definitions in the previous exercise, determine whether each of the following functions is odd, even, or neither.

a) $f(x) = 2 + x^2 + \sqrt{3}\, x^4$.

b) $g(x) = x + 3x^5$.

c) $h(x) = \dfrac{x(1 - x^2)}{x^2 + 1}$.

d) $F(x) = 2 + x^3$.

e) $g(x) = ax^3 + bx$.

f) $F(x) = 2^x + 2^{-x}$.

g) $G(x) = |x|$.

h) $f(\theta) = \sin \theta$.

i) $g(\theta) = \cos \theta$.

7. Let $f(x) = \sin x$, $g(x) = |x|$. Sketch the graphs of f, g, and F, G where $F(x) = f(g(x))$, $G(x) = g(f(x))$.

8. Let f and g be functions with a common domain.
   a) Show that the graph of the equation $(y - f(x))(y - g(x)) = 0$ consists of the combined graphs of f and g.
   b) Show that the graph of the equation
   $$(y - f(x))^2 + (y - g(x))^2 = 0$$
   consists of the points of intersection of the graphs of f and g.

9. Use the previous exercise to find the graphs of the following equations:
   a) $(y - 2x)(y - 3x) = 0$.   b) $y^2 - x^2 = 0$.
   c) $(y - x + 1)^2 + (y + x + 1)^2 = 0$.   d) $y^2 - x^4 = 0$.
   e) $(y - x)^2 + (y - |x|)^2 = 0$.

10. Sketch the graph of each of the following functions:
   a) $f(x) = \begin{cases} \frac{1}{3}x, & x \geq 0, \\ x, & x < 0. \end{cases}$ b) $g(x) = \begin{cases} x^2, & x \geq 0, \\ -x^2, & x < 0. \end{cases}$

   c) $H(x) = \begin{cases} 2x + 3, & x \geq 0, \\ 3, & x < 0. \end{cases}$ d) $G(x) = \begin{cases} \sin \pi/x, & x \neq 0, \\ 0, & x = 0. \end{cases}$

   e) $F(x) = \begin{cases} x \sin \pi/x, & x \neq 0, \\ 0, & x = 0. \end{cases}$ f) $h(x) = \begin{cases} x^2 \sin \pi/x, & x \neq 0, \\ 0, & x = 0. \end{cases}$

■ ■ ■ CHAPTER 4

In Exercises 1 and 2 find each limit.

1. a) $\displaystyle\lim_{x \to c} \frac{x^2 - c^2}{x - c}$.   b) $\displaystyle\lim_{x \to c} \frac{x - c}{x^2 - c^2}$.

   c) $\displaystyle\lim_{x \to a} \frac{x^2 - (a + b)x + ab}{x - a}$.   d) $\displaystyle\lim_{x \to -a} \frac{x + a}{x^3 + a^3}$.

2. a) $\displaystyle\lim_{x \to 4} \sqrt{x}$.   b) $\displaystyle\lim_{x \to 4} \sqrt{2 + \sqrt{x}}$.

   c) $\displaystyle\lim_{x \to 4} \sqrt{2 + \sqrt{2 + \sqrt{x}}}$.

3. Find $\displaystyle\lim_{x \to a} \frac{f(x) - f(a)}{x - a}$ in each of the following cases:
   a) $f(x) = bx + c$.   b) $f(x) = bx^2 + c$.   c) $f(x) = bx^3 + c$.

4. Find the derivative of each of the following functions:
   a) $f(x) = ax^2 + bx + c$.   b) $G(z) = \sqrt{1 - z^2}$.

   c) $h(\theta) = \dfrac{\theta^2 - 1}{\theta}$, $\theta \neq 0$.   d) $F(y) = \dfrac{ay + b}{y}$, $y \neq 0$.

   e) $g(\theta) = \dfrac{\theta}{\theta - 1}$, $\theta \neq 1$.

5. It can be proved (see Chapter 10) that $\displaystyle\lim_{x \to 0} \sin x = 0$ and that $\displaystyle\lim_{x \to 0} \cos x = 1$. Show that the sine, cosine, and tangent functions are continuous at the number 0. Find the following limits:
   a) $\displaystyle\lim_{x \to 0} (2 \sin x - 3 \cos x)$.   b) $\displaystyle\lim_{x \to 0} \sqrt{8 + \cos^2 x}$.

c) $\lim\limits_{\theta \to 0} \dfrac{1 + \sin \theta}{1 + \cos \theta}$.

d) $\lim\limits_{\theta \to 0} \sec^2 \theta$.

e) $\lim\limits_{x \to \pi/2} \sin (\pi - 2x)$.

f) $\lim\limits_{x \to -1} \cos^2 (x^2 - 1)$.

6. Define the following:
   a) F is continuous at c.
   b) G is continuous at a^2.
   c) f is continuous at x.
   d) g is continuous at $f(a)$.

7. Find an equation of the tangent line to the graph of f at the point $(a, f(a))$, if:
   a) $f(x) = x^{3/2}$; $a = 1$.
   b) $f(x) = x^{3/2} + k$; $a = 1$.

   c) $f(z) = cz^2 + d$; $a = 5$.
   d) $f(z) = \dfrac{k}{z^2 + 1}$; $a = 0$.

   e) $f(x) = (x + 1)\sqrt{x + 5}$; $a = 4$.

8. Sketch the graph of the given function, find an equation of the tangent line at the given point, and sketch the tangent line.
   a) $f(x) = -x^2$; $(-2, f(-2))$.
   b) $g(x) = 1 - x^2$; $(-2, g(-2))$.

   c) $F(x) = \dfrac{10}{x^2 + 1}$; $(-3, F(-3))$.
   d) $F(x) = \dfrac{10}{x^2 + 1}$; $(3, F(3))$.

   e) $G(x) = \dfrac{x}{x^2 + 1}$; $(0, G(0))$.

9. a) Show that if $f(x) = ax + b$ and if $f'(c) = 0$, $c \neq 0$, then $f(x) = b$.
   b) Show that if $f(x) = ax^2 + b$ and if $f'(c) = 0$, $c \neq 0$, then $f(x) = b$.
   c) Show that if

   $$f(x) = a_1 x^2 + b_1,$$

   $$g(x) = a_2 x^2 + b_2,$$

   and if $f'(c) = g'(c)$, $c \neq 0$, then

   $$f(x) = g(x) + k$$

   for some number k.   Find k.

10. Prove the theorem: If $f'(x)$ exists then $\lim\limits_{h \to 0} f(x + h) = f(x)$.   (See the proof of 4.28.)

11. a) Show that if $f(x) = |x|$, then $f'(x) = \dfrac{|x|}{x} = \dfrac{x}{|x|}$ if $x \neq 0$.
    b) Sketch the graph of f if $f(x) = |x|$, and interpret a) in terms of tangent lines.

12. a) Sketch the graph of the equation $y = x^3$, and sketch the tangent line at the origin.
    b) The graph of the equation $x = y^3$ has the same "form" as that of $y = x^3$, but it has a different position.   Sketch the graph of $x = y^3$.   What must be true of the tangent line to the graph of $x = y^3$ at the origin?

13. Let G be a function continuous in the interval (a, b), and let c be a number in (a, b) such that $G(x)$ is positive in (a, c) and $G(x)$ is negative in (c, b).   Prove that $G(c) = 0$.

14. Prove the theorem: Let g_1, g_2, f be functions such that

   $$g_1(x) \leq f(x) \leq g_2(x)$$

for every $x \neq a$ in some open interval containing a. If $\underset{x \to a}{\text{limit }} g_1(x) = \underset{x \to a}{\text{limit }} g_2(x)$ = b, then

$$\underset{x \to a}{\text{limit }} f(x) = b.$$

15. a) Show that if $\underset{x \to a}{\text{limit }} g(x) = b$ while $g(x) \neq b$ if $x \neq a$ in some open interval containing a and if $\underset{x \to b}{\text{limit }} f(x) = c$, then

$$\underset{x \to a}{\text{limit }} f(g(x)) = c.$$

(This theorem is sometimes useful if f is discontinuous at b. Compare this theorem with 4.20.)

b) Find $\underset{x \to 1}{\text{limit }} \dfrac{x - 1}{x^2 - 1}$.

Use a) with b) to find the following limits:

c) $\underset{x \to 0}{\text{limit }} \dfrac{(x + 1)^2 - 1}{(x + 1)^4 - 1}$.

d) $\underset{x \to 0}{\text{limit }} \dfrac{(x + 1)^{17} - 1}{(x + 1)^{34} - 1}$.

e) $\underset{\theta \to 0}{\text{limit }} \dfrac{\cos \theta - 1}{\sin^2 \theta}$.

f) $\underset{\theta \to 0}{\text{limit }} \dfrac{\sqrt{\cos \theta} - 1}{\cos \theta - 1}$.

g) Solve each of c) through f) without the use of a) and b).

16. Show that if $f(x) \leq k$ in some interval containing a and if $\underset{x \to a}{\text{limit }} f(x)$ exists, then $\underset{x \to a}{\text{limit }} f(x) \leq k$. Why is this theorem trivial if f is continuous at a?

■ ■ ■ CHAPTER 5

In Exercises 1 through 7 find $D_x y$.

1. $y = x^2 \pm 5$.

2. $y = \dfrac{x^2 + 1}{x^2 \pm 5}$.

3. $y = (x^2 + 1)(x^2 \pm 5)$.

4. $y = \sqrt{x^2 \pm 5}$.

5. $y = ax^4 + b\pi^2$.

6. $y = \dfrac{x}{a^2 \sqrt{a^2 + x^2}}$.

7. $y = \dfrac{x}{a^2 \sqrt{a^2 - x^2}}$.

In Exercises 8 through 13 differentiate each function.

8. $f(x) = ax^4 + bx^3 + cx^2 + dx + e$.

9. $g(x) = \dfrac{1}{ax^4 + bx^3 + cx^2 + dx + e}$.

10. $f(y) = \dfrac{\sqrt{y^2 - a^2}}{a^2 y}$.

11. $G(z) = \frac{2}{3}(az - 2b) \sqrt{az + b}$.

12. $f(x) = \dfrac{-\sqrt{a^2 - x^2}}{a^2 x}$.

13. $h(x) = \dfrac{x - a}{x + a}$.

In Exercises 14 through 18, find $\dfrac{dy}{dx}$ and $\dfrac{d^2y}{dx^2}$.

14. $y = (x - 1)^m \pm (x + 1)^n$.   **15.** $y = (x - 1)^m \cdot (x + 1)^n$.

16. $y = \dfrac{(x - 1)^m}{(x + 1)^n}$.   **17.** $y = ax^2 + bx + c$.

18. $y = \sqrt{ax^2 + bx + c}$.

Since $f(x)/g(x) = f(x)[g(x)]^{-1}$, every quotient may be written as a product. In Exercises 19 through 21 solve each problem twice: by use of 5.9 and by use of 5.8.

19. Find $f'(a)$ if $f(x) = \dfrac{x^2 - b}{x^2 + b}$.

20. Find $F'(z)$ if $F(z) = \dfrac{z}{\sqrt{z^2 + 1}}$.

21. Find $G'(c)$ if $G(y) = \dfrac{y + a}{\sqrt{y} + a}$.

22. Let $f(x) = \dfrac{x^2 + 2x + 2}{x + 1}$, $x \neq -1$.

   a) Use the quotient rule 5.9 to find $f'(x)$ and $f''(x)$.
   b) Note that $f(x) = x + 1 + (x + 1)^{-1}$, $x \neq -1$. Find
   $$D_x^2[x + 1 + (x + 1)^{-1}].$$

23. If n is a positive integer and if $g'(x)$ exists, use Definition 5.1 to prove that $D_x g^n(x) = ng^{n-1}(x)g'(x)$.

24. a) Using the same coordinate axes, sketch graphs of f, f', f'' where
   $$f(x) = x^3 - 3x.$$

   What can be said about the relation between
   a) the sign of $f'(x)$ and the graph of f?
   b) the sign of $f''(x)$ and the graph of f'?
   c) the sign of $f''(x)$ and the graph of f?

25. Recall that $|x| = \sqrt{x^2}$ and hence that $D_x|x| = \dfrac{x}{|x|} = \dfrac{|x|}{x}$, $x \neq 0$. Find the following derivatives:

   a) $D_x|x^3 - x^2|$.   b) $D_x\, 1/|x|$.

   c) $D_x^3 \dfrac{|x|}{x}\, (x^2 + 1)$.   d) $D_x(|x|^2 - 3|x| + 2)$.

   e) $D_x^2(x - 1)^2|x + 1|$.   f) $D_x^3 \dfrac{x|x|}{2}$.

26. Let r be a rational number, and let $f(x) = x^r$, $g(x) = rx^{r-1}$. Prove:
   a) If $f'(0)$ exists, then $g(0)$ exists and $f'(0) = g(0)$.
   b) If $g(0)$ exists, then $f'(0)$ exists and $f'(0) = g(0)$.

■ ■ ■ CHAPTER 6

In Exercises 1 through 6 sketch the graphs of the polynomial functions. Find extremal points and points of inflection.

1. $f(x) = x^2 - 4$.

2. $g(x) = (x^2 - 4)^2$.

3. $f(x) = x(x^2 - 1)$.

4. $g(x) = x^2(x^2 - 1)^2$.

5. $F(x) = 3x^5 - 40x^3 - 135x$.

6. $G(x) = x^4 - 4x$.

7. Let $g(x) = x^{1/2} + mx$, $x \geq 0$. Find the extrema of g when $m > 0$, $m = 0$, $m < 0$.

8. Discuss the graph of g if:

  a) $g(x) = x^{2/3}\sqrt{9 - x^2}$, $|x| \leq 3$.

  b) $g(x) = (x - 4)^{4/3} + 2(x + 4)^{2/3}$.

9. Let $f(x) = x^4 - 8x^2 + 4$. Sketch graphs of f, f', f'' on the same coordinate axes and interpret the relations between these graphs in terms of the theorems of this chapter.

10. Let $f(x) = (x - a)^n g(x)$ where $g'(a)$ exists, $g(a) \neq 0$, and n is a positive integer. Under what conditions on n will the graph of f cross the x-axis at $(a,0)$? Under what conditions is the x-axis the tangent line to the graph of f at $(a,0)$?

11. Find all the normal lines to the graph of the equation $y = x^2$ which are on the point $(0,2)$.

12. Let $f(x) = x|x|$. Sketch the graph of f. Show that $(0,0)$ is a point of inflection of this graph. Show that $f''(0)$ does not exist.

13. Find the absolute minimum value of f if $f(x) = x^2 - 2x + 4$. Hence show that $x^2 - 2x + 4 > 0$ for all x.

14. The total area of a page in a book is to be 96 in². The margins at top and bottom of the page are each to have width $1\frac{1}{2}$ in. and those at the sides are to have width 1 in. For what dimensions of the page is the printed area the greatest, and what is this maximum area?

15. A truck has a minimum speed of 10 mph. in high gear. When traveling x mph. in high gear, the truck burns diesel oil at the rate of

$$\frac{1}{300}\left(\frac{900}{x} + x\right) \text{ gal./mi.}$$

The truck cannot be driven over 50 mph. If diesel oil costs 20 cents per gallon, find:

  a) The steady speed that will minimize the cost of fuel for a 500-mile trip.

  b) The steady speed that will minimize the total cost of the trip if the driver is paid $1.50 per hour.

16. Two points A and B lie on the same side of the line L. Let P be on L. Without the use of the calculus determine the position of the point P such that $|AP| + |PB|$ is a minimum. Show that for this point AP and BP make equal angles with L.

■ ■ ■ CHAPTER 7

In each of Exercises 1 through 8 sketch the graph, paying attention to asymptotes.

1. $y = \dfrac{x^2 - 1}{x^3 - 8}$.

2. $y(x + 2) = 1$.

3. $y(x + 2)^2 = 1$.

4. $y = \dfrac{x}{x^2 - 1}$.

5. $y = \dfrac{x^2 + 1}{x^2 - 1}$.

6. $y = \dfrac{x^2 - 1}{x^2 + 1}$.

7. $y = \dfrac{(x + 1)^2}{x^2 - 1}$.

8. $y = \dfrac{x^2 - 1}{x^2 - 4}$.

To generalize the concept of asymptote we shall say that the line $y = mx + b$ is an asymptote of the graph of f if

$$\lim_{x \to \infty} (f(x) - (mx + b)) = 0 \quad \text{or} \quad \lim_{x \to -\infty} (f(x) - (mx + b)) = 0 \text{ or both.}$$

For example, in Exercise 9 $\lim_{x \to \pm\infty} (f(x) - (2x - 1)) = 0$ since

$$f(x) = (2x - 1) - \frac{1}{x}, \; x \neq 0.$$

Hence $y = 2x - 1$ is an asymptote of the graph of f.

In each of Exercises 9 through 14 sketch the graph of the function, paying attention to all asymptotes.

9. $f(x) = \dfrac{2x^2 - x - 1}{x}$.

10. $g(x) = \dfrac{x^3 - 8}{x^2 - 1}$.

11. $F(x) = \dfrac{x^2 - 1}{x}$.

12. $f(x) = \dfrac{x^3 - 1}{x^2 - 4}$.

13. $F(x) = \dfrac{(x + 1)^3}{x^2}$.

14. $G(x) = \dfrac{(x + 1)^3}{x^3 - 1}$.

15. Use the method discussed for Exercise 9 above to find the asymptotes and center of the hyperbola

$$\sqrt{3}\, x^2 - xy + (2 - \sqrt{3})x + y - 3 = 0.$$

Find equations of translation and rotation sufficient to remove the x, y, and xy terms of the equation.

16. a) Sketch the parabola $y = x^2$ and the hyperbola $y = \dfrac{1}{x}$ on the same coordinate axes. Let $f(x) = x^2 + \dfrac{1}{x}$. Where is the graph of f "close to" the parabola and where is it "close to" the hyperbola? Sketch the graph of f.

b) Sketch the graph of g as in a) if $g(x) = x^2 - \dfrac{1}{x}$.

c) Sketch the graph of F if $F(x) = x^3 - \dfrac{1}{x^2}$.

17. As analogues to 7.4 give definitions for $\lim\limits_{x \to a^+} f(x) = b$ and $\lim\limits_{x \to a^-} f(x) = b$.

Show that

a) $\lim\limits_{x \to 0^+} \dfrac{|x|}{x} = 1.$

b) $\lim\limits_{x \to 1^-} \dfrac{|x-1|}{x-1} = -1.$

c) $\lim\limits_{x \to 0^+} \dfrac{|x|}{x}(x-1) = -1.$

Referring to Exercise 17 when necessary, sketch the graph of each of the functions given in Exercises 18 through 25.

18. $f(x) = \dfrac{|x|}{x}.$

19. $g(x) = \dfrac{|x-1|}{x-1}.$

20. $h(x) = \dfrac{|x|}{x}(x-1).$

21. $F(x) = \dfrac{|x|}{x}(1-x).$

22. $G(x) = \dfrac{|x|}{x}(x^2-4).$

23. $f(x) = \dfrac{|x|}{x}|x-1|.$

24. $g(x) = \dfrac{|x|+1}{|x|}.$

25. $F(x) = \dfrac{|x|}{x}|x^2-1|.$

26. Show that the hyperbola $\dfrac{x^2}{144} - \dfrac{y^2}{16} = 1$ and the ellipse $\dfrac{x^2}{169} + \dfrac{y^2}{9} = 1$ are orthogonal where they intersect.

27. A satellite of a celestial body B describes an orbit that is (approximately) an ellipse one of whose foci is at the center of B. To obtain an equation of the orbit it is natural to choose a plane coordinate system in the plane of the orbit, with the origin at the center of B and with the coordinate axes coinciding with the axes of the ellipse. Let R be the radius of the earth. Let M be the apogee (maximum distance from B) and let m be the perigee (minimum distance from B) of an earth satellite. Derive an equation of the orbit.

28. The optical properties of the conic sections can be derived from the following exercises.

a) Show that the tangent line to the parabola $y^2 = 4px$ at the point P makes equal angles with a horizontal line through P and the line on P and F where F is the focus of the parabola.

b) Let F_1 and F_2 be foci of an ellipse or of an hyperbola. Show that a tangent line at the point P makes equal angles with the line on P and F_1 and the line on P and F_2.

■ ■ ■ CHAPTER 8

In Exercises 1 through 12, a, b, c, d are real numbers and m, n are positive integers. Find the integrals.

1. $\displaystyle\int_1^4 \left(\dfrac{1}{\sqrt{x}} + \dfrac{1}{\sqrt{2}} \right) dx.$

2. $\displaystyle\int_0^1 (1 - x + x^3)^2 (3x^2 + 1) \, dx.$

3. $\displaystyle\int_0^1 (1 + x + x^3)^2 (x + 1) \, dx.$

4. $\displaystyle\int_0^1 (2ax + b)(ax^2 + bx + c)^n \, dx.$

5. $\displaystyle\int_c^d \sqrt{ax + b} \, dx.$

6. $\displaystyle\int_c^d \dfrac{1}{\sqrt{ax + b}} \, dx.$

7. $\displaystyle\int_1^a x(x^2 - 1)^n \, dx.$

8. $\displaystyle\int_0^1 x(x^2 + a^2)^n \, dx.$

9. $\displaystyle\int_0^a \frac{x}{(x^2 + a^2)^n} \, dx, \; n > 1, \; a \neq 0.22.$

10. $\displaystyle\int_0^b x^{m-1}(x^m + b^m)^n \, dx.$

11. $\displaystyle\int_0^1 (x^2 + 2ax + a^2)^n \, dx.$

12. $\displaystyle\int_0^x \left[\int_1^t z^2 \, dz \right] dt.$

In each of Exercises 13 through 17 sketch the graph of f and the graph of g in the given interval and on the same coordinate axes, where $g(x) = \displaystyle\int_0^x f(x) \, dx.$

13. $f(x) = x + 1$, $[0,4]$.

14. $f(x) = (x - 1)^2$, $[0,3]$.

15. $f(x) = x - 1$, $[0,4]$.

16. $f(x) = x^2 - 4x + 3$, $[0,5]$.

17. $f(x) = x^3 - 4x^2 + 4x$, $[0,4]$.

18. Let $f(x) = \dfrac{1}{x^2}$ and $F(x) = -\dfrac{1}{x}.$ Find $F(1) - F(-1)$. Is

$$\int_{-1}^1 f(x) \, dx = F(1) - F(-1)?$$

Sketch the graph of f.

19. Find $\displaystyle\lim_{t \to \infty} \int_1^t \frac{1}{x^2} \, dx$ and interpret this result geometrically.

20. Let f' be continuous in $[a,b]$. Under what conditions is it true that

$$D_x \int_a^x f(x) \, dx = \int_a^x D_x f(x) \, dx$$

for every x in $[a,b]$?

21. a) Use the fundamental theorem of the calculus to show that if f is continuous in $[a,b]$, then

$$\int_a^b f(x) \, dx = \int_a^b f(z) \, dz.$$

b) Find $\displaystyle\int_1^x z^2 \, dz.$

c) Find $\displaystyle\int_a^x (z - a)^3 \, dz.$

d) Find $\displaystyle\int_a^{x^2} \sqrt[3]{z} \, dz.$

e) If $H(x) = \displaystyle\int_1^{3x^2} (2z - 3) \, dz$, find $H'(x)$.

f) Write a formula for

$$D_x \left\{ \int_a^{g(x)} f(z) \, dz \right\},$$

assuming that $g'(x)$ exists and that f is continuous in the closed interval with end points a and $g(x)$.

g) Find $D_x \left\{ \displaystyle\int_0^{x^2} \sqrt{1 - z^2} \, dz \right\}.$

h) Find $D_x \left\{ \displaystyle\int_0^{3x} \frac{1}{u^4 + 1} \, du \right\}.$

■ ■ ■ CHAPTER 9

In each of Exercises 1 through 4 find the limit if it exists.

1. $\displaystyle \operatorname*{limit}_{n \to \infty} \left(\frac{n^2 + 1}{n + 1} - \frac{n^2 + 2}{n + 2} \right).$

2. $\displaystyle \operatorname*{limit}_{n \to \infty} \left(\frac{n^2 + 1}{n + 1} \Big/ \frac{n^2 + 2}{n + 2} \right).$

3. $\displaystyle \operatorname*{limit}_{n \to \infty} \frac{1/n^2 - 4}{1/n^2}.$

4. $\displaystyle \operatorname*{limit}_{n \to \infty} \frac{(a + 1/n)^2 - a^2}{1/n}.$

5. Show that if $\displaystyle \operatorname*{limit}_{n \to \infty} (b_n - a_n) = 0$ and if c is a number such that $a_n \le c \le b_n$ for every positive integer n, then $\displaystyle \operatorname*{limit}_{n \to \infty} a_n = \operatorname*{limit}_{n \to \infty} b_n = c$. (Establish the inequality: $c - (b_n - a_n) \le a_n \le b_n \le c + (b_n - a_n)$).

6. a) Prove that if $\displaystyle \operatorname*{limit}_{n \to \infty} a_n = 0$, then $\displaystyle \operatorname*{limit}_{n \to \infty} |a_n| = 0$. (This is the converse of 9.9.)

   b) Prove that if $\displaystyle \operatorname*{limit}_{n \to \infty} a_n = 0$ and if there is a number M such that $|b_n| \le M$ for every positive integer n, then $\displaystyle \operatorname*{limit}_{n \to \infty} a_n b_n = 0$.

   c) Prove that if p is a rational number, $p > 0$, then $\displaystyle \operatorname*{limit}_{n \to \infty} \frac{(-1)^n}{n^p} = 0$.

7. Let $a_1, a_2, \cdots, a_n, \cdots$ be a sequence such that $\displaystyle \operatorname*{limit}_{n \to \infty} a_n = L$. Let f be a function such that the numbers $a_1, a_2, \cdots, a_n, \ldots$ are in the domain of f and f is continuous at L. Show that $\displaystyle \operatorname*{limit}_{n \to \infty} f(a_n) = f(L) = f(\operatorname*{limit}_{n \to \infty} a_n)$. (Compare this theorem with 4.20).

In Exercises 8 through 11 find the limit if it exists.

8. $\displaystyle \operatorname*{limit}_{n \to \infty} \sqrt{\frac{4n^2}{n^2 + 1}}.$

9. $\displaystyle \operatorname*{limit}_{n \to \infty} \sqrt{\frac{4n^2 - n + 1}{n^2}}.$

10. $\displaystyle \operatorname*{limit}_{n \to \infty} \frac{\sqrt{n^3 + n}}{n}.$

11. $\displaystyle \operatorname*{limit}_{n \to \infty} \left\{ 2 - \frac{(-1)^n}{n} \right\}^3.$

12. a) If $a_n = \dfrac{3n^2 - 1}{5n^2 + 1}$ and $b_n = a_{2n+1}$, $c_n = a_{n^2+1}$, find $\displaystyle \operatorname*{limit}_{n \to \infty} a_n$, $\displaystyle \operatorname*{limit}_{n \to \infty} b_n$, $\displaystyle \operatorname*{limit}_{n \to \infty} c_n$.

   b) Let u be a function such that $u(n)$ is a positive integer for every positive integer n and $u(n_1) > u(n_2)$ if $n_1 > n_2$. Prove that if $\displaystyle \operatorname*{limit}_{n \to \infty} a_n = L$ then $\displaystyle \operatorname*{limit}_{n \to \infty} a_{u(n)} = L$.

13. a) Let $S = \displaystyle \sum_{i=1}^{n} [(i + 1)^2 - i^2]$. Show that

$$S = [2^2 - 1^2] + [3^2 - 2^2] + \cdots + [(n + 1)^2 - n^2] = (n + 1)^2 - 1.$$

Since $(i + 1)^2 - i^2 = 2i + 1$, show that $S = 2 \displaystyle \sum_{i=1}^{n} i + n$. Hence derive 9.12.

b) Use the fact that $(i + 1)^3 - i^3 = 3i^2 + 3i + 1$ to derive 9.13.

c) Derive 9.14 and a formula for $\sum_{i=1}^{n} i^4$.

In Exercises 14 through 19 find the volume of the solid generated by revolving the region with given boundaries about the given axis.

14. The region with boundaries $x^2 = 4py$, $y = b$, where p and b are positive, about the x-axis.

15. The region in Exercise 14 revolved about the y-axis.

16. The region with boundaries $x^2 = 4py$, $y = 0$, $x = a$ where p and a are positive, about the x-axis.

17. The region in Exercise 16 revolved about the y-axis.

18. The region in Exercise 14 revolved about the line $y = b$.

19. The region in Exercise 16 about the line $x = a$.

20. A parabolic mirror of radius 4 in. is 1 in. thick at the center and 2 in. thick at the outer edge. Find the volume of the mirror and the position of the focal point.

21. The work necessary to raise an object of mass m from a position a meters from the center of the earth to a position b meters from the center of the earth is

$$W_a^b = \int_a^b \frac{kmM}{x^2}\, dx$$

where M is the mass of the earth. The work necessary to raise the object infinitely high from the surface of the earth is $W_R^\infty = \lim_{b \to \infty} W_R^b$ where R is the radius of the earth. Find W_R^∞.

The kinetic energy of the object is $\frac{1}{2}mv^2$ where v is its velocity. If the object is to travel infinitely high above the earth and has initial velocity v_0, then it has initial kinetic energy $\frac{1}{2}mv_0^2$ and by the principle of the conservation of energy $\frac{1}{2}mv_0^2 = W_R^\infty$. The velocity v_0 is called the *escape velocity*. Find a formula for v_0 and compute v_0 in meters per second if $M = 5.98 \times 10^{24}$ kg, $k = 6.67 \times 10^{-11}$, $R = 6.37 \times 10^6$. Find v_0 in miles per hour if 1 kilometer equals .621 miles.

■ ■ ■ CHAPTER 10

If $y = \sqrt{\dfrac{1 - x^2}{1 + x^2}}$, then $\ln y = \frac{1}{2}[\ln (1 - x^2) - \ln (1 + x^2)]$, and by implicit differentiation

$$\frac{1}{y}\frac{dy}{dx} = \frac{1}{2}\left[\frac{-2x}{1 - x^2} - \frac{2x}{1 + x^2}\right]$$

$$= \frac{-2x}{1 - x^4}.$$

Hence

$$\frac{dy}{dx} = \frac{-2xy}{1 - x^4} = \frac{-2x}{(1 - x^2)^{1/2}(1 + x^2)^{3/2}}.$$

Use this method (called *logarithmic differentiation*) to find $\dfrac{dy}{dx}$ in each of Exercises 1 through 6.

1. $y = \sqrt{\dfrac{a-x}{a+x}}$.

2. $y = \dfrac{x^3 + 1}{\sqrt{x^2 + x + 1}}$.

3. $y = (x^2 + 1)^x$.

4. $xe^y y^2 = 1$.

5. $xy^2 \tan y = 2$.

6. $y = \sqrt{\dfrac{\sec x + 1}{\sin x + 1}}$.

In Exercises 7 through 21 find each integral.

7. $\displaystyle\int_0^1 e^{ax}\, dx, \quad a \neq 0$.

8. $\displaystyle\int_0^a \dfrac{e^x}{(e^x + 1)^2}\, dx$.

9. $\displaystyle\int_0^1 \cosh x\, dx$.

10. $\displaystyle\int_1^e \dfrac{1}{x}\, dx$.

11. $\displaystyle\int_0^2 \dfrac{x}{x^2 + 1}\, dx$.

12. $\displaystyle\int_a^b \dfrac{1}{2x}\, dx, \quad a \cdot b > 0$.

13. $\displaystyle\int_1^e \dfrac{\ln x}{x}\, dx$.

14. $\displaystyle\int_e^{e^2} \dfrac{1}{x \ln x}\, dx$.

15. $\displaystyle\int_0^{\pi/2} \cos x\, dx$.

16. $\displaystyle\int_0^{\pi/6} \sin x\, dx$.

17. $\displaystyle\int_0^{\pi/2} \cos x e^{\sin x}\, dx$.

18. $\displaystyle\int_0^{\pi/2} \dfrac{\sin x}{1 + \cos x}\, dx$.

19. $\displaystyle\int_0^{\pi/3} \sin^2 \theta \cos \theta\, d\theta$.

20. $\displaystyle\int_{-\pi/4}^{\pi/4} \sec^2 \theta\, d\theta$.

21. $\displaystyle\int_0^{\pi/4} \dfrac{\sin x}{\cos x}\, dx$.

22. Find the area of the region bounded by one arch of the sine curve and the x-axis.

23. Show that $D_x\{e^{-kx}f(x)\} = e^{-kx}[f'(x) - kf(x)]$. Use this fact to solve the differential equation $f'(x) = kf(x)$. (If $g'(x) = 0$, then g is a constant function.)

24. Prove that $x > \sin x$ if $x > 0$. (Consider the minimum value of f if $f(x) = x - \sin x$.)

25. Since $1 - \dfrac{x^2}{2} < \cos x < 1$ if $0 < x < \pi/2$ by 10.28, we have that

$$\int_0^x \left(1 - \dfrac{x^2}{2}\right) dx \leq \int_0^x \cos x \leq \int_0^x dx,$$

or

$$x - \dfrac{x^3}{6} \leq \sin x \leq x, \quad 0 < x < \pi/2.$$

Show similarly that

$$1 - \dfrac{x^2}{2} \leq \cos x \leq 1 - \dfrac{x^2}{2} + \dfrac{x^4}{24}, \quad 0 < x < \pi/2.$$

Approximate $\sin .2$ and $\cos .2$.

26. Show that $\lim\limits_{x\to 0} \dfrac{\arcsin x}{x} = 1$ and that $\lim\limits_{x\to 0} \dfrac{\arcsin x}{\sin x} = 1$.

27. Let $s_n = \left(1 + \dfrac{1}{n}\right)^n$ and $t_n = \left(1 + \dfrac{1}{n}\right)^{n+1}$. Use supplementary Exercise 6(b) of Chapter 9 to show that $\lim\limits_{n\to\infty} (t_n - s_n) = 0$. (Note that $0 < s_n \le e$.) Hence use supplementary Exercise 5 of Chapter 9 to show that since $s_n \le e \le t_n$, then

$$\lim_{n\to\infty} s_n = \lim_{n\to\infty} t_n = e.$$

■ ■ ■ CHAPTER 11

1. $\displaystyle\int \frac{1}{x^2 - a^2}\, dx.$

2. $\displaystyle\int \frac{x}{x^2 - a^2}\, dx.$

3. $\displaystyle\int \frac{2x + 3}{x^2 - 4}\, dx.$

4. $\displaystyle\int \frac{2x + 3}{x^2 + 3x + 5}\, dx.$

5. $\displaystyle\int \frac{2x + 3}{\sqrt{x^2 + 3x + 5}}\, dx.$

6. $\displaystyle\int \frac{ax + b}{\sin (ax^2 + 2bx)}\, dx.$

7. $\displaystyle\int e^{ax+b}\, dx.$

8. $\displaystyle\int x^2\sqrt{x^3 - 1}\, dx.$

9. $\displaystyle\int \sec^4 \theta \tan \theta \, d\theta.$

10. $\displaystyle\int \frac{\sin \alpha}{1 + \cos^2 \alpha}\, d\alpha.$

11. $\displaystyle\int \frac{x}{\sqrt{x^2 - 2x}}\, dx.$

12. $\displaystyle\int \sec^{7/2} \theta \tan \theta \, d\theta.$

13. $\displaystyle\int \frac{e^{\log_2 x}}{x}\, dx.$

14. $\displaystyle\int \frac{e^{ax} - e^{bx}}{e^{ax} + e^{bx}}\, dx.$

15. $\displaystyle\int \sin ax \cos^r ax \, dx.$

16. $\displaystyle\int \frac{\cos \theta - \sin \theta}{2 \sin \theta \cos \theta}\, d\theta.$

17. $\displaystyle\int \frac{\sec^2 x}{1 - \tan x}\, dx.$

18. $\displaystyle\int \frac{\tan x}{1 + \sec x}\, dx.$

19. $\displaystyle\int \frac{\cos x}{\sin^2 x - 2}\, dx.$

20. $\displaystyle\int \frac{\cos x}{\sqrt{\sin^2 x + 2}}\, dx.$

Solve the following differential equations:

21. $(x - 2x^2) + (y - 2y^2)y' = 0.$

22. $\sin \theta + 3r^2 \dfrac{dr}{d\theta} = 0.$

23. $\dfrac{dy}{dx} = e^{ax+by}.$

24. $\dfrac{dy}{dx} = -x\sqrt{1 - x^2}.$

25. $y'' = \sin x.$

■ ■ ■ CHAPTER 12

Find the following indefinite integrals:

1. $\displaystyle\int \frac{1}{(x^2 - a^2)^2}\, dx.$

2. $\displaystyle\int \frac{1}{(x^2 + a^2)^2}\, dx.$

3. $\displaystyle\int x \csc^2 x \, dx.$

4. $\displaystyle\int x e^{x^2} \, dx.$

5. $\displaystyle\int \sin 2x \, e^{\sin x} \, dx.$

6. $\displaystyle\int \sin (\ln x) \, dx.$

7. $\displaystyle\int \frac{1}{(x^2 - a^2)^{3/2}}\, dx.$

8. $\displaystyle\int x^3 \sqrt{1 - x^2} \, dx.$

9. $\displaystyle\int \frac{1}{x^3 \sqrt{1 - x^2}}\, dx.$

10. $\displaystyle\int \frac{1}{x^3(1 - x^2)}\, dx.$

11. $\displaystyle\int \frac{4x^2 - 7x + 1}{x^3 - 2x^2 - x + 2}\, dx.$

12. $\displaystyle\int \frac{3x^3}{(x - 1)^2(x^2 + x + 1)}\, dx.$

If $z = \tan \dfrac{x}{2}$, $-\pi < x < \pi$, then $\sin x = 2 \sin \dfrac{x}{2} \cos \dfrac{x}{2}$

$$= 2\,\frac{\tan x/2}{\sec^2 x/2}$$

$$= \frac{2z}{1 + z^2}.$$

Similarly $\cos x = \dfrac{1 - z^2}{1 + z^2}$. Furthermore $x = 2 \arctan z$, and $dx = \dfrac{2}{1 + z^2}\, dz$. Use this transformation for Exercises 13 through 16.

13. $\displaystyle\int \frac{1}{2 + \cos x}\, dx.$

14. $\displaystyle\int \frac{1}{3 + \sin x}\, dx.$

15. $\displaystyle\int \frac{1}{1 + \sin x + \cos x}\, dx.$

16. $\displaystyle\int \frac{1}{\cot \theta + \csc \theta}\, d\theta.$

Solve the following differential equations:

17. $yy' = x \sin x.$

18. $\ln x + xyy' = 0.$

19. $r \dfrac{dr}{d\theta} = e^{ar + b\theta}.$

20. $\cos^3 x \dfrac{dy}{dx} = \cos y.$

■ ■ ■ CHAPTER 13

Approximate the following integrals by Simpson's rule for $n = 4$.

1. $\displaystyle\int_{.1}^{.2} \frac{\sin x}{x}\, dx.$

2. $\displaystyle\int_{.1}^{.4} \frac{\tan x}{x}\, dx.$

3. $\displaystyle\int_0^1 f(x)\,dx$ where $f(x) = \dfrac{\sin x}{x}$, $x \neq 0$, $f(0) = 1$.

The mean value of a function f in an interval $[a,b]$ is defined to be

$$M = \frac{\displaystyle\int_a^b f(x)\,dx}{b-a}.$$

In Exercises 4 through 7 find the mean value of the function in the given interval, sketch the graph, and interpret the mean value of f geometrically.

4. $f(x) = x^2$; $[0,3]$.

5. $f(x) = x^2$; $[-3,0]$.

6. $f(x) = \sin x$; $[0,\pi]$.

7. $f(x) = xe^x$; $[0,1]$.

In each of Exercises 8 through 11 find the centroid of the region with the given boundaries.

8. $y = xe^x$, $y = 0$, $x = 1$.

9. $y = xe^x$, $y = 0$, $x = -1$.

10. $y = \arctan x$, $y = 0$, $x = 1$.

11. $y = \cosh x$, $y = 0$, $x = -1$, $x = 1$.

12. In each of Exercises 8, 9, and 11 above find the volume of the solid generated by revolving the given region about the x-axis by the method of the theorem of Pappus (Exercise 10 of Section 5 of the text).

13. In each of Exercises 8, 9, and 11 above find the centroid of the solid generated by revolving the given region about the x-axis.

14. Develop a formula for the centroid of the solid of revolution described in Section 6 of Chapter 9.

■ ■ ■ CHAPTER 14

In Exercises 1 through 8 find each of the limits.

1. $\displaystyle\lim_{x \to 1} \frac{\ln x}{x^2 - x}$.

2. $\displaystyle\lim_{x \to 0} \frac{e^x - e^{-x}}{\sin x}$.

3. $\displaystyle\lim_{\theta \to \pi/2^-} (\sec \theta)^{\cos \theta}$.

4. $\displaystyle\lim_{\alpha \to \pi/2} (1 - \sin \alpha)\tan \alpha$.

5. $\displaystyle\lim_{x \to 0^+} x \ln (\sin x)$.

6. $\displaystyle\lim_{x \to 0^+} \frac{1}{x^{\sin x}}$.

7. $\displaystyle\lim_{x \to a} \frac{\sin x - \sin a}{x - a}$.

8. $\displaystyle\lim_{z \to 0^+} \frac{\ln z}{\cot z}$.

In Exercises 9 through 14 find the integral if it exists.

9. $\displaystyle\int_1^\infty \frac{1}{x^{3/2}}\,dx$.

10. $\displaystyle\int_0^\infty e^{-x} \sin x\,dx$.

11. $\displaystyle\int_0^\infty e^{-ax} \sin bx\,dx$, $a > 0$.

12. $\displaystyle\int_{-\infty}^0 xe^x\,dx$.

13. $\displaystyle\int_0^1 \frac{1}{e^x - e^{-x}}\,dx$.

14. $\displaystyle\int_{-\infty}^\infty \frac{1}{e^x - e^{-x}}\,dx$.

In each of Exercises 15 through 19 give the Maclaurin's formula for $n = 4$.

15. $f(x) = \sinh x.$ **16.** $f(x) = \cosh x.$ **17.** $g(x) = \dfrac{1}{2 - e^x}.$

18. $h(x) = x^4 - 1.$ **19.** $G(x) = e^{-x^2/2}.$

20. If $f(x) = \sin x$, find the Maclaurin polynomials $P_1(x)$, $P_3(x)$, $P_5(x)$. Sketch the graphs of f, P_1, P_3, P_5, paying particular attention to x-intercepts.

21. If $g(x) = \cos x$, find the Maclaurin polynomials $P_2(x)$ and $P_4(x)$. Sketch the graphs of g, P_2, and P_4, paying particular attention to x-intercepts.

22. In Exercise 20 above, plot the points $(.5, f(.5))$, $(.5, P_1(.5))$, $(.5, P_3(.5))$, $(.5, P_5(.5))$.

23. In Exercise 21 above, plot the points $(-.2, g(-.2))$, $(-.2, P_2(-.2))$, $(-.2, P_4(-.2))$.

■ ■ ■ CHAPTER 15

In each of Exercises 1 through 4:

  a) Determine the path by eliminating the parameter.

  b) Find an equation of the tangent line to the path at the given time t_1.

  c) Sketch the velocity and acceleration vectors at the time t_1.

1. $x = \cosh t$, $y = \sinh t$, $0 \leq t \leq 2$, $t_1 = 1$.

2. $x = \tan t$, $y = \sec t$, $0 \leq t \leq \pi/4$, $t_1 = \pi/6$.

3. $x = t - 3$, $y = 3t + 4$, $-4 \leq t \leq 2$, $t_1 = 0$.

4. $x = \cos t^2$, $y = \sin t^2$, $0 \leq t \leq \sqrt{2\pi}$, $t_1 = \sqrt{\pi/2}$.

5. Why is the acceleration vector in Exercise 4 above not directed toward the origin even though the path is a circle?

Sketch a graph of the equation $r = a + b \cos \theta$ in each of the following cases. (Choose appropriate values for a and b.)

6. $a = b > 0.$ **7.** $a > b > 0.$

8. $b > a > 0.$ **9.** $a < b < 0.$

10. $b < a < 0.$ **11.** $a < 0 < b.$

12. $b < 0 < a.$

13. a) Show that if $A^2 + B^2 = 1$, then there is an angle θ such that $\cos \theta = A$, $\sin \theta = B$. (Consider an angle in standard position whose terminal side is on the point (A,B).)

  b) Show that if $P(x,y)$ is on the graph of the equation $\dfrac{x^2}{a^2} + \dfrac{y^2}{b^2} = 1$, then there is an angle θ such that $x = a \cos \theta$, $y = b \sin \theta$.

  c) Let $a > b > 0$, and let $c = \sqrt{a^2 - b^2}$. Then $b = \sqrt{a^2 - c^2}$. Consider the points $F_1(-c,0)$, $F_2(c,0)$. Show that $|PF_1| + |PF_2| = 2a$. (This is a solution of Exercise 15, Section 5, Chapter 7 of the text.)

14. Use the method of the preceding exercise to solve Exercise 15, Section 6, Chapter 7. (Show that if $A^2 - B^2 = 1$, then the angle θ in standard position whose terminal line lies on the point $(1/A, B/A)$ is such that $\sec \theta = A$, $\tan \theta = B$.)

In each of Exercises 15 through 18 sketch the graph, find the area of the region
bounded by the graph, and find the length of the graph.

15. $r = 2 + 2 \sin \theta$.

16. $r = \cos \theta - 1$.

17. $r = \cos^2 \dfrac{\theta}{2}$.

18. $r = a \cos \theta + b \sin \theta$.

In Exercises 19 through 21 sketch the graphs of the pair of equations on the same
coordinate axes.

19. $r = 1 + \sin \theta, r = 1/(1 + \sin \theta)$.

20. $r = 1 + 2 \sin \theta, r = 1/(1 + 2 \sin \theta)$.

21. $r = 1 + \frac{1}{2} \sin \theta, r = 1/(1 + \frac{1}{2} \sin \theta)$.

22. Set up the integral for the arc length of an ellipse when the ellipse is described
in each of the following forms.

a) $\dfrac{x^2}{a^2} + \dfrac{y^2}{b^2} = 1, \quad a > b$.

b) $x = a \cos t, y = b \sin t, \quad a > b$.

c) $r = \dfrac{2ep}{1 + e \cos \theta}, \quad 0 < e < 1$.

Each of these integrals is called an elliptic integral and is known to have the
property that it cannot be evaluated by the use of elementary functions.

23. Show that the lines L_1 and L_2 with parametric equations $x = x_0 + a_1 t$,
$y = y_0 + b_1 t$ and $x = x_0 + a_2 s, y = y_0 + b_2 s$ intersect in the point $P_0(x_0, y_0)$.
Prove that L_1 and L_2 are perpendicular if and only if $a_1 a_2 + b_1 b_2 = 0$.

■ ■ ■ CHAPTER 16

In Exercises 1 through 12 determine the radius of convergence of the series.

1. $\displaystyle\sum_{k=1}^{\infty} \dfrac{kx^k}{2^k k(k+1)}$.

2. $\displaystyle\sum_{k=1}^{\infty} \dfrac{x^k}{k}$.

3. $\displaystyle\sum_{k=1}^{\infty} k^3 x^k$.

4. $\displaystyle\sum_{k=-4}^{\infty} \dfrac{kx^k}{k^2+1}$.

5. $\displaystyle\sum_{k=1}^{\infty} \dfrac{(kx)^k}{(k+1)^k}$.

6. $\displaystyle\sum_{k=0}^{\infty} \dfrac{a^k x^k}{k^2+1}, \quad a > 0$.

7. $\displaystyle\sum_{k=1}^{\infty} \dfrac{(b+1)^k x^k}{2^k 3^k + 1}, \quad b > 0$.

8. $\displaystyle\sum_{k=0}^{\infty} \dfrac{(x-a)^k}{a^k}, \quad a \neq 0$.

9. $\displaystyle\sum_{k=0}^{\infty} \dfrac{(x+2)^k}{(k+1)(k+2)}$.

10. $\displaystyle\sum_{k=0}^{\infty} \dfrac{(x-\pi)^k}{k!}$.

11. $\displaystyle\sum_{k=3}^{\infty} \dfrac{(2x+3)^{k-1}}{(2k+1)!}$.

12. $\displaystyle\sum_{k=0}^{\infty} \dfrac{(x^2+1)^k}{4^k}$.

Since $\sum_{k=0}^{\infty} \dfrac{x^k}{k!} = e^x$, the series in Exercise 10 above has the sum $e^{x-\pi}$. In Exercises 13 through 20 find the sum of each series.

13. $\sum_{k=0}^{\infty} \dfrac{(-1)^k \alpha^{2k+1}}{(2k+1)!}.$

14. $\sum_{k=0}^{\infty} \dfrac{(-1)^{k+1} \theta^{2k}}{(2k)!}.$

15. $\sum_{k=1}^{\infty} \dfrac{(-1)^{k+1} z^{2k}}{(2k+1)k}.$

16. $\sum_{k=0}^{\infty} \dfrac{(-1)^k (x - \pi/2)^{2k}}{(2k)!}.$

17. $\sum_{k=1}^{\infty} \dfrac{(x + 4)^k}{k}.$

18. $\sum_{k=1}^{\infty} \dfrac{(-1)^{k+1} (x - 1)^{2k-1}}{2k - 1}.$

19. $\sum_{k=0}^{\infty} \dfrac{x^{k+1}}{k!}.$

20. $\sum_{k=1}^{\infty} \dfrac{(-1)^{k+1} x^{2k-1}}{(2k)!}.$

■ ■ ■ CHAPTER 17

In Exercises 1 through 4 find parametric equations for the line containing the radial line to the given point of the sphere with given equation. Find an equation of the tangent plane to the sphere at the given point, and sketch the plane.

1. $x^2 + y^2 + z^2 = 9$; $(2,2,1)$.
2. $x^2 + y^2 + z^2 = 9$; $(-1,-2,2)$.
3. $x^2 + y^2 + z^2 + 4x + 4y - 2z = 0$; $(0,0,0)$.
4. $x^2 + y^2 + z^2 + 4x - 2z - 22 = 0$; $(3,1,2)$.

In Exercises 5 through 8 sketch the planes and their line of intersection if one exists. Find parametric equations for the line of intersection.

5. $2x + y + 4z = 4$; $x + 2y + 4z = 4$.
6. $3x + 3y + z = 3$; $x + y + 3z = 3$.
7. $x + y + z = 5$; $x + 5y + z = 5$.
8. $2x + y + 2z = 2$; $2x + y + 2z = 4$.

In Exercise 9 the two lines have the point $(1,2,1)$ as point of intersection. Show that the equations $x = 1 + t - s$, $y = 2 + t + 2s$, $z = +1 + 3t + s$ are parametric equations for the plane containing the two lines, and find an equation for this plane by eliminating the parameters t and s. In each of Exercises 10 and 11 show that the lines intersect, and find the plane containing the lines by the above method. Sketch the lines and the plane in each case.

9. $x = 1 + t, y = 2 + t, z = 1 + 3t$; $x = 1 - s, y = 2 + 2s, z = 1 + s$.
10. $x = 0, y = 3 - t, z = t$; $x = 3 - s, y = 0, z = s$.
11. $x = 0, y = 3 - t, z = t$; $x = 3 + 3s, y = 2 + s, z = -2s$.
12. In each of Exercises 9 through 11 above find parametric equations for the normal line to the plane determined by the two lines at their point of intersection.

In Exercises 13 through 20 use the methods of Sections 6 and 7 to discuss and sketch the graph of the equation. For example, in Exercise 13 it is possible to show by considering the trace in the plane $z = k$ that the surface is a surface of revolution.

13. $z = \dfrac{10}{1 + x^2 + y^2}.$

14. $z = \dfrac{1}{x^2 + y^2}.$

15. $z = x + y^2.$

16. $z = 4 - x^2 - y^2.$

17. $z = x^2 + 9y^2 - 9.$

18. $z = \dfrac{1}{x + y}.$

19. $z = \sqrt{x + y}.$

20. $z = e^{x^2 + y^2}.$

■ ■ ■ CHAPTER 18

The vector r is said to be a *linear combination* of vectors s and t if $r = as + bt$ for some real numbers a and b. Three vectors r, s, and t are said to be *linearly dependent* if one of them is a linear combination of the other two. If the vectors r, s, and t are not linearly dependent, they are said to be *linearly independent*.

1. Show that the vector $r = (5, -13, 12)$ is a linear combination of $s = (1, -3, 4)$ and $t = (-1, 2, 0)$. (*Hint:* If $r = as + bt$, then $5 = a - b$, $-13 = -3a + 2b$, and $12 = 4a$. Solve these equations for a and b.)

2. Show that the vector $s = (8, -12, 0)$ is a linear combination of $r = (\sqrt{2}, -3\sqrt{2}, -\sqrt{2})$ and $t = (5, -7, 3)$.

In each of Exercises 3–8, show that the vectors r, s, and t are linearly dependent.

3. $r = (-5, 7, 3)$, $s = (2, 0, -6)$, $t = (-12, 35/2, 6)$.

4. $r = (1, -1, 1)$, $s = (3, -3, 3)$, $t = (4, 0, 0)$.

5. $r = (-1, 0, 1)$, $s = (3, 0, 2)$, $t = (17, 0, 11)$.

6. $r = 3i - 4j$, $s = i + j + 7k$, $t = i - j + k$.

7. $r = 11a - 7b$, $s = a + 3b$, $t = 3a + 14b$, a, b any vectors.

8. r, s any vectors, $t = 0$.

9. Prove that the three vectors r, s, and t are linearly dependent if and only if there exist three numbers a, b, and c, not all zero, such that $ar + bs + ct = 0$. An equivalent theorem is that the three vectors r, s, and t are linearly independent if and only if the equation $ar + bs + ct = 0$ (in the three unknowns a, b, and c) has the unique solution $a = 0$, $b = 0$, and $c = 0$.

10. Show that the vectors i, j, and k, are linearly independent.

11. Show that the vectors $r = i + j$, $s = i + k$, and $t = j + 3k$ are linearly independent.

12. If a and b are any vectors and each of the vectors r, s, and t is a linear combination of a and b, then prove that the vectors r, s, and t are linearly dependent.

13. If r, s, and t are represented as position vectors in space, what is the geometrical interpretation of linear dependence and linear independence of the vectors r, s, and t?

14. If the vectors r, s, and t are nonzero and mutually perpendicular (so that $r \cdot s = r \cdot t = s \cdot t = 0$), then prove that they are linearly independent.

15. Given that the vectors r, s, and t are linearly independent and that

$$u = \frac{1}{|r|} r, \; a = s - (u \cdot s) u, \; v = \frac{1}{|a|} a,$$

$$b = t - (u \cdot t) u - (v \cdot t) v, \; w = \frac{1}{|b|} b,$$

prove that u, v, and w are mutually perpendicular unit vectors. Find u, v, and w in case

$$r = 3i + 4j, \; s = 25j + 8k, \; t = j + k.$$

16. Show the geometric relationship between the vectors r, s, t and u, v, w of the preceding exercise.

17. Show that $[(r_1 - r_0) \times (r_2 - r_1)] \cdot (r - r_0) = 0$ is an equation of the plane passing through the three endpoints of the position vectors r_0, r_1, and r_2. Find the equation in case:
a) $r_0 = (1,1,-2)$, $r_1 = (0,1,2)$, $r_2 = (0,0,3)$.
b) $r_0 = (-1,0,1)$, $r_1 = (1,-1,0)$, $r_2 = (1,1,-1)$.

18. Let line L_1 have equation $m_1 \times (r - r_1) = 0$ and line L_2 have equation $m_2 \times (r - r_2) = 0$, where $m_1 \times m_2 \neq 0$.
a) Show that the plane on L_1 that is parallel to L_2 has equation $(m_1 \times m_2) \cdot (r - r_1) = 0$.
b) Prove that the lines L_1 and L_2 intersect if and only if $(m_1 \times m_2) \cdot (r_2 - r_1) = 0$.
c) Find the point of intersection of L_1 and L_2 in case they intersect.

19. Do Exercise 15, p. 487, by methods of the preceding exercise.

20. Do Exercise 23, p. 484, by vector methods.

21. Let plane p_1 have equation $m_1 \cdot (r - r_0) = 0$ and plane p_2 have equation $m_2 \cdot (r - r_0) = 0$, where $m_1 \times m_2 \neq 0$. Prove that p_1 and p_2 intersect in the line $(m_1 \times m_2) \times (r - r_0) = 0$.

22. Do Exercise 13, p. 487, by methods of the preceding exercise. (*Hint*: The vector r_0 can be found by letting $z = 0$ and solving the resulting equations $4x + y = 7$, $x - 2y = 4$ for x and y. Then $r_0 = (x,y,0)$.)

23. Show that if $r'(t) \times r''(t) = 0$, then $r(t)$ is the position vector of a point moving on a straight line.

■ ■ ■ CHAPTER 19

In each of Exercises 1 through 3 verify that $f_{xy} = f_{yx}$, $f_{xxy} = f_{yxx}$, $f_{yyx} = f_{xyy}$.

1. $f(x,y) = xe^{x+y}$. 2. $f(x,y) = \dfrac{x}{y}$. 3. $f(x,y) = \dfrac{x}{1 + \sin y}$.

In each of Exercises 4 through 6 sketch the surface and the tangent plane to the surface at the given point.

4. $z = 10 - x^2 - y^2$; $(1,3,0)$. 5. $z = \dfrac{9}{1 + x^2 + y^2}$; $(2,2,1)$.

6. $y = \sqrt{x + z}$; $(1,2,3)$.

If $z = \dfrac{x}{x + y}$, find $\dfrac{dz}{dt}$ in each of the cases of Exercises 7 through 9.

7. $x = t,\ y = at.$ **8.** $x = \sin t,\ y = \cos t.$

9. $x = 2 + t,\ y = g(t).$

10. Let C be the curve of intersection of the surface $z = x^2 + y^2$ and the cylinder whose parametric equations are $x = \cos t,\ y = \sin t.$ Find $\dfrac{dz}{dt}$ and hence find parametric equations for the tangent line to C at the point where $t = \pi/4.$ Verify that this tangent line lies in the tangent plane to the surface $z = x^2 + y^2$ at the given point.

Find the extrema of each function in Exercises 11 through 13.

11. $f(x,y) = x^2 e^{x+y}.$ **12.** $F(x,y) = 4xy - 2x^2 - y^4.$

13. $g(x,y) = (x - 1) \ln y - x^2.$

14. If $f(x,y) = x^3 y + \sin y$, verify that

$$\frac{\partial}{\partial y} \int_0^x f(x,y)\, dx = \int_0^x f_y(x,y)\, dx,$$

$$\frac{\partial}{\partial x} \int_{\pi/4}^y f(x,y)\, dy = \int_{\pi/4}^y f_x(x,y)\, dy.$$

15. Define $D_\theta^2 f(x,y) = D_\theta\{D_\theta f(x,y)\}.$ Let $D(x,y)$ be defined as in 18.14. Show that if $D(a,b) > 0$ and $f_{xx}(a,b) > 0$, then $D_\theta^2 f(a,b) > 0$ for every $\theta.$ What is the geometric significance of this result?

16. Let $f_x(x,y) = f_y(x,y) = 0$ for every (x,y) in a rectangular region $R.$ Show that $f(x,y)$ is a constant in $R.$ (Use the mean value theorem on each of the terms of

$$f(x,y) - f(a,b) = [f(x,y) - f(a,y)] + [f(a,y) - f(a,b)]$$

where (a,b) is in $R.$)

17. Use Exercise 16 to show that if $f_x = g_x$ and $f_y = g_y$ in R, then f and g differ by a constant.

18. Prove theorems 18.12 and 18.13. Note that these theorems are analogues of 14.1 and 14.3, and that the analogue of 14.2 will be useful. It is also useful to employ the notation $[a,b;c,d]$ for the rectangle whose boundaries are $x = a$, $x = b;\ y = c,\ y = d.$

19. Prove that if $g_{xx}(x',y') < 0$, then $g(x',y')$ is not a relative minimum value of $g.$ (Consider the trace of the graph of g in the plane $y = y'.$)

20. If $p(z) = p(x + yi) = u(x,y) + v(x,y)i$, then $P(z) = 0$ if and only if $u(x,y) = 0$ and $v(x,y) = 0.$ Use this fact to solve the following equations:
a) $z^2 - i = 0.$ b) $z^2 = a + bi.$

21. Let F be a function of two variables continuous in the square $[a,b;a,b].$ Let $p_1, p_2, \cdots, p_n, \cdots$ be a sequence of partitions of the closed interval $[a,b]$ such that $\lim\limits_{x\to\infty} |p_n| = 0$ where

$$p_n = [x_{n0}, x_{n1}, \cdots, x_{nk_n}].$$

Prove that if w_{ni} and z_{ni} are numbers in $[x_{ni-1}, x_{ni}]$, then

$$\lim_{n\to\infty} \sum_{i=1}^{k_n} F(w_{ni}, z_{ni}) = \int_a^b F(x,x)\, dx.$$

Compare this theorem with 9.18 as to content and proof.

22. State and prove an analogue of 18.15 for a function of one variable.

▪ ▪ ▪ CHAPTER 20

Compare each of the integrals in Exercises 1 through 6.

1. $\int_0^1 dx \int_0^2 (x+y)\, dy.$ **2.** $\int_0^2 dy \int_0^1 (x+y)\, dy.$

3. $\int_{-1}^0 dx \int_1^2 dz \int_0^3 (x^2-y+z)\, dy.$ **4.** $\int_1^2 dz \int_0^3 dy \int_{-1}^0 (x^2-y+z)\, dx.$

5. $\int_0^2 dx \int_0^x (x^2+y^2)\, dy.$ **6.** $\int_1^2 dy \int_0^{y^2} (x+2y)\, dx.$

7. Interpret each of the integrals in Exercises 1, 2, 5, and 6 above as the volume of a solid.

8. Prove that

$$\int_a^b dx \int_c^d f(x)g(y)\, dy = \left\{ \int_a^b f(x)\, dx \right\} \cdot \left\{ \int_c^d g(y)\, dy \right\}.$$

In Exercises 9 through 12 use the theorem given in the preceding exercise.

9. $\int_0^1 dx \int_0^1 xy\, dy.$ **10.** $\int_0^{\pi/2} d\theta \int_0^1 r^2\theta\, dr.$

11. $\int_{-\pi}^{\pi} d\theta \int_0^1 r\sin\theta\, dr.$ **12.** $\int_0^1 dx \int_0^1 e^{x+y}\, dy.$

13. State and prove a theorem analagous to that of Exercise 8 above for triple integrals.

In each of Exercises 14 through 18 set up integrals sufficient to find the volume and the center of gravity of the solid with the given boundaries.

14. $x+y+z=2, \quad x=0, y=0, z=0.$

15. $z = \dfrac{1}{x^2+y^2}, \quad z=0, x^2+y^2=1.$

16. $z = \cos(x^2+y^2), \quad z=0. \quad (x^2+y^2 \le \pi/2).$

17. $z = \cos(x^2+y^2), \quad z=0 \ (3\pi/2 \le x^2+y^2 \le 5\pi/2).$

18. $\dfrac{x^2}{a^2}+\dfrac{y^2}{b^2}+\dfrac{z^2}{c^2}=1.$

▪ ▪ ▪ CHAPTER 21

Solve the following differential equations:

1. $(x+y+1)\, dx + (6x+10y+14)\, dy = 0.$

2. $(x+y+4)\, dx - (2x+2y-1)\, dy = 0.$

3. $(x+2y)\, dx + (2x-3y)\, dy = 0.$

4. $(ax+by+c)\, dx + (bx+ay+c)\, dy = 0.$

5. Show that under the transformation $z = cx + dy$ the differential equation $\dfrac{dy}{dx} = g(cx+dy)$ becomes separable.

6. Solve the equation $y' = \cos(x+y)$ by the method of Exercise 5.

7. If $x = x(t)$, $y = y(t)$ and if $M_y = N_x$, the differential equation

$$M(x,y)\frac{dx}{dt} + N(x,y)\frac{dy}{dt} = 0$$

is called exact. Show that the general solution is $F(x(t),y(t)) = C$ where $F_x = M$, $F_y = N$.

Assuming that $x = x(t)$, $y = y(t)$, solve the equations in Exercises 8 through 10.

8. $(6x + \ln y)\dfrac{dx}{dt} + \dfrac{x}{y}\dfrac{dy}{dt} = 0$.

9. $e^{-x}\sin y\,\dfrac{dx}{dt} - (e^{-x}\cos y + y)\dfrac{dy}{dt} = 0$.

10. $2xy\dfrac{dx}{dt} + (x^2 + y^2)\dfrac{dy}{dt} = 0$.

11. If $x = x(t)$, $y = y(t)$ and $M_y = N_x$, find the general solution of the equation

$$M(x,y)\frac{dx}{dt} + N(x,y)\frac{dy}{dt} = g(t).$$

12. Solve the equation

$$(y(t)e^{x(t)} - 2x(t))\frac{dx}{dt} + e^{x(t)}\frac{dy}{dt} = \cos t.$$

13. If x, y, and z are functions of t and M, N, and P are functions of x, y, and z, give a definition of the exactness of the equation

$$M\frac{dx}{dt} + N\frac{dy}{dt} + P\frac{dz}{dt} = 0.$$

Give the general solution of the equation

$$M\frac{dx}{dt} + N\frac{dy}{dt} + P\frac{dz}{dt} = g(t).$$

14. Solve the equation

$$e^{y(t)}\frac{dx}{dt} + x(t)e^{y(t)}\frac{dy}{dt} + \frac{dz}{dt} = e^t.$$

15. Let $q = \dfrac{1}{N}\left[\dfrac{\partial M}{\partial y} - \dfrac{\partial N}{\partial x}\right]$. If $q = f(x)\left(\text{i.e., if } \dfrac{\partial q}{\partial y} = 0\right)$, show that $I(x) = e^{\int f(x)\,dx}$ is an integrating factor for the equation $M\,dx + N\,dy = 0$. That is to say, show that the equation $I(x)M\,dx + I(x)N\,dy = 0$ is exact.

In Exercises 16 through 19 find integrating factors and solve.

16. $(1 - xy)\,dx + (xy - x^2)\,dy = 0$.   **17.** $(x^3 + y^4)\,dx + 8xy^3\,dy = 0$.

18. $xy' + y = 0$.   **19.** $y' + p(x)y = g(x)$.

20. Solve the equation $y' = x^2y$ as an exact equation and by series. Compare the results.

21. Solve by series the equation $y' = x^2(x + y)$.

Solve the following linear equations.

22. $y'' - 5y' - 6y = 0$.   **23.** $y'' - 5y' - 6y = e^{-x}$.

24. $y''' - 5y'' - 6y' = 0$.   **25.** $y''' - 5y'' - 6y' = \sin x$.

26. $y'' + 4y = x^2$.   **27.** $y''' + 4y' = x^2$.

28. $y''' - y'' + 4y' = \sin x$.   **29.** $y''' - y'' + 4y' - 4y = e^x$.

30. $y''' - 7y' + 6y = e^{-x}$.

Answers

Chapter 1

Section 2   **1.** $x < 2$ **3.** $x < \frac{3}{2}$ **5.** $x \leq \frac{5}{3}$ **7.** $4.9 < x < 5.1$
9. $-1.575 \leq x \leq -1.425$ **11.** $x \geq 4$ **13.** $x \leq b^2/4a$ if $a > 0$ **15.** $-1 < x < 3$
17. $x < -3$ **19.** no solution

Section 3   **1.** $-2 < x < 4$ **3.** $.45 < x < .55$ **5.** $-\frac{1}{3} < x < 3$ **7.** $-1 \leq x \leq 0$
13. $x < -2$ or $x > 2$ **15.** $x \leq -7$ or $x \geq 3$

Section 5   **1.** $(-6,-1)$ **3.** $[4,6]$ **5.** $(0,\frac{1}{4}]$ **7.** $(-1.505,-1.495)$ **9.** $(-2.5,-2]$

11. $[.009,.011]$ **13.** $[-1,2)$ **15.** $(0,.1)$ **19.** $(-\epsilon/5 - 2, \epsilon/5 - 2)$; $|x + 2| < \frac{\epsilon}{5}$

21. $(a - \epsilon\sqrt{a}, a + \epsilon\sqrt{a})$ **23.** $\left(a - \dfrac{\epsilon}{3a}, a + \dfrac{\epsilon}{3a}\right)$

Chapter 2

Section 2   **13.** $x = 2$ **15.** $y = 0, x = 0$ **17.** $x = \frac{3}{2}$ **19.** $y = x - 1$

Section 4   **1.** $x^2 + y^2 - 9x + y + 8 = 0$ **3.** $x^2 + y^2 - 2x - 24 = 0$
5. $x^2 + y^2 - 6y + 5 = 0$ **7.** $x^2 + y^2 + 2x + 6y + 1 = 0$
9. $x^2 + y^2 - 4x - 8y = 0$ **11.** $x^2 + y^2 + 8x - 8y + 16 = 0$ **13.** $(0,0), r = 4$
15. $(-3,5), r = 3$ **17.** $(0,-1), r = \sqrt{2}/2$ **19.** $(\frac{1}{3}, -\frac{2}{3}), r = \frac{1}{3}$
21. $x^2 + y^2 + 6x + 5 = 0$

Section 6   **15.** $D(6,7)$

Section 7   **1.** $x - 3y - 2 = 0$ **3.** $3x - y - 3 = 0$ **5.** $4x - y + 2 = 0$
7. $6x - y + 2 = 0$ **9.** $y - 1 = 0$ **11.** $mx - y - ma = 0$ **13.** $m = 2$.
$a = -\frac{3}{2}, b = 3$ **15.** $m = -\frac{1}{2}, a = -6, b = -3$ **17.** no slope, $a = -\frac{5}{3}$
19. $m = -5, a = -3, b = -15$ **21.** $2x + y - 9 = 0, x - 2y + 3 = 0$
23. $3x - 2y - 8 = 0, 2x + 3y - 1 = 0$ **25.** $4x + 7y = 0, 7x - 4y = 0$
27. $(2,10)$ **29.** $(5,-4)$ **31.** $(4,2), (-2,-6)$ **33.** $(2,4)$

Section 8 **13.** $y^2 = 4x$ **15.** $x^2 = -4y$ **17.** $x^2 = 4py$ **19.** $3x + 4y - 25 = 0$
21. $2x - 3y = 0$

Chapter 3

Section 1 **1.** $1; -1; 5; 1; 4 + 3\sqrt{3}; h^2 - 3h + 1$ **3.** $h - 1; 2x + h - 3$
5. $-1; 0; 2; (a^2 - 1)/(a^2 + 1); (z - 1)/(z + 1)$ **7.** $1/(2 + h);$
$2/(x + 1)(x + h + 1)$ **9.** $y = -3x$ **11.** $y - 3 = (2h + 7)(x - 3)$
13. $y + 2 = (2h + 3)(x - 2)$ **15.** $0,1; 0,3/(a + 1); \pm\sqrt{2}/2$ **17.** $f(r) = \pi r^2$
19. $G(A) = 4A$

Section 4 **1.** $f(x) + g(x) = x^2 + 3x, f(x) - g(x) = x^2 - 3x - 2,$
$f(x)g(x) = 3x^3 + x^2 - 3x - 1, \quad f(x)/g(x) = (x^2 - 1)/(3x + 1), \quad f(g(x)) = 9x^2 + 6x,$
$g(f(x)) = 3x^2 - 2$ **3.** $f(x) + g(x) = (x^2 + 2x - 1)/(x^2 - 1),$
$f(x) - g(x) = (x^2 + 1)/(1 - x^2), f(x)g(x) = x/(x^2 - 1), f(x)/g(x) = (x - 1)/x(x + 1),$
$f(g(x)) = (x - 1)/(2x - 1), g(f(x)) = -1/x$ **5.** $g(x) = \sqrt{x}, x \geq 0;$
$g(f(x)) = x$ if $x \geq 0, g(f(x)) = -x$ if $x < 0$ **7.** $f(f(x)) = |x|$

Section 5 **1.** decr. in $(-\infty,\infty); f(-2) = 5,$ max.; $f(1) = -1,$ min. **3.** decr. in
$(-\infty,-1]$; incr. in $[-1,\infty)$; $F(4) = 26,$ max.; $F(-1) = 1,$ min. **5.** decr. in $(-\infty,0)$
and $(0,\infty); G(-7) = -\frac{1}{7},$ max.; $G(-1) = -1,$ min. **7.** incr. in $(-\infty,0]$, decr. in
$[0,\infty); f(0) = 1,$ max.; there is no minimum. **9.** incr. in $(-\infty,\infty); g(20) = 8000,$
max.; $g(0) = 0,$ min. **11.** $\sqrt{f(u)},$ min.; $\sqrt{f(v)},$ max.

Chapter 4

Section 1 **1.** -13 **3.** -6 **5.** -1 **7.** $-\frac{1}{16}$ **9.** $\frac{1}{2}$ **11.** $3a^2$ **13.** $\sqrt{2}/4$
15. $0; 0$ **17.** $1/\sqrt{15}$

Section 2 **11.** 4 **13.** 3 **15.** 2

Section 3 **1.** 66 **3.** $\frac{1}{2}$ **5.** 4

Section 6 **1.** $-\frac{1}{4}$ **3.** $\frac{1}{4}$ **5.** $-\frac{1}{8}$ **7.** $-3/a^4$ **9.** $1/3a^2$

Section 7 **1.** $7; 1; 2a + 3; 2x + 3$ **3.** $-1; -\frac{1}{4}; -1/(a + 1)^2$ **5.** $-6; -4; 0; 2$
7. $6x - 2$ **9.** $2/(2 - z)^2$ **11.** $32t$ **13.** $x/\sqrt{x^2 + 1}$ **15.** $3\sqrt{x}/2$

Section 8 **1.** $-4; -2; 0; 2; 4$ **3.** $6x + y + 2 = 0$ **5.** $x + y - 3 = 0$
7. $x - y + 1 = 0$ **9.** $3x + y + 1 = 0$ **11.** $6\sqrt{2}x + y - 10 = 0$ **13.** $\frac{169}{8}$

Chapter 5

Section 2 **7.** $3x^2 - 4x + 5$ **9.** $t^4 - t^2$ **11.** kx^n **13.** $2u/(\pi + 1)$
15. $10x - 2$ **17.** $4x(x^2 + 1)$ **19.** $(15x^2 - 16x)/6$ **21.** $y = 2; y = -3x; y = -2$
23. $-2x/(x^2 + 1)^2; -5/(x + 2)^2; -9x^2/(x^3 + 1)^2$

Section 3 **1.** $24x^2$ **3.** $5\pi\sqrt{5}y^4 + 3\sqrt{10}y^2 - 2\pi y$ **5.** $15z^4 - 28z^3 + 15z^2$
7. $2/(x + 1)^2$ **9.** $1 - 1/(x - 1)^2$ **11.** $6a^3y^2/(y^3 + a^3)^2$ **13.** $3x^2 - 3/x^4$
15. $-5/x^2 - 4/x^3$ **17.** $2x - 2/x^3$

Section 4   **1.** $10x(x^2 + 2)^4$ **3.** $3(-3 + 2y)(2 - 3y + y^2)^2$
5. $-2(2x + 3)/(x^2 + 3x + 1)^3$ **7.** $160(t - 1)(16t^2 - 32t + 1)^4$
9. $12(1 - x^2)(3x - x^3)^3$ **11.** $2(x - 1)(4 + 3x)(6x + 1)$ **13.** $(8 - 6x)/(3x + 1)^3$
15. $-40x/(2x^2 + 1)^3$ **17.** $8x(x^2 - 1)/(x^2 + 1)^3$ **19.** $9x^2(x^3 + 1)^2/64$ **21.** $3\sqrt{x}/2$
23. $5x\sqrt{x}/2$ **25.** $x/\sqrt{x^2 + 1}$ **27.** $-1/\sqrt{1 - 2x}$ **29.** $2 \sin x \cos x$
31. $2 \cos 2x$ **33.** $3 \cos x/(4 - 3 \sin x)^2$ **35.** $10 \sin 5x \cos 5x$

Section 5   **1.** $(1 - 2x^2)/\sqrt{1 - x^2}$ **3.** $-1/(1 + z)\sqrt{1 - z^2}$ **5.** $1/\sqrt{(3t + 1)^2}$
7. $-4/x^2\sqrt{x^2 + 4}$ **9.** $\frac{3}{2}(1 + 1/y^2)\sqrt{y - 1/y}$ **11.** $6x - 1 + 1/2x^{3/2}$
13. $\sqrt{5}(1 + 1/x)/2\sqrt{x}$ **15.** $(10x^3 + 9x^2)/3(x + 1)^{2/3}$ **17.** $3/10\sqrt{3x + 1}$
19. $(\sqrt{2x} + 2)/2(\sqrt{2x} + 1)^2$ **23.** $\cos x/2\sqrt{\sin x}$ **25.** $-\cos y/\sqrt{3 - 2 \sin y}$
27. $(2 \cos t - \sin t \cos t)/2(1 - \sin t)^{3/2}$ **29.** $15 \sin 3x \cos 3x/(3 - \sin^2 3x)^{3/2}$

Section 6   **3.** $1/y$ **5.** x/y **7.** $-x/y$ **9.** $-(2x + y)/x$
11. $(2\sqrt{xy} + y)/(4\sqrt{xy} - x)$ **13.** $(3\sqrt[3]{x^2y^2} + y)/(2\sqrt[3]{x^2y} - x)$ **15.** $-y/x$
17. $(1 - 2xy - 3x^2)/(x^2 + 2y - 1)$

Section 7   **1.** $f''(x) = 6x - 6$ **3.** $F''(y) = 20y^3 - 18y$ **5.** $g''(t) = 15\sqrt{t}/4$
7. $f''(x) = -(x + 3)/4x^2\sqrt{x}$ **9.** $F''(x) = (8x^2 + 6)/(3 - 2x^2)^{5/2}$ **11.** $d^3y/dx^3 = 6$
13. $d^3y/dx^3 = 3/8(3 + x)^{5/2}$ **15.** $d^3y/dx^3 = 3(35x^{1/2} - 15x^{-1/2} + 4x^{-5/2})/8$
17. $d^3y/dx^3 = 640/27(4x + 1)^{8/3}$ **19.** $d^3y/dx^3 = 405/8(3x + 1)^{7/2}$

Chapter 6

Section 1   **1.** $7x + y + 2 = 0, x - 7y + 86 = 0$ **3.** $3x - y + 1 = 0,$
$x + 3y + 7 = 0$ **5.** $x + 18y - 9 = 0, 54x - 3y - 161 = 0$ **7.** $x - 3y + 9 = 0,$
$3x + y - 33 = 0$ **9.** $x - 2y - 3 = 0, 2x + y - 1 = 0$

Section 2   **1.** $f(2) = 5$, max.; $f(-1) = -1$, min.; any positive δ **3.** $F(-2) = -\frac{1}{2}$,
max.; $f(-1) = -1$, min.; any positive $\delta \leq \frac{3}{2}$ **5.** there is no maximum;
$f(2) = 0$, min.; any positive $\delta \leq 4$ **7.** decr. in $(-\infty,1]$; incr. in $[1,\infty)$;
$f(1) = -9$, absolute min.; $f(4) = 0$, max.; $f(1) = -9$, min.   **9.** incr. in $(-\infty,-2]$;
decr. in $[-2,\infty)$; $g(-2) = 8$, absolute max.; $g(-1) = 7$, max.; $g(4) = -28$, min.
11. decr. in $(-\infty,-1]$ and $[1,\infty)$; incr. in $[-1,1]$; $f(-2) = f(1) = 2$, max.;
$f(-1) = -2$, min.   **13.** incr. in $[\frac{1}{5},\infty)$ and $(-\infty,-1]$; decr. $[-1,\frac{1}{5}]$; $f(3) = 16$, max.;
$f(\frac{1}{5}) = -\frac{26244}{3125}$, min.   **15.** decr. in $(-\infty,-1]$ and $[0,1]$; incr. in $[-1,0]$ and $[1,\infty)$;
$G(-1) = G(1) = -1$, absolute min.; $G(-2) = 8$, max.; $G(\pm 1) = -1$, min.
17. decr. in $(-\infty,0]$; incr. in $[0,\infty)$; $G(0) = 1$, absolute min.; $G(-1) = G(1) = 2$, max.;
$G(0) = 1$, min.   **19.** incr. in $(-\infty,\infty)$; $g(3) = 2$, max.; $g(-\frac{179}{32}) = -\frac{1}{2}$, min.
21. incr. in $(-\infty,3]$; decr. $[3,\infty)$; $f(3) = 0$, absolute max.; $f(2) = 1 - \frac{1}{2}\sqrt[3]{9}$ min.

Section 3   **1.** $f(1) = -4$, min.; $f(-3) = 28$, max.   **3.** $h(0) = 0$, min.;
$h(-2) = 4$, max.   **5.** $F(0) = 6$, max.   **7.** $g(0) = 0$, max.; $g(\pm 1) = -1$, min.
9. $f(0) = 0$, max.; $f(\frac{6}{5}) = -\frac{26244}{3125}$, min.   **11.** $g(0) = 0$, max.; $g(2) = -3\sqrt[3]{4}$, min.
13. $F(1) = -1$, min.   **15.** $f(3) = \sqrt[3]{-6\sqrt{3}}$, min.; $f(-3) = \sqrt[3]{6\sqrt{3}}$, max.
17. no extrema   **19.** $G(\pm 1) = 1$, min.   **21.** $f(2) = 0$, min.
23. $F(-\frac{5}{2}) = \frac{37}{4}$, max.   **25.** no extrema   **27.** no extrema
29. $g(-2) = 0$, max.; $g(0) = -108$, min.   **31.** $f(\pm 2) = 0$, min.; $f(0) = 16$, max.
33. $F(-2) = -16$ and $F(1) = 38$, max.; $F(-1) = -38$ and $F(2) = 16$, min.

Section 4   **1.** $F(0) = 0$, min.   **3.** $f(3) = 4$, max.; $f(1) = 0$, min.
5. $g(0) = 0$, min.; $g(-4) = 32$, max.   **7.** $f(0) = f(2) = 0$, max.; $f(\frac{4}{5}) = -\frac{3456}{3125}$, min.
9. $G(-2) = 2$, max.; $G(-1) = \frac{4}{3}$, min.   **11.** $f(0) = 0$, max.; $f(4) = -48$, min.
13. if $m \geq 0$, $g(0) = 0$, min.; if $m < 0$, $g(0) = 0$, max. and $g(\frac{4}{9}m^2) = \frac{4}{27}m^3$, min.

Section 6   **1.** $f(\frac{1}{5}) = \frac{4}{5}$ min.   **3.** $g(-3) = 37$ max., $g(1) = 5$ min.
5. $F(2) = 3$ min.   **7.** $f(9) = \frac{2}{3}$ min.   **9.** $G(-1) = 4$ max.   **11.** $F(-\frac{1}{3}) = \frac{59}{27}$ max.,
$F(1) = 1$ min.; $(\frac{1}{3}, \frac{43}{27})$ pt. of infl.   **13.** $f(-1) = -2$ min., $f(0) = 3$ max.,
$f(2) = -29$ min.; pts. of infl. at $x = (1 \pm \sqrt{7})/3$ **15.** $g(-\sqrt{5}) = 10\sqrt{5}$ max.,
$g(\sqrt{5}) = -10\sqrt{5}$ min.   **17.** $G(\frac{5}{8}) = -15\sqrt[3]{25}/256$ min.   **19.** $F(-3) = 0$ max.,
$F(-2) = -2$ min.   **21.** $f(0) = 0$ min., $f(\frac{1}{2}) = 9\sqrt[3]{2}/8$ max., $f(2) = 0$ min.
23. $g(1/a) = \sqrt{a^2 + 1}$ max. if $a > 0$, min. if $a < 0$.   **25.** $(\pm 1, \frac{1}{4})$.   **27.** $(1, \frac{5}{6})$;
$15x - 6y - 10 = 0$.   **29.** $a = 1$, $b = -5$; min.

Section 7   **1.** 100×150 **3.** $(6 - 2\sqrt{3}) \times 4\sqrt{3} \times (12 + 4\sqrt{3})$
5. radius = height   **9.** length = 2(width)   **11.** height = $\sqrt{2}$(radius)   **13.** $5\sqrt{5}$
17. 3 miles from P **19.** 500

Section 8   **1.** $v = -32t + 80$, $a = -32$; $s(\frac{5}{2}) = 100$ max., $s(0) = 0$ min.
3. $v = 2t - 8$, $a = 2$; $s(4) = -12$ min., $s(-2) = 24$ max.   **5.** $v = 3t^2 - 3$, $a = 6t$;
$s(-1) = 2$ max., $s(1) = -2$ min.   **7.** $v = 1 - 2t - 3t^2$, $a = -2 - 6t$;
$s(-1) = 1$ min., $s(\frac{1}{3}) = \frac{59}{27}$ max.   **9.** $v = 2t - 16/t^2$, $a = 2 + 32/t^3$; $s(2) = 12$ min.
11. $r' = 1/\sqrt[3]{9\pi t^2}$; .082 in/sec   **13.** $d(t) = 4\sqrt{41t^2 - 120t + 225}$;
closest at 11:28 a.m.   **15.** $h(t) = \sqrt{2t}/3$; $\frac{1}{6}$ ft/min.

Section 9   **1.** $x - 2x^2 + 3x^3$ **3.** $2x^3 - 3x^2/2 + 5x$ **5.** $t^4/4 + t^3/3 - 7t^2/2$
7. $4x^5/5 - 3x^4/4 + x^3/3 + 2x$ **9.** $y^4/12 - y^3/6 + 3y^2/2$ **11.** $\sqrt{x}(x - 12)/3$
13. $4x^2 - 3x + 3$ **15.** $4x^3/3 + 3x^2 - 5x + 1$ **17.** $(3 - 2\sqrt{3})/3 + \sqrt{2}x - x^2 + x^3/3$
19. $4t^2 - 9t - 16$ **21.** 49 ft, 3.5 sec   **23.** 40 ft/sec   **25.** $s(t) = 4t^2$, $5\sqrt{2}$ sec,
34 ft/sec

Chapter 7

Section 2   **1.** $-\frac{1}{4}$ **3.** 0   **5.** $-\infty$ **7.** 0

Section 4   **1.** focus $(3,0)$, directrix $x = -3$ **3.** focus $(0, \frac{1}{4})$, directrix $y = -\frac{1}{4}$
5. focus $(-\frac{1}{2}, 0)$, directrix $x = \frac{1}{2}$ **7.** focus $(0, -2)$, directrix $y = 2$ **9.** $y^2 = 16x$
11. $x^2 = 8y$ **13.** $y^2 = 2x$ **15.** $y^2 = 4x + 4$

Section 5   **1.** vertices $(\pm 2, 0)$, foci $(\pm \sqrt{3}, 0)$ **3.** vertices $(0, \pm 5)$, foci $(0, \pm 4)$
5. vertices $(\pm \frac{3}{4}, 0)$, foci $(\pm \frac{9}{20}, 0)$ **7.** vertices $(0, \pm 1)$, foci $(0, \pm \sqrt{3}/2)$
9. $9x^2 + 25y^2 = 225$ **11.** $25x^2 + 4y^2 = 100$ **13.** $9x^2 + 4y^2 = 36$

Section 6   **1.** vertices $(\pm 2, 0)$,   foci $(\pm \sqrt{5}, 0)$,   asymptotes $x = \pm 2y$
3. vertices $(0, \pm 3)$, foci $(0, \pm 5)$, asymptotes $3x = \pm 4y$ **5.** vertices $(\pm 2, 0)$,
foci $(\pm 2\sqrt{2}, 0)$, asymptotes $x = \pm y$ **7.** vertices $(0, \pm \frac{4}{3})$, foci $(0, \pm 2\sqrt{13}/3)$,
asymptotes $2x = \pm 3y$ **9.** $3x^2 - y^2 = 12$ **11.** $16x^2 - 9y^2 = 576$
13. $4x^2 - y^2 = 16$

ANSWERS689

Section 7   **1.** parabola, vertex $(3,-2)$, focus $(3,-1)$ **3.** ellipse, center $(2,1)$,
vertices $(-1,1)$, $(5,1)$, foci $(2 \pm 2\sqrt{2},1)$ **5.** ellipse, center $(1,-2)$,
vertices $(1 \pm \sqrt{3},-2)$, foci $(0,-2)$, $(2,-2)$ **7.** hyperbola, center $(2,-2)$,
vertices $(2,-1)$, $(2,-3)$,   foci $(2,-2 \pm \sqrt{2})$,   asymptotes $y + 2 = \pm(x - 2)$
9. parabola, vertex $(\frac{3}{4},0)$, focus $(-\frac{5}{4},0)$ **11.** hyperbola, center $(3,0)$, vertices $(1,0)$, $(5,0)$,
foci $(3 \pm \sqrt{13},0)$, asymptotes $2y = \pm3(x - 3)$ **13.** $(y - k)^2 = 4p(x - h)$
15. $(x - h)^2/a + (y - k)^2/(a^2 - c^2) = 1$ **17.** $(x - h)^2/a^2 - (y - k)^2/(c^2 - a^2) = 1$

Section 8   **1.** ellipse, rotated equation $6x'^2 + y'^2 = 6$ **3.** ellipse,
rotated equation $x'^2 + 5y'^2 + (2\sqrt{3} - 1)x' + (\sqrt{3} + 2)y' - 12 = 0$ **5.** hyperbola,
rotated equation $6x'^2 - 4y'^2 = 3$ **7.** hyperbola, rotated equation
$3x'^2 - 2y'^2 - 3\sqrt{10}x' + 2\sqrt{10}y' - 12 = 0$

Chapter 8

Section 2   **1.** (a) $\frac{63}{4}$, $\frac{87}{4}$ (b) $\frac{275}{16}$, $\frac{323}{16}$ **3.** (a) $\frac{7}{16}$, $\frac{15}{16}$ (b) $\frac{175}{256}$, $\frac{207}{256}$
5. (a) $\frac{61}{144}$, $\frac{49}{36}$ (b) .55, 1.02

Section 3   **1.** -1.75, .25   **3.** .5, 2.5   **5.** -5.56, -2.78 **7.** -1.83, -1.08
9. .55, 1.02

Section 6   **1.** 4   **3.** 15   **5.** $\frac{136}{3}$ **7.** 10.1   **9.** $\frac{32}{3}$ **11.** $(3 - 2\sqrt{2})/2$
13. $-\frac{16}{81}$ **15.** $\frac{14}{3}$ **17.** 2   **19.** $\frac{1}{4}$

Section 8   **1.** $\frac{14}{3}$ **3.** 0   **5.** -14 **7.** $\frac{1}{3}$ **9.** $\frac{1}{4}$ **11.** $\frac{16}{3025}$ **13.** 0
15. $4(3\sqrt{3} - 2\sqrt{2})/3$

Section 9   **1.** 20   **3.** $\frac{32}{3}$ **5.** $\frac{64}{3}$ **7.** $\frac{4}{3}$ **9.** $\frac{1}{2}$ **11.** $\frac{8}{3}$ **13.** $\frac{125}{6}$
15. $2(2 - \sqrt{3})$

Chapter 9

Section 1   **1.** 3, $\frac{3}{2}$, 1, $\frac{3}{4}$, $\frac{3}{5}$; 0   **3.** $\frac{1}{2}$, $\frac{4}{5}$, 1, $\frac{8}{7}$, $\frac{5}{4}$; 2   **5.** -1, $\frac{1}{4}$, $-\frac{1}{9}$, $\frac{1}{16}$, $-\frac{1}{25}$; 0
7. $-\frac{1}{3}$, $\frac{1}{3}$, $\frac{7}{11}$, $\frac{7}{9}$, $\frac{23}{27}$; 1   **9.** 0, $\frac{7}{12}$, $\frac{5}{6}$, $\frac{39}{40}$, $\frac{16}{15}$; $\frac{3}{2}$ **11.** $\frac{4}{3}$, $-\frac{8}{3}$, $-\frac{108}{77}$, $-\frac{64}{63}$, $-\frac{500}{621}$; 0

Section 3   **3.** 132   **5.** 441   **7.** n^2 **9.** $n^2(2n^2 - 1)$ **11.** $S_n = 8(n - 1)/n$,
$T_n = 8(n + 1)/n$; 8   **13.** $S_n = 8(2n^2 - 3n + 1)/3n^2$, $T_n = 8(2n^2 + 3n + 1)/3n^2$; $\frac{16}{3}$
15. $S_n = 9(n - 1)(3n - 1)/2n^2$, $T_n = 9(n + 1)(3n + 1)/2n^2$; $\frac{27}{2}$
17. $S_n = 4(n + 1)(2n + 1)/3n^2 - 10(n + 1)/n - 8$, $T_n = 4(n - 1)(2n - 1)/3n^2 -$
$10(n - 1)/n - 8$; $-\frac{46}{3}$ **19.** $S_n = 4(n - 1)^2/n^2$, $T_n = 4(n + 1)^2/n^2$; 4   **21.** 8; 8
23. $9(4n^2 - 1)/4n^2$; 9   **25.** $2(2n^2 - 1)/n^2$; 4

Section 4   **1.** $32\pi/5$ **3.** 8π **5.** $2\pi/3$ **7.** $\pi/30$ **9.** $31\pi/160$ **11.** $4\pi r^3/3$
15. $32\pi p^3/15$

Section 6   **1.** $128\pi/5$ **3.** $64\pi/5$ **5.** $768\pi/7$ **7.** 6π **9.** $64\sqrt{2}\pi/3$
11. $4\pi(r^2 - R^2)^{3/2}/3$ **13.** $16\pi p^3/5$ **15.** $2\pi r^3(1 - \cos\theta)/3$

Section 7   **1.** 72 in. lbs   **3.** $84,375\pi/4$ ft lbs   **5.** $kW_1W_2(1/a - 1/b)$ ft lbs
7. 70,000 ft lbs   **9.** $1,125\pi$ ft lbs

Section 8   **1.** 1.10   **3.** 3.00   **5.** 3.13   **7.** 1.19

Chapter 10

Section 4   **1.** $a(e^{ax} - e^{-ax})$ **3.** $9e^{3x}(1 + e^{3x})^2$ **5.** $(1 + e^{2x} - 2xe^{2x})/(1 + e^{2x})^2$
7. $2x(1 + x^2)e^{x^2}$ **9.** $e^{2x}(18x^2 + 30x + 2)$ **11.** $-e^{-3x}(3x^2 + 2x + 3)/(x^2 + 1)^2$
13. $-e^x/(e^{2x} - 1)^{3/2}$ **15.** 1   **17.** $\sinh x$ **21.** $e^2 - 1$ **23.** $e - 1/e$
25. $(-1, -1/e)$ min. point, $(-2, -2/e^2)$ point of infl.   **27.** $(1,1/e)$ max. point,
$(2,2/e^2)$ point of infl.   **29.** $(0,1)$ max. point, $(\pm\sqrt{2}/2, 1/\sqrt{e})$ points of infl.
31. $(0,1)$ min. point

Section 5   **1.** $1, 2, 3, 4, -1, -2, -3, \frac{1}{2}, -\frac{1}{3}$ **3.** (a) 1   (c) $1/e$ (e) $2 + e^3$
4. (a) $x > e^2$ (c) $x \neq 0$, $-1/e < x < 1/e$ **13.** $f(0) = -5$, max.;
$f(\ln 2) = -8 + 4 \ln 2$, min.

Section 6   **1.** $1/(x + 1)$ **3.** $\ln |x^2 - 1| + 2x/(x - 1)$ **5.** $(2x \ln x - x)/\ln^2 x$
7. $e^x/(e^x + 1)$ **9.** $(1 - \ln x)/x^2$ **11.** $(\ln 2)2^x$ **13.** $1/\sqrt{x^2 + 1}$
15. $3e^{3x}[(e^{3x} + 1) \ln (e^{3x} + 1) - e^{3x}]/(e^{3x} + 1) \ln^2 (e^{3x} + 1)$ **17.** $(\ln x + 1)x^x$
19. $[\ln (x^2 + 1) + 2x^2/(x^2 + 1)](x^2 + 1)^x$ **21.** $(1/e, -1/e)$ min. point
23. $(1,1)$ min. point

Section 7   **1.** $-2 \log_2 e/(5 - 2x)$ **3.** $2x \log_{10} (3 + 2x^2) + 4x^3 \log_{10} e/(3 + 2x^2)$
5. $\pi(\ln x + 1)^{\pi-1}/x$ **7.** $(1 + e)(1 + \sqrt{x})^e/2\sqrt{x}$ **9.** $(2 \ln 2)2^{2x}$

Section 8   **1.** $f(t) = 10.2^{-t/140}$; 1.6 mg   **3.** 2.8 hrs   **5.** 6 mi/hr; 600 ft
7. $y = e^{2x}$ **9.** $y = 100 \cdot 2^x$ **11.** 3200

Section 10   **7.** $-3\pi/2, -\pi/2, \pi/2, 3\pi/2$ **9.** $-4\pi/3, -2\pi/3, 2\pi/3, 4\pi/3$
11. $-5\pi/3, -4\pi/3, \pi/3, 2\pi/3$ **13.** $-7\pi/4, -\pi/4, \pi/4, 7\pi/4$
15. $-7\pi/4 < \theta < -5\pi/4$, $-3\pi/4 < \theta < -\pi/4$, $\pi/4 < \theta < 3\pi/4$, $5\pi/4 < \theta < 7\pi/4$
17. 1

Section 11   **1.** $2(\cos^2 x - \sin^2 x)$ **3.** $2/(1 + \cos 2x)$ **5.** $(3/2) \tan^2 (x/2) \sec^2 (x/2)$
7. $2 \sec^2 x \tan x (\tan^2 x + \sec^2 x)$ **9.** $-2(\sin 2x + \cos 2x)$ **11.** $\sec x$
13. $2e^{2x}(\cos 2x - \sin 2x)$ **15.** $x \cos x$ **17.** $-2 \tan 2x \sec^2 2x/\sqrt{1 - \tan^2 2x}$
19. $3x^2 \sec x^3 \tan x^3$ **21.** $d^2y/dx^2 = 12 \csc^3 2x (3 \cot^2 2x + \csc^2 2x)$
23. $d^2y/dx^2 = 4 \sec^2 x \tan x (3 \sec^2 x - 1)$ **25.** $d^2y/dx^2 = [2x^2 \sin (1/x) -$
$2x \cos (1/x) - \sin (1/x)]/x^2$ **27.** $d^2y/dx^2 = -16 (\cos^2 2x - \sin^2 2x)$ **29.** $1/\cos y$
31. $1/\sec y \tan y$ **33.** $-[y \cos x + \sin (x + y)]/[\sin x + \sin (x + y)]$
35. $f(\pi/4) = \sqrt{2}$ max., $f(5\pi/4) = -\sqrt{2}$ min.   **37.** $F(0) = 1$ min., $F(\pi/3) = \frac{5}{4}$ max.,
$F(\pi) = -1$ min., $F(5\pi/3) = \frac{5}{4}$ max.   **39.** $g(\pi/6) = \sqrt{3}$ min., $g(5\pi/6) = -\sqrt{3}$ max.
41. $v(t) = 4 \cos t$, $a(t) = -4 \sin t$ **43.** $v(t) = -3\pi \sin \pi t$, $a(t) = -3\pi^2 \cos \pi t$

Section 12   **1.** $\pi/6$ **3.** $\pi/4$ **5.** $-\pi/4$ **7.** $\pi/2$ **9.** $-\pi/3$ **11.** $-\pi/2$
13. 0   **15.** $\sqrt{2}/2$ **17.** $\sqrt{3}$ **19.** 0

Section 13   **1.** $D_x \cos^{-1} x = -1/\sqrt{1 - x^2}$ **5.** $2/\sqrt{1 - 4x^2}$ **7.** $1/x\sqrt{16x^2 - 1}$
9. $6(1 + \arcsin 3x)/\sqrt{1 - 9x^2}$ **11.** $2/(1 + e^{4x}) - (2 \arctan e^{2x})/e^{2x}$ **13.** $\sin^{-1} x$

15. $1/x\sqrt{x^2-1}$ **17.** $1/2x\sqrt{x-1}$ **19.** $1/(1+x^2)\arctan x$ **21.** $2x^2/\sqrt{1-x^2}$
23. $6x^2\tan^{-1}x$ **25.** $c = -\pi/4$

Section 14 **1.** $f^{-1}(x) = x^3$; set of all real numbers **3.** $F^{-1}(x) = \tan^{-1}x$;
set of all real numbers **5.** $f^{-1}(x) = x - 2$; set of all real numbers **7.** $g^{-1}(x) = x/2$;
set of all real numbers **9.** $F^{-1}(x) = \log_a x$; set of all positive real numbers

Section 15 **1.** $\partial^2 f/\partial x \partial y = \partial^2 f/\partial y \partial x = 3$ **3.** $\partial^2 f/\partial x \partial y = \partial^2 f/\partial y \partial x = 2(x-y)/(x+y)^3$
5. $\partial^2 f/\partial x \partial y = \partial^2 f/\partial y \partial x = 4xye^{-x^2-y^2}$ **7.** $\partial^2 f/\partial x \partial y = \partial^2 f/\partial y \partial x = -y\sin xy + 1$
9. $\partial^2 f/\partial x \partial y = \partial^2 f/\partial y \partial x = 4x/y$ **11.** $\partial^2 f/\partial x \partial y = \partial^2 f/\partial y \partial x = -2(x+y)/[1+(x+y)^2]$

Chapter 11

Section 2 **1.** $\frac{1}{4}x^4 - \frac{1}{2}x^2 + 5x + C$ **3.** $\frac{2}{21}(3x+2)^{7/2} + C$ **5.** $\frac{1}{10}$
7. $\frac{2}{5}x^{5/2} + \frac{4}{3}x^{3/2} - 2x^{1/2} + C$ **9.** $x - 2\ln|x+1| + C$ **11.** $\frac{1}{5}x^5 + \frac{4}{3}x^3 + 4x + C$
13. $\ln 3 - \frac{4}{3}$ **15.** $\frac{1}{2}x^2 + 2x + \ln|x| + C$ **17.** $\frac{5}{2} - 3\ln 2$

19. $\frac{2}{3}x^3 - \frac{1}{2}x^2 - x + C$ **21.** $\dfrac{-2}{(x+4)^2} + C$ **23.** -34.1 **25.** $\frac{1}{2}$ **26.** 2

Section 3 **1.** $\dfrac{-1}{8(x^4+1)^2} + C$ **3.** $\frac{1}{2}\ln|x^2+2x+3| + C$ **5.** $\frac{1}{2}\sin^2 x + C$
7. $\frac{1}{2}\ln^2|x| + C$ **9.** $\frac{1}{4}\tan^4 x + C$ **11.** $\frac{1}{3}\ln|x^3+2| + C$ **13.** $\frac{2}{3}(\arctan x)^{3/2} + C$
15. $-\ln|1-x| + C$ **17.** $\dfrac{1}{e^{-x}+2} + C$ **19.** $-\frac{1}{2}\ln|1-2\sec x| + C$
21. $\dfrac{-1}{2\sin^2 x} + C$ **23.** $\frac{1}{4}\ln^2(1+x^2) + C$ **25.** $\dfrac{-1}{22}\left(\dfrac{1-x^2}{x^2}\right)^{11} + C$

Section 4 **1.** $\frac{1}{4}\sin 4x + C$ **3.** $-\frac{1}{6}\cos 3x^2 + C$ **5.** $-\frac{1}{2}\ln|\sec(1-2x)| + C$
7. $\frac{2}{3}\tan\dfrac{3x}{2} + C$ **9.** $2\ln\left|\sin\dfrac{x}{2}\right| + C$ **11.** $\sqrt{\sin 2x} + C$ **13.** $\frac{1}{18}\tan^6 3x + C$
15. $-\frac{1}{10}\cos^5 2x + C$ **17.** $-\frac{1}{3}\cot x^3 + C$ **19.** $\ln|\sec x| + C$
21. $-\cos(\ln|x|) + C$ **23.** $\dfrac{-1}{4(1+\sin 2x)^2} + C$ **25.** $2\tan x + 2\sec x - x + C$
27. $-\cot x + \csc x + C$ **29.** $\ln|\sec x + \tan x| + \ln|\sec x| + C$
30. $\ln|\sec x + \tan x| - \ln|\sec x| + C$

Section 5 **1.** $-\frac{1}{2}\cos 2x + \frac{1}{6}\cos^3 2x + C$ **3.** $\dfrac{2}{3}\sec^3\dfrac{x}{2} + C$
5. $\frac{3}{8}x + \frac{1}{4}\sin 2x + \frac{1}{32}\sin 4x + C$ **7.** $\frac{1}{9}\tan^3 3x - \frac{1}{3}\tan 3x + x + C$
9. $-\frac{1}{6}\cot^3 2x - \frac{1}{2}\cot 2x + C$ **11.** $\frac{1}{15}\sec^5 3x - \frac{1}{9}\sec^3 3x + C$
13. $\frac{2}{3}(\sin x)^{3/2} - \frac{2}{7}(\sin x)^{7/2} + C$ **15.** $\frac{2}{9}(\tan x)^{9/2} + \frac{2}{5}(\tan x)^{5/2} + C$
17. $-\frac{1}{8}\cos 4x + \frac{1}{4}\cos 2x + C$ **19.** $\frac{1}{10}\sin 5x + \frac{1}{2}\sin x + C$

Section 6 **1.** $\frac{1}{3}e^{3x-4} + C$ **3.** $e^{\tan x} + C$ **5.** $(-\frac{1}{2}\log_{10}e)10^{-2x} + C$
7. $\frac{1}{2}e^{2x} - 2x - \frac{1}{2}e^{-2x} + C$ **9.** $-\dfrac{1}{\ln 3}\left(\dfrac{1}{3}\right)^x + C$ **11.** $e^{\ln x} + C$ **13.** $\frac{1}{3}e^{3x} + C$
15. $-x + \ln(1+e^{2x}) + C$ **17.** $\dfrac{1}{a}$

Section 7 **1.** $\ln|x + \sqrt{x^2+4}| + C$ **3.** $\sqrt{x^2+4} + C$ **5.** $\frac{1}{6}\ln\left|\dfrac{x-3}{x+3}\right| + C$

7. $\frac{1}{2}\ln|x^2-9| + C$ **9.** $x + \dfrac{3}{2}\ln\left|\dfrac{x-3}{x+3}\right| + C$ **11.** $\frac{1}{2}\sec^{-1}\dfrac{u}{2} + C$

13. $-2\sqrt{9 - e^x} + C$ **15.** $\frac{1}{6}\tan^{-1}\frac{z^3}{2} + C$ **17.** $\frac{1}{3}\tan^{-1}\left(\frac{\tan x}{3}\right) + C$

19. $-\sin^{-1}(e^{-x}) + C$ **21.** $\sin^{-1}(x + 1) + C$ **23.** $\frac{\pi}{6}$ **25.** $\ln 3$ **27.** $\frac{\pi}{2}$

Section 8   **1.** $\frac{1}{3}\tan^{-1}\frac{x - 2}{3} + C$ **3.** $\sin^{-1}\frac{x - 2}{3} + C$ **5.** $-\frac{1}{x - 1} + C$

7. $-\frac{1}{3}\tan^{-1}\frac{x - 4}{3} + C$ **9.** $\sqrt{x^2 + 2x} + 2\ln|x + 1 + \sqrt{x^2 + 2x}| + C$

11. $\ln|4x^2 - 4x - 3| + \frac{1}{4}\ln\left|\frac{2x - 3}{2x + 1}\right| + C$ **13.** $\ln|x - 1 + \sqrt{x^2 - 2x}| + $
$\sec^{-1}(x - 1) + C$ **15.** $x - 4\ln|x + 2| + C$

Section 9   **1.** $xy = C$ **3.** $\frac{x^2}{2} + \frac{1}{y} = C$ **5.** $y - x + \ln\left|\frac{y - 1}{x}\right| = C$

7. $e^{-y} + e^{-x} = C$ **9.** $(\sec x + \tan x)\sec y = C$ **11.** (a) $58.9°$ (b) 4 min.
13. 3.5 sec   **15.** (a) $41.4°$ (b) 3.8 min.   **17.** $x^2 - 2x + y^2 = 3$

Chapter 12

Section 1   **1.** $\frac{x^2}{4}(2\ln x - 1) + C$ **3.** $\frac{2}{3}x^{3/2}(\ln x - \frac{2}{3}) + C$

5. $\frac{x^2 + 1}{2}\tan^{-1}x - \frac{x}{2} + C$ **7.** $x\sin x + \cos x + C$ **9.** $x\sin^{-1}x + \sqrt{1 - x^2} + C$

11. $(x^2 - 2x + 2)e^x + C$ **13.** $\frac{(2x + 1)^{1/2}(x - 1)}{3} + C$

15. $\frac{e^{2x}}{13}(2\sin 3x - 3\cos 3x) + C$ **17.** $-\frac{(1 - x^2)^{3/2}(3x^2 + 2)}{15} + C$

19. $x\ln(x^2 + 1) - 2x + 2\tan^{-1}x + C$ **21.** (a) $\frac{x^{r+1}}{(r + 1)^2}\{(r + 1)\ln x - 1\} + C$

(b) $\frac{(\ln x)^2}{2} + C$

Section 2   **1.** $\frac{2}{3}(x - 8)\sqrt{x + 4} + C$ **3.** $\frac{3}{28}(4x - 3)(x + 1)^{4/3} + C$

5. $2\sqrt{x} - 2\ln(1 + \sqrt{x}) + C$ **7.** $\frac{25}{2}\sin^{-1}\frac{x}{5} + \frac{x}{2}\sqrt{25 - x^2} + C$ **9.** $\sin^{-1}\frac{x}{5} + C$

11. $\frac{x}{2}\sqrt{9x^2 - 4} - \frac{2}{3}\ln|3x + \sqrt{9x^2 - 4}| + C$ **13.** $-\frac{1}{3}\ln\left|\frac{3 + \sqrt{x^2 + 9}}{x}\right| + C$

15. $-\frac{1}{16}\left\{\frac{2x}{x^2 - 4} + \frac{1}{2}\ln\left|\frac{x - 2}{x + 2}\right|\right\} + C$ **17.** $\sqrt{x^2 - a^2} - a\sec^{-1}\frac{x}{a} + C$

19. $-\frac{\sqrt{a^2 - x^2}}{x} - \sin^{-1}\frac{x}{a} + C$ **21.** $\frac{x}{2}\sqrt{x^2 + a^2} - \frac{a^2}{2}\ln|x + \sqrt{x^2 + a^2}| + C$

23. $\frac{x}{2}\sqrt{x^2 - a^2} + \frac{a^2}{2}\ln|x + \sqrt{x^2 - a^2}| + C$ **25.** $-\frac{1}{a}\ln\left|\frac{a + \sqrt{a^2 - x^2}}{x}\right| + C$

27. $\frac{1}{2}\left\{\tan^{-1}(x - 2) + \frac{x - 2}{x^2 - 4x + 5}\right\} + C$ **29.** $\frac{x}{2}\sqrt{x^2 + 1} + \frac{1}{2}\ln|x + \sqrt{x^2 + 1}| - $
$\sin y + y\cos y = C$

Section 3   **1.** $\ln\left|\frac{(x - 1)^2}{x}\right| + C$ **3.** $\frac{x^2}{2} + 2x + \frac{27}{4}\ln|x - 3| + \frac{1}{4}\ln|x + 1| + C$

5. $\frac{3}{4}\ln|2x - 1| - \frac{1}{4(2x - 1)} + C$ **7.** $\frac{5}{6}\ln|x + 2| + \frac{2}{3}\ln|x - 1| - \frac{1}{2}\ln|x| + C$

9. $\dfrac{1}{8} \ln \left|\dfrac{x-2}{x+2}\right| + \dfrac{1}{4} \tan^{-1} \dfrac{x}{2} + C$ 11. $x - \dfrac{1}{4} \ln |x| + \dfrac{9}{8} \ln |x-2| - \dfrac{7}{8} \ln |x+2| + C$

13. $2 \ln |x-2| - \dfrac{8}{x-2} - \dfrac{9}{2(x-2)^2} + C$ 15. $\ln (x^2 + 4) + \dfrac{1}{2} \tan^{-1} \dfrac{x}{2} + \dfrac{3}{2(x^2+4)} + C$

17. $\dfrac{1}{32} \ln \left|\dfrac{x+2}{x-2}\right| - \dfrac{7}{16} \left(\dfrac{1}{x-2}\right) + \dfrac{5}{16} \left(\dfrac{1}{x+2}\right) + C$

Chapter 13

Section 1   1. $dA = 2\pi r \, dr$ 3. $dy = \cos x \, dx$ 5. $dv = -\sin t \, dt$

7. $dM = m \, dv$ 9. $dF = \dfrac{-2m}{r^3} \, dr$ 11. $dy = .08, \Delta y = .0796$ 13. $dy = 6, \Delta y = 26$

15. $dy = -.025, \Delta y = -.0238$ 17. 4.021   19. ± 5 sq. ft.

Section 2   1. $\ln 3 = 1.1$ 3. $\dfrac{\pi^{3/2}}{12} (2\sqrt{2} + \sqrt{6})$ 5. .63   7. .464   9. .693

11. .981

Section 3   1. $(0,\frac{2}{7})$ 3. $(4,4)$ 5. $(\frac{1}{28}, -\frac{1}{14})$

Section 4   1. $(\frac{12}{5}, \frac{3}{4})$ 3. $(\frac{8}{5}, \frac{16}{7})$ 5. $(\pi/2 - 1, \pi/8)$ 7. $(e^2/4 + \frac{1}{4}, e/2 - 1)$

9. $\bar{x} = (\sqrt{2} - 1)/\ln(1 + \sqrt{2}), \bar{y} = \pi/8 \ln(1 + \sqrt{2})$ 11. $\bar{x} = \bar{y} = \dfrac{4r}{3\pi}$

13. $\bar{y} = \frac{1}{4}(\sinh a \cosh a - a)/(\cosh a - 1), \bar{x} = (a \cosh a - \sinh a)/(\cosh a - 1)$

Section 5   1. $(\frac{8}{3}, 0)$ 3. $\dfrac{\pi^2 + 4}{4\pi}, 0$.   5. $(\ln 5/2 \tan^{-1} 2, 0)$

Section 6   1. 416,667 lb   3. 9750 lb   5. 3,000,000 lb   7. 216.5 lb

Chapter 14

Section 1   1. Choose p so that $|p| < .01/95$. For example, $|p| = .0001$ and $p = [x_0, x_1, \cdots, x_{70.000}]$ where $x_i = -5 + .0001i$.   3. Choose p so that $|p| < .02$. For example, $|p| = .01$ and $p = [x_0, x_1, \cdots x_{300}]$ where $x_i = -1 + .01i$. $f(-\frac{1}{2}) = \frac{3}{4}$, min.; $f(2) = 7$, max.   5. Choose p so that $|p| < 2\epsilon$. $g(0) = 2$, min.; $g(4) = 4$, max. 7. Choose p so that $|p| < e\epsilon - 1$. For example, a regular partition $[x_0, x_1, \cdots x_n]$ where $n > (e - 1)/(e^\epsilon - 1)$. $g(1) = 0$, min.; $g(e) = 1$, max.   9. $f(-3) = f(3) = 18$ max., $f(0) = 9$ min.   11. $g(-1) = 7$ max., $g(2) = -20$ min.   13. $F(\pi/4) = \sqrt{2}$ max., $F(5\pi/4) = -\sqrt{2}$ min.   15. $f(2) = e^2$ max., $f(-1) = 1/e$ min.   17. $F(3) = 3$ max., $f(0) = 0$ min.   19. (a) none (c) $f(\pi/4) = 1$ max., $f(-\pi/4) = -1$ min.

Section 3   1. 1   3. 1   5. 1   7. 0   9. 2   11. -1 13. 0   15. $\frac{1}{6}$
17. $\frac{1}{5}$ 19. $\frac{2}{3}$ 21. $\ln 10 - 1$

Section 4   1. 0   3. 0   5. 0   7. $1/e$ 9. 0   11. 1   13. e^3 15. 1
17. e;

Section 5   1. 2   5. 2   7. 2   9. $\frac{3}{2}$ 11. $\pi/4$ 15. $1/2e$ 19. $\pi/2$
21. $3(1 + \sqrt[3]{2})$ 25. 1   27. -1

Section 6

1. $f(x) = -\left(x - \dfrac{\pi}{2}\right) + \dfrac{1}{3!}\left(x - \dfrac{\pi}{2}\right)^3 - \dfrac{1}{5!}\left(x - \dfrac{\pi}{2}\right)^5 - \dfrac{1}{6!}\left(x - \dfrac{\pi}{2}\right)^6 \cos z$

z between $\dfrac{\pi}{2}$ and x

3. $F(x) = \dfrac{\pi}{4} + \dfrac{1}{2}(x-1) - \dfrac{1}{4}(x-1)^2 + \dfrac{1}{12}(x-1)^3 - \dfrac{(x-1)^4 z(z^2-1)}{(z^2+1)^4}$

z between 1 and x

5. $f(x) = \sqrt{2} + \sqrt{2}\left(x - \dfrac{\pi}{4}\right) + \dfrac{3\sqrt{2}}{2}\left(x - \dfrac{\pi}{4}\right)^2 + \dfrac{11\sqrt{2}}{6}\left(x - \dfrac{\pi}{4}\right)^3$

$+ \dfrac{1}{24}\left(x - \dfrac{\pi}{4}\right)^4 (24\sec^5 z - 20\sec^3 z + \sec z)$, z between $\dfrac{\pi}{4}$ and x

7. $f(x) = x - \dfrac{x^3}{3!} + \dfrac{x^5}{5!} - \dfrac{x^7}{7!}\cos z$, z between 0 and x

9. $g(x) = x - \dfrac{x^2}{2} + \dfrac{x^3}{3} - \dfrac{x^4}{4} + \dfrac{x^5}{5} - \dfrac{x^6}{6}(z+1)^{-6}$, z between 0 and x

11. $F(x) = x + \dfrac{x^3}{3!} + \dfrac{3x^4}{4!}(1 - z^2)^{-7/2}(3z + 2z^3)$, z between 0 and x

13. $f(x) = 1 + \dfrac{x}{2} + \dfrac{1 \cdot 3}{2 \cdot 2^2}x^2 + \dfrac{1 \cdot 3 \cdot 5}{3! 2^3}x^3 + \dfrac{1 \cdot 3 \cdot 5 \cdot 7}{4! 2^4}x^4 + \dfrac{1 \cdot 3 \cdot 5 \cdot 7 \cdot 9}{5! 2^5}x^5(1 - z)^{-11/2}$

z between 0 and x

15. $g(x) = x + \dfrac{x^3}{3} + \dfrac{x^5}{15}(15\sec^4 z - 15\sec^2 z + 2)\sec^2 z$, z between 0 and x

17. $F(x) = \dfrac{1}{2} - \dfrac{1}{4}x + \dfrac{1}{48}x^3 + \dfrac{x^4}{24}(e^{3z} - 11e^{2z} + 11e^z - 1)$, z between 0 and x

Section 7

1. $\sin x = x - \dfrac{x^3}{3!} + \dfrac{x^5}{5!} \pm .000002$; $.479427$

3. $e^x = 1 + x + \dfrac{x^2}{2!} + \dfrac{x^3}{3!} + \dfrac{x^4}{4!} + \dfrac{x^5}{5!} \pm .005$; 2.716

5. $\ln(1 + x) = x - \dfrac{x^2}{2} + \dfrac{x^3}{3} - \dfrac{x^4}{4} + \dfrac{x^5}{5} - \dfrac{x^6}{6} \pm .002$; $.405$

7. $\sinh x = x + \dfrac{x^3}{3!} + \dfrac{x^5}{5!} \pm .008$; 1.175 **9.** $\tan^{-1} x = x - \dfrac{x^3}{3} \pm .0004$; $.1973$

11. 1.6487 **13.** $.99875026$ **15.** 1.0627 **17.** $.52110$ **19.** 1.949

Chapter 15

Section 1   **1.** $y = -\dfrac{x}{3} + 2$, entire graph   **3.** $(y - 1)^2 = 1 - x$, entire graph

5. $y = 1 - x^2$ in the first quadrant   **7.** $(y - 1)^2 + x^2 = 1$, entire graph
9. $y = x^{2/3}$, entire graph   **11.** $y^2 = x + 1$ in the first and fourth quadrants
13. Entire ellipse   **15.** Entire hyperbola

Section 2   **1.** $y = 3x - 4$ **3.** $y = -x - 2$ **5.** $y - \dfrac{3a}{5} = -\dfrac{4}{3}(x - 4a/5)$

7. $y - \dfrac{\pi}{6} = (1/\sqrt{3})(x + \ln 2)$ **9.** $y = 2x$ **11.** Hor. tang. at $(0, \pm 5)$; vert. tang.
at $(\pm 5, 0)$ **13.** Horiz. tang. at $(2n\pi, 3)$ if n odd, $(2n\pi, 1)$ if n even   **15.** Horiz. tang.
at $(2, 1)$, $(2, -3)$; vert. tang at $(5, -1)$, $(-1, -1)$ **19.** $d^2y/dx^2 = (2t - 3)e^{-3t}$
$d^2y/dx^2 = 1/3a \cos^4\theta \sin \theta$

Section 5
1. $\mathbf{r}'(t) = (2t,2)$; $\mathbf{r}''(t) = (2,0)$; $|\mathbf{r}(2)| = 2\sqrt{5}$
3. $\mathbf{r}'(t) = (2\cos t, -2\sin t)$; $\mathbf{r}''(t) = (-2\sin t, -2\cos t)$; $\left|\mathbf{r}\left(\frac{\pi}{4}\right)\right| = 2$
5. $\mathbf{r}'(t) = (-\sin t, -2\sin 2t)$; $\mathbf{r}''(t) = (-\cos t, -4\cos 2t)$; $\left|\mathbf{r}\left(\frac{\pi}{2}\right)\right| = 1$
7. $\mathbf{r}'(t) = (e^t, -e^{-t})$; $\mathbf{r}''(t) = (e^t, e^{-t})$; $|\mathbf{r}(0)| = \sqrt{2}$
9. $\mathbf{r}'(t) = (2\cos t, 2\sin t)$; $\mathbf{r}''(t) = (-2\sin t, 2\cos t)$; $\left|\mathbf{r}\left(\frac{\pi}{6}\right)\right| = 2$
11. $\mathbf{r}'(t) = (-a\omega\sin\omega t, a\omega\cos\omega t)$; $\mathbf{r}''(t) = (-a\omega^2\cos\omega t, -a\omega^2\sin\omega t)$; $|\mathbf{r}(t)| = a\omega$

Section 6 21. $r = 3$ 23. $r^2 = 2\csc 2\theta$ 25. $r = -4\cos\theta$ 27. $x^2 + y^2 = 2y$
29. $x^2 + y^2 = (x^2 + y^2 + y)^2$ 31. $y = 2$ 35. $r = a\sec\theta$

Section 9 1. $\frac{\pi^3}{48}$ 3. 1 5. $\frac{1}{4}(e^{2\pi} - 1)$ 7. $\frac{1}{2}\left(1 + \frac{\pi}{2}\right)$ 9. 25π 11. $\frac{3\pi}{2}$
13. $\frac{\pi}{2}$ 15. $\frac{1}{2}$ 17. $\frac{\pi a^2}{4n}$ 19. $\frac{1}{4}\left(\frac{\pi}{2} - 1\right)$ 21. $8\pi - 16$ 23. 0

Section 10 1. 12π 3. $\sqrt{5} + \frac{1}{2}\ln(2 + \sqrt{5})$ 5. $\sqrt{2}(e^2 - 1)$ 7. $\frac{8}{27}(10\sqrt{10} - 1)$
9. $\ln(2 + \sqrt{3})$ 11. $2\sqrt{17} + \frac{1}{2}\ln(4 + \sqrt{17})$ 15. $3\sqrt{2}$ 17. 2 19. $6a$

Section 12 1. $\frac{2\pi}{3}(10\sqrt{10} - 2\sqrt{2})$ 3. π 5. $\frac{\pi}{27}(145\sqrt{145} - 1)$
7. $\pi\left[\frac{e^6 - 1}{e^4}\sqrt{e^4 + 1} + 2 + \ln\frac{e^2 + \sqrt{e^4 + 1}}{1 + \sqrt{e^4 + 1}}\right]$ 9. $4\pi r^2$
11. $2\pi b^2 + \frac{2\pi a^2 b}{\sqrt{a^2 - b^2}}\sin^{-1}\left(\frac{\sqrt{a^2 - b^2}}{a}\right)$; $2\pi a^2 + \frac{2\pi ab^2}{\sqrt{a^2 - b^2}}\ln(a + \sqrt{a^2 - b^2})$
13. $\frac{4\sqrt{2}}{5}\pi a^2$

Chapter 16

Section 1 1. $\frac{35}{6}$ 3. $\sqrt{2}\pi/(\sqrt{2} - 1)$ 5. $\frac{68}{111}$ 7. $\sum_{k=1}^{\infty}\frac{1}{4k^2 - 1}$, converges to $\frac{1}{2}$
9. $\sum_{k=1}^{\infty}\frac{k^2 + k - 1}{k(k + 1)}$, diverges 11. $\frac{1}{2} - \frac{1}{2^2} - \frac{1}{2^3} - \cdots - \frac{1}{2^n} - \cdots = 0$
13. $\sum_{k=1}^{\infty}\frac{2k - 1}{(k^2 + 1)(k^2 - 2k + 2)}$, converges to 1

Section 2 1. conv. 3. conv. 5. div. 7. div. 9. div. 11. conv.
13. conv. 15. conv. 17. conv. 19. conv.

Section 3 1. conv. 3. div. 5. conv. 7. div. 9. conv. 11. .800
13. .969

Section 4 1. abs. conv. 3. div. 5. conv. 7. div. 9. abs. conv.
11. cond. conv.

Section 5   **1.** $(-\infty, \infty)$ **3.** $[-1,1)$ **5.** $(-\infty, \infty)$ **7.** $(-\frac{2}{3}, \frac{2}{3})$ **9.** $(-1,1)$

11. $(-2,4)$ **13.** $[-\sqrt{5} - 1, \sqrt{5} - 1]$ **15.** $\left(-\frac{1}{e}, \frac{1}{e}\right)$ **17.** $(-1,1]$ **19.** $[0,4)$

Section 6   **1.** $\ln 1.2 = .18232$ **3.** $\ln 3 = 1.09861$ **5.** $\displaystyle\sum_{n=1}^{\infty} \frac{(-1)^{n+1} x^n}{n^2}$

Section 7

1. $1 - \dfrac{1}{2} x + \dfrac{1}{2^2 2!} x^2 - \dfrac{3}{2^3 3!} x^3 - \cdots - \dfrac{1 \cdot 3 \cdots (2n-3)}{2^n n!} x^n - \cdots$

3. $\displaystyle\sum_{n=0}^{\infty} (-1)^n (n+1) x^n$

5. $1 + \dfrac{1}{2} x^2 + \dfrac{3}{2^2 2!} x^4 + \cdots + \dfrac{1 \cdot 3 \cdot 5 \cdots (2n-1)}{2^n n!} x^{2n} + \cdots$

7. $8x - 3x^2 + \dfrac{3}{16} x^3 + \cdots + \dfrac{3 \cdot 1 \cdot 3 \cdot 5 \cdots (2n-5)}{2^{3(n-1)} n!} x^{n+1} + \cdots$

9. $x + \dfrac{1}{2} \dfrac{x^3}{3} + \dfrac{3}{2^2 2!} \dfrac{x^5}{5} + \cdots + \dfrac{1 \cdot 3 \cdot 5 \cdots (2n-1)}{2^n n!} \dfrac{x^{2n+1}}{2n+1} + \cdots$

11. Since $\dfrac{1}{x\sqrt{x^2 - 1}} = x^{-2}(1 - 1/x^2)^{-1/2}$, $x > 1$,

$\sec^{-1} x = \dfrac{\pi}{2} - \dfrac{1}{x} - \dfrac{1}{6x^3} - \cdots - \dfrac{1 \cdot 3 \cdot 5 \cdots (2n-1)}{2^n n!(2n+1)x^{2n+1}} - \cdots$

Section 8

1. $\dfrac{\sqrt{2}}{2} \left[1 - \left(x - \dfrac{\pi}{4}\right) - \dfrac{(x + \pi/4)^2}{2!} + \dfrac{(x - \pi/4)^3}{3!} + \dfrac{(x - \pi/4)^4}{4!} \right.$

$\left. - \dfrac{(x - \pi/4)^5}{5!} - \dfrac{(x - \pi/4)^6}{6!} + \cdots \right], r = \infty$

3. $-(x+1) - \dfrac{(x+1)^2}{2} - \dfrac{(x+1)^3}{3} - \cdots - \dfrac{(x+1)^n}{n} - \cdots, r = 1$

5. $x + \dfrac{x^3}{3!} + \dfrac{x^5}{5!} + \cdots + \dfrac{x^{2n-1}}{(2n-1)!} + \cdots, r = \infty$

7. $\dfrac{x}{2!} - \dfrac{x^3}{4!} + \dfrac{x^5}{6!} - \dfrac{x^7}{8!} + \cdots + (-1)^{n+1} \dfrac{x^{2n-1}}{(2n)!} + \cdots, r = \infty$

9. $x^2 - \dfrac{2^3 x^4}{4!} + \dfrac{2^5 x^6}{6!} - \dfrac{2^7 x^8}{8!} + \cdots + (-1)^{n+1} \dfrac{2^{2n-1} x^{2n}}{(2n)!} + \cdots, r = \infty$

11. 1.3956 **13.** $.9962$ **15.** $.021372$

Chapter 17

Section 1   **1.** $(0,0,3)$, $(7,0,3)$, $(0,2,3)$, $(0,2,0)$, $(7,0,0)$, $(7,2,0)$ **3.** $(-1,1,5)$, $(2,1,5)$, $(-1,3,5)$, $(2,1,2)$, $(2,3,2)$, $(-1,3,2)$ **5.** $(0,-2,0)$, $(3,-2,0)$, $(0,1,0)$, $(3,-2,-1)$, $(3,1,-1)$, $(0,1,-1)$ **7.** $x^2 + y^2 + z^2 - x - 9y - 6z + 13 = 0$ **9.** $x^2 + y^2 + z^2 + 5x - y + z - 24 = 0$ **11.** Sphere: center $(1,0,0)$, radius $= 5$ **13.** Sphere: center $(0, \frac{3}{2}, -\frac{1}{2})$, radius $= \frac{3}{2}$ **15.** No graph   **19.** $x - 2y - z = 0$

Section 2   **1.** $\frac{1}{2}, \frac{1}{2}, 1/\sqrt{2}$; $60°$, $60°$, $45°$ **3.** $\frac{1}{3}, \frac{2}{3}, \frac{2}{3}$; $70°32'$, $48°11'$, $48°11'$ **5.** $1/\sqrt{3}, 1/\sqrt{3}, 1/\sqrt{3}$; $54°45'$, $54°45'$, $54°45'$ **7.** 2, 1, 2; $\frac{2}{3}, \frac{1}{3}, \frac{2}{3}$ **9.** $3, 3, 3$; $1/\sqrt{3}, 1/\sqrt{3}, 1/\sqrt{3}$ **11.** $0, 0, 4$; $0, 0, 1$

13. pos. x-axis: 1, 0, 0; 0°, 90°, 90°   neg. x-axis: -1, 0, 0; 180°, 90°, 90°
    pos. y-axis: 0, 1, 0; 90°, 0°, 90°   neg. y-axis: 0, -1, 0; 90°, 180°, 90°
    pos. z-axis: 0, 0, 1; 90°, 90°, 0°   neg. z-axis: 0, 0, -1; 90°, 90°, 180°
15. $\pi/3$ or $2\pi/3$

Section 4   **1.** $x + y - z - 1 = 0$ **3.** $4x + 7y - 2z + 9 = 0$
5. $3x + y - 4z = 0$ **7.** $2x + y - 4 = 0, 2x + z - 4 = 0, y + z - 4 = 0$
9. $x - 3y - 3 = 0, x + z - 3 = 0, z - 3y - 3 = 0$ **11.** $4x + y - 6 = 0, x = \frac{3}{2}$,
$y = 6$ **13.** $x = 6, 2x - 3z - 12 = 0, z = -4$ **15.** $x + y - 2z = 0$
17. $x - 2z - 3 = 0$ **19.** $6x + 10y - z - 23 = 0$ **21.** $x - y - 1 = 0$
23. $2x - 7y - 3z + 3 = 0$

Section 5   **1.** $x = 2t, y = t, z = 3t$ **3.** $x = 2 + 7t, y = 1, z = -1 - 5t$
5. $x = 4 + t, y = -4 - 6t, z = -3 + t$ **7.** $x = 11t, y = 7t, z = 2t$ **11.** $x = 5$,
$y = 1 + t, z = 2t; \dfrac{y-1}{1} = \dfrac{z}{2}, x - 5 = 0$ **13.** $x = 2 + 4t, y = -1 + 11t, z = 9t$;
$\dfrac{x-2}{4} = \dfrac{y+1}{11} = \dfrac{z}{9}$ **15.** $(-1,8,3)$ **17.** $3x + 4y - 9z - 2 = 0$ **19.** $x = 3t$
$y = 5t, z = -7t$ **21.** $x = -1 + 2t, y = 6 - t, z = 5 - 3t$

Section 8   **1.** $x = -2, y = -2s, z = \pi + x$ **3.** $x = 1 + s, y = 1 - s, z = s$
5. $x = 1 + 3s, y = 1 + s, z = 1 + 4s$ **7.** $x = 0, y = s, z = 0; x = 4 - 4s$,
$y = -2 + s, z = -8 + 12s; x = 9 + 6s, y = 3 + s, z = 27 + 27s$
11. $\sqrt{21} + \dfrac{5}{4}\ln\dfrac{4 + \sqrt{21}}{\sqrt{5}}$ **13.** $\dfrac{\pi}{2}\sqrt{\pi^2 + 2} + \ln(\pi + \sqrt{2 + \pi^2}) - \frac{1}{2}\ln 2$
15. 12   **17.** $9\sqrt{1 + \dfrac{25\pi^2}{4}}$

Chapter 18

Section 2   **3.** $\dfrac{2\sqrt{73}}{5}$
Section 4   **5.** $2\frac{1}{3}$ **7.** $12\frac{2}{3}$

Chapter 19

Section 2   **1.** $y \geq x; f_y = \frac{1}{2}(y - x)^{-1/2} = -f_x, f_{xy} = f_{yx} = -f_{yy} =$
$\frac{1}{4}(y - x)^{-3/2} = -f_{xx}$
3. $y \neq 0; g_x = \dfrac{e^{x/y}}{y}, g_y = \dfrac{-xe^{x/y}}{y^2}, g_{xx} = \dfrac{e^{x/y}}{y^2}, g_{yy} = \dfrac{x^2 + 2xy}{y^4}e^{x/y}$,
     $g_{xy} = g_{yx} = -\dfrac{x + y}{y^3}e^{x/y}$
5. $r \leq 1; F_\theta = F_{\theta\theta} = F, F_r = -\frac{1}{2}(1 - r)^{-1/2}e^\theta = F_{r\theta} = F_{\theta r}, F_{rr} = -\frac{1}{4}(1 - r)^{-3/2}e^\theta$
7. $y \neq -x; G_x = \dfrac{2y}{(x + y)^2}, G_y = \dfrac{-2x}{(x + y)^2}, G_{xx} = \dfrac{-4y}{(x + y)^3}, G_{yy} = \dfrac{4x}{(x + y)^3}$,
     $G_{xy} = G_{yx} = \dfrac{2x - 2y}{(x + y)^3}$
9. $x^2 + y^2 + z^2 \leq 4; f_x = -x/f(x,y,z)$
11. $x - 2y + 3z \neq n\pi + \dfrac{\pi}{2}; F_z = 3\sec^2(x - 2y + 3z)$

13. $g_{xx} = 2y \sin z$, $g_{yy} = 0$, $g_{zz} = -g$, $g_{xy} = g_{yx} = 2x \sin z$, $g_{xz} = g_{zx} = 2xy \cos z$, $g_{yz} = g_{zy} = x^2 \cos z$

15. $G_{uu} = \dfrac{-2v^2(uv + w)}{[1 + (uv + w)^2]^2}$, $G_{uv} = G_{vu} = \dfrac{1 + w^2 - u^2 v^2}{[1 + (uv + w)^2]^2}$

17. $\dfrac{\partial^3 G}{\partial y \partial x \partial x} = 2 \sin z$, $\dfrac{\partial^3 G}{\partial z^2 \partial y} = 2x \cos z$

19. $\dfrac{\partial F}{\partial x} = t^{(x+y) \sec y}[2x + y + (x^2 + xy) \sec y]$,

$\dfrac{\partial F}{\partial y} = 4 e^{(x+y) \sec y} \left\{ 1 + (x + y) \sec y[1 + (x + y) \tan y] \right\}$

21. $\dfrac{\partial F}{\partial r} = \dfrac{2rs(3r + s)(3r^2 - 6rs - s^2)}{(r - s)^2}$

29. $y = 3$, $x = 2 + t$, $z = 13 + 4t$

Section 4   **1.** $\dfrac{\partial z}{\partial u} = 2u$, $\dfrac{\partial z}{\partial v} = 0$ **3.** $\dfrac{\partial z}{\partial u} = \dfrac{2u}{\sqrt{1 - (u^2 - v^2)^2}}$

5. $\dfrac{\partial z}{\partial u} = \dfrac{5v}{(u + 2v)^2} e^{(2u-v)/(u+2v)}$ **7.** $\dfrac{\partial w}{\partial r} = \dfrac{3(r^2 + s^2 + t^2) - 2(3r - s - 2t)r}{(r^2 + s^2 + t^2)^2}$

9. $\dfrac{\partial w}{\partial u} = \sqrt{1 + v^2}$, $\dfrac{\partial w}{\partial v} = \dfrac{uv}{\sqrt{1 + v^2}}$ **11.** $\dfrac{dw}{dt} = \dfrac{2(t - 1)}{t^3} + \dfrac{2t}{(t + 1)^3}$

13. $\dfrac{dw}{dt} = t^3 \cos (t^3 \ln t)[1 + 3 \ln t] + \sin (t^3 \ln t)$

23. $\left(\dfrac{\partial H}{\partial V} \right)_P = g_V(P, V) + P = \left(\dfrac{\partial E}{\partial V} \right)_P + P$

Section 6   **1.** $\dfrac{dy}{dx} = -\dfrac{1 + y \cos xy}{2y + x \cos xy}$ **3.** $\dfrac{dy}{dx} = \dfrac{4}{x - 3y^2(x^2 + y^2)}$

5. $\dfrac{dy}{dx} = \dfrac{3x^2 - 4xy^2 - 3y}{4x^2 y - 3y^2 + 3x}$ **7.** $\dfrac{\partial z}{\partial x} = -\dfrac{2xz + y^2}{x^2 + 2yz - 3z^2}$ **9.** $\dfrac{\partial z}{\partial y} = \dfrac{3y^2 z + z^3}{3(x^3 + y^3) + (x + y)z^2}$

17. -1; $e/\sqrt{2}$; $-e/2$ **19.** (a) $\theta = \dfrac{\pi}{3}, \dfrac{4\pi}{3}$ (b) $\theta = \dfrac{5\pi}{6}$, min.: $\theta = \dfrac{11\pi}{6}$, max.

Section 7   **1.** $8x - 4y + z + 8 = 0$ **3.** $x + 2y + 2z - 9 = 0$
5. $z - 4x + 8y = 0$ **7.** $x + 4y - 18z + 13 = 0$ **9.** $x - y - 2z - 2 = 0$
15. $x = 1 + 2t$, $y = 2 + t$, $z = 2 - 2t$ **17.** $x = -2 + 2t$, $y = 1 + t$, $z = -1 - 3t$
19. $\nabla \cdot \mathbf{a} = 3$, $\nabla \times \mathbf{a} = (0,0,0)$ **21.** $\nabla \cdot \mathbf{c} = \cos x - \sin y + 1$, $\nabla \times \mathbf{c} = (1, -1, 0)$
23. $\nabla \cdot \mathbf{f} = e^y + e^x + e^z$, $\nabla \times \mathbf{f} = (-ye^z, -ze^x, -ze^y)$
Section 8   **1.** $f(0,0) = 0$, min.   **3.** $F(2,0) = -16$, min.   **5.** no extremum
7. $f(-\frac{1}{2}, 4) = -6$, max.   **9.** $F(2^{-1/5}, \pm 2^{3/10}) = 5 \cdot 2^{-2/5}$, min.   **11.** $\frac{3}{7}\sqrt{14}$ **17.** $\frac{4}{3}$

Section 9
3. $u(x,y) = x^3 - 3xy^2 + 5x + 7$, $v(x,y) = 3x^2 y - y^3 + 5y$
5. $u(x,y) = 2x^2 - 2y^2 + 2xy + \sqrt{2}\, x - 3y + 2$,
$v(x,y) = 4xy - x^2 + y^2 + 3x + \sqrt{2}\, y + 1$
7. $u(x,y) = x^3 - 3xy^2 - x + y$, $v(x,y) = 3x^2 y - y^3 - x - y$

Section 11   **1.** $F(x,y) = x \tan y$, $G(x,y) = x \tan y - 1$ **3.** $y \sec x$
5. $x\sqrt{1 - y^2} + \arcsin y$ **7.** $y \sin (x + y)$ **9.** $x \ln y$

Section 12   **1.** $6, 14\frac{2}{3}$ **3.** 42 **5.** 0

Section 13   **1.** (c) $\frac{3}{4}k$ **3.** $p(x,y) = -k \ln |xy|$, $w = k \ln \left| \dfrac{x_2 y_2}{x_1 y_1} \right|$

ANSWERS **699**

Chapter 20

Section 1

1. $L_2 = 20$, $U_2 = 60$, $L_4 = 30$, $U_4 = 50$, $L_n = 40 - 40/n$, $\iint_R (2x + y)\, dR = 40$

3. $L_4 = 34$, $U_4 = 76$, $L_n = \frac{8}{3}(19 - 27/n + 8/n^2)$, $\iint_R (x^2 + y)\, dR = \frac{152}{3}$

Section 2 **1.** $\frac{153}{2}$ **3.** $-\pi^2(e^2 - 1)/8e$ **5.** $\frac{11}{2}$ **7.** $-\frac{5}{24}$ **9.** $40\tan^{-1}2 - \frac{80}{3}$
11. $\frac{9}{2}$ **13.** $2/\pi + \frac{1}{6}$ **15.** $\frac{1}{12}$

Section 3 **1.** 5 **3.** 22 **5.** $\frac{32}{5}$ **7.** 16π **9.** $2r^3/3$ **11.** 6 **13.** $r^3/3$
15. 5π

Section 4 **1.** $4\pi(27 - 5\sqrt{5})/3$ **3.** $8\pi/3$ **5.** $10\pi/3$

Section 5 **1.** $(\frac{12}{5}, \frac{3}{4})$ **3.** $(2b/3, h/2)$ **5.** $\left(\dfrac{8a(\pi - 2)}{3\pi^2}, \dfrac{16a}{3\pi^2}\right)$
7. $([612 - 3\sqrt{2}\ln(3 + 2\sqrt{2})]/256, 0)$ **9.** $(16\sqrt{2}/35, 0)$ **11.** $h/2$ **13.** $(0, 8a/5\pi)$

Section 6 **1.** $|BC|/\sqrt{3}$ **3.** $\sqrt{3}|BD|/3$ **5.** $\sqrt{|AB|^2 + |BC|^2}/\sqrt{12}$ **7.** $a/2$
9. $\sqrt{5}a/2$ **11.** $\sqrt{15}a/5$ **13.** $ch^3/12$ (h the altitude on side c) **15.** $\sqrt{\pi}/4$

Section 7 **1.** 27, 0 **3.** 48π, 0 **5.** $16\sqrt{2}/3$, $-288\sqrt{2}/35$ **7.** $(1 - \ln 2)/2$, $\frac{1}{12}$
9. $2a^3/3$, $at/6$

Section 8 **1.** $(a/4, b/4, c/4)$ **3.** $(0, 0, \frac{1}{3})$ **5.** $(\frac{15}{8}, 0, -\frac{3}{4})$
7. $([2\sqrt{3} + \ln(2 + \sqrt{3})]/[4\sqrt{3} - 4\ln(2 + \sqrt{3})], 0,$
$[14\sqrt{3} - 17\ln(2 + \sqrt{3})]/[16\sqrt{3} - 16\ln(2 + \sqrt{3})])$
9. $(9\pi a/64, 3a/8, 9\pi a/64)$ **11.** $\displaystyle\int_{-a}^{a} dx \int_{-\sqrt{a^2 - x^2}}^{\sqrt{a^2 - x^2}} dy \int_{0}^{\sqrt{a^2 - x^2 - y^2}} (x^2 + y^2)\, dz$
13. $\displaystyle\int_{-\sqrt{h}}^{\sqrt{h}} dx \int_{-\sqrt{h - x^2}}^{\sqrt{h - x^2}} dy \int_{x^2 + y^2}^{h} (x^2 + y^2)\, dz$
15. $\displaystyle\int_{2}^{4} dx \int_{-\sqrt{x^2 - 4}}^{\sqrt{x^2 - 4}} dy \int_{0}^{2 - x/2} (x^3 + y^2)\, dz$ **17.** $abc(a^2 + b^2)/3$

Section 9 **1.** (cone has equation $\phi = \tan^{-1} a/h$) (a) $(3h/4, 0, 0)$ (b) $\pi a^4 h/10$
(c) $\pi a^2 h(3a^2 + 2h^2)/60$ **3.** (a) $([3(b^4 - a^4)]/[8(b^3 - a^3)], 0, 0)$ (b) $4\pi(b^5 - a^5)/15$
(c) $4\pi(b^5 - a^5)/15$ **5.** (1) $3\pi a^4 b/32$ (b) $(2a/3, 0, 5a^2 b/18)$

Chapter 21

Section 1 **9.** $y^2 = x^2 + C$ **11.** $y = Cx$ **13.** $y = Cx^2$
15. $y = x\ln|x| + C_1 x + C_2$

Section 3 **1.** $xy' = y$ **3.** $y' = 2x$ **5.** $yy' = x$
7. $(xy' - yy')^2 + (y - x)^2 = (x + yy')^2$ **9.** $y = x^2 + C$ **11.** $xy' + y = 0$
13. $y^2 + (x - 2)^2 = C$ **15.** $r^3 = -3\cos\theta + 1 + 3/\sqrt{2}$ **17.** $y^2 = (x + 1)^2 + 8$
23. $y = -x^3/3 + C'$ **25.** $2x^2 + y^2 = C'$

Section 5   **1.** $x^2 + 2xy + 2y^2 = C$ **3.** $2y(1 + e^x) - x^2 = C$ **5.** $y^2 + 2x \cos y = C$
7. $x^2 y + e^{xy} = C$ **9.** $y \tan x = C$ **11.** $y^2 - 2e^x \cos y = C$
13. $x^2 + y^4 - 2xy - 1 = 0$ **17.** $y = Cx$ **19.** $e^x(x + y - 1) = C$
21. $\ln(x^2 + y^2) + 2 \tan^{-1}(x/y) = C$

Section 6   **1.** $x^2 = C(x - y)$ **3.** $x^2 = (C - y^2)e^{y/x}$ **5.** $x^3 + 3xy^2 = C$
7. $\ln|y + 2x - 1| + \dfrac{x - 2}{y + 2x - 1} = C$

9. $\ln|x^2 + 3xy + y^2 + x - y - 1| - \dfrac{1}{\sqrt{5}} \ln \left| \dfrac{2y + 2 + (3 - \sqrt{5})(x - 1)}{2y + 2 + (3 + \sqrt{5})(x - 1)} \right| = C$

11. $y = C_1 e^x + C_2$ **13.** $y = -\sin x + C_1 x + C_2$ **15.** $y = \dfrac{C_1}{2} e^x + \dfrac{1}{2C_1} e^{-x} + C_2$

Section 7   **1.** $y = 1 + Ce^{-x^2/2}$ **3.** $y = c/b + ke^{-bx}, b \neq 0$ **5.** $y = \sin x + C \cos x$
7. $y = -e^{-2x} + Ce^{3x}$ **9.** $y = (x^2 + C)(x^2 + 1)$ **11.** $y = 1/(1 + Ce^{x^2/2})$
13. $y^2 = -\frac{2}{3}e^x + Ce^{4x}$

Section 8   **1.** $x = \dfrac{g}{r^2} \ln \dfrac{e^{rt} + e^{-rt}}{2}$ **3.** $y = 4p(x + p)$, Solution 2

5. $I(t) = \frac{1}{20}[1 - Ce^{-4t}]$ **7.** $I(t) = \dfrac{e^{-Rt/L}}{L} \left[\int e^{Rt/L} E(t)\, dt + C \right]$
9. $x(t) = 10[1 - 1/(10kt + 1)]$ **11.** $x(t) = a[1 - 1/(akt + 1)]$

Section 9   **3.** $y = C_1 e^{3x} + C_2 e^{-3x}$ **5.** $y = e^{-x}[C_1 e^{\sqrt{2}x} + C_2 e^{-\sqrt{2}x}]$

7. $y = C_1 e^{5x} + C_2 e^{-2x}$ **9.** $y = e^{-x/2} \left[C_1 \cos \dfrac{\sqrt{11}}{2} x + C_2 \sin \dfrac{\sqrt{11}}{2} x \right]$

11. $y = e^x[C_1 \cos \sqrt{2}x + C_2 \sin \sqrt{2}x]$ **13.** $y = e^{x/\sqrt{2}} \left[C_1 \cos \dfrac{\sqrt{26}}{2} x + C_2 \sin \dfrac{\sqrt{26}}{2} x \right]$

15. $y = e^{x/3} \left[C_1 \cos \dfrac{\sqrt{14}}{3} x + C_2 \sin \dfrac{\sqrt{14}}{3} x \right]$ **17.** $y = e^{\sqrt{3}x}[C_1 \cos \pi x + C_2 \sin \pi x]$
19. $y = 0$ **21.** $y = 2e^{2(x-1)} - e^{3(x-1)}$

Section 10
1. $L(\sin x) = -\sin x - 3 \cos x,\ L(e^{3x}) = 0$
3. $y = e^x[C_1 \cos x + C_2 \sin x] + \frac{1}{2}x^2 + x + \frac{1}{2}$
5. $y = e^{-x}[C_1 e^{\sqrt{2}x} + C_2 e^{-\sqrt{2}x}] - \frac{8}{13} \sin x - \frac{1}{13} \cos x$
7. $y = C_1 \sin x + [C_2 - \ln|\sec x + \tan x|] \cos x$
9. $y = C_1 e^x + C_2 e^{-x} - \dfrac{e^x}{5}[2 \cos x + \sin x]$
11. $y = C_1 - \frac{1}{4}[x^2 + x + C_2]e^{-2x}$
15. $y = C_1 e^{\sqrt{2}x} + C_2 e^{-\sqrt{2}x} - \frac{3}{2}x$
17. $y = C_1 + C_2 e^{-x} + \dfrac{e^x}{2}$
19. $I(t) = C_1 \cos t/\sqrt{10} + C_2 \sin t/\sqrt{10}$
21. $I(t) = e^{-t/2}[C_1 \cos t\sqrt{3}/2 + C_2 \sin t\sqrt{3}/2] - \frac{60}{13} \cos 2t + \frac{40}{13} \sin 2t$
23. $y = C_1 e^{-x} + C_2 e^x + C_3 e^{3x}$

Section 11

3. $y = C_0 \displaystyle\sum_{k=1}^{\infty} \dfrac{x^{2k}}{2^k k!} = C_0 e^{x^2/2}$

5. $y = C_0 \left[1 - \dfrac{x^3}{3!} + \dfrac{4^2 x^6}{6!} - \dfrac{7^2 4^2 x^9}{9!} + \dfrac{10^2 7^2 4^2 x^{12}}{12!} - \cdots \right]$
$+ C_1 \left[x - \dfrac{2^2 x^4}{4!} + \dfrac{5^2 2^2 x^7}{7!} + \dfrac{8^2 5^2 2^2 x^{10}}{10!} - \cdots \right]$

Supplementary exercises

Chapter 1   **1.** $u \leq v$ **3.** $c < x < d$ or $d < x < c$ **5.** $b \leq c$
7. $(-2,2)$; $[-.1,.1]$; $(4,6)$; $(-2 - \sqrt{7}, -2 + \sqrt{7})$; $[-2,0]$ **13.** $a > b$; $c > d$

Chapter 2   **1.** 1; 3.6; $.9\sqrt{5}$; 0; $1.5\sqrt{2}$ **3.** $2x - 7y + 39 = 0$; $7x + 2y + 4 = 0$;
$\frac{53}{7}, \frac{1325}{28}$ **5.** $(\frac{305}{183}, 1)$; $(\frac{102}{61}, \frac{84}{61})$ **7.** $(x + 3)^2 + (y - 3)^2 = 13$;
$(x - 2)^2 + (y + 4)^2 = 10$; $(x - 1)^2 + (y - 5)^2 = 5$ **9.** $(x - 1)^2 + (y - 1)^2 = 1$

13. $(0, -1)$; $(2,3)$ **17.** $c = \dfrac{r_1 a_2 + r_2 a_1}{r_1 + r_2}$, $d = \dfrac{r_1 b_2 + r_2 b_1}{r_1 + r_2}$; $\dfrac{r_1}{r_2} = 1$; $x_m = \dfrac{a_1 + a_2}{2}$,
$y_m = \dfrac{b_1 + b_2}{2}$

Chapter 3   **1.** $x \neq -1$; all real numbers; $x \geq 0$; $x \geq -\frac{5}{2}$; $x \neq \pm 2$; $x \geq 2$; $x = 1$;
$x \geq 2$; $0 \leq x \leq 2$

3. a) 7; $-x^2 + 3x + 10$; $\dfrac{x + 2}{5 - x}$; $-x + 7$;

   b) $x^2 + 2x - 3$; $2x^3 - 3x^2$; $\dfrac{x^2}{2x - 3}$; $(2x - 3)^2$;

   c) $\dfrac{2x^2}{x^4 - 1}$; $\dfrac{1}{x^4 - 1}$; $\dfrac{x^2 - 1}{x^2 + 1}$; $\dfrac{(x^2 - 1)^2}{1 + (x^2 - 1)^2}$;

   d) $2x^3 - 2$; $(x^3 - 1)^2$; 1; $(x^3 - 1)^3 - 1$
5. a) It is symmetric to the y-axis.   To the origin.
   b) When it contains only odd powers, resp. only even powers.

Chapter 4   **1.** $2c$; $\frac{1}{2}c$; $a - b$; $\frac{1}{3}a^2$ **3.** b; $2ab$; $3a^2 b$ **5.** -3; 3; $\frac{1}{2}$; 1; 0; 1

7. $y = \frac{3}{2}x - \frac{1}{2}$; $y = \frac{3}{2}x + \dfrac{2k - 1}{2}$; $y = 10cz - 25c + d$; $y = k$; $y = \frac{23}{6}x - \frac{1}{3}$

9. c) $k = b_1 - b_2$ **15.** $\frac{1}{2}$; $\frac{1}{2}$; $\frac{1}{2}$; $-\frac{1}{2}$; $\frac{1}{2}$

Chapter 5   **1.** $2x$ **3.** $4x^3 + 12x$ resp. $4x^3 - 8x$ **5.** $4ax^3$ **7.** $1/(a^2 - x^2)^{3/2}$

9. $-\dfrac{4ax^3 + 3bx^2 + 2cx + d}{(ax^4 + bx^3 + cx^2 + dx + e)^2}$ **11.** $a^2 z/\sqrt{az + b}$ **13.** $2a/(x + a)^2$

15. $(x - 1)^{m-1}(x + 1)^{n-1}[(m + n)x + m - n]$;
   $(x - 1)^{m-2}(x + 1)^{n-2}[((m + n)x + m - n)^2 + (x^2 - 1)(m + n)]$

17. $2ax + b$; $2a$ **19.** $4ab/(a^2 + b^2)^2$ **21.** $\dfrac{c - a + 2a\sqrt{c}}{2\sqrt{c}(\sqrt{c} + a)^2}$

25. $(3x^2 - 2x) \cdot \dfrac{|x - 1|}{x - 1}$, $(x \neq 1)$; $-\dfrac{1}{x^2} \cdot \dfrac{|x|}{x}$, $(x \neq 0)$; 0; $2x - 3\dfrac{|x|}{x}$, $(x \neq 0)$;

   $2(3x - 1) \cdot \dfrac{|x + 1|}{x + 1}$, $(x \neq -1)$; 0

Chapter 6   **1.** min. $(0, -4)$ **3.** min. $(\sqrt{3}/3, -2\sqrt{3}/9)$; max. $(-\sqrt{3}/3, 2\sqrt{3}/9)$;
infl. $(0,0)$ **5.** min. $(3, -756)$; max. $(-3,756)$; infl. $(0,0)$, $(-2, -494)$, $(2,494)$
7. min. $(0,0)$; min. $(0,0)$; max. $(0,0)$, min. $(4m^2/9, 20m^3/27)$ **11.** $\pm x + \sqrt{6}y = 2\sqrt{6}$;
$x = 0$ **13.** $\frac{3}{4}$
15. a) 30 mph; b) 50 mph $(15 \cdot \sqrt{14} > $ maximum speed of 50 mph$)$

Chapter 7   **15.** $y = \sqrt{3}x + 2 - \dfrac{1}{x-1}$; asymptotes: $y = \sqrt{3}x + 2$, $x = 1$; center:

$(1{,}2 + \sqrt{3})$; rotation: $x = \frac{1}{4}(\sqrt{6} + \sqrt{2})x' + \frac{1}{4}(\sqrt{6} - \sqrt{2})y'$, $y = -\frac{1}{4}(\sqrt{6} - \sqrt{2})x' +$ $\frac{1}{4}(\sqrt{6} + \sqrt{2})y'$; translation: $x'' = x'$, $y'' = y' - (\sqrt{6} + \sqrt{2})$

17. $\lim\limits_{x \to a^+} f(x) = b$, if for every $\epsilon > 0$ there exists a number $\delta > 0$ such that $|f(x) - b| < \epsilon$ for every x satisfying $0 < x - a < \delta$, and $\lim\limits_{x \to a^-} f(x) = b$, if for every $\epsilon > 0$ there exists a number $\delta > 0$ such that $|f(x) - b| < \epsilon$ for every x satisfying $0 < a - x < \delta$

27. $\dfrac{\left(x - \dfrac{M-m}{2}\right)^2}{\left(\dfrac{2R + M + m}{2}\right)^2} + \dfrac{y^2}{(R+M)(R+m)} = 1$

Chapter 8   **1.** $2 + 3\sqrt{2}/2$ **3.** $5\frac{547}{840}$ **5.** $\dfrac{2}{3a}[(ad+b)^{3/2} - (ac+d)^{3/2}]$

7. $\dfrac{1}{2(n+1)}(a^2 - 1)^{n+1}$ **9.** $\dfrac{2^{n-1} - 1}{(n-1)2^n a^{2(n-1)}}$ **11.** $\dfrac{1}{2n+1}[(1+a)^{2n+1} - a^{2n+1}]$

19. 1

Chapter 9   **1.** 1 **3.** No limit   **9.** 2 **11.** 8 **15.** $2\pi pb^2$ **17.** $\pi a^4/8p$

19. $\pi a^4/24p$ **21.** $W_{R}^{\infty} = kmM/R$; $v_0 = \sqrt{\dfrac{2kM}{R}} = 11{,}200\,\dfrac{\text{meters}}{\text{second}} = 25{,}000\,\dfrac{\text{miles}}{\text{hour}}$

Chapter 10   **1.** $-\dfrac{a}{(a-x)^{1/2}(a+x)^{3/2}}$ **3.** $(x^2+1)^{x-1}[2x^2 + (x^2+1)\ln(x^2+1)]$

5. $-\dfrac{2y^2}{4xy + x^2y^4 + 4}$ **7.** $\dfrac{1}{a}(e^a - 1)$ **9.** $\dfrac{1}{2}\left(e - \dfrac{1}{e}\right)$ **11.** $\frac{1}{2}\ln 5$ **13.** $\frac{1}{2}$

15. 1 **17.** $e - 1$ **19.** $\sqrt{3}/8$ **21.** $\frac{1}{2}\ln 2$ **23.** $f(x) = ce^{kx}$

25. $.1986 \le \sin .2 \le .2$; $.98 \le \cos .2 \le .98007$

Chapter 11   **1.** $\dfrac{1}{2a}\ln\left|\dfrac{x-a}{x+a}\right| + C$ **3.** $\frac{7}{4}\ln|x-2| + \frac{1}{4}\ln|x+2| + C$

5. $2\sqrt{x^2 + 3x + 5} + C$ **7.** $\dfrac{1}{a}e^{ax+b} + C$ **9.** $\frac{1}{4}\sec^4\theta + C$

11. $\sqrt{x^2 - 2x} + \ln|x - 1 + \sqrt{x^2 - 2x}| + C$ **13.** $\ln 2 \cdot e^{\log_2 x} + C$

15. $-\dfrac{1}{a(r+1)}\cos^{r+1} ax + C$ **17.** $-\ln|1 - \tan x| + C$

19. $\dfrac{1}{2\sqrt{2}}\ln\left|\dfrac{\sin x - \sqrt{2}}{\sin x + \sqrt{2}}\right| + C$ **21.** $3(x^2 + y^2) - 4(x^3 + y^3) = C$

23. $be^{ax} + ae^{by} = C$ **25.** $y = -\sin x + ax + b$

Chapter 12   **1.** $\dfrac{1}{4a^3}\ln\left|\dfrac{x+a}{x-a}\right| - \dfrac{1}{4a^2}\cdot\dfrac{2x}{x^2 - a^2} + C$ **3.** $-x\cdot\cot x + \ln|\sin x| + C$

5. $2(\sin x - 1)e^{\sin x} + C$ **7.** $-\dfrac{x}{a^2\sqrt{x^2 - a^2}} + C$

9. $-\dfrac{\sqrt{1 + x^2}}{2x^2} + \dfrac{1}{2}\ln\left|\dfrac{1 - \sqrt{1 - x^2}}{x}\right| + C$ **11.** $\ln\left|\dfrac{(x-1)(x-2)}{(x+1)^2}\right| + C$

13. $\dfrac{4}{\sqrt{3}}\tan^{-1}\left(\dfrac{\sqrt{3}\tan\frac{x}{2}}{3}\right) + C$ **15.** $\ln\left|1 + \tan\frac{x}{2}\right| + C$

17. $y^2 = -2x\cos x + 2\sin x + C$ **19.** $(ar + 1)be^{-ar} + a^2 e^{b\theta} = C$

Chapter 13   **1.** .09961   **3.** .099943   **5.** 3   **7.** 1   **9.** $\left(\dfrac{2e-5}{2-e}, \dfrac{e^2-5}{8e(2-e)}\right)$

11. $\left(0, \dfrac{e^4+4e^2-1}{8e(e^2-1)}\right)$ **13.** $\left(\dfrac{e^2+3}{2(e^2+1)}, 0, 0\right)$; $\left(\dfrac{19-3e^2}{2(e^2-5)}, 0, 0\right)$; $(0,0,0)$

Chapter 14   **1.** 1   **3.** 1   **5.** 0   **7.** $\cos a$ **9.** 2   **11.** $\dfrac{b}{a^2+b^2}$

15. $x+\dfrac{x^3}{3!}+\dfrac{\cosh z}{5!}x^5$ **17.** $1+x+\dfrac{3x^2}{2!}+\dfrac{13x^3}{3!}+\dfrac{e^{4z}+22e^{3z}+44e^{2z}+8e^z}{4!}x^4$

19. $1-\dfrac{x^2}{2!}+\dfrac{(z^4-6z^2+3)e^{-z^2/2}}{4!}x^4$ **21.** $1-\dfrac{x^2}{2!}; 1-\dfrac{x^2}{2!}+\dfrac{x^4}{4!}$

Chapter 15   **1.** $x^2-y^2=1$; $y=\dfrac{e^2+1}{e^2-1}x-\dfrac{2e}{e^2-1}$ **3.** $y=3x+13$; $y=3x+13$

5. The absolute value of the velocity vector (which always lies along the tangent line) is not independent of the parameter t, so that the point is not moving along the circle with constant speed.
15. 6π; 16   **17.** $3\pi/8$; 4

Chapter 16   **1.** 2   **3.** 1   **5.** 1   **7.** $6/(b+1)$ **9.** $[-3,-1]$

11. $(-\infty,\infty)$ **13.** $\sin a$ **15.** $\dfrac{1}{z}\int_0^z \ln(1+z^2)dz$ **17.** $-\ln(5-x)$

Chapter 17   **1.** $x=2+2t, y=2+2t, z=1+t$; $2(x-2)+2(y-2)+(z-1)=0$
3. $x=-2t, y=-2t, z=t$; $2x+2y-z=0$ **5.** $x=4t, y=4t, z=1-3t$
7. $x=t, y=0, z=5-t$ **9.** $5x+4y-3z=10$ **11.** $(0,1,2)$; $x+3y+3z=9$

Chapter 18   **1.** $r=3s-2t$ **3.** $t=\frac{5}{2}r+\frac{1}{4}s$ **5.** $r-28s+5t=0$
7. $r=35s-8t$ **11.** If $ar+bs+ct=0$, then $a+b=0, a+c=0$, and $b+3c=0$. Hence $a=0, b=0$, and $c=0$.   **15.** $u=\frac{3}{8}i+\frac{4}{8}j, v=-\frac{12}{17}i+\frac{9}{17}j+\frac{8}{17}k$,
$w=\frac{1}{85}(32i-24j+75k)$ **17.** (a) $(4,1,1)\cdot(x-1,y-1,v+2)=0$.

Chapter 19   **7.** 0   **9.** $\dfrac{g(t)-(2+t)\cdot g'(t)}{(2+t+g(t))^2}$ **11.** Minimum (0) for each point on the line $x=0$ **13.** A ridge (crest) above the curve $2x=\ln y$. Saddle point $(1,e^2,-1)$

Chapter 20   **1.** 3   **3.** 1   **5.** $\frac{16}{3}$ **7.** a) Frustum of right cylinder erected on the rectangle $(0,0), (0,2), (1,2), (1,0)$ in the xy-plane, and cut by the plane $z=x+y$. b) As a), the rectangle being $(0,0), (0,1), (2,1), (2,0)$.   c) Frustum of right cylinder erected on the triangle $(0,0), (2,0), (2,2)$ in the xy-plane, and cut by the paraboloid $z=x^2+y^2$.   d) Frustum of right cylinder erected on the rectangle $(0,0), (0,2), (\sqrt{2},2), (\sqrt{2},0)$ in the xy-plane, and cut by the plane $z=x+2y$ and by the right cylinder $x=y^2$.
9. $\frac{1}{4}$ **11.** 0

15. $V=4\int_0^1 dx\int_0^{\sqrt{1-x^2}}\dfrac{1}{x^2+y^2}dy$; $\bar{x}=\bar{y}=0, \bar{z}=\dfrac{4}{V}\int_0^1 dx\int_0^{\sqrt{1-x^2}}dy\int_0^{\frac{1}{x^2+y^2}}zdz$

17. $V=4\int_{\sqrt{3\pi/2}}^{\sqrt{5\pi/2}} dx\int_{\sqrt{3\pi/2-x^2}}^{\sqrt{5\pi/2-x^2}}\cos(x^2+y^2)dy$;

$\bar{x}=\bar{y}=0, \bar{z}=\dfrac{4}{V}\int_{\sqrt{3\pi/2}}^{\sqrt{5\pi/2}} dx\int_{\sqrt{3\pi/2-x^2}}^{\sqrt{5\pi/2-x^2}}dy\int_0^{\cos(x^2+y^2)}zdz$

Chapter 21   **1.** $(x+5y+9)^4=C(x+2y+3)$ **3.** $x^2+4xy-3y^2=C$
9. $2e^{-x}\sin y+y^2=C$ **11.** $F(x(t),y(t))=\int g(t)dt+C$

13. $M_y = N_x, N_z = P_y, P_x = M_z; F(x(t),y(t),z(t)) = \displaystyle\int g(t)dt + C,$ where $F_x = M,$

$F_y = N, F_z = P$

17. $7x^{1/2}y^4 + x^{7/2} = C$

19. $y \cdot e^{\int p(x)dx} = \displaystyle\int g(x)e^{\int p(x)dx}\,dx + C$

21. $y = C\left[1 + \dfrac{1}{3}x^3 + \dfrac{1}{4}x^4 + \dfrac{1}{6\cdot3}x^6 + \dfrac{1}{7\cdot4}x^7 + \dfrac{1}{9\cdot6\cdot3}x^9 + \dfrac{1}{10\cdot7\cdot4}x^{10}\right.$

$\left. + \dfrac{1}{12\cdot9\cdot6\cdot3}x^{12} + \dfrac{1}{13\cdot10\cdot7\cdot4}x^{13} + \cdots\right]$

23. $y = -\tfrac{1}{7}xe^{-x} + C_1e^{-x} + C_2e^{6x}$

25. $y = \tfrac{5}{74}\sin x + \tfrac{7}{74}\cos x + C_1 + C_2e^{-x} + C_3e^{6x}$

27. $y = \tfrac{1}{12}x^3 - \tfrac{1}{8}x + C_1\sin 2x + C_2\cos 2x + C_3$

29. $y = \tfrac{1}{5}xe^x + C_1e^x + C_2\sin 2x + C_3\cos 2x$

Index